PEARSON ALWAYS LEARNING

W. Stephen Damron

Introduction to Animal Science

Global, Biological, Social, and Industry Perspectives

Third Custom Edition for Oregon State University

Taken from:
Introduction to Animal Science: Global, Biological, Social, and Industry Perspectives, Fifth Edition
by W. Stephen Damron

D1441533

Cover photographs courtesy of The Department of Animal Sciences Staff at Oregon State University.

Taken from:

Introduction to Animal Science: Global, Biological, Social, and Industry Perspectives, Fifth Edition
by W. Stephen Damron
Copyright © 2013, 2009, 2006, 2003, 2000 by Pearson Education, Inc.
Published by Prentice Hall
Upper Saddle River, New Jersey 07458

All rights reserved. No part of this book may be reproduced, in any form or by any means, without permission in writing from the publisher.

This special edition published in cooperation with Pearson Learning Solutions.

All trademarks, service marks, registered trademarks, and registered service marks are the property of their respective owners and are used herein for identification purposes only.

Pearson Learning Solutions, 501 Boylston Street, Suite 900, Boston, MA 02116
A Pearson Education Company
www.pearsoned.com

Printed in the United States of America

10 16

000200010271710013

ML

ISBN 10: 1-256-87652-6
ISBN 13: 978-1-256-87652-6

For my wife, Rebecca, and our children, Joshua and Aubryana.
I am truly blessed.

brief contents

contents

5
Feedstuffs Classification 76

6
Genetics 93

7
Animal Breeding 113

8

Animal Reproduction 147

9

Beef Cattle 172

12
Swine 262

13
Sheep and Goats 290

14
Horses 324

15
Aquaculture 363

*By Dr. Louis R. D'Abramo, Professor; Dr. Martin W. Brunson, Extension Leader/Fisheries Specialist; and Dr. William H. Daniels, former Research Assistant, all with the Department of Wildlife and Fisheries. Publication 2003. Extension Service of Mississippi State University. Ronald A. Brown, Director. Mississippi State University Extension Service. Mississippi State University, http://ext.msstate.edu/pubs/pub2003.htm.

Preface

This book provides a text for introductory courses in animal science. The major, traditional biological disciplines and how the science of each of these contributes to the whole of animal science are included, as well as information on how to feed, manage, breed, and care for animals. Because the scope of animal science is so broad, this book examines how animals fit into all of society and how they contribute to the well-being of humans from a worldwide perspective. The textbook takes a brief tour to look at the various types of agriculture found around the world. It explores other uses that we have found for our domesticated animals. It individually considers the species that are of primary importance to humans. This textbook also discusses the industries that have arisen around those species and their effects on our society and our economy.

In the last 60 years or so, profound changes have taken place in the animal industries. Traditional animal husbandry has been joined by business interests and profound advances in science and technology to produce new approaches to animal production and care. Changes in the tastes and habits of consumers, economic considerations, and changes in the relative costs of animal products have all contributed to restructuring of the animal industries. The animal industries are assuming the role of dynamic, integrated parts of a greater food-providing system that is increasingly international in scope.

This textbook also acknowledges changing viewpoints toward the animals in our care. Profound societal changes have affected the animal industries and the people who work in them. Concerns over animal well-being, animal rights, food safety, biotechnology, ethical resource allocation, sustainability of agriculture, and other issues now affect animal use in a very real way. These issues and others are dealt with in the text.

A more affluent population has reached for new animals and new uses for animals, and consequently has turned to animal scientists to demand information. This text provides information concerning llamas, companion animals, and other species not traditional to the animal sciences. These species are now a part of animal science as surely as are the cow and the pig.

Written with sufficient flexibility, this textbook accommodates the three major approaches to animal science—the biological approach, the industry approach, and the species approach. The worldview information from Part One and the societal issues from Part Four round out all approaches.

This fifth edition accomplishes several goals. First, the statistics have all been updated to retain the currency that we feel is vitally important. Second, this edition has many new figures and illustrations. Because this is a color edition, a great deal of care was taken with selecting the images, and I am especially pleased with the art in this edition. In addition, new information has been added to virtually all chapters. Notable among those additions are sections in each of the species chapters on challenges to animal health, along with some excellent images. The biotechnology chapter is revamped and updated and wonderful new images added to it. The sheep and goat chapter underwent substantial revision to reflect the growing importance of meat goats, and the aquaculture chapter was also substantially revised to reflect the new reality of aquaculture's role in feeding the world's peoples. To make room for all the new images and information, and because of the increasingly easy access to information via the Internet, some tables were eliminated and others scaled back to make the text more succinct. One important thing that did not change was the educational philosophy of the previous editions. Those who used the earlier editions will quickly find all the aspects previously contained, including the "flavor."

To access supplementary materials online, instructors need to request an instructor access code. Go to **www.pearsonhighered.com/irc**, where you can register for an instructor access code. Within 48 hours after registering, you will receive a confirming e-mail, including an instructor access code. Once you have received your code, go to the site and log on for full instructions on downloading the materials you wish to use.

PEARSON AG IS GOING GREEN

Issues of sustainability and preserving our natural resources consistently rank among the most important concerns of our customers. To help do our part, Pearson AG is implementing the following eco-friendly initiatives to our publishing program.

- Printing all Pearson AG titles using paper fiber from managed forests certified by the Sustainable Forestry Initiative (SFI)
- Using vegetable-based ink products that contain a minimum of 45% renewable resource content and more than 5% by weight of petroleum distillates
- Offering alternative versions to traditional printed textbooks such as our **Student Value Editions** and e-book versions via **CourseSmart**
- Providing online supplemental materials such as PowerPoint Presentations, Test Banks, and Instructor Manuals through our Instructor Resource Center at **www.pearsoned.com**

For more information regarding the Sustainable Forestry Initiative please visit www. sfiprogram.org

SUSTAINABLE FORESTRY INITIATIVE

Certified Chain of Custody
Promoting Sustainable Forestry

www.sfiprogram.org
SFI-01042

ACKNOWLEDGMENTS

Writing a textbook requires the assistance of many people. In particular, I would like to thank colleagues for their continued support and help. Special thanks to David Freeman, Clement Ward, Derrell Peel, Bob Kropp, Christina DeWitt, Daniel Stein, Raluca Mateescu, Jennifer Hernandez Gifford, Marley Beem, Melanie Brashears, and Michael Davis of Oklahoma State University; David Buchanan of North Dakota State University; Tony Seykora of the University of Minnesota; Jim Horne of the Noble Research Center; Temple Grandin of Colorado State University; Michael Neary of Purdue University; and Siobhan Reilly, Food Protech, Stillwater, Oklahoma. Through the years, these people have graciously contributed ideas, figures, photos, and text for the book; reviewed chapters; helped find obscure materials I was seeking; and offered advice and suggestions on everything. They have done so with grace and enthusiasm for the book, and I will be forever in their debt for their participation in improving this textbook.

Invaluable assistance has been gladly accepted from Jon Beckett of Beckett Consulting; Ronald Brown, Martin Brunson, Robert Martin, Louis R. D'Abramo, and William Daniels of Mississippi State University; LaDon Swann of Illinois-Indiana Sea Grant Program, Purdue University; and An Peischel of the University of Tennessee. Students, current and former, have always been a part of this textbook. For the fifth edition, two provided particularly valuable assistance: Kellie Whipple and Ryan Robinson.

William Flowers, North Carolina State University; Dearl Lampley, Columbia State Community College; Laura Winstead, Henderson Community College; Semamawit Woldesenbet, Prairie View A&M University; and Ed Zweiacher, Redlands Community College provided feedback that was absolutely priceless. This text is better for their efforts and their diligence is appreciated.

Several individuals at Pearson Education provided invaluable assistance in ushering this book through the development and publishing stages. I would like to thank specifically William Lawrensen, Lara Dimmick, Kris Roach, and Alex Wolf. Many thanks also to Nancy Kincade of PreMediaGlobal for her efforts—couldn't have done it without her!

Finally, a special thanks to my family. My wife, Rebecca L. Damron, professor of English at Oklahoma State University, continues to provide assistance in response to, "Hey, hon, will you read this and tell me what you think?" and "Hon, how do you spell. . . ?" Thankfully, some things never change. To my children, Joshua and Aubryana, who have grown up with and become active participants in the development of this textbook, a big thanks for their contributions.

—W. Stephen Damron, Ph.D.
Oklahoma State University

part one
The Place of Animals and Animal Science in the Lives of Humans

1

Introduction to the Animal Sciences

Key Terms

Agriculture
Animal behavior
Animal breeding
Animal health
Animal science
Applied ethology
Biofuel
Biometry
Biotechnology
Civilization
Culture
Dairy product science
Diet
Domestic animals
Draft animal
Essential amino acids

Ethology
Farmer
Genetic code
Genetics
Green revolution
Heredity
Hunter-gatherer
Livestock revolution
Meat
Meat science
Nutrient density
Nutrition
Omnivore
Physiology
Renewable resources

Learning Objectives

After you have studied this chapter, you should be able to:

- Define *animal science* and all of its component parts.
- Describe how, why, and when domestication occurred.
- Give an overview of the distribution of agricultural animals worldwide.
- Explain to a nonagriculturist the contributions of domestic animals to humankind and state why domestic animals are so important to life as we know it.
- Describe the worldwide livestock revolution and its implications.

INTRODUCTION

Animals. We live with them, worship them, consume them, admire them, fear them, love them, care for them, and depend on them. They are part of our sustenance, our sociology, and our day-to-day lives. Because they are so important to us, we also study them and apply what we learn to improve their lives and enhance their roles in our lives. The branch of science that deals with domestic animals is **animal science,** which is the topic of this book.

Much of our use for animals revolves around their contributions to our food supply. Food comes from the land. To coax a more stable food supply from the land, humans developed a complicated resource management system called **agriculture.** In agriculture, domestic plants and animals are kept to produce for humankind's needs. Humans have practiced agriculture for thousands of years and, either directly or indirectly, every person on the planet depends on agriculture for his or her daily food (Figure 1–1). Because this is true, it is also ultimately true that all of humankind's other occupations are tied to agriculture. This is especially the case in the world's developed countries. In fact, the

Animal science The combination of disciplines that together comprise the study of domestic animals.

Agriculture The combination of science and art used to cultivate and grow crops and livestock and process the products.

Figure 1–1

Bolivian farmers cultivating potatoes on old Incan terraces. They use the same tools as those used by their ancestors. (FAO photo 22399/Roberto Faidutti. Used with permission by the Food and Agriculture Organization of the United Nations.)

Domestic animals Those species that have been brought under human control and that have adapted to life with humans.

Culture In this context, culture refers to the set of occupational activities, economic structures, beliefs/ values, social forms, and material traits that define our actions and activities.

Hunter-gatherer Hunter- gatherer peoples support their needs by hunting game, fishing, and gathering edible and medicinal plants.

Farmer Anyone who practices agriculture by managing and cultivating livestock and/or crops.

Civilization In modern context this refers to what we consider a fairly high level of cultural and techno- logical development.

entire urban industrial complex of the developed world is sustained only because of food surpluses generated by agriculturists. Humans have found many other uses for **domestic animals** in such areas as sports, recreation, manufacturing, religion, and as companions. Add these uses to food production and we discover that animals are at the core of virtually all of our lives, whether or not we are aware of it. Because agri- culture and its animals are integral to our existence, they have become a dominating part of our **culture,** our influence on the landscape, and, either directly or indirectly, our day-to-day activities.

Exactly when the individual animal species were domesticated is unknown. DNA sequencing technology suggests that the dog may have been domesticated from the wolf as long as 135,000 years ago, but archaeological evidence suggests that the dog was domesticated about 14,000 years ago (12000 B.C.). The earliest domestic food species (as most Westerners currently define it) was the sheep (some- where around 8000 B.C.), followed by goats, pigs, and cattle (6500 B.C.), llamas (5500 B.C.), horses (3500 B.C.), donkeys (4000 B.C.), reindeer (3000 B.C.), and chickens (6000 B.C.).

Humans did not plan their dependence on the animals they tamed and then domesticated. **Hunter-gatherers** (who first domesticated animals) used the meat, bones, and skins just as they had done before domestication. The only difference after domestication was convenience. The additional uses (milk, clothing, power, war, sport, and prestige) came later. This happened after people had lived in the company of animals for a long time in a more sedentary lifestyle.

Humans had hunted and consumed animals for 2 million years before domes- ticating them. The behavioral change required for hunters and gatherers to become **farmers** was a major cultural revolution and a major step toward what we call **civilization.**

With our acquisition of domestic animals came the need to ultimately manage them, care for them, and learn to use them to our best advantage. Those needs caused the development of the discipline of study that we call animal science.

ANIMAL SCIENCE SPECIALTIES

Animal science is simply the collective study of domestic animals. This includes every aspect, from conception to death, behavior to management, physiology to nutrition, and reproduction to product distribution. Animal science represents an accumulation of knowledge that began with observations of those hunter-gatherers who began the process of domestication long ago. As animal scientists have learned more and more about animals, the accumulated wealth of information has become too large for anyone to comprehend completely. Out of necessity, its study is divided into disciplines, or specialties, as a means of creating manageable pieces. These specialties may be broken down several ways, but the following categories illustrate the point:

- **Genetics** is the science of **heredity** and the variation of inherited characteristics. **Animal breeding** is the use of **biometry** and genetics to improve farm animal production. Genetics is an expanding field due largely to steady progress in deciphering the **genetic code.**

- **Nutrition** is the study of how organisms take in and use food/feed for body needs. Whether or not animals develop their genetic potential depends on their environment. The most important environmental factor is feed. Nutrition is the science that combines feeds with feeding management to bring about the economical production of livestock and/or health and long life to animal companions.

- **Physiology** is the study of the mechanisms of life from the single biochemical reactions in cells to the coordinated total of specialized cells that constitute a living animal. Because physiology is complex, we usually break down the study to the workings of physiological systems. Examples include reproductive physiology, renal physiology, and exercise physiology.

- **Animal health** is the study of how diseases, parasites, and environmental factors affect productivity and animal welfare. Disease is defined as any state other than a state of health. Once animals were domesticated, diseases and parasites began taking their toll.

- **Ethology** is the study of the biology of animal behavior. The specific study of behavior in domestic animals is **applied ethology.** This discipline developed along with the livestock industry's increased dependence on confinement rearing systems, which provide greater control over animals, reduce labor and feed costs, and help maximize genetic potential. They also present problems associated with behavior. Applied ethology includes many aspects of animal behavior, including animal welfare assessment, optimizing production, behavioral control, behavioral disorders, and behavioral genetics.

- **Meat science** deals with the handling, distribution, and marketing of finished meat products. **Meat** is defined as the edible flesh of animals that is used for food. Meat by-products are all of the products other than the carcass meat, some of which are edible and some of which are not.

- **Dairy product science** deals with the collection, handling, and marketing of milk in its many forms to the consuming public.

- **Biotechnology** involves technological applications of biology. This discipline has received new attention in animal science because of recombinant DNA technology and its many promises. Each of the other disciplines of animal science has benefited from biotechnology and will continue to do so at an ever-increasing rate.

Certainly, tremendous overlap occurs in these areas, and separations are made for our convenience. However, this convenience can also be a hindrance. By breaking the discipline of animal science down into smaller units, we have made it easier to learn but harder to grasp—we know the pieces of the puzzle better, but it is harder to put the pieces together. Always remember that it is the combination of the specialties that constitutes the whole discipline of animal science.

Genetics The science of heredity and the variation of inherited characteristics.

Heredity The transmission of genetic characteristics from parent to offspring.

Animal breeding The use of biometry and genetics to improve farm animal production.

Biometry The application of statistics to topics in biology.

Genetic code The set of rules by which information encoded in genetic material (DNA or RNA sequences) is translated into proteins (amino acid sequences) by living cells.

Nutrition The study of nutrients and how the body uses them.

Physiology The study of the physical and chemical processes of an animal or any of the body systems or cells of the animal.

Animal health The study and practice of maintaining animals as near to a constant state of health as is possible and feasible.

Ethology The study of animals in their natural surroundings.

Applied ethology The study of behavior in domestic animals.

Meat science The science of handling, distributing, and marketing meat and meat products.

Meat The flesh of animals used for food.

Dairy product science The science of providing milk and milk products as food.

Biotechnology A collective set of tools and applications of living organisms, or parts of organisms, to make or modify products, improve plants or animals, or develop microorganisms for specific uses.

ANIMAL DISTRIBUTION

There are approximately 4.5 billion large farm animals and 19.8 billion poultry distributed throughout the world (Table 1–1). The number of large farm animals has been increasing at an average rate of about 1% annually for three decades. During that time there have been shifts in the size of individual species populations

Table 1–1
AGRICULTURAL ANIMAL NUMBERS IN THE WORLD

	World Total	South America and the Caribbean	North and Central America	Oceania	Africa	Europe	Asia
Large Farm Animals							
Cattle (head)[1]	1,356,712,486	341,385,050	156,386,372	38,550,319	262,284,948	127,771,556	430,334,240
Sheep (head)	1,089,122,420	76,031,729	14,876,215	122,810,949	284,537,622	135,847,109	455,018,796
Pigs (head)	929,513,715	60,059,612	98,215,858	5,541,593	25,417,889	194,116,935	546,161,826
Goats (head)	839,855,010	25,600,260	11,991,274	972,755	284,846,006	17,951,905	498,492,809
Buffalo (head)	178,089,540	1,146,981		205	4,355,016	281,734	172,305,604
Horses (head)	58,851,371	16,347,025	17,201,053	416,357	4,445,260	6,364,559	14,077,117
Asses (head)	42,866,652	3,863,139	3,364,805	9,000	17,863,831	641,837	17,124,039
Camels (head)	24,369,291				20,635,089	7,143	3,727,058
Mules (head)	11,608,620	2,845,522	3,506,051		1,048,768	223,282	3,984,997
Other camelids (head)[2]	6,835,086	6,835,086					
Total	4,537,824,189	527,279,318	305,541,629	168,301,178	905,434,429	483,206,061	2,141,226,488
Rabbits and Rodents[3]							
Rabbits (1,000 head)	1,213,705	282,547	4,240		80,849	326,593	519,475
Other rodents (1,000 head)	67,500	67,500					
Poultry							
Chickens (1,000 head)	17,859,361	2,133,904	2,851,506	127,091	1,395,400	1,931,296	9,420,164
Ducks (1,000 head)	1,094,067	7,949	16,497	1,197	16,815	56,298	995,310
Geese & guinea fowl (1,000 Head)	342,168	398	300	78	12,362	21,730	307,300
Turkeys (1,000 head)	473,499	52,063	278,474	111,902	15,857	111,902	13,343
Total (1,000 head)	19,769,096	2,194,315	3,146,778	130,227	1,440,434	2,121,226	10,736,117
Insects							
Beehives (number)	64,750,626	5,520,872	5,098,466	699,079	16,167,361	16,174,450	21,090,398
Silkworm cocoons (MT)	422,510	8,097			170	1,246	413,000

Source: FAO, 2011.
[1]Includes yaks.
[2]Includes both llamas and alpacas.
[3]Producing animals slaughtered.
[4]Primarily guinea pigs.

Table 1–2
CONTRIBUTIONS OF ANIMALS TO HUMAN SOCIETIES

Food

Eggs	Blood
Meat	Fat
Milk	Edible slaughter by-products

Body Coverings

Wool
Leather, pelts, hides
Hair, fur, feathers

Work

Draft and other labor
Transportation

Body Wastes

Fuel	Construction material
Fertilizer	Animal feed

Other Uses

Income	Religion and other cultural needs
Storage of capital	Slaughter by-products
Storage of food	Recreation and sport
Biomedical research models	Pest and weed control
Contributions to the economy	Companionship and service
Buffer for fluctuating grain supplies	Pet foods and treats
Soil fertility enhancement	Conservation
Prestige	

Source: McDowell, 1991, and Turman, 1986.

and their worldwide distribution. Poultry numbers have increased more rapidly at an average rate of over 5% annually. Until very recently, greater than two-thirds of the large farm animals were found in developing countries, but they produced only about a third each of the meat, milk, and wool produced in the world. Reasons for the low productivity include environmental stresses, disease challenges, lack of access to technology, and different objectives of livestock production. However, the world agricultural order is undergoing profound changes, which are causing a greater percentage of the world's livestock to be found in the developing world. In addition, the productivity of the livestock in the developing world is improving dramatically.

Agricultural animals have made a major contribution to the welfare of human societies for millennia by providing a variety of products and services, as shown in Table 1–2. They are a **renewable resource,** and they use another renewable resource—plants—to produce these products and services.

Renewable resources Those resources that can be replaced or produced by natural ecological cycles or management systems.

CONTRIBUTIONS OF ANIMALS TO HUMANITY

A detailed look at animal use comes later in this book. This section briefly surveys some of the many contributions of livestock and other animals to humans.

Food Source

Humans are **omnivores,** consuming both plant- and animal-based foods. Figure 1–2 shows the contributions of different food sources to the world food supply. Although food is the most important contribution of agricultural animals to humans, plants

Omnivore An animal that eats both animal- and plant-based feeds.

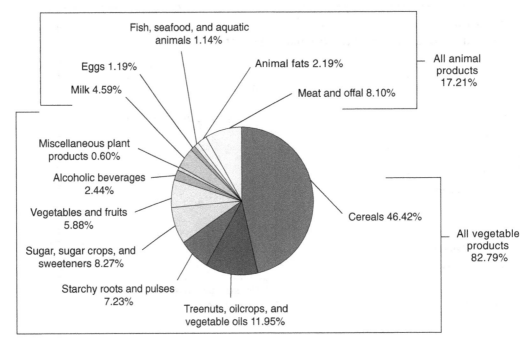

Figure 1–2

Contributions of food sources to human energy (calorie) consumption.

(Source: FAO, 2011a.)

supply a greater total quantity of food. Plants supply 82.8% of the total food energy consumed by the world's people, primarily because such a high percentage of the human diet in the developing countries is of plant origin. Animal products supply the remaining 17.2%. In developed countries, animals contribute a greater percentage of the total food energy. In the United States, for instance, they provide 27%. Animals are a more important source of protein than they are of calories (Figure 1–3), supplying 38.5% of the protein consumed in the world. Of the animal protein sources, meat provides approximately 49.5%, milk provides approximately 25.8%, fish supplies approximately 16%, and eggs supply 8.7%. Developed countries obtain a greater percentage of their total protein from animal products. The United States, for example, gets approximately 64% of its protein from animal products. Table 1–3 shows a more

Figure 1–3

Contributions of food sources to human protein consumption.

(Source: FAO, 2010a.)

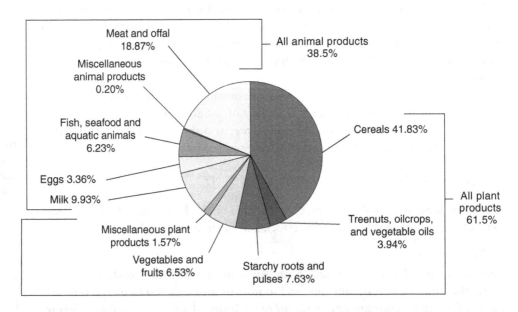

Table 1–3

PERCENTAGE CONTRIBUTION OF FOOD GROUPING TO VARIOUS NUTRIENTS IN THE U.S. FOOD SUPPLY

Nutrient	Meat, Poultry, Fish	Dairy (excl. butter)	Eggs	Total Animal	Vegetables	Legumes, Nuts, Soy	Grains	Fruits	Fats and Oils	Sugars and Sweeteners	Misc[1]
Energy	14	9	1	24	4	3	24	3	24	17	1
Protein	41	19	4	64	5	6	22	1	0	0	2
Total Fat	21	11	2	34	0	4	2	1	58	0	1
SFAs[2]	24	22	2	48	0	2	2	0	47	0	1
MUFAs[2]	22	7	2	31	0	4	1	1	62	0	1
PUFAs[2]	12	2	1	15	1	6	4	1	73	0	0
Cholesterol	45	14	35	94	0	0	0	0	5	0	0
Vitamin A	23	20	5	48	32	0	6	3	9	0	0
Vitamin E	4	2	2	8	6	6	4	3	74	0	0
Vitamin C	2	1	0	3	47	0	5	43	0	0	0
Thiamin	18	5	1	24	8	5	60	3	0	0	0
Riboflavin	17	27	6	50	5	2	39	0	0	1	1
Niacin	37	1	0	38	9	4	44	2	0	0	2
Vitamin B$_6$	38	6	2	46	21	4	19	7	0	0	0
Folate	4	3	3	10	11	10	61	6	0	0	1
Vitamin B$_{12}$	70	24	6	100	0	0	0	0	0	0	0
Calcium	4	70	2	76	7	4	5	3	0	1	2
Phosphorus	25	31	4	60	7	6	20	2	0	0	4
Magnesium	13	13	1	27	13	14	24	6	0	1	14
Iron	15	2	3	20	9	7	51	2	0	1	6
Zinc	37	17	3	57	6	6	26	1	0	0	4
Copper	21	3	2	26	11	19	21	5	0	2	16

Source: USDA, 2010.

[1]Coffee, tea, chocolate-liquor equivalent of coca beans, spices, and fortification of foods not assigned to a specific group.

[2]SFAs = saturated fatty acids; MUFAs = monounsaturated fatty acids; PUFAs = polyunsaturated fatty acids.

Nutrient density A measurement of the nutrients provided in a food compared to the calories it contains.

Diet The total of the foods and water being consumed by an individual or group.

Essential amino acids Those amino acids required by the body that must be consumed in the diet.

Undernourished Receiving inadequate nourishment for proper health and growth.

complete picture of the contribution of various foods to the U.S. food supply. Meat, eggs, and dairy products are important food sources because they are **nutrient dense.** This means they have many nutrients compared to their calories, and the nutrients are digestible and readily available. High-quality protein and biologically available levels of vitamins and minerals, as well as a significant amount of energy, are supplied to the **diet** by animal foods.

Animal foods are generally preferred over plant foods by human populations, and the vast majority of the world's population routinely chooses food produced from animals in its diet. A country's living standards can be gauged by the proportion of its food supply that consists of animal foods. Time and again, people have demonstrated that increasing animal-derived foods in their diet is one of the first things they will do when their income increases. Not only are animal foods palatable and delicious, they are also the most nutritionally complete foods. They are an important source of vitamins and minerals, and the protein in animal foods is more likely than are plant proteins to include the **essential amino acids** in the correct proportions.

Absolute food quantity and amount of animal products are more available to some of the world's peoples than to others. Approximately 27% of the calories in the average diet in North America is from animal products compared to 7.4% for the average African. There is also a tremendous difference in food distribution to the world's peoples. The average African eats only 66% of the daily calories eaten by the average North American. Globally, over 1 billion people are **undernourished.**

Most people include meat and dairy products in their diets whenever they can. Exceptions are almost always because of religious prohibitions (prohibitions against beef consumption by Hindus, for example) or because of prohibitive costs. The world's meat (excluding fish) is predominantly supplied by pigs, cattle, and poultry with lesser amounts from sheep, goats, buffalo, and horses. Several other species provide a significant amount of meat to the people of various geographic regions. Most milk comes from cows, but buffalo, goats, and sheep provide significant amounts of milk, and most domestic hooved animals are milked somewhere in the world.

Other Uses

In addition to food, other animal products are also of great importance to humans, who have used wool, hair and other fibers, feathers, and hides for millennia for clothing and other uses (Figure 1–4). Manure from animals is a valuable by-product used for fertilizer and other applications (Figure 1–5).

Figure 1–4
Hides are a slaughter byproduct that humans have used since long before domestication. (Photo courtesy of Adele M. Kupchik.)

Figure 1–5
Liquid manure from a hog-feeding operation in Iowa is being pumped onto cropland with a "honey wagon." (Photo by Tim McCabe. Courtesy of USDA Natural Resources Conservation Service.)

Slaughter by-products are the source of a large number of industrial and consumer products. Some examples include pharmaceuticals, insecticides, crayons, cosmetics, plastics, cellophane, glass, water filters, plywood adhesive, soap, gelatin, air filters, and animal feed (Figure 1–6).

Draft animals are vitally important to many Asian, African, and Latin American countries. Oxen plow fields; water buffalo work in rice paddies; yaks, donkeys, and camels still trudge over ancient trade routes; and dogs still pull sleds (Figure 1–7). Much of the world's food production in less developed regions is dependent on draft animals, as is transportation of goods to and from markets. Tasks such as carrying water and fuel are significant contributions of draft animals. As much as 80% of the nonhuman power of subsistence agriculture is provided by draft animals.

Draft animal An animal whose major purpose is to perform work that involves hauling or pulling. An ox or horse pulling a plow or wagon is a draft animal.

Animals are used as models for humans in biomedical research. Thirty years have been added to the average American life span since 1900. In addition, the quality of life for people afflicted with chronic diseases has been improved dramatically. Medical research depends on the use of animals as models. It will continue to do so

Figure 1–6
Slaughter by-products are used in the manufacture of a variety of industrial and consumer products. (Photo courtesy of Adele M. Kupchik.)

Figure 1–7
Draft animals are still the most important nonhuman power source in developing countries.

in the foreseeable future (Figure 1–8). In addition, animals are used in research to benefit animal health, resulting in healthier, longer-lived pets and healthier, more productive livestock.

Animal companionship is important to people around the world, enhancing human physical, emotional, and spiritual well-being. Specially trained animals assist people with visual disabilities (guide animal), hearing disabilities (hearing or signal animal), and other disabilities (service or assistance animal), helping people live more independently (Figure 1–9). Therapy animals are commonplace.

In addition, many entertainment industries such as racing, rodeos, and bull-fighting are based on animal use (Figure 1–10).

Agricultural animals convert inedible feeds to valuable products. About two-thirds of the feed used in the U.S. livestock industry is not suitable for human

Figure 1–8
Biomedical research depends on the use of animals as research models. This two-year-old Spanish goat underwent a successful cleft palate repair in utero. Goats were first developed as an animal model for the study of lupine-induced crooked calf syndrome. The model is now playing a role in developing proce-dures for prenatal repair of cleft palate in children. (Photographer Peggy Greb. Courtesy of USDA-Agricultural Research Service.)

Figure 1–9
Service dogs help people with disabilities. Here, a Seeing Eye® dog in action, with student and instructor, on the streets of Morristown, New Jersey. The dog has stopped the person from proceeding across the driveway as the van turns. (Photo courtesy of The Seeing Eye, Inc. Used with permission.)

Figure 1–10
Many entertainment industries are based on animal use. Horse racing is among the most popular. (Source: Clarence Alford/Fotolia)

consumption. Hay, pasture, coarse forages, by-products, garbage, and damaged food are examples. Animal use diversifies agriculture, the food supply, and the economy. Diversified agriculture is more stable and more sustainable.

THE FUTURE OF LIVESTOCK PRODUCTION

Global livestock production is undergoing huge increases in animals and products with further increases predicted. To keep pace with demand, many are predicting the need to double animal product output by 2050. This increasing animal production is being referred to as the **livestock revolution,** and it is being likened to the cereal grains boom of the **green revolution,** which began in the 1960s and is credited with saving millions of lives and building many national economies.

The forces driving increased global demand for animal products are simple: human population growth and increasing income. Unprecedented economic development around the world is increasing **per capita** income. The world's human population is increasing and is projected to reach approximately 9 billion by 2050. These factors are causing increased per capita consumption of animal products and large increases in total demand. Most of the new demand for animal products is in

Livestock revolution
Large increases in supply and demand of livestock and animal products worldwide at the end of the 20th century and into the 21st century.

Green revolution Dramatic improvements in grain production in developing countries during the 1960s to the 1980s because of technological innovation and application.

Per capita Per unit of population: by or for each person.

Biofuel Gas or liquid fuel made from biological materials, such as crops and animal waste.

developing countries, which are expected to soon produce the majority of the world's meat and milk. Along with the increased demand for animal products is an increased demand for other agricultural commodities to feed people and livestock. In addition, the world's developing demand for **biofuel** production will increasingly play a role in food availability and prices.

The challenges associated with these profound changes in agriculture are significant. The prime agricultural lands are already in use, and, worldwide, the potential new agricultural lands are covered by forests, under human settlements and infrastructure, or likely to be marginally productive. With increased human population, agricultural land per person will continue to decrease. Therefore, agricultural land will need to be more productive. To make this happen, there is a pressing need for research and subsequent technology development to increase productivity per unit of land. Agriculture of all kinds has the potential to affect the environment both negatively and positively. For the sake of future generations, we must achieve these massive increases in yield while protecting air, soil, and water quality. Combined, the opportunities and the challenges suggest an unprecedented dynamic period in the world agricultural order.

SUMMARY AND CONCLUSION

Animal science has its roots in the challenges that the first domesticators of animals encountered many millennia ago when they permanently brought in animals from the wild. Today, animal science is a vital field with specialties in genetics and animal breeding, nutrition, physiology, animal health, animal behavior, meat and dairy product science, and biotechnology. Animals are used for a myriad of purposes, including food, fiber, work, research, companionship, and entertainment.

Although agricultural animals have come under attack in recent years by those who feel they are a luxury, the numbers of agricultural animals are steadily increasing, and they are becoming more important in helping to feed the human population. For this reason, we should learn something about the factors that determine the kinds of agricultural animals found throughout the world. Chapter 2 explores in depth the contributions animals make to humankind.

STUDY QUESTIONS

1. Define animal science. When did animal science begin?
2. Explain why all of the world's occupations are tied to agriculture.
3. When did animal domestication occur? When were each of the major species domesticated? Was domestication a conscious decision by humans?
4. Define the specialties of animal science.
5. Why is the specialization in animal science disciplines both a help and a hindrance?
6. Study Table 1–1, which gives livestock numbers in the world. Notice the relative numbers of each species. Offer some reasons why animals are distributed as they are. Based on the numbers in this table, what are the world's major farm species?
7. Table 1–2 gives an overview of the goods and services derived from domestic animals by humans. (These are explored in detail later in the text.) Develop a list of uses from this table that are ranked from "most useful" to "least useful" from your current perspective. (At the end of the book, come back to your list and see if your perspective has changed.)
8. What proportion of human food energy and protein comes from animal products?
9. What proportion of the U.S. calorie and protein supply comes from animal products? How do other countries compare?
10. If a person does not eat meat, what are the most common reasons?
11. Which animals supply most of the world's meat?
12. Meat is important as a food for the human population because it is nutrient dense. What does "nutrient density" mean?
13. List some of the important products made from by-products of the slaughter industry.

14. How important are draft animals to subsistence agriculture? Name six important draft animals.

15. What is the role of animals in medical research?

16. Briefly discuss some of the ways that animals provide companionship, recreation, and entertainment to humans.

17. What types of humanly unusable feeds do animals convert to valued products?

18. Why is a diversified agriculture important, and what role do animals have in diversification?

19. What is the livestock revolution, and what are some of its challenges?

REFERENCES

A.D.A.M. Medical Encyclopedia [Internet]. Atlanta (GA): A.D.A.M., Inc.; ©2005. Malnutrition; [updated 2009 May 12; cited 2010 June 10]. Available from: http://www.nlm.nih.gov/medlineplus/ency/article/000404.htm#Definition

Allport, S. 2000. *The Primal Feast: Food, Sex, Foraging, and Love.* Harmony Books, New York, NY.

American Association for Laboratory Animal Science. 2010. Use of Animals in Biomedical research: understanding the issues. http://www.aalas.org/pdf/08-00007.pdf

Bourden, R. M. 2000. *Understanding animal breeding.* Upper Saddle River, NJ: Prentice Hall.

Council for Agricultural Science and Technology. 1980. *Food from animals: Quantity, quality and safety.* Report No. 82. Ames, IA: Council for Agricultural Science and Technology.

Council for Agricultural Science and Technology. 1997. *Contribution of animal products to healthful diets.* Report No. 131. Ames, IA: Council for Agricultural Science and Technology.

Council for Agricultural Science and Technology. 1999. *Animal agriculture and global food supply.* Report No. 135. Ames, IA: Council for Agricultural Science and Technology.

Delgado, C., M. Rosegrant, H. Steinfeld, S. Ehui, and C. Courbois. 1999. *Livestock to 2020: The next food revolution.* Washington, DC: International Food Policy Research Institute.

FAO. 2002. *World agriculture: Towards 2015/2030.* Rome: Food and Agricultural Organization of the United Nations.

FAO. 2009. *The state of food and agriculture: Livestock in the balance.* Rome: Food and Agricultural Organization of the United Nations.

FAO. 2009a. *The state of food insecurity in the world 2009.* Accessed online July 2010. ftp://ftp.fao.org/docrep/fao/012/i0876e/i0876e.pdf.

FAO. 2011. *FAOSTAT statistics database: Production: Live animals.* http://faostat.fao.org/site/573/default.aspx#ancor.

FAO. 2011a. *FAOSTAT statistics database: Food supply.* http://faostat.fao.org/site/345/default.aspx

FAO. 2010. *Draught animal power: An overview.* http://www.fao.org/ag/ags/agse/chapterps1/chapterps1-e.htm

Foundation for Biomedical Research. 2008. *Proud achievements of animal research.* 6th ed. Washington, DC: Foundation for Biomedical Research.

Gillespie, J. R. 1987. *Animal nutrition and feeding.* Albany, NY: Delmar.

Houpt, K. A. 2005. *Domestic animal behavior.* 4th ed. Ames, IA: Blackwell Publishing Professional.

Jensen, P. 2002. *The ethology of domestic animals.* Wallingford, UK: CAB International.

Jordan-Bychkov, T. G., M. Domosh, R. P. Neumann, and P. L. Price. 2008. *The human mosaic: A thematic introduction to cultural geography.* 10th ed. New York: W. H. Freeman.

Larsen, C. S. 2003. Animal source foods and human health during evolution. Journal of Nutrition 133(11 Suppl 2):3893S–3897S.

McDowell, R. E. 1984. The need to know about animals. In *World food issues,* M. Droskoff, ed. Ithaca, NY: Center for Analyses of World Food Issues, Cornell University.

McDowell, R. E. 1991. *A partnership for humans and animals.* Raleigh, NC: Kinnic Publishers, Kinnickinnic Agri-Sultants.

Otten, J. J., J. P. Hellwig, and L. D. Meyers, eds. 2006. *Dietary reference intakes: The essential guide to nutrient requirements.* Washington, DC: National Academies Press.

OECD-FAO. 2010. *OECD-FAO agricultural outlook 20010–2019.* Paris: Organization for Economic Co-operation and Development; Rome: Food and Agricultural Organization of the United Nations.

Reed, C. A. 1974. *The beginnings of animal domestication in animal agriculture in the biology, husbandry, and use of domestic animals.* 2nd ed. H. H. Cole and W. N. Garrett, eds. San Francisco: W. H. Freeman.

Smith, B. D. (1995) *The emergence of agriculture.* Scientific American Library, New York, NY.

Steckel, R. S. & Rose, J. C., eds. (2002) *The backbone of history: health and nutrition in the western hemisphere.* Cambridge University Press, New York, NY.

Taylor, R. E., and T. G. Field. 2008. *Scientific farm animal production.* 9th ed. Upper Saddle River, NJ: Prentice Hall.

Turman, E. J. 1986. *Agricultural animals of the world.* Stillwater: Oklahoma State University.

USDA. 2010. *Agricultural statistics.* Washington, DC: National Agricultural Statistics Service. Accessed online June 27, 2010. http://www.nass.usda.gov/index.asp

2

The Value of Animals to Humanity

Key Terms

By-products
Civilization
Companion animal
Compost
Conservation
Draft
Essential fatty acids
Food and Agricultural Organization
   of the United Nations (FAO)
Health research
Hides
Meat
Metric ton

Milk
Nutrient density
Nutrients
Per capita
Pest control
Pesticides
Poultice
Power
Recombinant DNA
Spectator sport
Storage of capital
Wool
Xenotransplantation

Learning Objectives

After you have studied this chapter, you should be able to:

- Describe the value of animal products in providing for the world's food.
- Explain the current rates of growth or decline of animal products on a worldwide basis.
- Elaborate on the milk-producing species, state their importance to world milk production, and understand what is happening to world milk production.
- Describe the value of eggs in feeding the world's people.
- Develop a modest understanding of some miscellaneous food uses for the world's animals.
- Explain the value of animal products in the human diet.
- Give a good overview of all the many nonfood uses humans have for the world's animals.

INTRODUCTION

What did humans derive from domestication? Why do we need domestic animals in today's world? The answer to both questions is essentially the same, and the answer comes in several parts: Food is the first answer. When humans turned from hunters to farmers by domesticating animals and plants, we created a much more readily available food supply and set the stage for great advancement in culture. What we think of as civilization began to develop.

Goods and services from the world's animal populations supply many social, religious, and economic functions in addition to food. The importance of each good or service varies depending on many factors, including the ethnicity of the owners, the country, and the environment. Nonfood uses for animals are generally more important in wealthier societies than they are in less wealthy ones, although there are notable exceptions. In this chapter, we examine the major contributions of agricultural animals to humanity.

THE FOOD USES OF AGRICULTURAL ANIMALS

Red Meat and Poultry Production

Nutrients Chemical substances that provide nourishment to the body. Essential nutrients are those necessary for normal maintenance, growth, and functioning.

Per capita Per unit of population, by or for each person.

The **nutrients** provided by meat are important for human survival. Protein and energy are quantitatively and qualitatively important and substantial shares of the vitamins and minerals in our diet are also contributed by meat. Annual **per capita** meat supply ranges from over 300 lbs in affluent countries to very little in poor countries (Figure 2–1). World meat production has increased steadily for many years at an average rate of 2% per year. Table 2–1 shows the meat production for most meat-producing species. The pig is the most important meat source, producing 38% of the world's meat (Figure 2–2). Chicken is next at 28%, followed by beef with approximately 23% (Figure 2–3). Together, these three sources produce 89% of all meat. Pork production is increasing at the rate of approximately 1–2% per year.

Figure 2–1

Per capita meat supply in pounds, selected countries and the world.

(Source: FAO, 2011.)

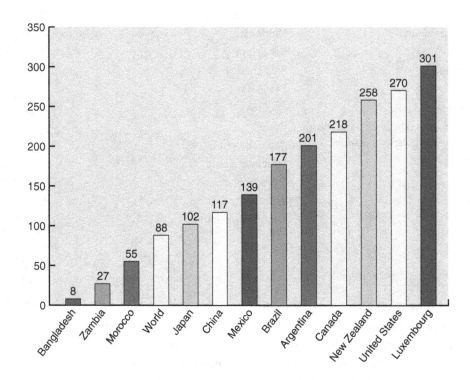

Table 2–1
WORLD MEAT PRODUCTION (1,000 METRIC TONS)

	1990	2000	2005	2009
Meat, total	179,860	233,404	259,132	281,559
Pig meat	69,922	89,787	99,064	106,069
Chicken meat	35,350	58,307	69,188	79,596
Beef and buffalo meat	55,318	59,100	62,145	65,146
Sheep meat	7,031	7,664	7,881	8,109
Duck, goose, and guinea fowl meat	1,853	4,779	5,413	6,321
Turkey meat	3,717	5,071	5,161	5,320
Goat meat	2,656	3,770	4,636	4,939
Rabbit	933	1,294	1,476	1,645
Equine	584	993	1,008	1,018
Meat, all other	856	716	1,070	1,222

Source: FAO, 2011.

Figure 2–2
The pig is the most important meat-producing species. Many pigs are unimproved animals that either scavenge or are fed household wastes.

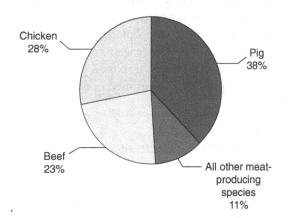

Figure 2–3
Relative contribution of the major meat species to world meat supplies.
(Source: FAO, 2011.)

Production from most other meat-producing species is increasing 1–2% yearly. Poultry meat production is growing the most rapidly at almost 3% per year, more than doubling since 1990. Poultry meat is increasing much faster than the average rate for all other meats and thus is becoming an increasingly larger part of total world meat production (Figure 2–4). Poultry meat could overtake pork as the world's most popular meat by 2020. Some developing countries are undergoing phenomenal production increases with several producing three times as much poultry meat per year as they were producing 10 years ago. This increase is primarily in response to two things. First, the technology, genetics, and management know-how associated with

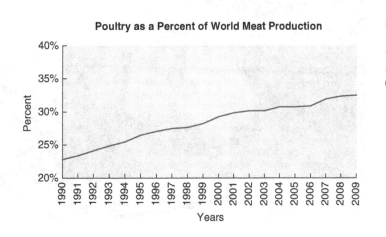

Figure 2–4
World poultry-meat production is increasing more rapidly than any other meat.
(Source: FAO 2011.)

the poultry industry have made its production much more cost effective. Second, economic development in many countries has increased incomes, thus providing the economic means to a better diet for more people. Invariably, people demonstrate their willingness to purchase more meat for their diets as soon as they are able to afford it.

Edible Slaughter By-Products

Once the products of greatest value are removed from a carcass, the substances and products remaining still have value. We commonly refer to these as *by-products*. Some of these by-products are edible, and others are not. Table 2–2 provides a partial list of edible by-products of meat animals. In developed countries, these by-products are usually considered specialty foods and are called variety meats. Most are organ meats such as liver, kidney, tongue, sweetbread, brain, heart, and tripe. These products are often considered delicacies (Figure 2–5). However, in the United States, we are not as fond of them as is the rest of the world, so we export large quantities to Europe and other countries. Liver is the most widely used. Brains and spinal cords are no longer consumed in many parts of the world because of the concerns over transmission of bovine spongiform encephalopathy.

An additional large share comes from edible fat, and both blood and blood plasma are eaten and used in food processing. Additionally, hides and bones are processed to produce gelatins used in desserts and food processing.

Table 2–2
EDIBLE BY-PRODUCTS FROM ANIMALS

Brain	Pancreas
Cheek meat, ears, and snouts	Spleen
Feet, pigs' feet, knuckles, and calves' feet	Stomach
Head meat	Sweetbreads (thymus)
Heart	Tail or oxtails
Intestines (often used as sausage casings)	Tallow and lard
Kidney	Testes
Lips	Tongue
Liver	Tripe (usually rumen and reticulum)
Lungs	Udders
Melts (spleen)	Uteri

Figure 2–5
Offered side by side in this Mexican meat market are hearts, lungs, other organ meats, feet, tripe, and carcass meat, fresh and still warm from the morning's premarket slaughter. Food tastes and traditions vary, and not all people agree on what is the product of a carcass and what is a by-product.

Milk and Milk Products

Milk provides much-needed protein, energy, minerals, and vitamins to humankind's diet. Annual per capita whole milk supply ranges from over 500 lbs per year in some countries to little or none in others. The total production of milk in the world has increased slowly for the last two decades. Total world milk production is increasing by approximately 2% per year. World milk production for the major species is given in Table 2–3. On a worldwide basis, approximately 83% of milk is from cattle, 13% is from buffalo, and most of the remainder is from sheep, camels, and goats (Figure 2–6). Humans use almost 700 million **metric tons (MT)** of milk per year. This includes fluid milk and processed milk. Table 2–4 shows the world production of the major processed milk products. Often, dairy products supply the major source of fat in human diets. In addition to adding flavor to high-starch foods such as rice and root crops, fats also provide needed calories and **essential fatty acids** to the diet.

Metric ton (MT) Approximately 1.1 U.S. tons. Equal to 1 million grams, or 1,000 kilograms.

Essential fatty acids Fatty acids required in the diet.

Ghee Clarified liquid butter.

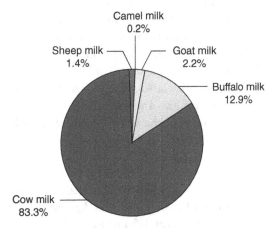

Camel milk
0.2%

Sheep milk
1.4%

Goat milk
2.2%

Buffalo milk
12.9%

Cow milk
83.3%

Figure 2–6
Relative percentage of world milk supply by species.
(Source: FAO, 2011.)

Table 2–3
MILK PRODUCED IN METRIC TONS BY THE WORLD'S MAJOR SPECIES

	1980	1990	2000	2009	Rank in 2009
Cow milk (whole, fresh)	422,351,163	479,029,292	490,130,037	580,481,508	1
Buffalo milk	27,525,084	44,075,742	66,500,380	90,333,830	2
Goat milk	7,738,026	9,979,850	12,652,528	15,128,186	3
Sheep milk	6,822,721	7,978,108	8,034,961	8,974,689	4
Camel milk	1,220,464	1,353,394	1,440,565	1,636,123	5
Total milk	465,657,460	542,416,356	578,758,472	696,544,346	

Source: FAO, 2011.

Table 2–4
WORLD DAIRY PRODUCT PRODUCTION IN METRIC TONS

	1980	1990	2000	2009	Rank in 2009
Cheese	11,514,659	14,834,708	16,530,939	19,358,614	1
Butter and **ghee**	6,955,142	7,838,819	7,408,557	9,639,570	2
Evaporated and condensed milk	4,339,639	4,240,879	4,046,042	4,732,761	3
Skim milk and buttermilk, dry	4,177,542	4,280,474	3,360,387	3,322,310	4
Dry whole cow milk	1,726,766	2,085,963	2,503,471	2,957,307	5

Source: FAO, 2011.

Dairying has been promoted in the developing countries for several decades by several major international agencies. Dairy industry promotion assists development in several ways. In addition to improving nutrition, it also provides year-round employment (as opposed to crops that have seasonal labor needs). The year-round income bolsters the overall economy. Dairying is also a very efficient means of converting animal feed to people food.

Poultry and Eggs

In addition to meat (Table 2–1), the various poultry species produce a second high-quality food for human consumption—eggs. Poultry offer great potential for improving the nutritional levels of all the world's peoples. As food producers, they have many advantages. Poultry require a low initial investment and, if necessary, can produce some food for their owners with only a minimal input in terms of feed, equipment, and housing. They are also generally fairly hardy and prolific.

Eggs are a very important global food source from both a volume and quality perspective. Chickens produce most of the eggs for human consumption (Table 2–5). Their production is increasing at a rate of approximately 2.2% per year worldwide. Ducks, turkeys, geese, and guinea fowl also contribute, but to a much lesser degree. Eggs are an excellent source of high-quality protein and fat. The protein is important to all economic classes. For poor societies, the fat content is a positive factor because it provides calories and essential fatty acids. Note that the number of metric tons of eggs produced in the world is only slightly less than the amount of meat from beef and exceeds meat production from many other species.

Miscellaneous Food Uses

Animals provide several additional foods for humans. World production of honey is estimated by the **Food and Agricultural Organization of the United Nations (FAO)** at just over 1.5 million MT per year (Figure 2–7). A rather exotic way in

Food and Agricultural Organization of the United Nations (FAO)
The largest autonomous agency within the United Nations system. FAO works to alleviate poverty and hunger by promoting agricultural development.

Table 2–5
WORLD EGG PRODUCTION IN METRIC TONS

	1980	1990	2000	2009
Hen eggs, in shell	26,217,375	35,245,563	51,113,006	62,426,378
Other bird eggs, in shell	1,199,336	2,302,657	4,057,432	4,981,371
Total	27,416,712	37,548,221	55,170,439	67,407,749

Source: FAO, 2011.

Figure 2–7
Honey is favored around the world for its sweetness and unique flavor. When fermented with water and yeast it becomes mead or "honey wine." Beeswax also has many uses, including candles and craft-making.
(Source: FAO/19181/M. Marzot. Used with permission by the Food and Agriculture Organization of the United Nations.)

Figure 2–8
The large tails of the fat-tailed sheep breeds are fat storage organs. To acquire this fat, the tail is cut and a hollow reed used to suction out the fat for use in cooking.

which living animals are used for food is as a source of blood collected by venous puncture. Tibetan nomads and African tribesmen (especially the Masai) do this. The fat from the tails of fat-tailed sheep is collected from live animals in Africa and Asia (Figure 2–8). Hides and skins (especially roasted pig) are used for food in many countries, and cattle hides are eaten in Africa and a few other places (Figure 2–9).

The Value of Animal Products in the Human Diet

Animal products are a very important part of human diets because they are high-quality food. They are excellent sources of protein, energy, minerals, and essential vitamins. The nutrient availability is good and the **nutrient density** is high. In wealthy societies, meat and fish are the foods around which meals are built—the meat or fish is chosen first, and the rest of the meal is selected to complement it. In most developed countries, meat accounts for the largest share of food cost. Affluent families in developing countries spend similar amounts. Low-income groups spend less, due to cost. However, these groups identify animal products of all types as desirable or essential food items. In addition to the nutritive value, animal products supplement the taste of the bland, starchy foods that, of necessity, form the bulk of their diets.

Nutrient density A measurement of the nutrients found in a food compared to the caloric content.

Figure 2–9
Roasted pigskins are a popular food in many countries. They are eaten as is or used in cooking. These were roasted and spiced and on sale in bulk.

THE NONFOOD USES OF AGRICULTURAL ANIMALS

Table 2–6 lists the great variety of important contributions that various species of domestic animals provide for humans in addition to food. Some of these uses are outside the social context of people who live in developed countries, which makes it difficult for us to understand the great magnitude of these contributions to people's

Table 2–6
ANIMAL CONTRIBUTIONS OF SERVICES AND NONFOOD PRODUCTS

Classification	Contribution	Main Sources
Draft power	Crop production	Cattle, buffalo, yaks, camels, horses, donkeys, mules
	Cartage	Cattle, buffalo, yaks, camels, horses, mules, donkeys, reindeer
	Packing	Camels, yaks, horses, mules, donkeys, reindeer, llamas, sheep, goats
	Herding	Horses, mules, camels, asses
	Irrigation pumping	Buffalo, cattle, camels, asses
	Threshing grains	Cattle, horses, asses
	Transportation	Horses, donkeys, mules, buffalo, camels, reindeer
	Human leisure time	All working species
Storage in animals	Capital	All domestic species
	Grains	Buffalo, cattle, sheep, pigs, poultry
Conservation	Grazing	All domestic herbivores
	Seed distribution	All domestic herbivores
	Soil through crop rotation	Most grazing animals
Ecological	Maintenance	Most animals
	Restoration	Most animals
Pest control	Weeding crops	Domestic ruminants, ducks, geese
	Insects in crops	Poultry, ducks, geese
	Irrigation canals	Buffalo, ducks, geese
Cultural uses	Exhibitions and sports	Horses, cattle, goats, sheep, pigs, buffalo, chickens, dogs, cats
	Bride price	Cattle, goats, sheep, camels
	Religious sacrificial	Sheep, goats, cattle, poultry, buffalo, pigs
	Fighting	Chickens, cattle, buffalo, sheep, dogs, camels
	Pet	All species
	Racing	Horses, cattle, dogs, camels, buffalo
	Status symbol	Horses, cattle, pigs, buffalo, camels, fighting cocks, most species to some degree
	Blood and death restitution	Horses, cattle, buffalo, camels, pigs
Income	Security	Cattle, buffalo, goats, sheep, pigs, all poultry
	Liquidity	All species
	Reduce risks of cropping	All species
Nonarable lands	Income	Cattle, camels, goats, sheep
	Soil fertility in cropping	Cattle, goats, sheep, buffalo
Research	Biomedical and numerous other	All domestic species and fowl
Fiber	Wool, hair, feathers	Sheep, camels, llamas, alpacas, yaks, horses, goats, other mammals
		All fowl
Skins	Hides, pelts	Almost all species
Wastes	Fertilizer, fuel, methane gas, construction material, feed (recycled)	Almost all species
Inedible products	Fat, horns, hooves, bones, tankage, endocrine extracts	All species

Source: McDowell, 1991, pp. 17, 45. Various other sources.

lives. This section explores some of these contributions in greater detail and gives us all the opportunity to have an enhanced appreciation for human dependence on domestic animals.

Body Coverings

The most important products from some animals are their body coverings. Examples are sheep (wool, Persian lambskins, Figure 2–10), goats (cashmere and mohair), and alpacas (Figure 2–11). For other species, the body covering is a by-product rather than the main product. A major advantage of the fiber products is that they are renewable—they can be harvested repeatedly from the same animal. Skins and hides are nonrenewable, at least from the same animal. In countries with a highly developed agriculture, the skins and hides obtained at the time of slaughter are a valuable by-product. However, their contribution to the total value

Figure 2–10
The Karakul sheep produces Persian lambskins that are used in the manufacture of luxurious coats. (Photo courtesy Keith Ramsay.)

Figure 2–11
Alpaca fibers are used to make many products, including novelty items such as this Peruvian crafted rug/wall hanging made exclusively from different colors of alpaca fiber.

Table 2–7
WORLD HIDE AND FIBER PRODUCTION IN METRIC TONS

	1980	1990	2000	2009	Rank in 2009
Cattle hides, fresh	5,658,314	6,307,585	7,393,408	7,869,020	1
Wool, greasy	2,794,157	3,347,708	2,318,537	2,080,190	2
Sheepskins, fresh	1,108,708	1,345,602	1,763,805	1,916,847	3
Goatskins, fresh	390,168	579,437	852,953	1,084,038	4
Buffalo hides, fresh	478,623	613,667	792,824	860,739	5
Silkworm cocoons, reelable	341,660	363,587	342,454	497,529	6
Hair of horses	110	100	130	140	7

Source: FAO, 2011.

of the slaughter is relatively small compared to the value of the carcass. Often, they are shipped to a developing country for processing. In poorer countries, hides or skins (rather than the meat) may be the most valuable animal export product, and they may provide valuable foreign currency. In addition, wool, hair, and feathers are often used in cottage industries to produce clothing, pillows, bedding, carpets, brushes, and handicrafts. World hide and fiber production is shown in Table 2–7. As one might expect, cattle hides, wool, and sheepskins are produced in greatest volume.

Goats yield two types of body coverings that are used for making fabrics—mohair and cashmere. Mohair is clipped from the Angora goat each year just as the fleece is shorn from sheep (Figure 2–12). The average yield is about 6 lbs. Angora goats are raised in several parts of the world. Cashmere, also called pashmina, is the very fine underfur of the Kashmir goat. Kashmir goats are really a type rather than a breed. Almost all goats produce some cashmere. It must be combed out of the coarse, outer guard hair by hand. The average yield is only about 4 oz. Kashmir goats are raised in the high plateaus of Tibet, China, and northern India.

Yaks produce a coarse fiber from which clothing and one of the best horse blankets are made. The long hair of the camel is woven into cloth or blankets primarily for use by the people who own the camels. Camel-owning nomads also use camel

Figure 2–12

The Angora goat produces mohair, which is a valuable fiber in fine-clothing manufacture.

hair as tent fabric material. Camel hair paintbrushes are highly valued by some artists. The other domestic animals of the camel family that yield fiber are the llama and alpaca native to the Andes Mountains of South America. The alpaca produces wool that is of higher quality than most sheep wool.

The Karakul and Kuche are fur-bearing breeds of sheep. Lambs are slaughtered within a few days of birth and the pelts are removed. The Karakul is the best known of the two, yielding Persian lambskins used in the manufacture of very expensive coats. The Karakul thrives in very dry environments. Most are produced in Afghanistan and Namibia. The skins are exported to the developed countries. The pelt of the Kuche is used in making fur hats, collars, and coats. It is seldom exported out of northern Asia.

Feathers are used for pillows, bedding, and clothing (down coats), for jewelry and adornments on clothing (hats), for fishing lures, and as a protein supplement to feed animals. Silk from silkworms is important in production agriculture in China, India, and Uzbekistan, with nine countries producing at least 1,000 MT annually (Figure 2–13).

Power Sources

In a developed agriculture, almost all farm power is provided by machines rather than by animals. In developing countries, however, 50% of the arable land is tilled by **draft** animals. Animals are used for plowing, pulling carts or sleds, and packing. As a general rule, the poorer the country, the greater the dependence on animal power. Oxen, donkeys, horses, buffalos, mules, and camels are the major animal species used for draft purposes. Several other species are used in specific geographic locations, such as yaks, llamas, goats, reindeer, and dogs. Oxen and buffalo are the most powerful in pulling, with oxen being faster on dry land. Horses and mules move the fastest, which is an advantage if high-quality implements are available. Donkeys and camels carry the heaviest loads in relation to body size and are preferred in drier climates. Yaks are best adapted to high altitudes. For many of the world's people, there is no alternative to draft power (Figure 2–14).

Draft To move loads by drawing or pulling. A draft animal is one that is used to draw or pull loads.

Figure 2–13
Silk is one of the most valued natural fibers in the world and is often woven into fine fabrics such as these.
(Brynn Bruijn/ Saudi Aramaco World/ SAWDIA. Used with permission.)

Figure 2–14
Family coming to market in a donkey-powered cart. Oxen, donkeys, horses, water buffalo, mules, and camels are the major draft species, but yaks, llamas, goats, reindeer, and dogs are also used for work.

Body Wastes

Manure   As many as half of the world's farmers depend on animal manure and **compost** from plant residues as their only source of fertilizer (Figure 2–15). Manure is preferred over chemical fertilizers by small farmers who till the land by hand or use crude plows because manure improves soil texture. Manure is also used in the developed countries as a source of soil fertility but not very efficiently. A recent study determined that only 5% of U.S. cropland is fertilized with livestock manure, and most of that is from dairy and hog operations. In many of the poorer areas of the world, manure must be used as a fuel. This is particularly true in very densely populated areas where trees have been cut and used as fuel or for other purposes. In these areas, dried manure, particularly from cattle and buffalo, is an important source of fuel for cooking and heating (Figure 2–16). At higher elevations, yak dung becomes especially important. The sale of this product is an important source of income for many farm families who take dried dung cakes to the cities and sell them. A third use of manure is for construction. Many people in Africa and Asia use cow and/or buffalo manure as plaster for their huts (Figure 2–17). In the upper elevations of Peru and Uruguay, houses are built of blocks made from a mixture of approximately 50% manure plus soil and straw. In other cultures, cow manure is used as an important ingredient in **poultices** for wound healing.

Compost Decayed organic matter used for fertilizing and conditioning land.

Poultice A soft moist mass held between layers of cloth, usually warm, and applied to some area of the body.

Figure 2–15
Body wastes and compost from crops are preferred crop fertilizers for millions of farmers around the world. (Source: FAO Photo/18658/ G. Blank. Used with permission by the Food and Agriculture Organization of the United Nations.)

Figure 2–16
Manure is commonly used for fuel in many places around the world. Shown here are dried-manure-and-straw cakes stacked beside a house for easy access.

Figure 2–17
In many parts of the world, manure is used as a construction material. This Masai hut is plastered with a mixture of mud and dung. (Photo courtesy of R. Dudley and Barbara B. Koy. Used with permission.)

Urine Urine is used to enhance soil fertility in many parts of the world due to its nitrogen, phosphorous, and potassium content. In Asia, cow urine is sprinkled on dirt floors to control dust and pests. In Africa, urine and blood are used to extend the low volume of milk available for human food. Some systems of leather making use urine, and it has historically been used in some methods of textile manufacture and dyeing. It is even used as a rinse for hair, in medicinals, and in religious ceremonies.

Pest and Weed Control

Land that is being left to fallow (rest) can be grazed by animals to control weeds. Their manure rejuvenates the soil. Grazing animals are also frequently used along the edges of canals to control vegetation. Grazing the canals also helps control snailborne diseases in the human population because large numbers of snails are killed under the hooves of the grazing animals. Ducks are also used in irrigation canals because they eat snails and leeches. It is common to use ducks in rice fields after harvest to pick up missed grain and reduce insect populations (Figure 2–18). Animals provide a tremendous service globally by reducing weeds and crop residues on cropland, which must be removed if the land is to be prepared by hand

Figure 2–18
Animals serve important roles in pest and weed control. Ducks are invaluable in rice paddies. They pick up dropped grain after harvest, reduce snail and insect populations, and provide their manure for the next crop. (Photo courtesy of Suzanne Tolleson. Used with permission.)

tools or animal-drawn plows. One method used to accomplish this is to stock the land heavily with animals to remove the weeds, grasses, and residues just before planting. Farmers and pastoralists in Africa often have a centuries-old arrangement to provide mutual service to each other in this way. Consumption of these nuisances adds additional economic value to the cropland through the animal product gained. In Africa, close grazing of vegetation around cropped areas reduces insect numbers by creating a vegetation-free barrier around the crop. The use of animals to control insects and weeds has potential for the developed world as a means of reducing the use of **pesticides** in certain areas.

Pesticides Any agent or poison used to destroy pests including fungicides, insecticides, herbicides, and rodenticides.

Storage of Capital and Food

In many of the poorer developing countries, banks are nonexistent. Even if they exist, people either do not have access to them or do not trust them. As an alternative to banks, people use livestock (particularly cattle) as a vehicle for storing their surplus capital. If money is needed, animals can be sold or often bartered for other needed items (Figure 2–19). Use of livestock for storage of capital has several undesirable effects. Clearly, large herds are desirable, and when they are acquired and maintained, severe overgrazing often results. This is a major reason why desertification increases when the human population increases. A second very undesirable effect is the reluctance of people to sell animals unless money is needed. This prevents the development of an orderly program of marketing and slaughtering of animals such as that found in the developed countries. For maximum utilization of the livestock of a country, such a marketing program must be in place.

Figure 2–19
Cattle are often used to store wealth. When cash is needed, they are sold or bartered, like these animals photographed at a trade day in a remote part of Luzon, Philippines.

The use of animals as storage of food is very important in many countries of the world because animals represent one of the most reliable reserve food supplies. In the richer countries of the world, livestock populations can support the energy and protein requirements of the population for a year or more. Most poor countries have inadequate facilities for storing grain (especially for any long period) without suffering large losses from pests. This is not a problem with animals. Animals assume even greater importance in the storage of food in countries subjected to periodic and prolonged droughts. When the rains do not come, crops fail. Animals can continue to survive for several months, even years, and may be the only means of survival of the human population.

Cultural Uses

For some of the world's peoples, the roles of animals in food supplies and other services can be less important than the cultural roles the animals hold. The most important reason to a given group of people for keeping animals may be cultural.

Religion is a very important cultural role that is given high priority by the world's people. The following is a partial listing of the contributions animals make to cultures.

Exhibitions and Spectator Sports   The animal industries have long used shows as a means of promoting their breeding stock to potential buyers. However, the love of competition is also an important part of this activity. Some people believe the purebred livestock industry in the United States would disappear without this social dimension. The excitement of this activity is catching, as evidenced by 4-H and FFA club animal projects (Figure 2–20). Horses, dogs, cats, small mammals, llamas, and other species are also exhibited in many countries. Activities such as rodeos, fighting (bulls, buffalo, sheep, and chickens), and racing (camels, horses, buffalo, dogs, fowl, turtles, and frogs), together provide billions of person days of recreation annually. In many developing regions, these combined animal recreation events represent the largest source of entertainment for people. In developed countries, they provide viable outlets for viewers and participants and contribute to the economy.

Companionship and Service   The dog and the cat have long and venerable histories of companionship and service to humans (Figure 2–21). However, other species, such as ferrets and small rodents (hamsters, gerbils, rabbits, and so on), and several new species, such as alpacas, llamas, small pigs, hedgehogs, and small primates, are also used. Domestic livestock are also used extensively as pet species in both developed and developing countries. Modern research has demonstrated a myriad of benefits to

Figure 2–20
Exhibition of livestock has a social dimension, in addition to helping promote breeding stock to potential buyers. Here, 4-H and FFA students show their animals at a youth livestock exposition. (Photo courtesy of Kellie Whipple. Used with permission.)

Figure 2–21
Dogs and other animals have long and venerable histories of companionship and service to humans. (Photo courtesy of Dawne Damron-Belote. Used with permission.)

humans from animal companionship. In addition, Seeing Eye dogs, hearing-ear dogs, monkeys to assist paraplegics, drug-search dogs, and a variety of others make valuable contributions to humanity.

Social Structure   The less developed the agriculture, the more livestock are a part of the cultural fabric of the people. In pastoral societies, animals are the wealth left to the next generation. This is especially true of nomads. Animals play an important role in the traditional way that formal contracts are sealed and social obligations met. Marriage contracts involve exchanges of livestock. In tribes where polygamy is practiced, there is pressure to accumulate animals to obtain additional wives. In some tribes, the traditional bride price is so high that young men must work for several years to obtain the necessary livestock for payment. This thus serves an important social function in birth control.

Nonfood or Inedible Slaughter By-Products

Opinions vary about what is edible on a carcass and what is not. Many things that people in developed countries consider inedible are eaten in developing countries. However, a large number of nonfood products are derived from slaughter at all levels of development. A partial listing of sources and products is provided in Table 2–8. In developing countries, various by-products become jewelry, religious implements, tools, fuel, construction material, fly swatters, or musical instruments. These products are often considered indispensable for daily life. In developed countries, many pharmaceuticals and drugs are extracted from animal organs and other tissues. Intestines become sutures; pigskin is used to help burn victims; heart valves are harvested from pigs and used to replace defective valves in human hearts. Many of the inedible meat products are used in pet foods and livestock feeds. Bones and hooves are converted to fertilizer and mineral supplements; inedible fat is used for a variety of purposes, such as lubricants, candles, detergents, crayons, plastics, insecticides, shaving cream, and livestock feeds. These represent multibillion-dollar industries worldwide.

Human Health Research

The number of animal applications to health research are simply too numerous to mention. The average American life span increased by 30 years in the 20th century. Much of that increase was due to health research conducted on animals. In addition,

Table 2–8
NONFOOD SLAUGHTER BY-PRODUCTS

Source	Some Products
Blood	Glue, feed, vaccines, serums
Bones	Buttons, jewelry, gelatin, glue
Digestive tract	Feed, fertilizer
Endocrine glands	Pharmaceuticals
Hides	Leather
Inedible fat	Fatty acids, fuel, soap, candles
Hooves	Gelatin, glue
Horns	Handicrafts, cultural symbols

Source: Adapted from McDowell, 1991, p. 42. Used with permission.

the quality of life for people afflicted with chronic diseases has been improved immeasurably. During World War II, biomedical research began making extraordinary strides in the pursuit of human health. Animals have been used extensively as models in that research. Rats, mice, guinea pigs, hamsters, and rabbits have been the most important species used. In recent decades, more dogs and cats have been used, and currently, pigs and other traditional livestock species are proving very useful. Medical research depends on the use of animals as models and will continue to do so for the foreseeable future. **Recombinant DNA** technology is making animals in research an even more promising aid in fighting disease; for example, animals have been genetically engineered to mimic human disease conditions. Such developments greatly reduce the amount of time needed by scientists to offer cures and treatments for diseases. In addition, **xenotransplantation,** the replacing of human organs with those from animals, is an active and promising area of research.

Recombinant DNA DNA molecules that have had new genetic material inserted into them. A product and tool of genetic engineering.

Xenotransplantation The transplanting of animal organs into humans.

Income

In developed countries, the economic structure depends on specialization. This is true of agriculture as well as other sectors of the economy. Animal agriculture is a highly specialized means of using land and labor to generate earnings. The yearly earnings from animal products represent roughly half the total from agriculture in the United States. Annual cash receipts from animal agriculture exceed $110 billion, with a general upward trend. The average annual increase in cash receipts from animal agriculture was $2.2 billion during the 2000s.

Developing-country agriculture also depends on animals for income. This is evident in the most developed of the developing countries. Their economic systems are operating in much the same way as the developed countries they hope to join in economic status. However, it is also true of the least-developed countries as well. In subsistence systems, animals are frequently the major source of income generated from the farm. Extra income from the livestock is used to buy items such as fertilizer and improved seeds that help the farmers increase overall productivity and increase the standard of living for the family. The local economy is stimulated through increased availability and demand of jobs and products.

Conservation

Domestic animals play vital roles in many land- and water-conservation practices. These roles include controlling pests and adding manure to lands being left to fallow; using alley-cropping systems where leguminous trees are planted in strips with animals and crops alternated between them; and providing alternative use in

Figure 2–22

Sheep grazing under a stand of rubber trees eat weeds and other plants that would otherwise compete with the rubber trees. Valuable food and fiber products are then harvested from the sheep flock.

Stover Parts of the plant left after grain harvest.

tree-cropping systems and weeding stands of palms and other trees (Figure 2–22). The entire concept of sustainable agriculture often depends on having animals in the system.

SUMMARY AND CONCLUSION

Agricultural animals help humans extend their use of the available resources by converting nonedible material to humanly edible food. This conversion is not always efficient or fast. However, allowing animals to eat wheat straw or corn **stover**, or to browse brush or even catch their own insects, reptiles, and rodents, is the only way these resources can be converted to food for humans. People have historically consumed animal products and will go to great lengths to procure them. In so doing, we are balancing our diet, which might otherwise be of a very low quality. The high biological value of protein, coupled with needed vitamins and minerals, makes animal products an essential part of the human diet.

Animals provide humans with a myriad of services in addition to providing food. Without the goods and services provided by animals in addition to food, peoples in developed and developing countries would find it difficult to maintain their living standard and perhaps even to survive. New products are constantly being developed that increase that dependence.

STUDY QUESTIONS

1. Using numbers, compare and contrast the quantity of meat consumed by people in developed and developing countries.
2. What species provide most of the world's meat?
3. Describe the rates of growth in the production of the various meats used by human societies in the world.
4. Cattle produce approximately what percentage of the total milk produced in the world? Which species produces the second largest amount of total milk?
5. Describe the value that dairying can bring to economic development of a country.
6. What species is most important to world egg production?
7. Describe some miscellaneous food uses of animals.
8. Describe the differences in the ways in which meals are selected in wealthy versus poor societies.
9. What is the physiological and nutritional significance of animal products in the human diet?
10. List ten nonfood uses for animals that are most important to you.

11. What are the various body coverings provided by animals? Which animal produces which product?

12. What is meant when we say that skins and hides are nonrenewable but wool is renewable?

13. What is different about the Karakul and the Kuche breeds of sheep as compared to other sheep?

14. What is the value of animal fibers, feathers, and so on, in the cottage industries of poor countries?

15. What are the various uses of draft power? What places in the world rely most on draft power? What species provide the bulk of draft power?

16. Describe the various uses humans have found for the body wastes of animals.

17. Explain how animals are used in pest and weed control. With the expanding number of ranchettes and hobby farms in the United States and other developed countries, can you see opportunities for a resurgence of interest in this low-tech approach to pest control?

18. Explain how animals can be used as storage for capital and food.

19. Describe the significance of animals as a provider of cultural dimensions to people's lives.

20. Compare and contrast the various uses the people of developed and developing countries have for nonfood slaughter by-products.

21. Human health research depends on the use of animals as models for humans. Most diseases for which we have a cure are under control because of the contributions of animals. Which animals are the most important to this research?

22. How do animal industries contribute to income generation in developed and developing countries?

23. How do animals aid in land conservation?

REFERENCES

Bradford, G. E. 1999. Contributions of animal agriculture to meeting global human food demand. *Livestock Production Science* 59: 95–112.

Donald J. M., M. O. Ribaudo, M. J. Livingston, J. Beckman, and W. Huang. 2009. *Manure use for fertilizer and for energy.* Report to Congress. Washington, DC: USDA-Economic Research Service.

FAO. 2000. Animal production service fact-file—draught power. http://www.fao.org/WAICENT/FAOINFO/AGRICULT/aga/agap/factfile.draught.htm.

FAO. 2011. *FAOSTAT statistics database: Agricultural production and production indices data.* http://apps.fao.org/.

Jasiorowski, H. A. 1998. Constraints and opportunities for the future use of animals in human society. In *Proceedings, Special Symposium and Plenary Sessions, The 8th World Conference on Animal Production.* Seoul: Seoul National University.

Kaushik, S. J. 1999. Animals for work, recreation, and sports. *Livestock Production Science* 59: 145–154.

McDowell, R. E. 1977. Ruminant products: More than meat and milk. Winrock Report, Sept. Morrilton, AR: Winrock International Livestock Research and Training Center.

McDowell, R. E. 1991. *A partnership for humans and animals.* Raleigh, NC: Kinnic Publishers, Kinnickinnic Agri-Sultants, Inc. *Author's note.* This chapter borrows very heavily from R. E. McDowell's 1991 work and is done so with his permission.

Marchello, J. A. and E. V. Marchello. 2005. Contributions to Society: Slaughter by-products. In *Encyclopedia of Animal Science,* W. G. Pond and A. W. Bell, eds. New York: Marcel Dekker.

Ramaswany, N. 1994. Draught animals and welfare. *Review of Science and Technology* 13:195–216.

Sansoucy, R., S. Ehui, and H. Fitzhugh. 1996. The contribution of livestock to food security and sustainable development. Keynote paper, Proceedings of the Joint FAO/ILRI Roundtable on Livestock Development Strategies for Low Income Countries. Rome: FAO.

Seré, C., and H. Steinfeld. 1996. World livestock production systems. FAO Animal production and health paper 127. Rome: FAO.

Taylor, R. E. 1995. *Scientific farm animal production.* 5th ed. Upper Saddle River, NJ: Prentice Hall.

Turk, K. L. 1975. Significance of animals in farming systems and in the provision of farm power and pleasure. Prepared for the Rockefeller Foundation Review of the Role of Animals in the Future World Food Supply, April 21–22, New York.

part two
The Biological Sciences of Animal Science

3

Introduction to Nutrition

Key Terms

Applied or production nutritionist	Feedstuff
Ash	Finishing
Balance trial	Growth
Basic nutritionist	Maintenance
Bomb calorimeter	Metabolism trial
Carbohydrates	Minerals
Cellulose	Monogastric
Crude fiber	Nitrogen-free extract (NFE)
Crude protein	Nutrient
Diet	Nutrient requirement
Digestibility	Nutrition
Digestion trial	Palatability
Dry matter	Production
Energy	Protein
Estrous cycle	Ration
Ether extract	Reproduction
Fats	Ruminant
Feed	Van Soest fiber analysis
Feed analysis	Vitamin
Feeding trial	Work

Learning Objectives

After you have studied this chapter, you should be able to:

- Define nutrition and understand the reasons for studying nutrition.
- Explain what a nutrient is and know the difference between dietary essential and nonessential nutrients, classify the nutrients, and list the 50 dietary essential nutrients.
- Describe the general uses of nutrients in the body and discuss the major factors that affect an animal's needs for nutrients.
- Explain in detail the three major types of animal trials that nutritionists use.
- Define and explain feedstuff analysis.
- Summarize the feeds evaluation procedures described in this chapter.

INTRODUCTION

Nutrition is the study of how the body uses the nutrients in feed to sustain life and for productive purposes. Nutrition is a very complicated science. To study nutrition adequately, we must study the nutrients and consider how animals consume, digest, absorb, transport, metabolize, and excrete them. We must further consider how the body uses nutrients for productive purposes, and then consider the economics of feeding and the potential effects to the human population of various feeds, additives, medicinals, and so on. Good nutrition is basic to good health and production.

In commercial livestock production, it is important to study nutrition to be able to feed livestock cost effectively. Depending on the type of enterprise, the cost of feed and feeding is 45–75% of the total cost of livestock production. You cannot make money in animal production agriculture without properly feeding the livestock.

Nutrition The study of the body's need and mechanism of acquiring, digesting, transporting, and metabolizing nutrients.

The study of nutrition is important for several other reasons. Nutrition affects general health and well-being, physical abilities, and susceptibility to and ability to recover from disease. Nutrition is also an intricate part of many body systems. If we understand nutrition, we can understand those systems. Studying nutrition provides an excellent opportunity to understand the basic "bio-logic" of life—you cannot understand nutrition without understanding the basis of life, and you cannot understand the basis of life without understanding nutrition.

The field of nutrition is broad and encompasses much information: nutritionists thus need to specialize. This specialization allows the individual nutritionist to keep up with the rapidly changing industries and the rapidly advancing science. Specialty areas for animal nutritionists are divided into two categories, based on whether the animals studied are monogastric or ruminant. **Monogastric** nutritionists focus on one-stomached animals such as poultry, swine, horses, dogs, cats, fish, rats, mice, guinea pigs, monkeys, and some zoo animals. **Ruminant** nutritionists specialize in sheep, goats, dairy/beef cattle, and other wild or captive species that have a rumen. Most nutritionists tend to fall into one or the other of two additional camps: **basic nutritionists** or **applied/production nutritionists**.

Basic nutritionists study the metabolism of the animals, and they are most interested in the biochemical mechanisms of nutrient metabolism. They are sometimes concerned with knowledge for its own sake rather than practical applications. What basic nutritionists learn is important to production nutritionists, who take the basic nutritionists' findings and determine real-world applications. Applied or production nutritionists are more interested in maximal, cost-effective feeding of animals in a production setting. They explore the many possibilities for using feedstuffs in the best possible way to make money. Often thought of as "feed-em and weigh-em" research, applied nutrition is really a complicated and often challenging attempt to translate basic science into real-world application. We often find nutritionists who bridge several categories or even defy categorization. Even a specialist must know something about several disciplines in order to be a good nutritionist. These disciplines include biochemistry, cytology, economics, marketing, endocrinology, genetics, inorganic chemistry, mathematics, microbiology, neurology, organic chemistry, physics, physiology, veterinary medicine, and waste management.

NUTRIENTS AND THEIR USES

If we are to understand nutrition, we must understand **nutrients**. Nutrients are substances required for life processes. They are used in body metabolism to maintain the body and for reproduction, growth, and lactation. Nutrients provide energy and building material for the body, as well as metabolic regulators. Nutrients are classified as either dietary essentials or dietary nonessentials. Dietary essential nutrients must be a part of the diet. The nutrient classifications are water, carbohydrates, vitamins, minerals, proteins, and fats (lipids). Energy is needed by the body but is not a nutrient per se. Carbohydrates, proteins, and fats all provide energy to the animal through their breakdown products. Figure 3–1 lists the 50 dietary essential nutrients.

Water is frequently neglected in many discussions of nutrition. This seems odd, considering that the body will die more quickly from water deprivation than from the deprivation of any other nutrient. Water is used by the body as a lubricant; as a regulator of body temperature; as a solvent for the body's solid components; as a

Monogastric Having only one stomach.

Ruminant Hooved animals that have a rumen and chew their cud.

Basic nutritionist A nutritionist interested in elucidating basic metabolism and nutrient action and interaction.

Applied or production nutritionist The practical nutritionist. An applied nutritionist works on practical questions such as cost effectiveness, method of delivery, and carcass effects.

Nutrient A substance in the diet that supports the normal functions of the body.

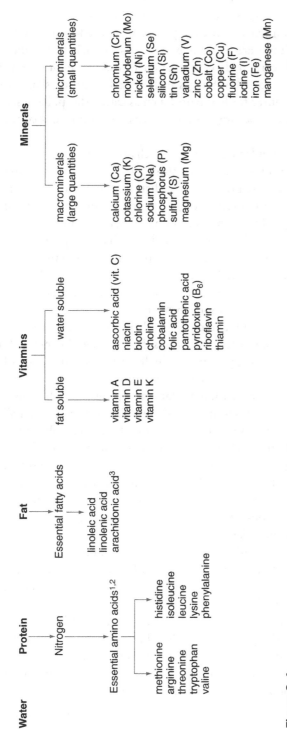

Water

Protein

Nitrogen

Essential amino acids[1,2]

methionine   histidine
arginine   isoleucine
threonine   leucine
tryptophan   lysine
valine   phenylalanine

Fat

Essential fatty acids

linoleic acid
linolenic acid
arachidonic acid[3]

Vitamins

fat soluble

vitamin A
vitamin D
vitamin E
vitamin K

water soluble

ascorbic acid (vit. C)
niacin
biotin
choline
cobalamin
folic acid
pantothenic acid
pyridoxine (B$_6$)
riboflavin
thiamin

Minerals

macrominerals
(large quantities)

calcium (Ca)
potassium (K)
chlorine (Cl)
sodium (Na)
phosphorus (P)
sulfur[4] (S)
magnesium (Mg)

microminerals
(small quantities)

chromium (Cr)
molybdenum (Mo)
nickel (Ni)
selenium (Se)
silicon (Si)
tin (Sn)
vanadium (V)
zinc (Zn)
cobalt (Co)
copper (Cu)
fluorine (F)
iodine (I)
iron (Fe)
manganese (Mn)

Figure 3–1

The essential nutrients.

[1]Mnemonic device for remembering essential amino acids = MATT HILL VP.

[2]For poultry, two additional amino acids are needed: glycine and proline.

[3]Arachidonic acid can be synthesized from linoleic acid if it is available, so it is only essential if linoleic acid is absent or in short supply.

[4]Authors vary on whether or not to list sulfur as a macromineral or micromineral. The discrepancy arises because only a very small amount of inorganic S is needed, but the sulfur-containing amino acids (organic S) are needed in larger quantities.

transporting medium in body fluids such as blood, lymph, urine, and sweat; and as a necessary participant in the chemical reactions of the body. Animals meet their needs for water by drinking and eating feed that has water in it, and with metabolic water produced by the chemical reactions that break down protein, carbohydrates, and fats in the body. A direct, positive correlation exists between how much water an animal needs and how much of the other nutrients it consumes.

Carbohydrates are sugars, starches, and cellulose. The primary use of carbohydrates is to provide animals with energy. Energy is used to do the body's work (chemical reactions). Grains are fed to livestock because their starch and sugar contents are easily digestible carbohydrates that animals readily use for energy. **Cellulose** is the major carbohydrate found in forages such as fresh pastures, silage, and hays. It is an important energy source for herbivores such as cattle, sheep, llamas, and horses. Carbohydrates account for the largest single percentage of nutrient content in most commonly fed feedstuffs.

Proteins are compounds made up of long chains of amino acids. Their primary uses in the body are as components of lean tissue, enzymes, hormones, and body metabolites. If excess proteins are present in the diet, they are used for energy. Animals typically need very different amounts of protein depending on the feeds used and the age and use of the particular animal. Young animals need protein to build their bodies (grow); mature animals must only replace exhausted proteins in the body. Pregnancy, milk production, and some other production functions require a substantial amount of protein. Oil seed meals such as soybean meal and cottonseed meal are common protein feedstuffs, as well as fishmeal, alfalfa meal, and dried skim milk. However, virtually all feeds contain some protein.

Fats are esters of fatty acids and glycerol. They are used by the body as a source of energy and as a source of essential fatty acids. Fats are high in energy. On average, they have 2.25 times more energy than carbohydrates on an equal weight basis. They are also important carriers of the fat-soluble vitamins. Common feedstuffs used for their fat content include tallow, lard, horse fat, and various vegetable oils.

Vitamins are organic compounds needed by the body in very small amounts. They are classified as either fat-soluble or water-soluble. The fat-soluble vitamins tend to be involved in regulating body functions such as vision, blood clotting, and tissue maintenance, and growth such as bone development. The water-soluble vitamins tend to be used more for body metabolic regulation. Many feeds are rich in vitamins, but some are very poor vitamin sources. We are able to isolate, synthesize, or otherwise gather vitamins into commercially prepared vitamin supplements that are heavily used in modern feed formulations and mixes.

Minerals are the inorganic constituents of bones and teeth and an important part of the body's enzyme systems. Virtually all feedstuffs contain some minerals. Supplemental minerals are provided in various forms including salt, trace mineralized salt, oyster shells, lime, and bone meal.

The nutritive value of feeds is quite variable. Feeds must be selected to provide an appropriate **diet** for the purpose intended. For example, some feeds are high in energy-furnishing nutrients and are used in finishing rations or for producing milk and eggs. When protein-rich feeds and vitamin and mineral mixes are added to the energy feeds, a **ration** of optimum production is born.

BODY FUNCTIONS AND NUTRIENT NEEDS

Animals need nutrients to run the body's metabolic machinery for maintenance, production, and reproduction. How much of these essential nutrients does an animal need? The amount required depends on many different things. Definite differences

Carbohydrates Chemically defined as polyhydroxy aldehydes or ketones, or substances that can be hydrolyzed to them.

Cellulose A carbohydrate composed of thousands of glucose molecules that forms the support structure of plants.

Protein Compounds composed of combinations of α-amino acids.

Fats One of a class of biomolecules called lipids. Chemically, fats are triacylglycerides, which are composed of the alcohol glycerol, with three fatty acids attached.

Vitamin A term used to group a dissimilar set of organic substances required in very small quantities by the body.

Minerals In nutrition, the specific set of inorganic elements thus far established as necessary for life in one or more animal species.

Diet All the feeds being consumed by an animal, including water.

Ration The specific feed allotment given an animal in a 24-hour period.

Figure 3–2
Body functions dictate nutrient needs. Piglets need nutrients specifically for growth, and sows need specific amounts of specific nutrients for lactation. (Photo by Keith Weller. Courtesy USDA-Agricultural Research Service.)

between species are linked to the species' type of digestive tract as well as peculiarities of the species' metabolism. Other factors such as the level of production and the specific product or products being produced (work, fetus, growth, milk, eggs, and fiber) are important. Nutrient needs are additive and must be fed in sufficient amounts to simultaneously meet all of the animal's current needs (Figure 3–2). Nutrients often have influence on each other owing to interactions that may increase or decrease the needs of the individual animal. Thus, the job of the nutritionist is a complicated one. An understanding of the needs of the body is essential if nutritionists are to do their job. Individual discussions of the body's needs follow.

Maintenance, in its simplest form, refers to maintaining the body at a constant weight and temperature. The maintenance nutrient requirement is a combination of the nutrients needed for basal metabolism (activities such as heartbeat and breathing) and those for normal animal movement. Normal activity levels often vary tremendously. Imagine the difference in essential activity between a relatively sedentary riding horse standing knee-deep in good grass with a bucket of oats given to him twice a day, compared to a free-ranging mustang that has to search for every bite and avoid all kinds of hazards as well. It is rarely our goal to simply maintain animals in a production setting. However, the needs of maintenance must be met before the animal will produce any useful product. Thus, maintenance is the first requirement that must be met in a production setting. Because energy is a big portion of maintenance, feeds relatively high in fats and carbohydrates are generally used for providing maintenance requirements.

Growth is the process of increasing the body weight by adding tissue like that already present. In growth, the body requires good-quality nutrients in relatively large amounts to build its structural units. All of the required nutrients are needed and balance is very important. Every system in the body is changing and developing, so the nutrient needs are high in the growth phase and nutrient deficiencies become readily apparent.

Finishing is the final growth and fattening phase of the production of meat animals. All nutrients are needed for the finishing phase, but energy is needed during this phase in much higher proportions. Energy feeds are required during finishing to provide the energy needed for the formation of lean tissue, bone, and fat. Less protein as a percentage of the total diet is needed during this phase than is needed for growth or production. We rely on feeds high in carbohydrates and fats during the finishing phase because their cost is usually lower than the cost of protein-rich foods (Figure 3–3).

Maintenance The needs of the animal exclusive of those required for a productive function such as growth, work, or milk production.

Growth The process of adding tissues similar to those already present in the body to increase the size of an organism toward the goal of maturity when growth stops.

Finishing Usually refers to the final feeding stage when animals are readied for market.

Figure 3–3
Finishing cattle for slaughter involves feeding for maintenance, growth, and fat deposition. (Photo by Brian Ptechtel. Courtesy USDA-Agricultural Research Service.)

Production The general term used to describe the output of usable products and services by animals.

Production refers to the output of products such as eggs, milk, and wool. The nutrients needed for production vary with the product. Lactation is the most demanding of all the production functions in mature animals. Milk contains water, protein, fat, vitamins, and minerals, and additional energy is required to produce it. Eggs contain protein, fats, minerals, vitamins, and water. Diets must be selected and rations must be balanced for these nutrients to accomplish cost-effective feeding. Other types of production require levels of nutrients specific to the product or combination of products being produced (Figure 3–4).

Work Physical exertion as a production function.

Work is a specialized production function and the major product of some species such as working horses, working dogs, and packing llamas (Figure 3–5). The major nutrient increase needed for work is energy. Carbohydrates are generally the most cost-effective means of increasing energy in the diet, so carbohydrate-rich feeds are generally used to meet this need.

Figure 3–4
Production of eggs, milk, and wool requires levels of nutrients specific to the product being produced.

Figure 3–5
Work is a specialized production function that requires additional energy in the animal's diet. (Photo courtesy of Paige Rabalais. Used with permission.)

Figure 3–6
This 2-year-old beef cow must provide milk for her newborn calf, rebreed, and gestate her next calf, all while still growing. (Photo by Scott Bauer. Courtesy USDA-Agricultural Research Service.)

Reproduction of live normal offspring is a basic biological necessity for a species to survive. For efficient, cost-efficient agriculture, we must provide for the arrival of a new generation at the same time we are receiving the products from the current one. Providing adequate nutrition for the reproductive function must be accomplished in addition to maintenance and production. Poor nutrition can be manifested in abnormal or delayed **estrous cycles**; reduced calf and lamb crops; small and weak litters in swine, dogs, and other litter-bearing species; and poor egg production and/or hatchability in poultry. The high-producing animals are often the ones with whom we have the most difficulty. The third trimester of a pregnancy is the most critical for the reproducing female (Figure 3–6). Energy and protein must be increased, and the need for several minerals and vitamins is increased during this period as well.

Reproduction The combined set of actions and biological functions of a living being directed at producing offspring.

Estrous cycle The time from one period of sexual receptivity in the female (estrus or heat) to the next.

FEED ANALYSIS

Properly feeding livestock requires knowledge of the nutrients found in the feedstuffs available and balancing of these nutrients to meet the physiological needs for the species in question. A comprehensive evaluation procedure discovers nutrient

Digestibility A measure of the degree to which a feedstuff can be chemically simplified and absorbed by the digestive system of the body.

Palatability The acceptability of a feedstuff or ration for consumption.

Feed Foods used to feed animals.

composition, **digestibility**, productive value, **palatability**, and the physical or handling characteristics of **feeds**. Feeds analysis also provides useful information about feed growing, harvesting and storing methods, thus helping to obtain the highest quality feed for the animals and the most profit to the producer (Figure 3–7).

Three basic types of analytical methods are commonly used to analyze feeds for nutrient content. *Chemical procedures* are standard chemistry applied to feeds. *Biological procedures* use animals to test the feeds. This is more time consuming, labor intensive, and expensive but gives a better estimate of how the animal will use the feed. We also use some species of animals as models for other species to save money (i.e., rats for pigs). *Microbiological procedures,* the third type, are similar to biological procedures but use bacteria in place of higher animals.

Proximate analysis is a set of chemical/analytical procedures designed to partition feedstuffs into water, ash, crude protein, ether extract, crude fiber, and nitrogen-free extract. Although proximate analysis is the most common set of chemical tests used on feedstuffs, the information it provides is sometimes misleading or even inaccurate. However, proximate analysis is still used and will continue to be used. Thus, good nutritionists must learn its limitations as well as its value.

Dry matter Everything in a feed other than water.

Dry matter is determined by heating a feed sample until all water has evaporated. The percentage of the sample that is not water is then referred to as the dry matter of the sample. To balance a ration properly and know how much of each ingredient to mix into a ration, the dry matter must be determined.

Ash The mineral content of a feed.

Ash is considered the mineral content of the feedstuff. It is determined by burning a dry sample in a very hot oven (500–600°C) to burn off all of the organic matter. The actual value in knowing ash content is marginal. However, we must know how much ash is in the feedstuff to make other calculations. In some feeds, ash content can be quite high. More detailed mineral analyses are needed to help the nutritionist balance a ration for the various minerals.

Crude protein An estimate of protein content obtained by multiplying the nitrogen content of a substance by a factor, usually 6.25.

Crude protein (CP) is determined by the Kjeldahl process, which isolates and measures the nitrogen in a feed. An average protein contains 16% nitrogen. Crude protein can then be calculated by multiplying total nitrogen by 6.25. As

Figure 3–7

Feeds analysis is used to discover nutrient composition, productive value, palatability and physical/handling characteristics. It can also be used to help improve feed harvesting and storing methods. (Photo by Scott Bauer. Courtesy USDA-Agricultural Research Service.)

the name implies, this is a crude measure of nutritional value. Any nitrogen found in the feed is called crude protein. The crudeness of the measurement is not much of an issue for the functional ruminant, which can use nitrogen that is not in protein form (**NPN**) to make real protein in the rumen. For monogastric and immature ruminants, crude protein has less value because amino acid content is the information needed. Modern analytical techniques may soon make this laboratory procedure obsolete.

To determine **ether extract** (EE) (fat), a dry feed sample is extracted with diethyl ether. The ether extracts the fat. Unfortunately, some plant materials other than fat are also ether soluble. These include many organic compounds such as chlorophyll, volatile oils, resins, pigments, and plant waxes that have little nutritional value. The goal of the test is to isolate the portion of the feed that has high-caloric density. The value of the results depends on the feed being analyzed.

Carbohydrates (CHO) are not determined by direct analysis. For the sake of analysis, carbohydrates are considered to be measured in two fractions: (1) **crude fiber** (CF) and (2) **nitrogen-free extract (NFE)** or nonfiber carbohydrates. The crude fiber procedure is an attempt to simulate digestion in the true stomach and the small intestine. Crude fiber is made up of cellulose, hemicellulose, and insoluble lignin. Nitrogen-free extract is determined by subtraction rather than by a direct chemical method. There is no extract, per se, which makes this method confusing and sometimes hard to understand. The water, ash, crude protein, fiber, and fat found in the feed are added together and subtracted from the number 100. In theory, NFE should be the readily available carbohydrates, such as the sugars and starches. In reality, because it is derived from subtraction, it contains the errors of all the analyses and is generally considered to contain some hemicellulose and lignin. The error is especially true of forages that contain more of these materials. The most problematic limitations to the proximate analysis system are with crude fiber and NFE fractions. Sometimes NFE is less digestible than CF, especially for forages. This discrepancy would not happen if the individual tests were actually measuring what they should be. Because carbohydrates are such a large portion of animal diets, and the different species have very different capabilities of using the different carbohydrates, this shortcoming in the proximate analysis system is a major problem.

The Van Soest method is an alternative fiber analysis (Figure 3–8) that was developed as a means of better describing forages in response to the limitations of proximate analysis. The cell content is almost completely digested by the ruminant, but the cell wall is highly variable in its digestibility by the animal. Much of this variation can be explained by the species of plant and the stage of maturity. The Van Soest method has several uses. It can be used to predict the intake and digestibility of feedstuffs by animals and is a means of evaluating heat damage in forages.

Vitamins must be assayed individually. Biological assays are used for some; others are determined by chemical analysis.

The *determination of the energy content* of common feedstuffs is a very important part of nutrition. An instrument called a **bomb calorimeter** is used to determine the gross energy content of feedstuffs. Gross energy is expressed in **calories**. Gross energy itself has little value, but it is useful in calculating other values. For example, if we know how much gross energy is in both feed and feces, we can calculate how much was digested and absorbed.

Other methods of feed analysis are also used, and more are sure to be developed, to help the nutritionist. For example, infrared light rays are being used for feed analyses. Moisture, lipid, protein, and fiber contents are frequently determined this way, although calcium, phosphorus, salt, and a few other ingredients are also

NPN Nonprotein nitrogen. Any nitrogen found in a feedstuff that is not part of a protein molecule.

Ether extract In proximate analysis, the portion of a sample removed by extraction with a fat solvent such as ethyl ether.

Crude fiber In proximate analysis, the insoluble carbohydrates remaining in a feed after boiling in acid and alkali.

Nitrogen-free extract (NFE) In proximate analysis, a measure of readily available carbohydrates calculated by subtracting all measured proximate components from 100.

Bomb calorimeter A device into which a substance can be placed and ignited under a pressurized atmosphere of oxygen.

Calorie A measure of food energy. The heat required to raise the temperature of 1 g water from 14.5° to 15.5°C. About 4.2 joules.

Figure 3–8

Flow diagram for Van Soest fiber analysis.

[1]Cell contents include sugar, starch, soluble carbohydrates, pectin, protein, NPN, lipids, and miscellaneous vitamins.

[2]Cell wall components include cellulose, hemicellulose, lignin, silica, and heat-damaged protein.

(Source: Jurgens, M. H. 1993, p. 58. Used with permission.)

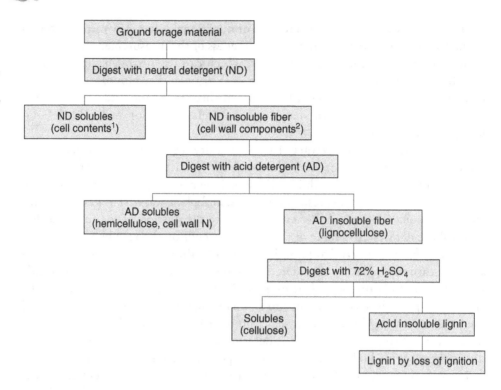

determined. This type of analysis has the major advantage of being much quicker than other methods. However, calibrating the machine requires a wide variety of samples of a wide variety of feeds. Cost is also a problem because instruments are expensive.

Determining the Value of Feedstuffs to Animals

Although chemical analysis of feed is important, it is only one step in determining the value of a **feedstuff** to animals. We must combine the chemical analysis with information about how feed affects the animal. To do this, we conduct trials in which the animal is fed the feed in question. Three major types of animal trials are used: **feeding trials**, **digestion trials**, and **metabolism trials**.

Information gathered from these types of trials allows us ultimately to develop feeding standards and recommendations for feeding animals at different levels of production. Many factors affect nutrient utilization of feeds by animals, including species of animal and type of digestive tract, age, physiological state, (pregnant, growing, lactating, and so on), physical form of the feed (pelleted, cracked, steamrolled, and so on), nutrient balance, and many more. In general, the types of trials used to determine the value of feeds are the same from species to species, with only minor changes in procedures needed.

A feeding trial is used to determine if animals will eat a feedstuff and how they will perform on the feedstuff. It doesn't tell us why things do or don't happen. It only tells us what happens. Common types of feeding trials include growth trials, lactation trials, egg production, endurance (for horses), or even measurement of some specified body function (sperm count, bone levels of calcium, and so on).

Digestion trials are used specifically to discover the degree to which a feedstuff is digested and absorbed by the animal. Digestion trials can be conducted on any nutrient in a feed. In a digestion trial, we feed a feedstuff or diet that has been chemically analyzed to determine its nutrient makeup. During the feeding period, we collect the fecal matter. The fecal material is then analyzed to determine chemically the nutrients that remain in it. We then calculate a digestion coefficient by taking the difference in the nutrients fed and then excreted and calculate a percent disappearance. Digestion

Feedstuff Any substance used as animal feed.

Feeding trial A comparatively simple experimental tool in which animals are fed to determine their performance on specific feeds or substances added to feeds.

Digestion trial An experimental tool used to determine the digestibility of a specific feedstuff, nutrient, or ration.

Metabolism trial An advanced form of digestion trial that measures the body's use of nutrients.

coefficients can be calculated for all nutrients. The terms *digestion coefficients* and *percent digestibility* are identical in meaning. The following formula is used to calculate digestion coefficients:

$$\text{Nutrient digestibility (\%)} = \frac{\text{Nutrient intake} - \text{Nutrient in feces}}{\text{Nutrient intake}} \times 100$$

The basic procedure for calculating a digestion coefficient is given in the following example:

> During a digestion trial, a steer ate 88 lbs of hay. The hay was 11.8% crude protein. The digestion trial was 7 days long. During the trial, the steer excreted 203 lbs of feces, which were analyzed and found to contain 1.3% protein.

1. Calculate a digestion coefficient for the protein in the hay.

$$\text{Protein digestibility} = \frac{\text{Total protein consumed} - \text{Total protein excreted}}{\text{Total protein consumed}}$$

$$= \frac{(88 \text{ lbs} \times 11.8\%) - (203 \text{ lbs} \times 1.3\%)}{(88 \text{ lbs} \times 11.8\%)} \times 100$$

$$= \frac{10.38 - 2.64}{10.38} \times 100$$

$$= \frac{7.74}{10.38} \times 100$$

$$= 74.6\%$$

2. Calculate the digestible protein content (DP) of the hay:

$$\text{DP} = \text{Crude protein content} \times \% \text{ Digestibility}$$

In this example, the crude protein content of the forage is 11.8% and the digestibility of the protein is 74.6%. Therefore, $11.8 \times 74.6 = 8.8$ DP in the hay.

TDN (total digestible nutrients) is a measure that historically was used extensively to balance rations for livestock. It is considered to be the digestible energy content of a feed expressed in terms of a carbohydrate equivalent basis. TDN is calculated using digestion coefficients for the crude protein, ether extract, crude fiber, and NFE portions of a feed sample. Only the energy-containing components (not water or ash) are included. The basic procedure for calculating TDN is indicated by the following example:

Fraction	Amount in Feed (%)	×	Percent Digestibility	=	Contribution to TDN (%)
Crude protein	10	×	75	=	7.5
Ether extract	5	×	80 × 2.25	=	9.0
Crude fiber	5	×	60	=	3.0
NFE	70	×	90	=	63.0
			% TDN in feed	=	82.5

Note: One of the most confusing problems for some students is how to handle the decimal point. When you multiply a percent × a percent and you want your answer in a percent (as in the TDN example), move the decimal two places to the left on only one number (either one), and your decimal will then be where you want it to be in your answer.

Expressing Feed Composition on a Dry-Matter (DM) Basis

The nutrient contents of a feed are commonly expressed on either an air-dry (as-is) basis or a dry-matter basis. To balance and feed rations, it is important to be able to convert them back and forth. The following example demonstrates how to make the conversion using a TDN as an example:

$$\frac{\text{TDN value on air-dry basis}}{\text{Dry-matter content of feed}} \times 100 = \text{TDN on dry-matter basis}$$

For hay, TDN was calculated to be 50.4% on an air-dry, "as-is," or "as-fed" basis. The following steps convert it to a dry-matter basis:

$$\frac{50.4}{0.91 \text{ (moisture content was 9\%)}} \times 100 = 55.4\% \text{ TDN}$$

The step can be repeated for the other nutrients, as demonstrated for crude protein (CP):

$$\frac{13.0 \text{ (protein content on air-dry basis)}}{0.91 \text{ (Dry-matter content of feed)}} \times 100 = 14.3\% \text{ CP on dry-matter basis}$$

Measures of Energy

Energy is needed by different animals in very different amounts. Choosing the correct unit can help keep the math simple and the numbers easier to read. The units of energy measurement most frequently used are:

Calorie (cal)   = Amount of heat or energy needed to raise 1 g of H_2O 1°C from 14.5° to 15.5°C

Kilocalorie (kcal)   = Energy required to raise 1,000 g of water from 14.5° to 15.5°C
                       = 1,000 calories

Megacalorie (Mcal) = 1,000 kcal or 1,000,000 calories.

In human nutrition, the term *kilocalorie* is used to measure and describe energy, although by convention we use the term *large calorie (symbol Cal),* which is equivalent to 1,000 small calories of about 4.2 kilojoules. For pet species, kcal is commonly used. In livestock nutrition, Mcal are most frequently used because of the large amount of energy these species need. The figures 80 Mcal and 80,000 kcal represent the same amount of energy. The smaller number is more convenient to use when performing the math associated with ration formulation.

Energy Content of Nutrients

Carbohydrates, proteins, and fats all provide energy to the animal. However, their energy contents (energy densities) are very different. Carbohydrates have approximately 4.0 kcal/g, whereas proteins have approximately 5.65 kcal/g on the average. However, about 1.65 kcal/g are lost as urea in the urine. The actual average gross energy value of most carbohydrates is about 4.4 kcal, but some energy is not digested, so we normally adjust the value to 4.0 kcal/g to compensate. The

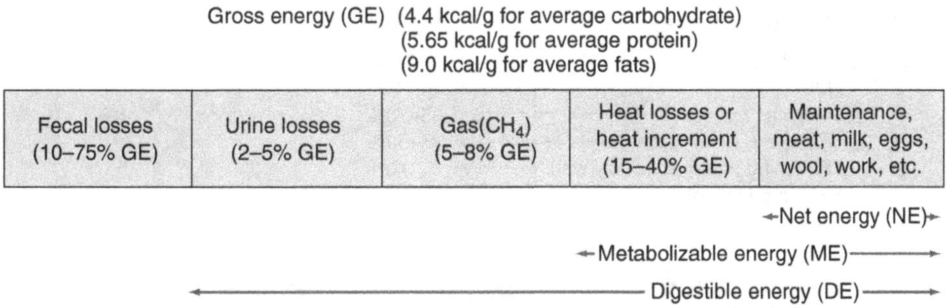

Gross energy (GE)   (4.4 kcal/g for average carbohydrate)
(5.65 kcal/g for average protein)
(9.0 kcal/g for average fats)

Fecal losses (10–75% GE)	Urine losses (2–5% GE)	Gas(CH$_4$) (5–8% GE)	Heat losses or heat increment (15–40% GE)	Maintenance, meat, milk, eggs, wool, work, etc.

←Net energy (NE)→

←Metabolizable energy (ME)——————→

←———————— Digestible energy (DE)————→

Figure 3–9
Schematic diagram for partitioning energy values of feeds. (Source: Adapted from Wagner, 1977. Used with permission.)

Therefore, formulas for calculating the various energy values (DE, ME, and NE) of feeds are as follows:

GE – fecal loss   = DE
DE – gas and urine = ME
ME – heat losses   = NE

gross energy value for protein (5.65 kcal/g) is higher than for carbohydrates, but approximately 1.65 kcal/g is lost as urea in the urine when protein is used as an energy source, so the net value is about the same as for carbohydrates: 4.0 kcal/g. Therefore, carbohydrates and protein are given the same value in calculating TDN. Fats have approximately 9.0 kcal/g. Fat is given a value that is 2.25 times greater (9.00/4.00 = 2.25) than the values of the carbohydrate and protein because it does have a higher energy content per unit of measurement. This is the reason for the 2.25 correction factor for fat in a TDN calculation, and this is why TDN is considered an estimate of the digestible energy (DE) of a feed on a carbohydrate equivalent basis (Figure 3–9).

The amount of energy lost from feed in the various compartments represented in Figure 3–9 depends on several factors, including the kind of feed, its digestibility, and the animal. The numbers in parentheses in Figure 3–9 represent the range of the losses. Losses in the feces are generally the largest and most variable. Highly digestible feeds have minimal losses in the feces; poorly digested feeds have much higher losses. These losses occur during digestion and metabolism and include heat of fermentation of the microbial population in ruminants and horses. Heat losses are usually the second largest and most variable losses.

Efficiency of Energy Use

The purpose of all the energy conversions in the body of animals is to convert energy into something useful, such as maintenance of the animals, and products such as meat, milk, work, wool, and eggs. Heat losses are also useful in the overall scheme because they help the animal maintain body temperature. The better the feed, the greater the efficiency of net energy production from feeds. Metabolizable energy is used with different efficiency for various productive functions, some of which are more important in some species than in others. For this reason, we use different units of energy in ration formulation for different animal species. Figure 3–10 summarizes the varying efficiencies of energy utilization for the various productive functions of the body. This all relates back to TDN. The following formula is used to convert TDN to digestible energy and metabolizable energy:

1 lb TDN = 2.0 Mcal DE or 1.7 Mcal of ME

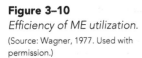

Figure 3–10
Efficiency of ME utilization.
(Source: Wagner, 1977. Used with permission.)

	Productive function	Efficiency
ME	Maintenance	~ 70%
	Milk	70%
	Growth	65–70%
	Fattening (beef cattle)	35–58%
	Fattening (simultaneously with milk production)	70%
	Work	70%

Metabolism trials are more advanced digestion trials and include measures of such things as urine and hair loss. One particular type of metabolism trial is a **balance trial.** The goal of a balance trial is to measure total intake and excretion so that retention in the animal's body can be calculated. Net retention of a nutrient within the body is positive balance and net loss is negative balance. Thus, a metabolism trial also provides information on nutrient use after absorption by the animal. Balance trials are usually conducted to study protein, energy, and minerals. Collections include feces, urine, expired air, milk, eggs, sloughed skin, shed hair, dropped feathers, sweat, and measurement of heat loss.

Nutrient Requirements

The outcome of all the chemical tests and all the animal trials has been the development of a set of nutrient requirements for the various species of animals commonly used in agriculture, research, and as companions. The National Research Council, a branch of the National Academy of Science, publishes these nutrient requirements and recommendations for feeding animals in various stages of production. The publications are updated and republished periodically. Included in these publications is general nutrition information and nutrient requirements of the various species as well as information on the feeding value of the commonly used feeds for the species.

Examples of the type of information found in these publications are given in Tables 3–1 and 3–2. The publications include, *Nutrient Requirements of Beef Cattle, Nutrient Requirements of Dogs and Cats, Nutrient Requirements of Fish, Nutrient Requirements of Dairy Cattle, Nutrient Requirements of Horses, Nutrient Requirements of Laboratory Animals, Nutrient Requirements of Mink and Foxes, Nutrient Requirements of Non-Human Primates, Nutrient Requirements of Poultry, Nutrient Requirements of Rabbits, Nutrient Requirements of Small Ruminants,* and *Nutrient Requirements of Swine.*

Ration Formulation

The amount of feed offered to an animal during a 24-hour period is called a ration. Providing the proper nutrients for a given animal to accomplish its specific production function is what we try to accomplish when we balance, mix, and subsequently feed a ration. If we accomplish this, we can say we are feeding a *balanced* ration. In addition to being balanced, a good ration must be palatable and free of damaging amounts of molds, diseases, and other quality-lowering factors. The ration should be economical and not have any negative effects on the general health and well-being of the animal or product quality. As an example, some substances in feeds and weeds give undesirable odors and flavors to the milk of dairy cows and off colors in eggs. Others cause undesirable carcass characteristics. Such feeds must be carefully managed if they are to be used at all. Tables 3–3, 3–4, 3–5, 3–6, 3–7, and 3–8 give examples of balanced rations for some classes of animals.

Balance trial A type of metabolism trial designed to determine the retention of a specific nutrient in the body.

Table 3–1

SELECTED NUTRIENT CONTENT OF FEEDS COMMONLY FED TO POULTRY AND SWINE ON AN AS-FED BASIS

Feedstuff	(IFN)	DM (%)	CP (%)	Lysine (%)	Vitamin E (mg/kg)	Niacin (%)	Thiamine (%)	Ca (%)	Fat (%)	ME Swine (kcal/kg)	ME Poultry (kcal/kg)
Alfalfa meal	1-00-023	92	17.4	0.7	111.0	37.0	3.4	1.4	2.8	1,705	1,480
Bakery waste	4-00-466	92	9.8	0.3	41.0	26.0	2.9	0.1	11.7	3,600	3,630
Corn, gluten meal, 60%	5-28-242	90	61.2	1.0	23.4	60.0	0.3	—[1]	1.8	3,585	—
Molasses, beet	4-00-668	78	6.6	—	4.0	41.0	—	0.1	0.2	2,320	1,980
Oats, grain	4-03-309	89	11.8	0.4	14.9	14.0	6.0	0.08	4.7	2,735	2,543
Wheat, bran	4-05-190	87	15.5	0.6	14.3	197.0	8.4	0.13	4.0	2,268	1,270

Source: Various National Research Council publications. Information has been simplified and numbers rounded.
[1] — indicates that a feed does not have a significant amount of that nutrient.

Table 3–2
DAILY NUTRIENT REQUIREMENTS OF HORSES

Animal	Weight (kg)	DE (Mcal)	Crude Protein (g)	Lysine (g)	Calcium (g)	Phosphorus (g)	Vitamin A (10^3 IU)
Mature horses							
Maintenance	600	18	650	27	24	17	18
Stallions (breeding)	600	26	950	40	36	22	27
Lactating mares							
Foaling to 3 months	600	33.7	1,711	60	67	43	36
Working horses							
Very heavy exercise	600	41.0	1, 200	52	48	35	27
Growing horses							
4 months	200	16.0	800	35	47	26	9

Source: Nutrient Requirements of Horses, 6th ed., 2007, pp. 300–301, National Research Council. Information has been simplified and numbers rounded.

Table 3–3
BALANCED CREEP DIETS FOR LAMBS

	Diet 1 (%)	Diet 2 (%)	Diet 3 (%)	Diet 4 (%)
Corn grain	48	48	29	24
Wheat			21	
Milo				24
Soybean meal	9			
Cottonseed meal		9	7	9
Molasses	4	4	4	3
Limestone	1	1	1	2
Alfalfa hay or pellets	38	38	38	38

Source: Courtesy of Dr. Jerry Fitch, Oklahoma State University. Used with permission.

Table 3–4
A TOTAL MIXED RATION (TMR) FOR LACTATING DAIRY COWS

	Per Cow Daily
Alfalfa hay	10.0 lbs
Corn silage	36.0 lbs
Shelled corn	21.1 lbs
Soybean meal	7.4 lbs
Dicalcium phosphate	3.8 oz
Limestone	5.2 oz
Sodium bicarbonate	7.1 oz
Trace mineralized salt	2.4 oz
Vitamin A	59,200 U
Vitamin D	29,600 U

Source: Adapted from Dunham and Call, 1989, p. 10.

Table 3–5

SUGGESTED MODERATE NUTRIENT DENSITY DIETS FOR GROWING SWINE USING SORGHUM GRAIN AND/OR BARLEY AS MAJOR GRAIN SOURCES[1]

Ingredient	Diet 1 (lb)	Diet 2 (lb)	Diet 3 (lb)	Diet 4 (lb)
Sorghum grain	1,514	1,375	1,444	—
Barley	—	—	—	1,532
Soybean meal, 44%	437	—	—	319
Soybean meal, 48%	—	—	424	—
Soybeans, full fat (cooked)	—	577	—	—
Fat	—	—	80	100
Calcium carbonate	17	17	18	18
Dicalcium phosphate	22	21	24	21
Salt	7	7	7	7
Trace mineral and vitamin mix	3	3	3	3
Totals	2,000	2,000	2,000	2,000

Source: Luce et al., 1995, p. 10.
[1]Suggested for average and high lean gain barrows 75–140 lbs, average gilts 75–140 lbs, and high lean gain gilts 140 lbs to market.

Table 3–6

EXAMPLE RATIONS FOR SOME COMPANION SPECIES (PERCENTAGE OF RATION)

	Dog	Cat	Rabbit	Guinea Pig	Hamster
Ground yellow corn	56.0	33.77	—	—	52.93
Ground wheat	5.0	9.0	36.5	23.6	13.47
Ground oats	—	—	—	25.25	7.54
Cornstarch	—	—	—	—	36.67
Molasses	—	—	3.0	—	0.70
Corn gluten meal (60% CP)	5.0	12.8	—	—	—
Soybean meal (48% CP)	15.0	10.0	6.0	12.0	22.0
Meat and bonemeal	10.0	3.0	—	—	—
Fish meal	—	1.0	—	—	4.85
Poultry meal	—	17.4	—	—	—
Cellulose	—	—	—	—	2.04
Alfalfa meal	—	—	54.0	35.0	20.0
Animal digest	—	1.0	—	—	—
Animal fat	7.0	6.0	—	—	—
Soybean oil	—	—	—	1.5	1.25
Vitamin/mineral premix	—	—	—	0.40	—
Vitamin premix[1]	0.8	0.8	—	—	0.08
Trace mineral premix[1]	0.5	0.5	—	—	0.05
Dicalcium phosphate	0.2	—	—	0.50	1.8
Ground limestone	—	—	—	—	0.5
Calcium carbonate	—	1.16	—	1.0	—
Salt	0.5	0.7	0.5	0.75	0.50
Potassium chloride	—	0.48	—	—	—
Phosphoric acid solution	—	2.3	—	—	—
Citric acid	—	0.01	—	—	—
Taurine	—	0.08	—	—	—
Brewer's yeast	—	—	—	—	6.46
Choline	—	—	—	—	0.14
DL-Methionine	—	—	—	—	0.05

Sources: *Nutrient Requirements of Laboratory Animals*, 4th ed., 1995, National Research Council; Pond et al., 2005, pp. 522, 527.
[1]The specific premixes are different for each species.

Table 3–7
RATIONS FOR BEEF CALVES (PERCENT OF RATION)

	Feed for Growing Cattle	Supplement for Grazing Steers
Cottonseed hulls	14.0	—
Cottonseed meal	—	86.0
Alfalfa pellets	19.0	—
Soybean meal	10.3	—
Salt	0.25	—
Calcium carbonate	0.6	—
Vitamin/mineral/additive premix	0.05	3.0
Dicalcium phosphate	0.6	—
Wheat middlings	—	7.0
Corn	51.0	—
Molasses	4.2	4.0

Source: Adapted from Lalman, 2008, pp. 156, 159.

Table 3–8
RATIONS FOR MATURE HORSES

	As-Fed Basis		Dry-Matter Basis	
All Feeds in the Ration	(lbs/day)	(%)	(lbs/day)	(%)
Bermuda grass, late	13.001	70.000	12.091	70.898
Oats, grain	3.715	20.000	3.313	19.429
Corn, dent, grain	1.393	7.500	1.226	7.188
Soybean meal 44% PRO	0.371	2.000	0.331	1.941
Sodium chloride	0.046	0.250	0.046	0.272
Calcium carbonate	0.046	0.250	0.046	0.272
Total ration	18.573	—	17.054	—

Source: Freeman, 2011.

SUMMARY AND CONCLUSION

Nutrition is a dynamic and very complicated science. It is essential that we understand nutrition because feeds and the methods of feeding comprise a large portion of the costs of livestock production. This chapter will not make you a world-famous nutritionist. However, it does give you a broad working knowledge on which to build. The key to understanding the interconnectedness of nutrition is in reducing it to its essentials:

1. Nutrition is the study of how the body uses nutrients for maintenance and production.

2. Nutrients are the chemical entities that the body requires. We need to know which nutrients and how much of each is required for the animal we are feeding.

3. Feeds contain nutrients. We must determine just how much of a particular nutrient is in each feed and then determine how much the animals can actually use.

4. When we know an animal's nutrient needs and a feed's nutrient availability for that animal, we can balance a ration from those ingredients to meet the animal's needs.

STUDY QUESTIONS

1. Define nutrition and explain why one might choose to study it.
2. Why is the proper feeding of livestock such an important practical consideration?
3. Describe the disciplines of nutrition including the areas of specialty for nutritionists. Explain the differences between basic and applied nutritionists.
4. Name and describe at least five disciplines involved in the study of nutrition.
5. Describe how you would set up an experiment to determine whether a nutrient is essential. How would you interpret the results?
6. List the nutrient categories. Why isn't energy a nutrient? Is it required for life?
7. List the essential amino acids. Are there any additional amino acids for poultry? Are there any deviations from this list?
8. List the fat-soluble vitamins.
9. List the water-soluble vitamins.
10. What is the difference between macro- and microminerals?
11. List all of the macrominerals and microminerals.
12. What are the overall body functions for which an animal uses nutrients?
13. What is the purpose of having feeds chemically analyzed?
14. What are the three general types of analytical methods used to evaluate feedstuffs? Briefly define each method.
15. What nutrients are measured by proximate analysis? What are the limitations of each individual test?
16. Describe in detail how carbohydrates are determined by proximate analysis. How is this process different from the way the other proximate constituents are determined?
17. What individual carbohydrate fractions are determined in each part of the proximate carbohydrate fractions?
18. What is the major problem with the proximate analysis?
19. Why was the Van Soest fiber determination method developed? What advantages does it offer over proximate analysis?
20. Why is there no standard test for determining the vitamin content of feeds?
21. Describe in detail the tests for determining the energy content of a feed. What are the units used to express energy content?
22. How do feeding trials help to generate feeding standards for animals?
23. List the factors that may have an effect on nutrient utilization.
24. What are the common types of feeding trials?
25. Describe how a feeding trial, a digestion trial, and a metabolism trial differ.
26. What is the difference between values for a feed expressed on an as-fed basis compared to a dry-matter basis?
27. Describe the differences in the energy content of an average carbohydrate compared to an average protein and an average fat.

REFERENCES

Cheeke, P. R. 1991. *Applied animal nutrition.* 3rd ed. New York: Macmillan.

Church, D. C., and W. C. Pond. 1988. *Basic animal nutrition and feeding.* 3rd ed. New York: Wiley.

Dunham, J. R., and E. P. Call. 1989. *Feeding dairy cows.* MF-754 (Revised). Manhattan: Cooperative Extension Service, Kansas State University.

Fitch, G. Q. 2007. Personal communication. Oklahoma State University, Stillwater.

Freeman, D. W. 2011. Personal communication. Oklahoma State University, Stillwater.

Gillespie, J. R. 1987. *Animal nutrition and feeding.* Albany, NY: Delmar.

Jurgens, M. H. 1993. *Animal feeding and nutrition.* 8th ed. Dubuque, IA: Kendall/Hunt.

Lalman, D. 2008. Supplementing and feeding calves and stocker cattle. In *Beef cattle manual.* Stillwater, OK: Cooperative Extension Service. Division of Agricultural Sciences and Natural Resources, Oklahoma State University.

Luce, W. G., A. F. Harper, D. C. Mahan, and G. R. Hollis. 1995. Swine diets. In *Pork industry handbook*. Stillwater: Oklahoma Cooperative Extension Service. Division of Agricultural Sciences and Natural Resources, Oklahoma State University.

NRC. 1995. *Nutrient requirements of laboratory animals*. 4th ed. Washington, DC: National Academy Press.

Perry, T. W., A. E. Cullison, and R. S. Lowery. 1999. *Feeds and feeding*. 5th ed. Upper Saddle River, NJ: Prentice-Hall.

Pond, W. G., D. C. Church, K. R. Pond, and P. A. Schoknect. 2005. *Basic animal nutrition and feeding*. 5th ed. New York: Wiley.

Preston, R. L. 2011. Feed composition tables. *Beef magazine*. March 1, 2011. New York: Penton Media. Accessed online March 2011. http://beefmagazine.com/march11/

Wagner, D. G. 1977. *Livestock feeding*. Stillwater: Oklahoma State University.

4

The Gastrointestinal Tract and Nutrition

Key Terms

Abomasum	Herbivore
Anaerobic	Ileum
Bacteria	Jejunum
Bolus	Mastication
Carbohydrates	Micturation
Carnivore	Monogastric
Cecotrophy	Omnivore
Cellulase	Papillae
Cellulose	Peristalsis
Chyme	Prehension
Colic	Protein
Coprophagy	Protozoa
Defecation	Proventriculus
Deglutition	Rumen
Denature	Ruminal bloat
Digestion	Ruminant
Duodenum	Rumination
Enzymes	Salivation
Eructation	Symbiosis
Fermentation	Vitamin
Forestomachs	Volatile fatty acid (VFA)

Learning Objectives

After you have studied this chapter, you should be able to:

- Describe the methods of the breakdown of food.
- Classify digestive systems according to stomach type and type of diet consumed.
- Describe the steps of digestion.
- Identify the differences and similarities in the digestive processes of animals.
- Explain the importance of the complex stomach of the ruminant and its benefits to the animal.

INTRODUCTION

Feeds and feedstuffs are chemically complex mixtures of substances that contain the nutrients an animal needs. The digestive tract breaks down those complex materials to their constituent parts so the nutrients can be absorbed and metabolized by the body. Breakdown of food by the digestive system in preparation for absorption is called **digestion** and is accomplished in three ways: (1) the physical or mechanical actions of chewing (mastication) and muscular action of the digestive tract (peristalsis); (2) the chemical action of hydrochloric acid, which is used by the stomach to denature proteins and bile used in the small intestine to help digest fats; and (3) the action of enzymes, which increase the speed of the breakdown of the chemical bonds in foods by the addition of a

Digestion The physical, chemical, and enzymatic means the body uses to render a feedstuff ready for absorption.

Enzymes Proteins capable of catalyzing reactions associated with a specific substrate.

water molecule (hydrolytic enzyme). **Enzymes** can be produced by the digestive tract and accessory organs (liver, pancreas), or by microorganisms living in symbiosis with the animal. Enzymes are biological catalysts that speed the rate at which a particular reaction reaches equilibrium. Many enzymes are found in the system and are needed for faster and more efficient digestion.

One of the intriguing things we know about nutrient metabolism and the metabolic pathways for different species is that they are essentially the same. *E. coli* and giraffes have much the same thing happening at the cellular level. However, they have different nutrient requirements, consume different types of feed, and digest food very differently. This difference in digestive types has allowed dissimilar species to fit into different places in the food chain and carve a niche for themselves. The type of digestive system an animal has dictates what the animal can successfully use as feed. The more complicated the feed (like forage), the more complicated the digestive tract. Thus, the ruminant system is designed to retain feed for several days, which is a long time compared to the few hours that a feed is held in a carnivore's simple tract (Figure 4–1).

CLASSIFICATION OF DIGESTIVE SYSTEMS

Monogastric Having only one stomach. Also, nonruminant.

We classify the different digestive systems anatomically by the type of stomach an animal has. **Monogastrics,** or nonruminants, are one-stomached, or simple-stomach, animals. They can have a very simple tract, as in the mink and dog, or a cecal digestion, as in the horse, rabbit, or rat. Monogastrics that have a cecal fermentation can use much more fibrous feedstuffs than can a simple monogastric. Others, like the kangaroo, rely on a sacculated stomach to retain fibrous material for better digestion. The **ruminants**—cattle, sheep, goats, and pseudoruminants (llamas)—are more complex-stomached animals that have more than one stomach compartment. These compartments are located before the true stomach. A complicated fermentation takes place there to help the animal make use of fibrous feeds. These tracts usually also have a cecum, which helps to retain the feed even longer.

Ruminant Hooved animals that have a rumen and chew their cud.

We also classify digestive systems according to the type of diet the animal normally consumes. There are three digestive categories based on diet. **Carnivores** are flesh-eating animals, for example, cats and birds of prey. **Omnivores** eat both animal and vegetable matter; examples include chickens, pigs, and humans. **Herbivores** eat vegetable-based feeds. They are able to digest this plant material with the help of **cellulases** provided by bacteria during the fermentation process. Horses, cows, rabbits, guinea pigs, llamas, kangaroos, elephants, and many others are herbivores. All herbivores have some specialized way to help them digest **cellulose**.

Carnivore An animal that subsists on meat.

Omnivore An animal that selects a diet of both plant matter and meat.

Herbivore An animal that eats a diet of only plant material.

Cellulase An enzyme that specifically attacks and digests cellulose.

Cellulose A carbohydrate composed of thousands of glucose molecules that forms the support structure of plants.

Prehension The act of seizing and grasping.

AN OVERVIEW OF THE STEPS OF DIGESTION

Prehension, the means an animal uses to bring food into its mouth, is the first step of digestion. Animals use a variety of prehension methods, including use of their upper limbs, head, beak, and claws, and their mouth, teeth, and lips. Herbivores use the tongue, teeth, or lips to grasp forage. Ruminants have no upper incisor teeth, therefore the cow uses its flexible tongue to bring forage into its mouth and cuts the forage off with the lower incisor teeth and upper dental pad. Sheep use their teeth and cleft upper lip to permit them to graze close to the ground, which can lead to overgrazing. Horses make use of their mobile, prehensile upper lip, as well as upper and lower incisor teeth.

Sheep (*Ovis aries*)
Body length: 110 cm

0 cm 20

Pony (*Equus caballus*)
Body length: 164 cm

0 cm 20

Rabbit (*Oryctolagus cuniculus*)
Body length: 48 cm

0 cm 10

Figure 4–1
Mammalian digestive tracts.
(Source: Swenson, 1984. Used by permission of the publisher, Cornell University Press.)

Dog (*Canis familiaris*)
Body length: 90 cm

0 cm 10

Kangaroo (*Macropus giganteus*)
Body length: 115 cm

0 cm 10

Pig (*Sus scrofa*)
Body length: 125 cm

0 cm 20

Rat (*Rattus norvegicus*)
Body length: 17 cm

0 cm 5

Mink (*Mustela vison*)
Body length: 42 cm

0 cm 5

Mastication, or chewing, involves the vertical and lateral action of the jaw and teeth to crush food. Carnivores chew only to the extent needed to reduce the size of their meat so it can be swallowed. All herbivores need thorough mastication of their feed, mostly forage, to allow bacterial enzymes access to the cellulose. Ruminants first form a bolus and then swallow it without much chewing. Later they regurgitate the feed and thoroughly chew it. This process is one of the key elements

Mastication The process of chewing.

Figure 4–2
Salivary glands of the pig.

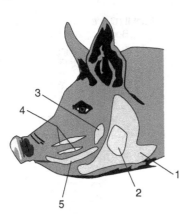

Salivary glands
1. Parotid
2. Mandibular (submaxillary)
3. Palatine
4. Buccal
5. Sublingual

Rumination The process in ruminants where a cud or bolus of rumen contents is regurgitated, remasticated, and reswallowed for further digestion.

Salivation The elaboration of the mixed secretion (saliva) produced primarily by three bilateral pairs of glands in the mouth known as salivary glands.

of **rumination.** A typical dairy cow chews between 40,000 and 50,000 times a day. Cecal fermentors and some simple monogastrics must chew thoroughly before swallowing because the food goes directly into the glandular stomach for digestion. They don't regurgitate their feed.

Salivation includes secretion and mixing of saliva with food. Three main paired salivary glands produce saliva (Figure 4–2). These are the parotid (below the ear), the submaxillary (mandibular) (at the base of the tongue), and sublingual (under the tongue). Saliva is mixed with food during chewing and has many functions. The first function is to lubricate food so the animal can chew and swallow it. All animals depend on this most irreplaceable salivary function. Both the water content and the protein mucin, found in saliva, are responsible for the lubricating function. Think how hard it would be for you to eat a cracker or for herbivores to eat forage without saliva. The solvent action of saliva dissolves small portions of food, allowing it to come into contact with taste buds, and gives food its taste. Saliva may also stimulate the taste nerves. The washing action of saliva cleanses the mouth and prevents decay of leftover food particles. The enzyme lysozyme supplies a disinfectant action that kills bacteria that could harm teeth and gums. Dogs and other carnivores have especially large amounts of lysozyme. Ruminants rely heavily on the bicarbonates in saliva to buffer the acids produced by the microorganisms in the rumen. The acids would soon damage the rumen wall if they weren't buffered. Saliva provides readily available nutrients for rumen microorganisms and helps maintain the proper pH for the microorganisms. Mucin, which is a protein, is digested and used by the microorganisms once it reaches the lower tract. Urea is harvested from the blood by salivary glands and secreted with the saliva. The microorganisms use it to manufacture protein. Salivary phosphorus (P) and sodium (Na) are also used by the microorganisms. The antifrothing property of saliva helps prevent **ruminal bloat** from being a daily occurrence. It prevents formation of a stable foam that would interfere with eructation (belching). Saliva also has an excretory function.

Ruminal bloat More correctly called *ruminal tympany.* An overdistention of the rumen and reticulum with the gases of fermentation. Commonly referred to as *bloat.*

Deglutition The act of swallowing. Passing material from the mouth through the esophagus to the stomach.

Bolus A rounded mass ready to swallow.

Peristalsis The progressive squeezing movements produced by the contraction of muscle fibers found in the wall of the digestive tract.

Swallowing, or **deglutition,** is the passing of food and water (or anything else) from the mouth to the first stomach compartment via the esophagus. The swallowing reflex is involuntary and under neural control. It is caused by the presence of material in the back of the mouth. The tongue is responsible for forming a **bolus** of the food in the mouth and voluntarily pushing it to the back of the mouth. Muscle contractions (**peristalsis**) move the food to the stomach. The cardiac valve is a valve located at the end of the esophagus that prevents feed in the stomach from coming back into the esophagus in some species.

In the ruminant, the feed makes its first stop in the rumino-reticulum for fermentation. Fermentation is an important topic and discussed at length later in this chapter. In the monogastric, the first stop is in the true stomach, which represents the next stop after the forestomachs for the ruminants.

Significant chemical and enzymatic digestion begins in the glandular stomach, which is similar in most animals. In the chicken, the stomach is called the **proventriculus,** and in the cow, it is called the **abomasum**. Physical breakdown of food occurs because of the churning action created by the contractions of the strong stomach muscles. The churning action also mixes the food (ingesta) with chemicals and enzymes. Chemical digestion is provided by hydrochloric acid (HCl), which is secreted by gastric glands in the stomach. HCl **denatures** proteins, a crucial first step in their digestion. In the native state, proteins are poorly digested. In denatured form, enzymes readily hydrolyze them. HCl activates the enzyme pepsin from its precursor pepsinogen. HCl provides an acidic pH in the stomach that is needed for gastric enzymes to work. HCl kills bacteria, which renders the stomach almost sterile. Several enzymes secreted in the stomach gastric juice provide enzymatic digestion of food. These include pepsin, gastricin, and rennin, all of which work on proteins. Rennin hydrolyzes the milk protein casein. This enzyme is not important in the adult animal, but it is especially important in young ruminants. Gastric lipase acts on fat.

In addition to digestion, the stomach stores food, another important function. This allows the animal to eat at a much faster rate than if digestion had to occur as rapidly as the food was consumed. The food is then metered into the lower gut as it is capable of digesting it.

The small intestine is divided into three portions. The **duodenum** is the first part. It extends from the pylorus of the stomach to the beginning of the jejunum. In most species, the duodenum is in the form of a loop and is often referred to as the duodenal loop. It is generally only about 1 ft long. Bile and pancreatic secretions enter in this portion of the small intestine. Excluding microbial fermentation, the duodenum is the main site of food breakdown in the entire digestive system. The **jejunum** is the second and longest part of the small intestine. Digestion continues here, but its major function is the absorption of digestive end products. The jejunum is several feet long. The **ileum** is the third part. Its major job is to form the connection to the large intestine, but absorption occurs here also. The entire small intestine is lined with **mucous membranes**. There are folds within this layer that serve to increase the surface area considerably. The jejunum portion of many species is covered with microscopic villi, which may number in the millions. They increase the absorptive surface tremendously. Nutrients are absorbed into the villi and pass into the lymphatic system or the circulatory system. Carbohydrates, amino acids, short-chain fatty acids, water-soluble vitamins, and most minerals absorbed from the small intestines enter the bloodstream. They go first to the liver and then are distributed to the rest of the body. The rest of the lipids and fat-soluble vitamins are transported by the lymphatic system to the thoracic duct, and they empty into the vena cava to be further transported.

The small intestine is the chief site of food digestion and nutrient absorption for monogastrics. When **chyme** leaves the stomach, it is very acidic. Chyme is mixed in the duodenum with three alkaline secretions, all very important to digestion. These secretions are bile, pancreatic juice, and succus entericus. Bile is formed in the liver. It is concentrated (up to 20 times for some species) and stored in the gallbladder until needed for digestion. Some species, like the rat and horse, don't have a gallbladder. Because they eat many small meals throughout the day, they secrete bile continually. Bile salts, which are derivatives of cholesterol, assist in the digestion and absorption of fats.

Pancreatic juice, the second alkaline secretion of importance, contains the really important, very potent digestive (hydrolyzing) enzymes. In hydrolysis, a compound

Proventriculus The glandular stomach in fowl.

Abomasum The true glandular stomach in the ruminant.

Denature In protein chemistry, to disrupt the structure of a native protein causing it to lose its ability to perform its function.

Duodenum The first segment of the small intestine.

Jejunum The second and longest portion of the small intestine.

Ileum The last short portion of the small intestine.

Mucous membrane Cell layer covered in epithelial cells that both absorb and secrete.

Chyme The name given to the material consisting of food, saliva, and gastric secretions.

is split into two or more simpler compounds by the uptake of the H and OH parts of a water molecule on either side of the chemical bond cleaved. The main enzymes are trypsin, chymotrypsin, carboxypeptidase, aminopeptidase, intestinal lipase, and amylase.

The third secretion, succus entericus (intestinal juice), is secreted by glands in the small intestine itself in large amounts. For example, a human may secrete 20 liters per day. Its function is to lubricate, dilute, and increase the pH of the food mixtures.

Relative capacities of the large intestine and ceca vary greatly from species to species. Monogastric herbivores have the large intestine of greatest relative volume and carnivores have the smallest. The large intestine contains no villi; thus absorption is restricted. Mucous glands line the large intestine to provide lubrication. Note that no digestive enzymes are secreted in the large intestine by the animal. Any enzymes found there must be left over from secretions found earlier in the tract or are provided by microorganisms. The large intestine has three parts: colon, cecum, and rectum. The material that enters from the small intestines is liquid and contains cells, undigested foodstuffs, and digestive secretions. Water, electrolytes, vitamins, minerals, and volatile fatty acids (VFAs) are absorbed from this material, with emphasis on water and electrolytes. The contents of the large intestine are not sterile. The feces contain about 50% bacteria by weight. A variety of bacteria grow in feces, the most common being coliform bacteria (fecal bacteria). These bacteria produce some vitamins. Large intestinal vitamin K is very important in chickens, for instance. Bacteria also produce gases, the most important of which are carbon dioxide and methane.

Monogastric herbivores like the horse, rabbit, guinea pig, and elephant have an extensive colon and functional cecum. Carnivores, by contrast, have a very short large intestine with nonfunctional ceca. The combined colon and cecum of the monogastric herbivores is comparable in size to the rumen of ruminants and has a large fermentation capacity. The large intestines and ceca in monogastric herbivores function much as the rumen does but with less advantage to the animal. The reason is twofold. Much of the good nutrient content has already been removed from the feed by the digestion and absorption of the digestive tract prior to the feed reaching the cecum. Thus, the cecum has lower quality feed to work with than does the rumen. The second reason is that absorption is less from the cecum than the rumen. Very significant digestion does take place, however. Microorganisms break down cellulose in the cecum and large intestine, much as in the rumen. B-complex vitamins are produced. VFAs are produced, absorbed, and used in all monogastric herbivores as an energy source, similar to what happens in the ruminant. A large amount of bacterial protein is also manufactured in the cecum. However, animals must employ behavioral adaptation to be able to use this protein because there are no digestive secretions into the large intestine by the animal. The large intestine can only absorb free amino acids, not whole proteins, so the microbial protein remains unused. The adaptive mechanism is called **cecotrophy,** which is a form of pseudorumination. Animals who practice cecotrophy eat the contents of their cecum and digest it after it has been fermented in the cecum. Rabbits, for example, practice cecotrophy. They have two types of feces. One is the pellet type, which is what people usually see. The other is a soft feces that the rabbit eats. This soft feces is material that has been fermented in the cecum. The bacterial protein produced by the fermentation is digested the second time around by the upper gut. If a rabbit is denied the option of practicing cecotrophy and is on a poor diet, it will die of malnutrition because it will be deficient in protein and B vitamins. Cecal fermenters who do not practice cecotrophy, such as horses, depend more on dietary protein and B vitamins than do rabbits or ruminants. Thus, they need more dietary proteins and B vitamins in their diet.

Cecotrophy The process by which mucus-covered soft fecal pellets are expelled from the intestine and consumed by the animal.

The omnivore large intestine is generally less capable than that of the herbivore, but more capable than that of the carnivore. Vitamin synthesis and water and electrolyte absorption are similar to that of the carnivores. Cellulose digestion in these animals is a function of retention time. The longer it is retained, the more likely some digestion will take place. Studies indicate that up to 18–20% crude fiber digestion in high-fiber diets fed to swine is possible. The usefulness of this is unclear, however, because the role of volatile fatty acid absorption and utilization in the pig is poorly understood. Because swine in modern swine production facilities are rarely fed much fibrous feed, the argument is moot.

Defecation is the discharge of excrement from the body via the rectum or cloaca. Internal and external anal sphincters control the exit of material from the body. Defecation is initiated by the defecation reflex, which is stimulated by the pressure of feces in the rectum. This reflex is assisted by parasympathetic nervous signals that intensify the peristaltic waves of the large intestines. Many animals also use the Valsalva maneuver. They breathe deeply, close the glottis, and then flex the abdominal muscles. This puts pressure on the fecal contents and helps expel them.

The contents of the fecal material include undigested feed, residues of digestive enzymes, sloughed cells, and bacteria. The quantity of feces is affected by how well the feed is digested. Feeds low in digestibility contribute more undigested material to the feces. In addition, the poorly digested material causes an increase in the amount of sloughed cells from the wall of the intestine.

Micturition is urination. The components of urine include the nitrogen compounds—urea in mammals and uric acid in birds and other species. Uric acid requires much less water from the body to excrete. Also included are minerals and water. The kidney is a major regulatory mechanism for keeping the body appropriately hydrated and for removing various wastes from the body.

Defecation The act of expelling fecal matter from the large intestine via the rectum or cloaca.

Micturition The act of urinating.

DIGESTION IN THE PIG

The pig is omnivorous and monogastric (Figure 4–3). A pig's mouth is used primarily for grinding feed by the teeth and mixing with saliva. The saliva, which has a pH of about 7.4, moistens feed and helps in the chewing and swallowing process. The

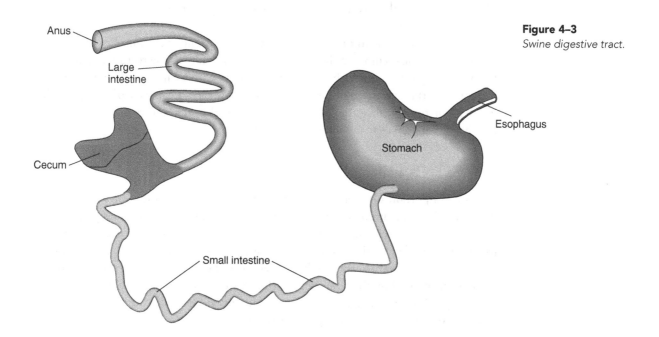

Figure 4–3
Swine digestive tract.

Anus

Large intestine

Cecum

Small intestine

Esophagus

Stomach

pig is the only farm mammal in which any amount of the enzyme salivary amylase is secreted in the saliva. The salivary amylase is relatively weak compared to that in human saliva, which is about 100 times more powerful. Amylase begins to break down the starch in the feed. However, this is of very little nutritional importance because the feed does not stay in the mouth long enough for starch breakdown. The pH is too low (acidic) in the stomach for amylase to act on the starches. The stomach of the full-grown pig has a capacity of about 2 gals.

The enzymes contained in the gastric juices of the pig are those expected in a monogastric animal. One exception is that rennin, the enzyme that coagulates milk, is not found in the pig's gastric juice. Digestion of protein is completed in the intestine and most fat digestion occurs in the small intestine. The pig requires about 24 hours to empty a full stomach.

The small intestine of the full-grown pig is about 60 ft long, has a capacity of about 2.5 gals, and is divided into three sections. The function of the small intestine is to continue the process of digestion by means of the pancreatic juice, bile, intestinal juice, and movements of the intestinal wall. A large amount of absorption of nutrients also occurs in the small intestine of the pig.

Pancreatic juice contains a number of enzymes that aid in the digestion of proteins, fats, and carbohydrates, as well as sodium carbonate and sodium bicarbonate, which neutralize acid from the stomach. The pancreas also produces insulin, which plays an important role in carbohydrate metabolism. Trypsin is initially secreted as trypsinogen and activated by calcium ions and the enzyme enterokinase, which is found in the intestine. Trypsin breaks down protein into amino acids and peptides. Chymotrypsin is secreted as chymotrypsinogen and activated by the action of trypsin in the intestine. It converts proteins into peptides and amino acids and has a coagulating action on milk. Carboxypeptidase acts on peptides and breaks them down to amino acids. All three of these enzymes continue the protein digestion that was started by pepsin in the gastric juice, and attack undigested proteins. Pancreatic lipase (steapsin) converts fats into fatty acids and glycerol. This action is most effective after the bile has emulsified the fats. Pancreatic amylase (amylopsin or pancreatic diastase) converts starch to maltose. Maltase changes maltose into glucose. Sucrase (invertase) changes sucrose to glucose and fructose. Lecithinase hydrolyzes the phospholipid lecithin.

Bile assists in digestion and absorption of fats and aids in absorption of fat-soluble vitamins. Bile may also activate pancreatic lipase and accelerate the action of pancreatic amylase.

The large intestine in the adult pig is about 16 ft long, has a capacity of 2.5 gals, and consists of the cecum and the colon, which terminates as the rectum and anus. In the mature pig, the cecum is about 9.5 in. in length, with a capacity of about 0.5 gals. The colon in the mature pig is about 16 ft long and has a capacity of 2.0 gals. The primary functions of the large intestine are to absorb water and to act as a reservoir for the waste materials that constitute the feces.

DIGESTION IN THE RUMINANT

The most important difference between ruminants and nonruminants is the complex stomach of the ruminants and the very different digestion that takes place there. Because ruminants represent the largest percentage of the domestic herbivores, we discuss them in detail. The main function of the complex stomach of the ruminant is to allow the animal to use roughage (cellulose) as a source of energy. Microbial populations housed by the ruminant in the first three compartments ferment feed. The end products of the fermentation provide nutrients to the animal that would otherwise be unavailable for any productive use.

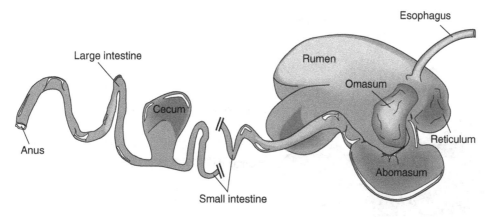

Figure 4–4
Digestive system of the ruminant. (Source: Modeled on Jurgens, 1993, p. 44.)

A ruminant typically fills the **rumen** rapidly, taking little or no time to chew its meal, and then finds a place to rest and chew. During rumination, the animal regurgitates the food eaten earlier and spends time chewing it. The particle size of the feed is broken down mechanically in this way and its surface area is increased manyfold. This increased surface area allows the microorganisms many more places of access than would otherwise be available. When one mouthful is sufficiently chewed, it is re-swallowed, another is regurgitated, and the process is repeated. A ruminant may spend a third of its life in this process. The more fiber in a diet, the more the animal will ruminate, and vice versa. Straw stays in the rumen much longer than feed of higher quality like corn silage, because of the need to ruminate and thereby help the microorganisms.

Anatomy of a typical ruminant stomach is shown in Figure 4–4. The complex stomach is comprised of four compartments: rumen, reticulum, omasum, and abomasum. Common names for these compartments are *paunch* for the rumen, *honeycomb* and *hardware stomach* for the reticulum, *manyplies* and *Stockman's Bible* for the omasum, and *true stomach* for the abomasum. The rumen and reticulum are often called the *rumino-reticulum* or *reticulo-rumen complex* because material passes freely between them and no wall separates them.

The contents of the rumen generally equal about 20% of the body weight of the adult animal. The combined capacity of the rumen, reticulum, and omasum is approximately 50 gals in an adult dairy cow, which provides significant fermentation capacity. The relative volume of the rumen is 80%, the reticulum 5%, the omasum 7–8%, and the abomasum 8–9%. The relative amount of dry versus wet material in the rumen is variable depending on what the animal has consumed and what has been absorbed. This can range from 5–60 gals of liquid and from 5–50 lbs of solid.

The rumen, reticulum, and omasum are collectively known as the **forestomachs.** The lining of these organs is nonglandular and does not produce mucus or enzymes. The abomasum, or true stomach, is lined with a true mucous membrane, and gastric juice is secreted, as in the stomachs of all mammals. Generally speaking, from the abomasum to the anus, the ruminant tract is much the same as a monogastric tract.

The reticular groove contracts and forms a tube that acts as a bypass of the rumen and empties into the omasum (Figure 4–5). This groove functions to keep milk out of the young ruminant's undeveloped rumen. If a calf drinks milk too quickly or if the groove does not close, milk can get into the rumen of the calf. The milk can't be adequately digested in the immature rumen and rots. The calf develops a severe case of diarrhea (scours) owing to the proliferation of bacteria and production of toxins in the rumen.

Rumen The largest of the ruminant forestomachs. Contains microorganisms that degrade complex carbohydrates and produce volatile fatty acids, amino acids, and vitamins to the host animal.

Forestomachs The name given to the three digestive compartments of the ruminant tract that are placed anatomically before the true stomach.

Figure 4–5
Side view (right side) of the rumen.

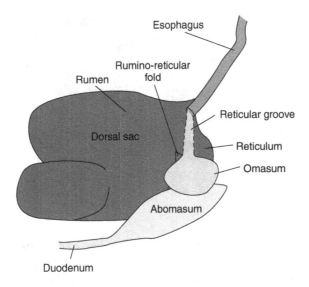

The main function of the rumen is to act as a site of anaerobic bacterial fermentation. Undeveloped at birth, it begins developing in response to the young animal's eating solid food and can have some fermentation as early as 4–8 weeks of age. All of the food consumed by the ruminant animal enters the reticulo-rumen. Some passes through quickly and isn't affected, but 85–95% is fermented to some degree. The bacteria in the rumen digest carbohydrates (cellulose, starch, and so on) and other plant materials and produce volatile fatty acids (VFAs) as an excretory by-product. VFAs are absorbed by the animal across the rumen wall and supply about 50% or more (maybe up to 70% in some cases) of the energy requirement for the ruminant. The rumen wall is covered with small fingerlike projections called **papillae.** Papillae function to increase the absorptive surface of the rumen.

A major benefit of microbial fermentation is the protein manufactured by the microorganisms as they live and reproduce. Bacteria can even convert non-protein nitrogen (NPN) such as urea into bacterial protein, which the animal subsequently uses. The bacteria pass out of the rumen and down the tract with the feed and are digested in the abomasum and small intestine. The amino acids released by the action of the animal's enzymatic digestion often meet the protein requirements of the animal. The microorganisms are about 50% crude protein with 3% lysine content. Their quality is similar to that of soybean meal, which is an excellent quality feedstuff. The bacteria also contain energy, vitamin K, and water-soluble vitamins that the animal is able to digest, absorb, and use. The formation of these vitamins by the rumen bacteria frees the ruminant from dietary water-soluble requirements under normal circumstances. The microorganisms do not synthesize vitamins A, D, and E. The bacteria also produce enough essential fatty acids for the animal.

Another important function of the rumen is to store food. This is probably how ruminants evolved—they would eat rapidly, run and hide in the woods, and chew their meal. This helped them avoid predators by minimizing their time in the open grasslands where they were vulnerable to predators.

The reticulum functions as a site of microbial action just the same as the rumen. The reticulum also acts as a pacemaker of rumen contractions. The contractions start with the reticulum and spread to the rumen. These rumen contractions are very strong and caused by contraction of the powerful rumen muscles. They function to mix the rumen contents and are essential for optimum microbial

Papillae Small fingerlike projections that greatly increase the surface area of the small intestine.

digestion. These contractions also serve to move the contents through the digestive tract. The heavier particles settle in the reticulum and are passed on through the omasum to the abomasum. The lighter particles float on the top of the rumen; these particles are then regurgitated and subjected to remastication.

The omasum absorbs water, electrolytes, and VFAs and reduces particle size of feed before it enters the abomasum.

The abomasum of the ruminant is equivalent to the true glandular stomach in monogastrics and has the same functions. Folds in the wall of the ruminant abomasum provide extra capacity and help the ruminant handle the large volume of dietary fiber.

Eructation is a very important mechanism for ruminants. The large quantities of gas produced by the rumen microorganisms as a by-product during fermentation (up to 600 L/day in a dairy cow) must be removed. Contractions of the upper sacs of the rumen force the gas toward the esophagus, which dilates, and the gas escapes. Much of the gas goes into the trachea and lungs. This provides a muffling effect and reduces the noise level considerably from what it would otherwise be. This too probably developed as a defense mechanism. It did little good for the herd to hide in the woods if a chorus of belching noises attracted every predator within hearing distance.

Eructation Belching. Removing gas from the rumen via the esophagus.

The Fermentation Process

Rumen microorganisms and the ruminant animal live in **symbiosis.** The animal benefits because the microorganisms digest feeds it could not otherwise use and generate nutrients it needs. This makes feeding the ruminant more complicated because feeding the ruminant actually involves feeding the microorganisms as well as feeding the animals. The ruminal environment is maintained by the animal to support the microorganisms, which are thus provided with a near ideal set of living conditions. These include warmth, moisture, a food supply, removal of the end products of digestion, darkness, and an **anaerobic** environment. In addition, ruminal contractions keep the contents mixed, and rumination reduces the particle size of the feed for easy access by the microorganisms.

Symbiosis A relationship where dissimilar organisms live together or in close association.

Anaerobic Conditions that lack molecular oxygen.

Many different bacteria are found in the rumen and include populations that specialize in digesting cellulose, hemicellulose, starch, proteins, sugars, acids, and producers of ammonia, vitamins, and methane. Concentrations can range from 15–50 billion/mL of rumen fluid.

Nearly 40 species of ciliate protozoa also occupy the rumen. Typically, any individual animal has only a dozen or so different species. Many factors affect the concentrations of protozoa, which can number up to a million per milliliter of rumen fluid. Protozoa use the same substrates as the bacteria and dine on bacteria as well. Some believe they help prevent bacterial overgrowth. Protozoa are closely associated with the food particles and tend to stay in the rumen rather than passing on down the tract for digestion.

Virtually everything the ruminant consumes is affected by the rumen fermentation. Some feeds are changed tremendously; others less so. Both simple and complex carbohydrates are fermented in the rumen. VFAs are a major product of ruminal fermentation. The VFAs commonly produced in the rumen are acetate, propionate, butyrate, isobutyrate, valerate, and isovalerate. The VFAs are very important. As an energy source, they may provide as much as 50–70% of the total energy needs of the animal. Bacterial cells provide 5–10% of the energy to the animal, and feed that is digested enzymatically amounts to 20–30% (Figure 4–6).

Much of the protein is broken down by microorganisms to ammonia and organic acids. The microorganisms then use the ammonia to manufacture amino acids for their own use. NPN sources can also be used by the microorganisms.

Figure 4–6

VFA synthesis in the rumen by microorganisms.

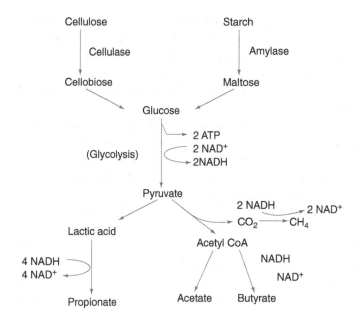

This allows us to feed urea and other NPN sources to ruminants as a means of reducing costs. Most plant sources are low in lipids, and those found in feeds aren't changed much by the fermentation process. High levels of fat are bad for the microbes and reduce the overall ability of the microorganisms to do their job.

Gas is a major product of fermentation and may amount to up to 600 L/day, as we mentioned earlier. Heat is also a major product of fermentation. The heat of fermentation is a part of the total heat increment of the animal, which is useful in winter to keep the body warm but can be detrimental in hot weather.

Advantages and Disadvantages of the Ruminant System

There are both advantages and disadvantages to the ruminant digestive system when compared to that of the nonruminant animal. Microbial fermentation has the potential to digest feedstuffs that the animal's enzymatic digestion processes cannot. This increases the feeding value of such feeds as prairie hay, corncobs, and wheat straw. Essential nutrients not found in the animal's diet such as vitamins, amino acids, and fatty acids are manufactured by the microbes and absorbed and used by the animal. If microbial fermentation occurred only in the cecum, most of these nutrients would be excreted in the feces.

A disadvantage is that the fermentation processes in the reticulo-rumen have the potential to decrease the overall quality of the ruminant animal's diet by destroying essential nutrients such as vitamins, amino acids, and fatty acids that are found in the feed. Much current interest has been expressed in bypassing high-quality feedstuffs such as soybean meal and starch and not allowing the microbes to digest them. The fermentation process also requires and wastes a considerable quantity of energy. A significant portion of the dietary energy is lost as heat and gaseous products of incomplete bacterial metabolism. This explains in part why the feed consumption required to result in 1 lb of body weight gain is about 4–8 lbs for a growing steer compared with about 3 lbs for a growing pig. Fortunately, we do not have to feed ruminant animals high-quality feeds throughout their production cycle. The ruminant animal provides us with an ideal mechanism to convert low-quality feeds not fit for human consumption into high-quality food products. Greater susceptibility to digestive upsets such as bloat (the accumulation of massive quantities of gas in the rumen) and acidosis (reduced rumen pH), which damages the rumen wall and leads to lowered productivity and liver abscesses, are other disadvantages.

DIGESTION IN THE AVIAN

The digestive organs of fowl (Figure 4–7) are similar to those of other monogastrics except for the lack of teeth and the presence of the gizzard and the crop. The mouth is not sharply separated from the pharynx. Most birds have no soft palate or teeth, and only small numbers of poorly developed salivary glands. Salivary amylase exists in the saliva but is of little value. There is no digestion in the mouth. The esophagus in the avian tract is modified. The crop is a dilation of the esophagus that is present in most species, but not all. It functions as a food storage organ and as a moistening reservoir. The size of the crop varies with the eating habits of the bird and between species. In doves and pigeons, the crop produces "pigeon milk" or "crop milk," which is used to feed the young. Fermentation occurs in the crop in some species.

The proventriculus is equivalent to the glandular stomach in mammals or the abomasum in ruminants. It is small in some species, such as chickens or pigeons. It is large in some fish-eating species (i.e., those consuming high-protein diets). The proventriculus is the site of gastric juice production (HCl and pepsin) and has a pH of 4. Ingesta passes through in a matter of seconds, so virtually no digestion takes place. Carnivorous birds are an exception—there is digestion in their proventriculus.

The gizzard, or ventriculus, is a highly specialized grinding organ. It is very muscular but varies in muscularity depending on the type of food consumed. It may

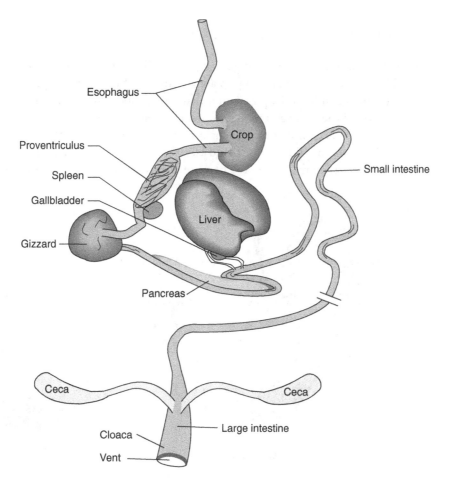

Figure 4–7
Digestive system of the avian.

be large and well developed in wild animals and smaller and less developed in commercially raised species that eat preground rations. In free-ranging birds, the gizzard contains grit to aid in the grinding of feed to smaller particles; however, with modern preground rations, grit is unnecessary. No enzymes are secreted; however, the enzymes from the proventriculus work here.

The small intestine functions in digestion and absorption of feed and nutrients just as in other monogastrics. The first part of the small intestine is the duodenum just as in other animals, but there is no specifically separated jejunum or ileum like that of mammals. The length of the duodenum varies among and between species, especially with eating habits. It is longer in herbivorous than in carnivorous birds. Generally the same enzymes found in mammalian species are present except for lactase. Milk by-products are rarely fed to chickens for this reason.

The ceca are located at the junction of the small and large intestine. There are two ceca in the avian. The size is influenced by the type of diet—the ceca are larger when the animal consumes high fiber. They open into the large intestine via the muscular ileocecal valves. Water reabsorption occurs in the ceca along with some fiber digestion; perhaps as much as 18% of total fiber and water-soluble vitamin synthesis occurs in the ceca by bacteria. The modern chicken is fed little fiber and therefore does not make use of its ceca.

The large intestine is relatively short in birds, only 2–4 in. It is not divided into a distinct rectum or colon as it is in mammals. From a digestive perspective, the large intestine is more important in water absorption than in any other function. However, vitamin K synthesis and absorption do occur here in the chicken. The cloaca is the common orifice for waste elimination (feces and urine), copulation, and egg laying in females.

DIGESTION IN THE HORSE

Figure 4–8 illustrates the horse digestive system. The horse is a nonruminant herbivore. Horses, rabbits, and guinea pigs are all capable of using roughage because they have an active cecal bacterial population that digests fiber. In this section, we explore the digestion of the horse as a model for the cecal fermenters.

The horse accomplishes prehension with its teeth, a flexible upper lip, and tongue. The horse has both vertical and lateral jaw movements. In addition, the upper jaw is wider than the lower jaw. Because of this, horses chew on only one side of

Figure 4–8
Digestive system of the horse.

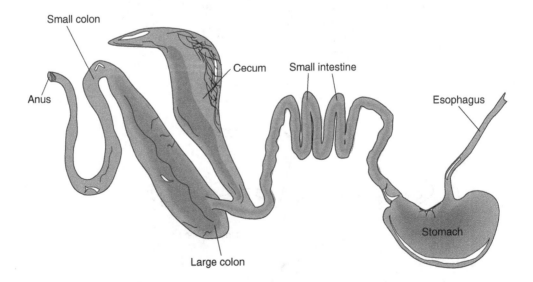

the mouth at a time. The saliva of the horse contains no enzymes but is important as a lubricant for the coarse material the horse eats. Total secretion is copious. A mature horse may secrete up to 10 gals per day if it is consuming hay or other similar material. The esophagus of the horse has only one-way peristaltic movements, which makes it almost impossible for the horse to regurgitate.

The stomach of the horse has some important distinctions compared to the stomachs of other mammals. Perhaps the most distinctive is that the stomach capacity is smaller. A pig less than half the size of a horse can have a stomach as large. A cow of equal size has an abomasum that is 50% larger. The horse's stomach provides only 8% of the capacity of the tract, or approximately 3–4 gals of capacity. The horse stomach is also unique in that it does not have equivalent muscular activity to that of other species. The feed tends to arrange itself in layers because of this lesser activity. These two factors result in the horse being more susceptible to stomach disorders than are other species. **Colic** and ruptured stomachs both occur, with colic very common. Horses should be fed small portions several times daily if possible. At a minimum, twice-a-day feeding is desirable with sufficient hay to help avoid stomach disorders.

Colic A broad term that means digestive disturbance, especially in horses.

The small intestine of the horse is similar to that of other monogastrics except for the absence of a gallbladder. The horse evolved as a continual eater and had no need for storage of bile to help with digestion of food consumed in meals. Instead, bile is secreted directly and fairly continually into the duodenum at a rate of approximately 300 mL/hr.

The large intestine of the horse is divided into the cecum, large colon, small colon, and rectum and is 25 ft long in an average-sized horse. It accounts for over 60% of the total gut capacity and is equal to about three-fifths the size of the large intestine capacity in a comparably sized ruminant. The cecum and large colon contain a bacterial population similar to that of the rumino-reticulum of ruminants in both numbers and kinds of microorganisms. Bacterial fermentation produces VFAs similar to those of the ruminant, which are absorbed and used by the animal. The horse on a forage diet receives the majority of its energy in the form of these VFAs from the large intestine. These bacteria also synthesize water-soluble vitamins that are absorbed from the large intestine, but in limited amounts. Bacterial synthesis of protein occurs, but the horse is not able to absorb this product because of the lack of enzymes and absorptive mechanisms. Because this protein is not subject to action of the digestive juices, the horse benefits little from it unless it practices **coprophagy.** Sometimes, horses on a poor diet practice coprophagy in an attempt to balance their nutrient needs. The cecum is the primary area of water reabsorption from intestinal contents, although additional amounts are absorbed from the colon.

Coprophagy The act of eating feces.

The soluble carbohydrates are digested and absorbed in the small intestine much as in any monogastric. The fiber fractions are fermented in the large intestine and colon. The products are essentially the same as those of a rumen fermentation. The VFAs are even produced in almost identical molar concentrations as those in the rumen. The VFAs are absorbed from the large intestine and used as an energy source by the cells of the horse. The horse is only about two-thirds as effective at fiber digestion as the ruminant. This is generally believed to be because feed has a much more rapid rate of passage through the horse than the ruminant. The fats found in a horse's ration are digested and absorbed in the small intestine.

The absence of a gallbladder does not seem to cause the horse any problem. Fats in rations of up to 20% fat are digested 90% or better. Proteins are digested in the horse similarly to other monogastrics and must receive the essential amino acids in the diet. Horses should receive better feed than cattle receive if we expect them to perform to their potential.

SUMMARY AND CONCLUSION

Different species have very different digestive tracts. These differences are both anatomical and functional and in many ways dictate how animals must be fed. However, for all their differences, there are also tremendous similarities. The overall goal of digestion is the same for all species: to release nutrients for the animal to absorb and metabolize in order to maintain and produce.

STUDY QUESTIONS

1. Define digestion.
2. What are the three major methods of digestion? Describe them.
3. Why do different animals use very different kinds of feeds?
4. What are the stomach types in livestock?
5. Define carnivore, omnivore, and herbivore.
6. What is prehension?
7. Define mastication. How do different animals accomplish this?
8. What is salivation? How do mastication and salivation help the animal?
9. What do you think dictates the amount of saliva that various species produce?
10. What are the components and functions of saliva?
11. Define deglutition.
12. What is the role of the stomach in digestion?
13. What are the three portions of the small intestine, and what is the function of each?
14. What does bile do? Where does it come from?
15. What does pancreatic juice do? Include a description of the function of each enzyme found in pancreatic juice.
16. What is the function of the large intestine? What do bacteria do in the gut of a monogastric herbivore?
17. Why do rabbits practice cecotrophy?
18. Describe how an animal defecates.
19. What are the components of urine?
20. Describe how a bite of feed is digested by the pig from prehension to defecation.
21. What is the major anatomical difference in ruminants and nonruminants?
22. Describe the anatomy of the ruminant tract. What are the common names of the four ruminant digestive compartments found between the esophagus and the small intestine?
23. What is the relative volume of each compartment in the ruminant "stomach"?
24. What is the reticular groove and what does it do?
25. What is the function of the rumen?
26. Why are VFAs of importance to the ruminant, and what does the animal do with them?
27. What is the relative quality of the protein manufactured in the rumen?
28. Name the nutrients produced by rumen fermentation.
29. What is the function of the reticulum? The omasum? The abomasum?
30. Describe eructation and discuss the consequences if a ruminant is unable to eructate.
31. Describe symbiosis. How do ruminants and their microbes qualify for status as symbiotic partners?
32. What kinds of microorganisms are found in the rumen?
33. What is the relative importance of VFAs to the energy contribution of a ruminant animal?
34. What is the composition of the gas coming off a ruminant fermentation?
35. State clearly the advantages of the ruminant digestive system.
36. Why don't ruminants practice cecotrophy?
37. What are the disadvantages of the ruminant digestive system?
38. Why is the feed conversion ratio for ruminants so much poorer than it is for monogastrics?
39. What are the major anatomical differences in the avian and the pig? Describe each along with its function.
40. How does digestion occur in the avian? What are the differences in the digestive processes of a chicken and of a pig?
41. Describe the significance to the horse of being a cecal fermenter.
42. How much saliva does the horse produce?
43. What are the unique features of a horse's stomach?
44. Describe in detail what happens in the large intestine and cecum of the horse.
45. Why must we feed essential amino acids to horses but not to cows?

REFERENCES

Cheeke, P. R. 1999. *Applied animal nutrition: Feeds and feeding.* 2nd ed. Upper Saddle River, NJ: Prentice Hall.

Church, D. C., and W. G. Pond. 1988. *Basic animal nutrition and feeding.* 3rd ed. New York: Wiley.

Duke, G. E. 1984. Avian digestion. In *Duke's physiology of domestic animals*, 10th ed., Melvin J. Swenson, ed. Ithaca, NY: Cornell University Press.

Ensminger, M. E., J. E. Oldfield, and W. W. Heinemann. 1990. *Feeds and feeding digest.* Clovis, CA: Ensminger.

Evans, J. W., A. Borton, H. Hintz, and L. D. Van Vleck. 1990. *The horse.* New York: W. H. Freeman.

Gillespie, J. R. 1987. *Animal nutrition and feeding.* Albany, NY: Delmar.

Hibberd, C. A. 1990. *Animal nutrition manual.* Stillwater: Oklahoma State University, Animal Science Department.

Jurgens, M. H. 1982. *Animal feeding and nutrition.* 5th ed. Dubuque, IA: Kendall/Hunt.

Jurgens, M. H. 1993. *Animal feeding and nutrition.* 7th ed. Dubuque, IA: Kendall/Hunt.

Kellems, R. O., and D. C. Church. 1999. *Livestock feeds and feeding.* 4th ed. Upper Saddle River, NJ: Prentice Hall.

Maynard, L. A., J. K. Loosli, H. F. Hintz, and R. C. Warner. 1979. *Animal nutrition.* 7th ed. New York: McGraw-Hill.

McDonald, P., R. A. Edwards, and J. F. D. Greenhalgh. 1988. *Animal nutrition.* 4th ed. New York: Wiley.

Perry, T. W., A. E. Cullison, and R. S. Lowery. 1999. *Feeds and feeding.* 5th ed. Upper Saddle River, NJ: Prentice-Hall.

Pond, W. G., D. C. Church, K. R. Pond, and P. A. Schoknecht. 2005. *Basic animal nutrition and feeding.* 5th ed. New York: Wiley.

Swenson, M. J., ed. 1984. *Duke's physiology of domestic animals.* 10th ed. Ithaca, NY: Cornell University Press.

Teeter, R. G. 1988. *Animal nutrition manual.* Stillwater: Oklahoma State University, Animal Science Department.

Umphrey, J. E. and C. R. Staples. 2003. *General anatomy of the ruminant digestive system.* Gainesville: The University of Florida. Publication # DS31. Accessed online March 2011. http://edis.ifas.ufl.edu/ds061.

5

Feedstuffs Classification

Learning Objectives

After you have studied this chapter, you should be able to:

- Describe feedstuff classification and identify feedstuff categories and characteristics.
- Identify the nutritive characteristics in various feedstuff categories.

Key Terms

Anaerobic

Energy feed

Ensiling

Feed

First-limiting amino acid

Forage

Green forage

Lignin

Mineral supplement

National Research Council

Nonnutritive additive

Nutritive value

Pasture

Protein quality

Protein supplement

Range plants

Roughage

Silage

Vitamin supplement

Weathering

INTRODUCTION

Feeds of many origins, qualities, and availabilities are used in animal diets in the United States and around the world. The nutritive content varies tremendously among them. Making sense of it all can be a daunting task. The National Research Council, a branch of the National Academy of Science, publishes a series of reports entitled *Nutrient Requirements of Domestic Animals*. Those publications use eight categories to group feedstuffs with others that have common characteristics. Feedstuffs within a group generally have similar nutritive values as well as other common characteristics. These categories help us organize types of feeds and give us a way to think about how we go about balancing a ration. In practical terms, most rations are balanced with the use of computers and databases that have information on every available feedstuff programmed into them. The category a feed falls into is not important to the computer. However, with the limits of the human mind, it is still useful to be able to put feeds into these categories: (1) dry forages and roughages; (2) pasture, range plants, and green forages; (3) silages; (4) energy feeds; (5) protein supplements; (6) mineral supplements; (7) vitamin supplements; and (8) nonnutritive additives.

FEEDSTUFF CATEGORIES

Dry Forages and Roughages

Feeds placed in this category contain at least 18% crude fiber, with values ranging up to 50% crude fiber. Dry **forages** and **roughages** are high in cellulose, hemicellulose, and possibly lignin and low in readily digested carbohydrates such as starch and sugars. Consequently, they generally have a lower digestibility and therefore lower energy values than do concentrates. The protein content varies from nearly 30% for alfalfa to 2–3% for some straws. Because ruminants and cecal fermenters generally use these feeds, the quality of the protein is not usually a concern. It is hard to make general statements about the mineral and vitamin contents of these feeds because they vary so widely. Examples of feeds in this category are legume hay, grass hays, wheat straw, cornstalks, corncobs, cottonseed hulls, peanut hulls, and rice hulls (Figures 5–1, 5–2, and 5–3).

Forage Fiber-containing feeds, such as grass or hay. Contain at least 18% fiber but have high digestible energy (more than 70%).

Roughage A bulky feedstuff with low weight per unit volume. Contains at least 18% fiber but can range up to 50%. Less digestible than forages.

Pasture, Range Plants, and Green Forages

Examples of feeds in this category are Bermuda grass pasture, sorghum-sudan grass, tall-grass prairie species, and wheat pasture (Figure 5–4). Many of these feeds could be harvested as dry feeds that would be classed in the previous category. The moisture

Figure 5–1
Hay is an example of a dry forage and roughage.
(Photo by Norm Klopfenstein. Courtesy USDA–Natural Resources Conservation Service.)

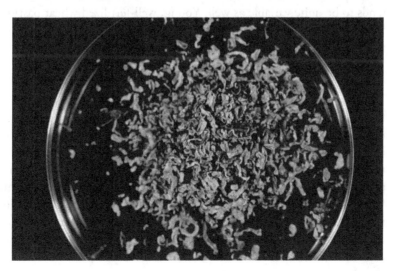

Figure 5–2
Beet pulp is a by-product of sugar production. It is often used in dairy rations and feeds for show cattle.

Figure 5–3
Cottonseed hulls are a by-product of the cotton industry and an excellent fiber source.

Figure 5–4
Grazing is the world's most common use of growing forage. These cattle are grazing native switchgrass pasture, which offers pasture for cattle in midsummer, when the cool-season species are less productive.
(Photo by Lynn Betts. Courtesy USDA–Natural Resources Conservation Service.)

content of these feeds is usually between 50–85% but can be quite variable. Winter range pasture in the range states may contain as little as 15–30% moisture, whereas wheat pasture can be as high as 90% moisture. The dry-matter nutritive content tends to be quite variable as well. Young, well-fertilized wheat pasture can have very high crude protein and can be very digestible, whereas late season prairie hay is the opposite.

Silages

Ensiling The process of producing silage from forage.

Anaerobic Conditions that lack molecular oxygen.

The process of **ensiling** plant material under **anaerobic** conditions produces silage (Figure 5–5). This is a common storage method for livestock feed. The plant material undergoes a controlled fermentation that produces acids. The acids then kill off the bacteria, molds, and other destructive organisms. As long as the silage is left undisturbed, it will keep for years. Many different materials can be ensiled. Corn silage is produced by chopping and ensiling the whole corn plant after the ears have formed. Other grain-producing species also produce good-quality silage, as do legume forage species, cannery waste, and roots and tubers. One common misconception is that ensiling improves the nutritive content of a feed. The opposite is actually true. The fermentation process uses nutrients and thus reduces the nutritive content of the material.

Figure 5–5
Silage is plant material allowed to ferment under anaerobic conditions in a silo such as the bunker silo pictured here. Samples are taken to be analyzed for nutritive value and moisture content. (Photo by Stephen Ausmus. Courtesy USDA–Agricultural Research Service.)

This category of feedstuff also causes some confusion because the ensiling process can be used to preserve other products such as high-moisture corn. However, these other products are not automatically classified as silage just because they are ensiled.

Characteristics

The three categories previously discussed in this section have much in common in terms of the plants found in each category, and thus their nutritive values are similar. Most of the feeds from these three categories are commonly referred to as either roughages or forages without further classification. A forage is generally considered to be of higher quality than a roughage (Figure 5–6). Feeds in these categories provide the bulk of the diets of the herbivorous species (ruminants and cecal fermenters) and as such are the major feeds available for animal use in the United States and the rest of the world. For these reasons, a general discussion of them seems in order before discussing the remaining categories.

The characteristics of good-quality forage generally include being relatively immature when harvested by animals or by mechanical means; being green and leafy; having soft, pliable stems; being free from mold or mustiness; being palatable; and being free from foreign material. The further a feed gets from this ideal, the poorer the quality and the more likely it will be thought of more as a roughage than a forage. For example, under most range conditions an excess of high-quality forage is available during the growing season. However, animals need feed all year long. Thus, a

(a)

(b)

Figure 5–6
The hay (a) is a fine-stemmed forage of high nutritive value. The wheat straw (b) is a roughage of low nutritional value.

part of the growth must be retained to provide feed during the nongrowing months of the year. This feed is consumed as a mature, weathered, low-quality feed during the winter months and thought of as roughage.

It is common to divide forages and roughages into legumes (e.g., alfalfa, lespedeza, soybeans, and clovers) and grasses (e.g., prairie grasses, timothy, Bermuda grass, and wheat). Legumes are generally better quality feed than grasses because the former have a lower stem and a higher leaf content. Of course, there are exceptions. Although wheat pasture is a grass, it may contain from 20–34% crude protein when it is in a young vegetative state. This protein level is higher than that of most legumes. For some nutrient parameters, there is actually little difference between legumes and grasses of equal maturity, but for other parameters, legumes are much higher in nutrient value. As a general rule of thumb, legumes and grasses have about the same energy content, but legumes have much higher protein, calcium, and carotene contents.

Many variables affect the nutritive content of forages and roughages. These include maturity at the time of harvesting, weather damage, soil fertility, plant species, and harvesting method. Maturity at the time of harvesting is perhaps the most important factor because all nutrients, except fiber, decrease in number with advancing maturity. Fiber increases with maturity. Young plants may contain only 20% crude fiber, but mature plants may have 40% or more. **Lignin** also increases as fiber increases.

The digestibility and palatability of a forage decrease with advancing maturity and increasing fiber level (Figures 5–7, 5–8). The rate of change is much greater for some plants than for others. For example, timothy, brome grass, and buffalo grass retain good palatability over a wide range of maturities. Orchard grass and lovegrass are very palatable and digestible when young, but they lose these characteristics quickly as they mature. The effects of maturity are more pronounced for grasses than for legumes. Nutrient changes with advancing maturity and **weathering** are illustrated in Table 5–1. Table 5–2 gives the nutrient content of some representative forages and roughages.

Lignin Polymers of phenolic acids found in plants as part of the structural components of the plant.

Weathering Loss in nutritive value through exposure to the elements.

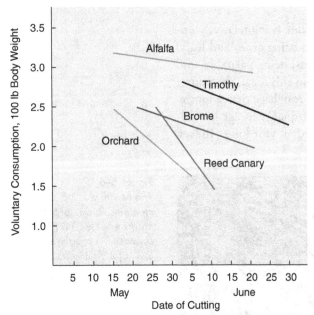

Figure 5–7

Effect of maturity on voluntary intake of first cutting forages by sheep. The later in the season the hay harvested, the less of it animals will willingly eat. (Source: Wagner, 1988, p. 50.)

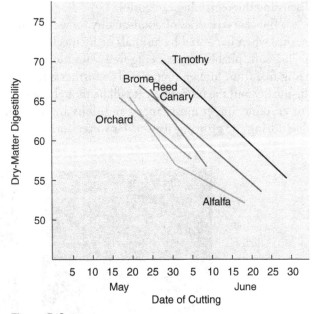

Figure 5–8

Effect of maturity on dry-matter digestibility of first cutting forages. As forages mature, the dry-matter digestibility declines. (Source: Wagner, 1988, p. 51.)

Table 5–1

AVERAGE CHEMICAL COMPOSITION OF FOUR NATIVE GRASSES DURING DIFFERENT MONTHS OF THE YEAR[1,2]

Month	Dry Matter (%)	Crude Protein (% on DM basis)	Crude Fiber (% on DM basis)	Calcium (% on DM basis)	Phosphorous (% on DM basis)	Carotene (mg/kg)
May	44.0	10.01	30.69	0.30	0.13	174.8
June	45.5	7.84	32.23	0.30	0.99	195.6
July	48.3	6.04	33.11	0.35	0.09	145.2
August	56.5	4.92	34.83	0.31	0.08	81.4
September	60.8	3.99	35.51	0.28	0.07	40.4
October	66.5	3.79	35.80	0.32	0.06	20.2
November	81.4	2.55	38.56	0.25	0.03	3.6
December	94.4	2.63	38.07	0.30	0.04	0.9
January	93.4	2.49	38.45	0.34	0.09	0.4
February	93.6	2.52	37.21	0.29	0.04	0.3
March	96.0	1.95	43.19	0.21	0.03	0.0
April	92.6	2.91	39.97	0.29	0.04	0.6

[1]Data taken from *Chemical Composition of Native Grasses in Central Oklahoma from 1947 to 1962* by Waller, Morrison, and Nelson, Bulletin B-697, January 1972.
[2]Values represent averages for 15 years.
Source: Wagner, 1988, p. 47.

Energy Feeds

Energy feeds primarily include the cereal grains, by-product feeds made from cereal grains (e.g., corn hominy feed, wheat bran), and fruits and nuts. All are low in protein.

Feeds placed in this category contain less than 18% crude fiber or less than 35% cell wall and have a protein content of less than 20% (Figure 5–9). They are usually high in starch and NFE and are thus high in energy content. Protein supplements, which are discussed next, may have similar energy content but have greater than 20% crude protein. The cereal grains are very low in crude fiber, with the range being about 2–10%. Corn (Figure 5–10), sorghum (Figure 5–11), and wheat contain about 2%, barley about 6%, and oats 10–12%. Seeds that have a fibrous outer hull are higher in crude fiber. The lower the fiber levels, the higher the energy content tends to be because more readily digested carbohydrates such as starch and sugars will be present. The energy value of grains is high, with the TDN as high as 90%

Figure 5–9

Energy feeds, generally the cereal grains or their by-products, contain less than 18% crude fiber (35% cell wall) and have a protein content of less than 20%. They are usually high in starch and NFE and are thus energy dense. Ground wheat is pictured here.

Table 5–2
Selected Nutrient Analysis of Some Forages and Roughages

Feedstuff	As Fed (% DM)	TDN (%)	NE$_m$ (Mcal/lb)	NE$_g$ (Mcal/lb)	CP (%)	EE (%)	CF (%)	ADF (%)	Ash (%)	Ca (%)	P (%)	K (%)	Mg (%)
Alfalfa, hay	90.6	60.0	1.31	0.74	18.6	2.39	26.1	33.8	8.57	1.4	0.28	2.43	0.28
Bermuda grass, fresh	30.3	64.0	1.44	0.86	12.6	3.70	28.4	36.8	8.1	0.49	0.27	1.7	0.17
Citrus pulp, silage	21.0	78.0	0.86	0.57	7.3	9.7	15.6	25	5.5	2.04	0.15	0.62	0.16
Corncobs, ground	90.0	50.0	0.44	0.19	3.2	0.7	36.2	35	1.7	0.12	0.04	0.87	0.07
Orchard grass, fresh, early bloom	23.5	68.0	1.57	0.97	12.8	3.70	32.0	30.7	8.1	0.25	0.39	3.38	0.31
Potato silage	25.0	82.0	0.91	0.61	7.6	0.4	4.0	5	5.5	0.04	0.23	2.13	0.14
Rice hulls	92.0	12.0	0.00	0.00	3.3	0.8	42.9	72	20.6	0.10	0.08	0.57	0.83
Sorghum silage, 30% DM	30.0	60.0	0.60	0.34	7.5	3.0	27.9	38	8.7	0.35	0.21	1.37	0.29
Wheat straw	89.0	44.0	0.34	0.10	3.6	1.8	41.6	54	7.8	0.18	0.05	1.42	0.12

Source: Bath et al., 1997; NRC, 1996
TDN = total digestible nutrients
NE$_m$ = net energy for maintenance
NE$_g$ = net energy for gain
CP = crude protein
EE = ether extract
CF = crude fiber
ADF = acid detergent fiber
Ca = calcium
P = phosphorous
K = potassium
Mg = magnesium

Figure 5–10
Corn is the most common feed grain in the United States. This corn has been steam flaked.

Figure 5–11
Grain sorghum is an excellent energy feed grown in drier parts of the United States.

on a dry-matter basis. These values are because of the high starch content (as high or higher than 70%), low fiber content, and high digestibility. The by-product feeds in this category usually have somewhat lower energy content because they contain more fiber and less starch as a result of processing (Figure 5–12). These feeds are fed to

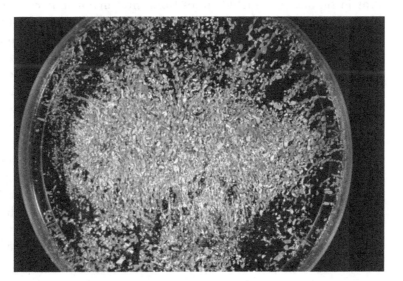

Figure 5–12
Wheat shorts are an energy feed that is also a by-product feed. By-product feeds usually have lower energy values and higher fiber levels than the original grain before processing.

Table 5–3
SELECTED NUTRIENT ANALYSIS OF SOME COMMON ENERGY FEEDS

Feedstuff[1]	Dry Matter (%)	Crude Protein (%)	Ruminant TDN (%)	Poultry (kcal/kg)	ME (kcal/kg)	Swine TDN (%)	ME (kcal/kg)
Bakery products, dried	91	10.0	82	1,650	3,630	1,635	3,600
Barley, grain	89	11.5	74	1,250	2,750	1,305	2,870
Corn, yellow, grain	86	7.9	80	1,540	3,390	1,520	3,350
Hominy feed, corn expeller	89	11.5	86	1,390	3,060	1,530	3,365
Molasses, cane, dried	91	7.0	80	1,080	2,375	1,165	2,560
Oats, grain	90	11.0	68	1,160	2,550	1,215	2,670
Oat groats (dehulled oats)	92	16.0	90	1,500	3,300	1,545	3,400
Sorghum, milo, grain	89	11.0	71	1,505	3,310	1,470	3,230
Wheat, hard, grain	88	13.5	76	1,440	3,170	1,465	3,220
Wheat, soft, grain	86	10.8	79	1,460	3,210	1,550	3,415
Wheat bran	89	14.8	62	590	1,300	1,055	2,320

[1]All table data are "as fed."
Source: Dale, 1997. Used with permission.

ruminants and cecal fermenters to increase the energy density of their rations, and to monogastrics as the primary source of energy for their diets.

Energy feeds are by definition below 20% in crude protein content. The cereal grains range between 8% and 12%. Some of the by-product feeds are higher. The protein digestibility ranges from 50–80% but the protein quality is generally poor. This is because the essential amino acid content is usually poor for grains. Lysine, methionine, and tryptophan are frequently the **first-limiting amino acids** in these feeds. If not first, they tend to be second or third limiting.

In general, cereal grains are invariably very low in calcium (Ca), modest in phosphorus (P), and low in most trace minerals. Grains are very low in both vitamin D and carotene, which is a precursor for vitamin A. However, they are generally a good source of vitamin E and do contain some B vitamins. Table 5–3 shows the nutrient content of some representative energy feeds.

First-limiting amino acid
The first amino acid whose lack of availability restricts the performance of the animal.

Protein Supplements

Protein supplements include feeds from three major sources. They are either of plant origin (e.g., soybean meal, cottonseed meal, and corn gluten meal), animal origin (e.g., fish meal, dried skim milk, and tankage), or nonprotein nitrogen (NPN) sources (e.g., urea, purified amino acids, and ammonium salts). Protein supplements are generally expensive feeds. Although balanced rations require less total protein than energy sources, the protein sources are expensive and represent the second largest source of expense in the ration. In some management and feeding situations, protein supplements are the largest out-of-pocket expense in the entire program.

Feeds placed in this category contain more than 20% crude protein. Some have high-energy contents as well. However, economics dictates that they be used to satisfy the protein needs of the animal. Because ruminants can convert the poorer quality proteins to higher quality microbial protein, an effective cost-reduction strategy is to feed the NPN sources to ruminants and avoid the higher quality, and thus more expensive, of these. Very-high-quality, and thus very expensive, feeds must be used for some rations (e.g., baby pig rations, milk replacers).

Feedstuff[1]	Swine TDN (%)	Carotene (mg/kg)	Vitamin A (IU/g)	Vitamin E (mg/kg)	Calcium (%)	Total Phosophorus (%)	Ash (%)
Bakery products, dried	79	5	3.9	25	0.1	0.35	8.0
Barley, grain	70	—	—	36	0.08	0.42	2.5
Corn, yellow, grain	80	2	1.7	22	0.01	0.25	1.1
Hominy feed, corn expeller	82	9	15.3	—	0.05	0.5	3.0
Molasses, cane, dried	65	—	—	5.4	1.18	0.9	8.0
Oats, grain	65	—	—	20	0.3	0.35	4.0
Oat groats (dehulled oats)	84	—	—	15	0.07	0.45	2.2
Sorghum, milo, grain	78	—	—	12.2	0.04	0.29	1.7
Wheat, hard, grain	79	—	—	15.5	0.05	0.41	2.0
Wheat, soft, grain	83	—	—	15.5	0.05	0.3	2.0
Wheat bran	57	—	—	10.8	0.14	1.17	6.4

The protein feeds of plant origin are primarily derived as products of the extraction of the oil from a group of seeds referred to as *oilseeds* because of their high fat content (Figure 5–13). These protein sources are thus referred to as *oilseed meals*. The most important of these sources are soybeans and cottonseed (Figure 5–14). However, significant amounts of flax, peanut, sunflower, sesame, and others are also available. The protein content is generally at least 40% and is highly digestible. The **protein quality** varies but is generally good. Lysine, cystine, and methionine levels are commonly low. Soybean meal is different in that its lysine level is usually higher. As you recall, the essential amino acid content is usually poor for grains with lysine, methionine, and tryptophan frequently being the first-, second-, and third-limiting amino acids in these feeds. These amino acids may need to be provided as purified amino acids, or animal-based protein supplements can be added to make up the deficiencies. The energy content varies depending on how much of the oil was removed in the extraction process. In general, oilseeds are low in calcium and high in phosphorus. Caution must be used when balancing rations for monogastrics because half

Protein quality A measure of the presence and digestibility of the essential amino acids in a feedstuff.

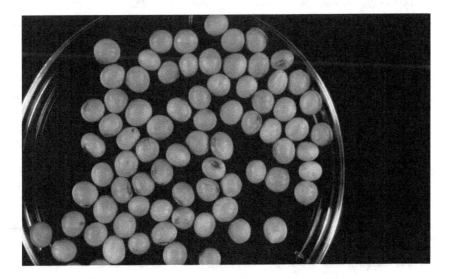

Figure 5–13
Whole soybeans can be used as livestock feed. However, they are usually processed to remove their oil content for human consumption. The remaining soybean meal is a high-quality protein supplement.

Figure 5–14

Cottonseed is a by-product of cotton production. After the oil is extracted from the seeds for human use, cottonseed meal, a high-quality protein supplement, remains.

or more of the phosphorus can be tied up as phytic-bound forms and is unavailable to the animals. The trace mineral content is variable but is generally considered to be low. Oilseeds are low in carotene, which is a precursor for vitamins A and E. They are low-to-moderate sources of B vitamins.

The protein feeds of animal origin are primarily derived as end products of the meat packing, dairy processing, and marine industries. The most important of these are meat meal, bonemeal, blood meal (Figure 5–15), feather meal, dried milk, and fish meal. The milk products are the highest quality of the end products and generally the most expensive. Good fish meals can rival milk products in quality. In addition, they generally contain much higher quantities of total protein. The lysine content of fish meal is considerably higher than that of other commonly available protein sources. Fish meals are usually good mineral and B vitamin sources. Milk and fish products are usually used for monogastric and young ruminant rations because of their high quality and subsequent cost. The quality of the protein in the meat products is usually lower than that of the milk and fish products. However,

Table 5–4
CRUDE PROTEIN AND AMINO ACID CONTENT OF SOME PROTEIN SUPPLEMENTS[1]

Ingredients	Dry Matter (%)	Crude Protein (%)	Methionine (%)	Cystine (%)	Lysine (%)	Tryptophan (%)	Threonine (%)
Blood meal, animal	89	80.0	1.0(91)	1.4(76)	6.9(86)	1.0	3.8(87)
Brewers dried grain	93	27.9	0.6	0.4	0.9	0.4	1.0
Brewers dried yeast	93	45.0	1.0	0.50	3.4	0.8	2.5
Canola meal	91	38.0	0.7(90)	0.47(75)	2.3(80)	0.44	1.71(78)
Casein, dried	90	80.0	2.7(99)	0.3(84)	7.0(97)	1.0	3.8(98)
Cottonseed meal, 41%, direct solvent	90	41.0	0.51	0.62	1.76	0.52	1.35
Feather meal, poultry	93	85.0	0.55(76)	3.0(59)	1.05(66)	0.4	2.8(73)
Fish meal, herring, Atlantic	93	72.0	2.2	0.72	5.7	0.8	2.88
Meat and bonemeal, 45%	92	45.0	0.53	0.26	2.2	0.18	1.8
Milk, whole dried, feed grade	96	25.5	0.62	0.4	2.26	0.41	1.03
Peanut meal, solvent	92	48.0	0.42	0.73	1.77	0.5	1.16
Soybean meal, solvent	90	44.0	0.65	0.67	2.9	0.60	1.7
Yeast, Torula, dried	93	48.5	0.80	0.6	3.8	0.5	2.6

[1]Numbers in parentheses represent percentage availability.
Source: Dale, 1997. Used with permission.

Figure 5–15
Blood meal is an example of a slaughter by-product used as a protein supplement.

the quality is still good and their use is usually restricted to monogastrics. Some of the meat products have high mineral contents, depending on the percentage of bone they contain. The vitamin content is highly variable but generally low because of the types of processing required to make these feeds usable. Feather meal is a low-quality protein supplement, but it is very high in total protein content (over 90%). It is best used in ruminant rations, although it can be used as a part of monogastric rations.

The NPN sources technically include such a wide range of material that generalizations are impossible. Purified amino acids are technically NPN. However, because of the costs of such feeds, the practical use of the term NPN is for urea (Figure 5–16) and other similar products. Urea and similar products must be used with functional ruminants only—and then, very carefully. The ruminant microbes are able to use substantial amounts of NPN and, because they are frequently of lower cost than proteins, they are often used to cheapen a ration. They are not a significant source of other nutrients as a rule. Table 5–4 shows the crude protein and amino acid contents of some commonly used protein supplements.

Ingredients	Isoleucine (%)	Histidine (%)	Valine (%)	Leucine (%)	Arginine (%)	Phenylalanine (%)
Blood meal, animal	0.8(78)	3.05(84)	5.2(87)	10.3(89)	2.35(87)	5.1(88)
Brewers dried grain	2.0	0.47	1.69	3.2	1.3	1.82
Brewers dried yeast	2.2	1.3	2.37	3.2	2.2	1.86
Canola meal	1.51(83)	1.10(85)	1.94(82)	2.6(87)	2.3(90)	1.5(87)
Casein, dried	5.7(98)	2.5(96)	6.8(98)	8.7(99)	3.4(97)	4.6(99)
Cottonseed meal, 41%, direct solvent	1.33	1.1	1.82	2.4	4.66	2.23
Feather meal, poultry	2.66(85)	0.28(72)	4.55(82)	7.8 (82)	3.92(83)	2.66(85)
Fish meal, herring, Atlantic	3.0	1.91	5.7	5.1	5.64	2.56
Meat and bonemeal, 45%	1.7	1.5	2.4	2.9	2.7	1.8
Milk, whole dried, feed grade	1.33	0.77	1.74	2.57	0.92	1.33
Peanut meal, solvent	1.76	0.95	1.88	3.70	4.55	2.04
Soybean meal, solvent	2.5	1.1	2.4	3.4	3.4	2.2
Yeast, Torula, dried	2.9	1.4	2.90	3.5	2.6	3.0

Figure 5–16
Feed-grade urea is used as a nonprotein nitrogen source in ruminant rations.

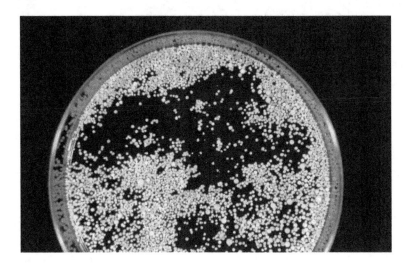

Mineral and Vitamin Supplements

Virtually all feeds contain at least some vitamins and minerals. Animals need these nutrients in much smaller amounts than they do the other nutrients. Nevertheless, dietary needs must be met in a satisfactory manner to achieve good animal performance and economical production. Depending on the feeds used to balance the ration for the other nutrients, concentrated sources of vitamins and/or minerals may be needed.

Mineral supplements in common use include salt (often trace mineralized) (Figure 5–17), bone meal, oyster shell (Figure 5–18), calcium carbonate, limestone, and fairly pure forms of other specific minerals such as selenium, cobalt, and others. In addition, a wide variety of premixed, complete, mineral supplements are generally available. The minerals of concern usually include sodium, calcium, phosphorus, magnesium, copper, iron, manganese, zinc, cobalt, and selenium. Table 5–5 shows the mineral content of some representative mineral supplements.

Vitamin supplements include such products as ensiled yeast, liver meal, fish oil, and wheat germ oil, as well as purified forms of individual vitamins. Although rations can be formulated and balanced for each individual vitamin easily with

Figure 5–17
NaCl and a variety of trace minerals are collectively referred to as trace mineral salt. It is used in loose form such as this for mixing with other feeds, or it may be fed in blocks that animals lick when they crave salt.

Table 5-5
MINERAL CONTENT OF SOME REPRESENTATIVE MINERAL SUPPLEMENTS

	Calcium (%)	Total Phos. (%)	Ash (%)	Sodium (%)	Potassium (%)	Magnesium (%)	Fluorine (%)	Manganese (ppm)[1]	Iron (ppm)	Copper (ppm)	Zinc (ppm)	Selenium (ppm)
Bonemeal (steamed)	24.0	12.0	71.0	0.46	n/a[1]	0.64	n/a	30.4	840	16.3	424	n/a
Calcium carbonate	38.0	—[1]	95.8	0.06	0.06	0.5	n/a	279	336	24	n/a	0.07
Diammonium phosphate (N-18%)	0.5	20.0	34.5	0.04	—	0.45	0.2	500	15,000	80	300	n/a
Deflourinated phosphate	33.0	18.0	99.0	4.5	0.09	—	0.2	220	9,200	22	44	0.6
Dicalcium phosphate	20.0	18.5	85.6	0.08	0.07	0.6	0.18	300	10,000	80	220	0.6
Phosphoric acid, 75%	—	23.8	n/a	n/a	n/a	n/a	—	n/a	5	n/a	n/a	n/a

	Potassium (%)	Magnesium (%)	Iron (%)	Copper (%)	Manganese (%)	Zinc (%)	Cobalt (%)	Sulfur (%)	Selenium (%)	Sodium (%)
Copper sulfate (CuSO₄5H₂O)	—	n/a	n/a	25.0	n/a	n/a	—	—	—	—
Ferrous sulfate (FeSO₄7H₂O)	—	0.04	21.0	0.001	0.002	—	—	11.0	—	—
Manganese sulfate (MnSO₄H₂O)	—	0.05	0.01	0.01	25.0	0.01	—	19.0	—	—
Magnesium sulfate (MgSO₄)	—	20.0	0.04	0.001	0.12	—	—	26.6	—	—
Potassium sulfate (K₂SO₄)	44.8	—	n/a	n/a	n/a	n/a	—	18.3	—	—
Sodium selenite (Na₂SeO₃)	—	—	—	—	—	—	—	—	45.6	26.6
Zinc oxide (ZnO)	—	—	0.8	—	—	73.0	—	—	—	—
Copper sulfate (CuSO₄5H₂O)	—	0.5	—	0.07	0.01	—	—	1.0	—	—

[1]ppm = parts per million; n/a = data not available; — indicates that the ingredient does not contain a significant amount of nutrient.
Source: Dale, 1997. Used with permission.

Figure 5–18
Oyster shell, a valuable source of calcium, is frequently used in laying-hen diets.

modern computer balancing programs, in practice, vitamin supplements are often added without regard for the amounts that may be found naturally in the feeds used in the ration. This is because of the highly variable availability of vitamins found in natural feedstuffs. Those vitamins usually supplemented in animal rations include vitamins A, D, and E for functional ruminants; and vitamin K, riboflavin, pantothenic acid, niacin, choline, folic acid, biotin, and cyanocobalamine for other species. Table 5–6 shows the vitamin content of a standard vitamin premix supplement (Figure 5–19).

Table 5–6
VITAMIN PREMIX FOR SWINE[1]

Vitamin	Amount/lb of Premix[1]	Suggested Source
Vitamin A	2,000,000 IU[2]	Vitamin A palmitate-gelatine coated
Vitamin D	200,000 IU	Vitamin D_3—stabilized
Vitamin E	10,000 IU	dl-Tocopherol acetate
Vitamin K (menadione equivalent)[2]	800 mg	Menadione sodium bisulfite
Riboflavin	1,200 mg	Riboflavin
Pantothenic acid	4,500 mg	Calcium pantothenate
Niacin	9,000 mg	Nicotinamide
Choline	20,000 mg	Choline chloride (60%)
Vitamin B_{12}	5 mg	Vitamin B_{12} in mannitol (.1%)
Folic acid	300 mg	Folic acid
Biotin	40 mg	D-biotin

[1]Premix is designed to be used at a rate of 5 lbs per ton of complete feed for sows and baby pigs, and 3 lbs per ton of complete feed for growing-finishing swine.
[2]A standard unit of potency. Defined by the International Conference for Unification of Formulae.
Source: Luce et al., 1998. Used with permission.

Figure 5–19
Vitamins are often mixed in appropriate individual quantities and blended with an inert carrier so they can be added to rations. Such vitamin supplements facilitate the balancing of rations and improve the accuracy of ration mixing.

Nonnutritive Additives

This is a catchall category for a large group of feed ingredients added to rations for some reason other than their nutritive value. They may be used to stimulate growth or some other type of production, improve feed efficiency, enhance health, or alter metabolism. Feedstuffs in this category include antibiotics, coloring agents, flavors, hormones, and medicants. Examples of substances in this category include monensen sodium (makes rumen fermentation more efficient), butylated hydroxytolulene (antioxidant), aluminum sulfate (used as an anti-gelling agent for molasses), monosodium glutamate (flavor enhancer used in pet foods), propylene glycol (emulsifying agent), and aluminum potassium sulfate (color additive). Not all additives are fed. Some can be given to the animal as an injection or implant.

The list of nonnutritive additives changes over time. Those additives classified as drugs must be approved by the Food and Drug Administration (FDA). A good reference to become familiar with is the *Feed Additive Compendium*. Updated yearly, this is an invaluable resource for nutritionists.

SUMMARY AND CONCLUSION

This chapter was designed to give you an overview of feeds and their general uses and nutritive values. The system of categorizing feedstuffs used in this chapter is the one found in the NRC publications, which is generally used and accepted. Although the chapter has provided generalities about the feeds classifications, exceptions are easy to find. Research is continually telling us more about feeds and their nutrient availabilities. Even identical species of plants can produce different nutrient levels in a feedstuff because of the many environmental factors that affect nutrient content. The by-product feeds tend to change because the processes that generate them change. Plant breeders are continually developing new and nutritionally different crops. With the advent of accelerating recombinant DNA technology, even more rapidly changing nutritive values can be expected. All of these changes tend to blur the lines between nutrient classes. It is important to keep up with changes in the values of the various feedstuffs. Consult current NRC publications and scientific journals. An additional important resource with high credibility with academics and industry leaders is the annual *Feedstuffs Reference Issue*.

STUDY QUESTIONS

1. What are the eight categories of feedstuffs as recognized by the NRC?
2. What are the similarities and differences in the first three categories described in this chapter?
3. What is the difference between a forage and a roughage? What are the characteristics of a good-quality forage?
4. What is the definition of an energy feed? What is the definition of a protein feed? What is the difference between an energy feed and a protein feed?
5. What are the differences and similarities of protein supplements from the three major sources of protein supplements?
6. What are the major similarities and differences in vitamin supplements and mineral supplements?
7. For what purposes are nonnutritive additives added to rations?
8. Why must one have a good, current source of nutrient composition for feedstuffs?

REFERENCES

Bath, D., J. Dunbar, J. King, S. Berry, and S. Olbrich. 1997. Byproducts and unusual feeds. *Feedstuffs* 69(30):32.

Dale, N. 1997. Ingredient analysis table: 1997 edition. *Feedstuffs* 69 (30):24.

Feed additive compendium. 1998. Minnetonka, MN: Miller Publishing Co., and Alexandria, VA: The Animal Health Institute.

Luce, W. G., A. F. Harper, D. C. Mahan, and G. R. Hollis. 1998. Swine diets. *Pork industry handbook*. Lafayette, IN: Media Distribution Center.

NRC. 1996. *Nutrient requirements of beef cattle*. 7th ed. Washington, DC: National Academy Press.

Pond, W. G., D. C. Church, K. R. Pond, and P. A. Schokhecht. 2005. *Basic animal nutrition and feeding*. 5th ed. New York: Wiley.

Thaler, R. C., and R. C. Wahlstrom. 1998. Vitamins for swine. *Pork industry handbook*. Lafayette, IN: Media Distribution Center.

Wagner, D. G. 1988. *Livestock feeding*. 2nd ed. Stillwater: Oklahoma State University.

6

Genetics

Key Terms

Additive gene action
Alleles
Aneuploidy
Animal breeding
Artificial selection
Autosomes
Biotechnology
Centromere
Chromosome
Codominance
Crossbreeding
Deoxyribonucleic acid (DNA)
Diploid
DNA polymerase
DNA replication
Dominant
Epistasis
Expression
Gametes
Gametogenesis
Gene
Gene frequency
Genetic drift
Genetic engineering
Genome
Genotype
Genotypic frequency
Haploid
Heritability
Heterosis
Heterozygous
Homologous chromosomes
Homozygous
Inbreeding
Inbreeding depression
Incomplete dominance
Inheritance

Linebreeding
Locus
Marker-assisted selection
Meiosis
Messenger RNA
Migration
Mitosis
Monosomy
Multiple alleles
Mutations
Natural selection
Nucleotide
Outbreeding
Phenotypic frequency
Polymerization
Polyploidy
Population genetics
Principle of independent assortment
Principle of segregation
Purines and pyrimidines
Qualitative traits
Quantitative traits
Recessive
Ribonucleic acid (RNA)
Ribosomes
Selection
Selection differential
Sex-influenced inheritance
Sex-limited traits
Sex-linked inheritance
Somatic cells
Testcross
Transcription
Transfer RNA (tRNA)
Transgenic
Translation
Trisomy

Learning Objectives

After you have studied this chapter, you should be able to:

- Explain the role that genetics plays in animal production.
- Describe the location of genes within a cell.
- Explain the process of cellular division with relation to the replication of cells containing a full complement of genetic information.
- Explain the process of cellular division that ultimately produces cells containing only half of the genetic information.
- Describe how variation in traits is passed from parent to offspring.
- Describe how gene frequencies change in a population.
- Explain the concept of relationship between individuals.
- Describe several systems of mating individuals.
- Summarize the implications of genetic engineering, the promise it holds for future animal production, and the opportunities that animals will have to provide even greater benefits to humanity.

INTRODUCTION

Genetics can be termed the foundation of life, for without the ability to transfer genetic information from one generation to the next, existence would be impossible. In the nature versus nurture debate, genetics is the nature side. Inheritance takes place by the transmission of genes, in the form of chemical entities, from parent to offspring at the time of conception. During this transfer of molecular material, certain information is passed on to the offspring that is combined to form a blueprint of characteristics that will describe both the physical appearance and the molecular composition of the animal. An animal's genetic makeup, or **genotype**, sets the stage for disposition, coat type, coat color, speed, gait types, body composition, growth, reproduction, milk production, disease resistance, and other traits.

A large part of how efficiently animal products can be produced is related to the genetic composition of the animal or herd of animals. The **expression** of the genotype into traits of economic importance provides the basis for the animal's worth when marketed. Because there are many ways to market an animal, it is important to produce animals with the necessary genotype for maximum value in the target market.

Within each major animal species, producer and consumer preferences set the pace for desired characteristics in the animals that are produced. From a livestock producer standpoint, efficiency of production might be the most important overall goal in regard to other traits, such as disposition, which also receive consideration because of the effect such traits have on the producer's ability to care for the animals. However, when viewing animals from a consumer's position, tenderness, flavor, color, and leanness might top the list of important characteristics. This is not to say that these characteristics don't overlap between the producer and the consumer, because they surely do. For instance, the consumer is interested in cost, which is related to efficiency of production. However, the priorities on each side are often different. In the companion species, there too may be differences in producer and consumer concerns. An elite breeder may strive to breed an international champion. The average consumer may just want a healthy dog with no major flaws and a good disposition that will be a good companion.

Applied genetics in animals is usually referred to as *animal breeding* (Figure 6–1). It is the science that helps in the quest to breed better animals. The practice of breeding and selection has led to remarkable changes in animal species. The wolf has been transformed into dogs as different as the Saint Bernard and the Chihuahua. The wild aurochs became the specialized milk, meat, or work breeds of modern cattle. The wild boar, the Red Junglefowl, the vicuña, the Siberian hamster, and several score

Genotype The genetic makeup of an organism.

Expression Manifestation of a characteristic that is specified by a gene.

Figure 6–1

The application of animal breeding and selection techniques has led to remarkable changes, such as arranging the genes of the wild boar (a) into those of the modern meat-type hog (b).

(a)

(b)

of other wild animals have been converted to the modern domestic species we know today. Interestingly, the greatest changes in domestic species through the practice of animal breeding occurred before the science was named, and before the scientific basis of inheritance was discovered. Dogs have been dogs rather than wolves for at least 10,000 years. **Deoxyribonucleic acid (DNA)**, the stuff genetic codes are made of, was determined to be the genetic material relatively recently, in 1952. However, research in **genetic engineering** has made possible advances that may come to dwarf those earlier accomplishments, and it will likely do so in the span of a few decades rather than a few millennia.

THE GENE

The nucleus of the cell contains the **chromosomes**. Chromosomes are large molecules composed of DNA and protein. Within these large molecules are smaller segments of DNA called **genes**. The genes contain the information that controls all of the biochemical processes of the cell. By controlling the biochemical processes of the cell, genes control the life processes. A gene is a segment of DNA that codes for a specific protein. These DNA molecules are in the shape of a double helix. DNA comprises chromosomes, which are found in pairs. It is this arrangement of genes, DNA, and chromosomes that provides the basis for inheritance (Figure 6–2).

Because genes are segments of DNA, we should look at the structure of DNA to determine the existence of genetic material. Deoxyribonucleic acid (DNA) consists of two strands comprised of alternating sequences of the sugar deoxyribose and phosphate bonds. At each sugar, there is a bridge of nitrogen **bases** composed of chemical compounds called **purines and pyrimidines**. The purines present in a DNA molecule are adenine (A) and guanine (G); the pyrimidines are thymine (T) and cytosine (C). The bridges are always combined, with adenine attaching to thymine and guanine with cytosine. The bases are attached with hydrogen bonds (Figure 6–3). The segment of deoxyribose, phosphate, and one of the bases is called a **nucleotide**. A gene is a segment of the double helix consisting of several nucleotides. These segments produce a genetic code that specifies the chemical composition of proteins, which ultimately are the end product of genetic expression. The entire genetic material of an animal is termed its **genome**.

Genomes of organisms vary in size, with simpler organisms having genomes substantially smaller than those of complex multicellular organisms. Because chromosomes comprise the genome, there is an issue of how this genetic information is held in such small spaces. DNA segments can be of varying lengths, and this is important when they must be packed into small sections of the chromosome. DNA is supercoiled in such a way that it becomes very compact and is able to fit into extremely small sections of the chromosome. Imagine a DNA molecule that has ends attached in such a way as to produce a circle. Now imagine twisting this circle so it decreases in width by half, and now one circle is lying on top of the other. Picture a coiled garden hose that has been twisted in this manner. With each twist, the circumference of the circle decreases but gets deeper or thicker as the hose stacks up on top of itself. This same concept is true of supercoiled DNA. As this sequence progresses, the DNA molecules in a chromosome become much more compact and the chromosome shortens and thickens, thus becoming smaller in overall size.

There is some potential for variation in chromosome numbers because of the many processes that must first take place for inheritance to be possible. One such variation in chromosome numbers is called **polyploidy**. A polyploid individual has

Deoxyribonucleic acid (DNA) Chemically, a complex molecule composed of nucleotides joined together with phosphate sugars. Chromosomes are large molecules of DNA.

Genetic engineering The term most frequently used to describe the technologies for moving genes from one species to another.

Chromosome The DNA-containing structures in cells. Composed of segments called genes.

Gene A short segment of a chromosome. Genes direct the synthesis of proteins or perform regulatory functions.

Bases One of the four chemical units on the DNA molecule that form combinations that code for protein manufacture. The four bases are adenine (A), cytosine (C), guanine (G), and thymine (T).

Purines and pyrimidines Organic ring structures made up of more than one kind of atom (heterocyclic compounds). Purines and pyrimidines contain nitrogen in addition to carbon.

Nucleotide The building blocks of nucleic acids. Each nucleotide is composed of sugar, phosphate, and one of four nitrogen bases.

Genome The complete genetic material of an organism.

Polyploidy Having more than two full sets of chromosomes.

Figure 6–2

Location and structure of genetic material. (Source: Adapted from Alcamo, 1996, p. 10.)

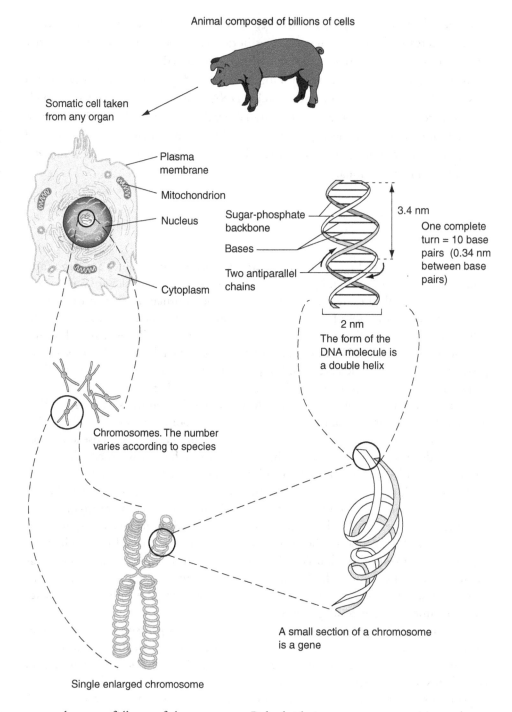

more than two full sets of chromosomes. Polyploidy is very uncommon in vertebrates but quite widespread in plants. This is beneficial in some situations. Many times polyploidy causes failure of meiosis because there is more than one pairing partner for each chromosome and the result is just a few small seeds; for example, seedless watermelons.

Figure 6–3

Chemical nature of DNA. This structure is the double helix form of DNA. A & T are joined with double hydrogen bonds; G & C are joined with triple hydrogen bonds.

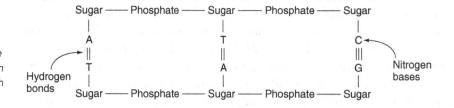

Another example of variation is **aneuploidy**, in which there is variation in chromosome number with respect to individual chromosomes. If an organism is missing a chromosome ($2n - 1$), it is said to be **monosomic**. If an organism contains an extra chromosome ($2n + 1$), it is possible for development to be either normal or slightly abnormal. This is referred to as **trisomy**. Monosomies and trisomies are frequently lethal unless the affected chromosome is one of the smallest chromosomes. A common nonlethal example of trisomy is Down syndrome in humans, which is caused by trisomy of autosome number 21. Trisomy is often related to failure of the chromosomes to separate properly in meiosis, producing a gamete with two copies of the chromosome.

DNA is a sequence of base pairs (i.e., ATCG with TAGC) that represents the code for a specific gene. A sequence of four bases can be arranged in 256 different ways; therefore, it is easy to see how sequences of many more base pairs can be arranged in exponentially many more ways. This concept provides the complexity of DNA and thus the code for many different genes.

DNA replication is the process of making a copy of a DNA molecule. Replication must occur accurately so the daughter cell (the cell being produced) inherits the same information contained in the parent cell. This process of synthesizing DNA is carried out by unzipping the existing DNA strand between base pairs (i.e., unzipping between A-T and C-G) to expose each base. **DNA polymerase** is the enzyme that forms the sugar–phosphate bond between adjacent nucleotides in a chain. For DNA polymerase to act, an RNA primer must be present to which the DNA polymerase attaches to begin the replication process. The process of **polymerization** is carried out by DNA polymerase. More specifically, this consists of deoxynucleotides being added to the existing single strand of DNA, thereby producing a complete DNA molecule with matching base pairs and sequences just like the initial molecule. Thinking through this process, it is easy to visualize the splitting of a DNA molecule to produce two strands of DNA. Then the addition of nucleotides that complement the existing bases (i.e., ATGC) forms a complete DNA molecule. By starting with one DNA molecule, this process ultimately produces two identical molecules.

The next step is to look at how this genetic information is used to specify the type of molecule to be produced. DNA is located in the nucleus of the cell, but proteins are produced by **ribosomes** located in the cytoplasm. Because the purpose of the DNA is to serve as a template for the construction of a protein, the genetic message found in the DNA must be transported from within the nucleus out to the ribosome. **Ribonucleic acid (RNA)** molecules are fitted especially for this process. RNA molecules are built to complement the DNA. This process is known as **transcription**. DNA serves as a template and codes for the manufacture of RNA. Once a complementary RNA has been synthesized, it is processed to remove sections of base pairs from the primary transcript that are not part of the coding sequence for the specific protein needed. The end product of this processing is a **messenger RNA (mRNA)** that contains only the sequences of base pairs used to code for the specific protein. The DNA also codes for a second RNA called **transfer RNA (tRNA)**, which is used to collect the amino acids needed to build the protein. The mRNA leaves the nucleus and attaches to the ribosome, where it is used as the template to manufacture the protein. The tRNA moves into the cytoplasm and attaches to the amino acid for which each is coded. Next, the ribosomes move along the length of the mRNA and align with the tRNA, which brings the amino acids into the chain. As they are aligned, the amino acids chemically bond to each other. A chain of amino acid sequences is thus constructed. This process is known as **translation** of the mRNA code for the protein being built. When the tRNA comes to a three-base sequence for which it has no match, the process is complete. The resulting chain of amino acids is a protein. The protein is now ready to do its work in the cell.

Aneuploidy A condition in which an organism has a chromosome number that is not an exact multiple of the monoploid (m) number.

Monosomy The absence of one chromosome from an otherwise diploid cell.

Trisomy The presence of one extra chromosome in an otherwise diploid cell.

DNA replication The cellular process of making a copy of a DNA molecule.

DNA polymerase The enzyme that forms the sugar–phosphate bonds between adjacent nucleotides in a chain so that replication can occur.

Polymerization The process of building high molecular weight molecules by repeatedly chemically bonding the same compound to itself.

Ribosomes A component of cells that contain protein and tRNA. They synthesize proteins.

Ribonucleic acid (RNA) Long chains of phosphate, ribose sugar, and several bases.

Transcription In protein manufacture, the process of building RNA that is complementary to DNA.

Messenger RNA (mRNA) Nucleic acid that carries instructions to a ribosome for the synthesis of a particular protein.

Transfer RNA (tRNA) Molecules of RNA coded by DNA to bond with a specific amino acid. tRNA molecules "collect" the amino acids from the cytoplasm that the ribosomes use to manufacture proteins.

Translation In protein manufacture, the process of building an amino acid sequence according to the code specified by mRNA.

PRINCIPLES OF INHERITANCE

Alleles One of two or more alternative forms of a gene occupying corresponding sites (loci) on homologous chromosomes.

Homologous chromosomes Chromosomes having the same size and shape, occurring in pairs, and affecting the same traits.

Locus The specific location of a gene on a chromosome.

Homozygous When two genes of a pair are the same.

Heterozygous When two genes in a pair are not the same.

Inheritance The transfer of gene-containing chromosomes from parent to offspring.

Gametes The sperm from the male parent and the egg from the female parent.

Principle of segregation Mendel's first law; often called the law of segregation. The law states that when gametes are formed, the genes at a given locus separate so that each is incorporated into different gametes.

Principle of independent assortment Mendel's second law. It says that in the formation of gametes, separation of a pair of genes is independent of the separation of other pairs.

In 1866, Gregor Mendel discovered the principles of inheritance while working with garden peas. He sought to understand why peas were consistent within lines but different between lines. Our understanding of how traits are inherited has sprung from the simple experiments of this monk.

The various forms of a given gene are called **alleles**. Alleles affect the same trait, but each allele causes the production of a different protein and thus differences in the way the trait is expressed. Genes are located on molecules called chromosomes. Chromosomes that have the same size and shape and occur in pairs are called **homologous chromosomes**. Homologous chromosomes have genes that affect the same traits. The number of chromosomes containing the genetic information of an individual differs among species (Table 6–1). An animal that has matching alleles at a given point on the chromosome, or **locus**, is said to be **homozygous** (*AA*), and one with different alleles is **heterozygous** (*Aa*).

The method by which these alleles are passed on from one generation to the next is known as **inheritance**. Each parent produces reproductive cells called **gametes**, and within each gamete is a single allele for each gene. In the formation of these gametes, the parental alleles separate so that each gamete contains only half of the genetic code the parent possesses. Two important principles come into play at this point:

> The **principle of segregation** states that alleles separate so that only one (randomly chosen) is found in any particular gamete.

> The **principle of independent assortment** states that in the formation of gametes, separation of a pair of genes is independent of the separation of other pairs.

When the gametes combine to produce an individual, these alleles are brought together and coding for a protein begins. Any given gamete contains one allele for each gene in the genotype. A genotype is the entire genetic composition of the animal; however, genotype can also mean only the alleles of genes of interest to a particular situation.

The concept of sex determination is important in the formation of gametes. The male gametes are *sperm* and the female gametes are *eggs*. In mammals, female genotypes contain a pair of X chromosomes and males have an X and

---

Table 6–1
NUMBER OF CHROMOSOMES BY SPECIES

Species	Number of Chromosomes (2*n*)
Human	46
Cattle	60
Swine	38
Sheep	54
Goat	60
Horse	64
Chicken	78
Bison	60
Llama	74
Cat	38
Dog	78

Source: Compiled from Bourdon, 2000, and Van Vleck et al., 1987.

a Y chromosome. Thus a female can contribute only an X chromosome to her offspring; a male is capable of passing on either an X or a Y. The pairing of these sex chromosomes in the zygote ultimately determines the sex of an individual. In this situation, the male contributes the gamete that will determine the sex of the offspring. In the avian species, the female gamete contains pairs that do not match, making her the parent that passes on the chromosome that carries the information for sex differentiation; the male passes on gametes with only one type of sex chromosome.

Each normal body tissue cell, or **somatic cell**, of an individual has two sex chromosomes, or one pair. However, every somatic cell also has $(2n - 2)$ **autosomes**, which are simply all chromosomes other than sex chromosomes. In other words, for each somatic cell of an organism, such as a human, that has 46 chromosomes (23 pairs), two chromosomes (1 pair) are sex chromosomes and the other 44 chromosomes (22 pairs) are autosomes. Each gamete cell has one sex chromosome and $(n - 1)$ autosomes. In the human, a gamete contains 1 sex chromosome and 22 autosomes. A visual representation of the chromosomes of a species is called a *karyotype*. Karyotypes are put together by using pictures of individual chromosomes taken at metaphase (see following section). They are then arranged by chromosome number so that visual comparisons can be made (Figure 6–4).

The production of gametes is responsible for providing the means by which inheritance takes place. By applying the aforementioned principles, it is possible to understand how variation exists in a population. The principle of segregation, when combined with the principle of independent assortment, provides a means for randomization of alleles within the gametes.

Chromosomes occur in pairs in somatic cells. Thus a somatic cell contains a **diploid** $(2n)$ number of chromosomes. The germ cells, sperm and egg, contain only a **haploid** number (n). A chromosome can be thought of as long strands of genes. Chromosome size depends on how many genes are located on each respective chromosome. Another feature of the chromosome is the **centromere**, which can be located anywhere along the chromosome. The centromere serves as the point of attachment for the spindle fibers during cell division. The location of the chromosome is another feature that can be used to identify chromosomes. To understand the method by which somatic cells and gametes obtain their respective number of chromosomes, it is important to identify the different types of cell division.

Somatic cells All cells in the body other than gametes.

Autosomes All chromosomes other than the sex chromosomes.

Diploid Having two sets of chromosomes as opposed to the one set found in gametes.

Haploid A cell with half the usual number of chromosomes. Sex cells are haploid.

Centromere The region of a chromosome where spindle fibers attach.

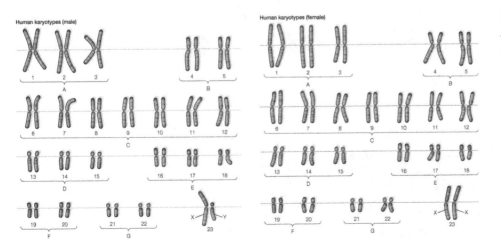

Figure 6–4
A false-color light micrograph of a normal human karyotype.

MITOSIS AND MEIOSIS

Mitosis

Mitosis is the process of somatic cell division (Figure 6–5). It occurs in normal body tissues and is responsible for the everyday maintenance of the body and for growth in young animals. Mitosis is really just replication of cells. A diploid cell undergoes division that allows the production of two diploid cells. This is a replicational process whereby a (2*n*) cell has produced a pair of matching (2*n*) cells.

Meiosis

Gametogenesis is the development of the sex cells, (i.e., **sperm** and **oocyte**). This is a reductional process (2*n* to *n*) responsible for forming cells that contain half of the genetic message. The cell division that occurs in gametogenesis is called **meiosis** and consists of two divisional procedures (Figure 6–6). During the first division, one diploid cell (2*n*) divides into two haploid cells (*n*). The second division consists of a replication of each of the two haploid cells to produce four haploids. This process of gametogenesis is efficient in that one diploid cell divides and replicates in such a way as to produce four haploid cells. These are the cells passed on in the form of sperm or oocytes that, when combined, produce a cell with the full genetic complement of DNA.

Mitosis The process of somatic cell division.

Gametogenesis The formation of gametes.

Sperm The gamete from the male.

Oocyte The gamete from the female.

Meiosis The process that forms sex cells. Cells formed through meiosis have half the chromosomes of the parent cells.

Figure 6–5

Mitosis (Source: Levine, 1980. Used with permission.)

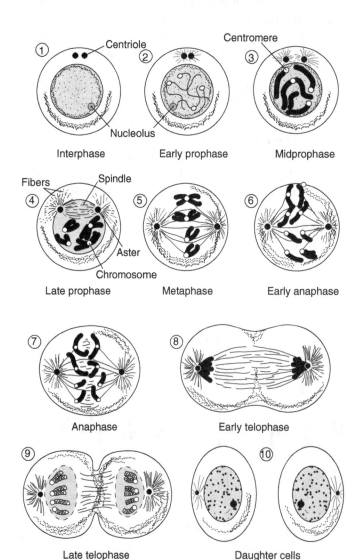

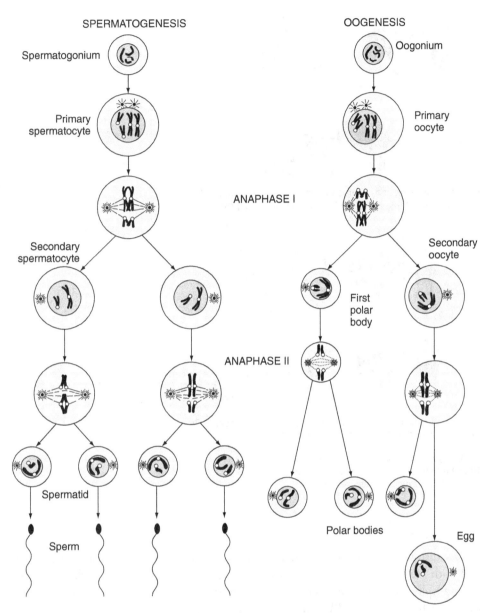

SPERMATOGENESIS

Spermatogonium

Primary
spermatocyte

Secondary
spermatocyte

Spermatid

Sperm

OOGENESIS

Oogonium

Primary
oocyte

ANAPHASE I

Secondary
oocyte

First
polar
body

ANAPHASE II

Polar bodies

Egg

Figure 6–6
Meiosis (Source: Levine, 1980.
Used with permission.)

GENE EXPRESSION

Dominant and Recessive Expression

Once the alleles have combined to determine the genetic makeup of an individual, the methods by which they become interpreted into traits, or are expressed, becomes important. **Dominant** alleles, signified by a capital letter (*A*, for example), express themselves over **recessive** alleles (*a*). For example, *R* stands for an allele that codes for black coat color, and *r* represents red coat color. If an individual receives *R* from each parent, then its genotype is *RR* and the phenotype, or physical appearance, is black. Likewise, an individual with an *Rr* genotype would also express a black coat color. In this case, the dominant allele masks the recessive and the phenotype is representative of the dominant allele. However, if an individual inherited an *r* allele from each parent, its genotype is *rr*, and the animal will express a red coat color. For the individual to have a phenotype representative of the recessive allele, both of the inherited alleles must be of the recessive form. This concept is illustrated in Figure 6–7.

Dominant One member of a gene pair is expressed to the exclusion of the other.

Recessive The member of a gene pair that is only expressed when the dominant allele is absent from the animal's genome.

Figure 6–7
The behavior of simple dominant and recessive traits.

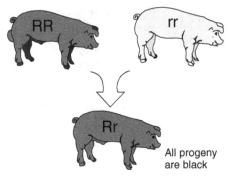

All progeny are black

R represents black and r represents red. All progeny are black because the R gene each received from the sire masks the expression of r.

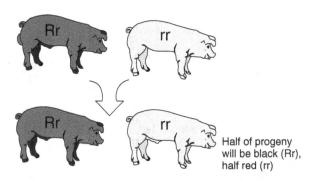

Half of progeny will be black (Rr), half red (rr)

In this mating half the offspring receive an rr and half receive Rr. Thus half the progeny are red and half are black.

RR is the homozygous dominant condition.
Rr is the heterozygous dominant condition.
rr is the homozygous recessive condition.

Codominance

Codominance Both alleles are expressed in the phenotype when present in the heterozygous state.

An exception to the rule of dominance occurs when neither allele masks the other and both are expressed in the phenotype. This situation is known as **codominance**. An example would be that of coat color in Shorthorn cattle. An animal that inherits one of each type of allele *RW* will express both red and white in its coat color to produce what is called a *roan color pattern*. This is illustrated in Figure 6–8.

Incomplete Dominance

Incomplete dominance Condition in the heterozygote where both genes are expressed in a way different from either homozygous condition.

Incomplete dominance is a situation in which no dominance exists and a heterozygous individual will appear as an intermediate between the two alleles. We can illustrate this with an example of coat color. Assume that a particular breed expresses incomplete dominance such that a heterozygote will produce a color that is neither white nor black but rather a smutty gray that is intermediate between white and black. The terms *incomplete dominance* and *codominance* are easy to confuse. To help remember, use the Shorthorn cattle example above. The roan color in the Shorthorn is produced from codominance. If Shorthorn color were instead inherited by incomplete dominance, the coat color would be pink.

Epistasis

The previous examples discussed inheritance of genes for which gene expression is a function of only that single pair of genes. However, many gene pairs act in concert with one another to produce gene expression. In such cases, the expression of one

Red MALE

	R	R
W	RW (Roan)	RW (Roan)
W	RW (Roan)	RW (Roan)

White FEMALE

White MALE

	W	W
R	RW (Roan)	RW (Roan)
W	WW (White)	WW (White)

Roan FEMALE

Figure 6–8
Codominance.

gene is influenced by the presence of another. This is known as **epistasis**, which is capable of causing the appearance of a dramatic departure from the principles of Mendelian inheritance. A gene may express a typical action when another specific gene is not present, but when this gene does exist and epistasis exists as well, the gene could have a totally different action. Coat color in many species is affected by epistasis. For example, horses either have black hair or they don't. This is controlled at the *E* locus. However, whether they have black hair all over their bodies or just on the **points** is controlled by the extension gene at another locus. Those with genotype *Ea* are black all over. Those with genotype *EA* are bay in color, which is typically some shade of reddish-brown body with black only on the points.

Epistasis Interaction among genes at different loci. The expression of genes at one locus depends on alleles present at one or more other loci.

Points Legs, mane, and tail.

Multiple Alleles

Remember that only two alleles can exist on each locus for an individual animal. However, there could be many alleles of a gene present in a population. This is known as a system of **multiple alleles**. A common example used to represent this concept is the A-B-O blood types in humans. Type A and type B are both dominant to type O, and types A and B are codominant to each other. In other words, if a person's genotype is *AA* or *AO*, he or she has the antigen A produced in his or her blood. Likewise, if the genotype is *BB* or *BO*, the antigen B is produced. If, however, the person has both the *A* and *B* alleles, codominance is in effect and the blood type is AB, in which both antigens are present in the blood. When the individual contains two alleles of the O blood group, the genotype is *OO*. In this case, no antigen is present in the blood.

Multiple alleles Genes with three or more alleles.

Testcrossing

It would be beneficial to be able to look at an animal and determine its genotype based on its phenotypic appearance. This would make the selection process much more efficient. It is not possible to do this when dominance is in effect. An animal that is homozygous recessive for a gene such as coat color could easily be identified because it has to have both alleles of the recessive gene. Therefore, it will express the recessive form in its phenotype. However, animals that phenotypically express the dominant form of the gene cannot be as easily identified genetically. An animal could be heterozygous or homozygous dominant, either of which will express the dominant phenotype. For instances such as this, a **testcross** can determine whether the animal is homozygous or heterozygous. A testcross can be conducted by mating this individual to one with a homozygous recessive genotype, which can only contribute a recessive allele. If an offspring is produced with the recessive phenotype, then it must be homozygous recessive, which means the test animal is heterozygous. If all offspring are produced with the dominant phenotype, we can conclude the test animal is homozygous dominant, and the animal is considered to be "true breeding."

SEX-RELATED INHERITANCE

Sex-Linked Inheritance

Some genes are located only on the X or Y chromosome and therefore are inherited only when that respective chromosome is passed on. This is referred to as **sex-linked inheritance**. X and Y chromosomes are homologous to each other in certain regions. This means they contain the same, or nearly the same, genetic sequence. Sex-linked genes are those that reside in the nonhomologous portions of the X and Y chromosomes. *X*-linked genes reside in the nonhomologous area of the X chromosome and can be inherited through the acquisition of that chromosome. *X*-linked genes can be passed on to either male or female offspring because each has at least one X chromosome. For males, it is easy to determine the genotype from the phenotype for *X*-linked genes. The male has only one *X* chromosome, so the phenotype representative of X-linked genes is easily recognizable. For females, however, the genotype is more difficult to determine. Females have two X chromosomes, and the phenotype can be portrayed as either of those respective genes. *Y*-linked genes reside in the nonhomologous portion of the Y chromosome and are inherited only with that chromosome, meaning only males can have a phenotype representative of that gene.

Sex-Influenced Inheritance

The genes for **sex-influenced inheritance** traits are carried on the autosomes. In sex-influenced inheritance, the phenotypes are not expressed in the same way in the two sexes. Let's examine an example of horns in sheep. In the male, the gene for horns (*H*) is dominant to the recessive form (*h*) for polledness. However, in females the *h* gene is dominant to *H*. In either case, when the genotype *HH* is present, the animals will have horns. Likewise, when either sex contains the *hh* genotype, no horns are present. In a case in which a male is heterozygous (*Hh*), horns will be present. However, if the heterozygous form of the gene is inherited in a female, she will be polled.

Sex-Limited Traits

Another example of sex-related inheritance is that of **sex-limited traits**. In this case, traits are unique to only one sex. Some examples are milk production, litter size, and egg production by females. Both sexes carry genes for these traits, but only one sex is capable of expression.

POPULATION GENETICS

Gene Frequency

Knowing how often genes occur in a population of animals is important to make genetic change. **Gene frequency** is defined as the proportion of loci in a population that contain a particular allele. Thus the **genotypic frequency** can be defined as how often a particular genotype occurs in a population. The proportion of individuals in

Testcross Mating with a fully recessive tester animal to determine if an individual is homozygous or heterozygous.

Sex-linked inheritance Traits inherited on the X or Y chromosome and therefore inherited only when that respective chromosome is passed on.

Sex-influenced inheritance When the same genotype is expressed differently depending on the sex of the animal.

Sex-limited traits Traits expressed in one sex or the other such as milk production in females. Both sexes carry genes for the trait.

Gene frequency The proportion of loci in a population that contain a particular allele.

Genotypic frequency The frequency with which a particular genotype occurs in a population.

a population that express a particular phenotype is the **phenotypic frequency**. In a population of cattle in which half are horned and half are **polled**, the phenotypic frequency for polledness is 0.5, as is the frequency of horned cattle. Because many pairs of genes control most traits, it is important to expand these concepts of frequencies beyond just one pair of genes.

Animal Breeding and Population Genetics

The study of how gene and genotypic frequencies change, and thus change genetic merit in a population, is called **population genetics**. The principles of genetics discussed previously affect not only the proportion of genes in an individual, but also the occurrence of these genes in a population. The science of using the principles of genetics to make improvement in a livestock species is **animal breeding**. Robert Bakewell is given credit for being the first animal breeder. He lived in Dishley, England, from 1726 to 1795. In his productive life as a stockman, he made significant improvements in the English Longhorn breed of cattle, the Leicester breed of sheep, and the Shire breed of horses. He practiced "breeding the best to the best," even when the animals were blood relatives. This is said to have scandalized some of his neighbors. However, others saw the merits of what he was doing and joined him in his efforts. As a result, the discipline of animal breeding was born.

Animal breeders seek to influence population genetics. In a population of animals, represented either by an entire breed or just a set of animals within that breed, various factors play a role in the type of animals produced. Genetic merit of the population is influenced by many interactions among genes, as well as the frequency of genes in the population. Production animal breeders must incorporate an understanding of the principles of genetics into their production practices to make the necessary genetic changes within their herd.

Mutation and Genetic Drift

To understand how gene frequencies remain stable and how they change from one generation to the next, we must define some ways in which change is made. **Mutations** are changes in the chemical composition of a gene that alter DNA. This causes the production of new alleles that can affect gene and genotypic frequencies. However, the frequency of mutations that directly affect phenotype in a population is very small. Another method by which gene frequencies change is **genetic drift**. This is a change in gene frequency owing to chance that cannot be controlled in direction, but can be controlled in amount by the size of the population. As the population gets larger, the amount of genetic drift decreases. Mutations and genetic drift cannot be used to cause genetic improvement, but direct changes in gene frequency can be accomplished using migration and selection.

Migration and Selection

Migration is the process of bringing new breeding stock into a population. Migration can be performed on a herd, a breed, or on an industrywide basis. Large changes in gene frequencies can be made quickly by this method. An important factor in migration is that the frequency of genes in the existing herd and the migrants must be different. Bringing a new sire into a population is a way to cause migration, but only if the sire's genotype is different from that of the existing population. When genotypes are very different, gene frequency can be changed quickly. **Selection** is the process of allowing some animals to be parents more than others. Selection can be expanded to include how many offspring each animal is allowed to produce and how long that animal stays in the breeding population. Two types of selection can occur.

Phenotypic frequency The proportion of individuals in a population that express a particular phenotype.

Polled Having no horns.

Population genetics The study of how gene and genotypic frequencies change, and thus change genetic merit in a population.

Animal breeding The science of using the principles of genetics to make improvement in a livestock species.

Mutations Changes in the chemical composition of a gene.

Genetic drift A change in gene frequency of a small breeding population owing to chance.

Migration The process of bringing new breeding stock into a population.

Selection The process of allowing some animals to be parents more than others.

Figure 6–9
Through artificial selection, animals within a species have been developed into breeds as diverse as the Rottweiler and the Chihuahua. (Courtesy of Justin and Tamra Beard. Used with permission.)

Natural selection Selection based on factors that favor individuals better suited to living and reproducing in a given environment.

Natural selection is based on the fact that some animals are more suited and/or have more natural opportunity to be parents than are others. This fact is controlled by nature and can be illustrated in domestic animals using the example of a herd of cows that run with several bulls. Some bulls will sire more offspring than others will because of their aggressiveness, age, and reproductive ability. Thus in managed populations, natural selection is still a very important force. Wild populations are selected through natural selection exclusively.

Artificial selection The practice of choosing the animals in a population that will be allowed to reproduce.

The other type of selection, **artificial selection**, is controlled by the herd manager. Artificial selection is based on management decisions to allow certain animals more opportunity to mate and produce offspring than others. (In common usage, the term *artificial selection* is shortened to *selection*.) Selection involves culling less desirable animals and choosing superior replacements. Selection is a very valuable tool to the animal producer, but it has limitations as well. The effect of selection is limited by the rate at which offspring are produced or by the generation interval (Figure 6–9).

Now that an understanding of possible methods of changing gene frequency has been established, we can apply an important principle to reinforce this concept:

> The *Hardy-Weinberg law* states that in a large, random mating population where mutation, migration, and selection are nonexistent, gene and genotypic frequencies will remain stable from one generation to the next, and if there are two alleles with frequency of p_A and q_a, the genotypic frequencies are $p_A{}^2$ *AA*, $2p_A q_a$ *Aa*, and $q_a{}^2$ *aa*.

Practically speaking, if the desired genetic merit of the herd has been achieved, no methods of selection, migration, or mutation are occurring, and the herd is large, then the gene frequencies will remain constant within that herd from one generation to the next.

QUANTITY VERSUS QUALITY TRAITS

Qualitative and Quantitative Traits

Qualitative traits Those traits for which phenotypes such as coat color can be classified into groups.

Quantitative traits Those traits that are numerically measured and are usually controlled by many genes, each having a small effect, such as milk or egg production.

Qualitative traits are those for which phenotypes can be classified into groups rather than numerically measured. Examples of such traits are coat color and the presence of horns. **Quantitative traits** are those that are numerically measured and usually controlled by many genes, each having a small effect. One can rarely pinpoint the contribution of any particular gene to the quantitative phenotype of an animal. Most often, it is necessary to measure these traits with some kind of measuring tool. Evaluating the growth rate of pigs requires the use of scales, for example. Quantitative traits are influenced by the same types of gene action as qualitative traits are. If there is no dominance at a locus, it is referred to as **additive gene action**. Additive effects deal with individual genes, which allow for more efficient selection. For each individual gene, a representative effect on the trait occurs. For instance, if one A^+ represents a calf that is 2 lbs heavier at birth, then an animal with the genotype of A^+A^+ will be 4 lbs heavier than one with the alleles AA. Likewise, a calf with the genotype A^+A would be 2 lbs heavier than a calf with the genotype AA.

> **Additive gene action** When the total phenotypic effect is the sum of the individual effects of the alleles.

Just as the type of inheritance affects a specific trait, the environment in which the animal is raised has an effect on the expression of quantitative traits. The genetic merit is very valuable in producing animals with certain characteristics or animals that perform to certain levels. However, factors such as climate, management practices, and health determine whether the animal performs to its genetic potential. This nongenetic source of variation is one that must be considered when evaluating animals based on quantitative traits. Using this understanding, it is easy to realize that the phenotype is a result of the genotype and environmental interaction.

Heritability

Differences in the phenotypes of animals are due to genetics and environment. Only the additive genetic effects are inherited. The proportion of the difference in individuals that is due to additive gene effects is known as **heritability**. Practically speaking, heritability is a measure of the proportion of phenotypic variation that can be passed from parent to offspring. Heritability is thus used as an indicator of the amount of genetic progress that can be achieved by choosing superior parents. The range of values for heritabilities is from zero to one, and they can be thought of as percentages or proportions. Heritability estimates have been calculated for most important traits for the different livestock species and can be used to give an indication of how much progress can be made in traits from generation to generation.

> **Heritability** A measure of the proportion of the phenotypic variation that is due to additive gene effects.

We can use an example of litter size here to demonstrate how heritability acts. Assume a group of sows is averaging 7 pigs per litter and a producer wishes to improve this number. For his next matings, he chooses boars and sows from litters averaging 11 pigs. The first step is to calculate a **selection differential**. This selection differential is the phenotypic advantage of those chosen to be parents. The selection differential here is 11 − 7, or 4 pigs. Now, assuming that the heritability of litter size is 0.10, we can expect only 10% of the 4-pig selection differential to be inherited, or 0.4 of a pig per litter. Thus, we would expect the litters from these selected parents to be 0.4 pigs bigger, or 7.4 pigs per litter compared to 7 pigs. This might not seem like much progress. However, litter size is a trait that is quite important from an economical standpoint and improvement of .4 pigs per litter would make a big difference in a large swine operation. It is easy to see that traits with higher heritability estimates can be selected with much greater efficiency. Lowly heritable traits don't express much change from generation to generation from selection.

> **Selection differential** The phenotypic advantage of those chosen to be parents. The difference in the mean of those chosen to be parents and the mean of the population.

As a rule, carcass merit traits are considered to be highly heritable (0.4–0.6), which is encouraging because there is increased interest in, and demand for, specific carcass characteristics to meet today's market needs. This enthusiasm should be tempered by the knowledge that carcass traits are difficult to measure accurately in potential parents. Moderately heritable traits are those having heritabilities of 0.2–0.4. Growth traits are examples of moderately heritable traits and are selected for less progress when compared to carcass traits. Traits such as reproductive ability have low heritabilities (0–0.2), which is unfortunate considering they are among the most economically important traits in animal production.

Through the process of making genetic improvement in a population, animals begin to share similarities in their genetic composition. The relationship between two animals can be thought of as the proportion of genes they are expected to have in common. Siblings or offspring that have at least one parent in common inherit some of their genes from that parent, and thus the brothers and sisters have some of those gene pairs in common. The relationship coefficient can range from 0–1 and is most often by a factor of half. The following is a list of common relationships:

	R
Full-sibs	0.5
Half-sibs	0.25
Parent-offspring	0.5
Grandparent-offspring	0.25
Great-grandparent	0.125
Great-great-grandparent	0.0625
First cousin	0.125

These values are an indication of how closely related the individuals are. Notice that the further back in the animal's pedigree a relative exists, the smaller the value of the relationship.

Systems of Mating

Inbreeding The mating of closely related individuals.

Inbreeding is the mating of closely related individuals (Figure 6–10). It is used to increase homozygosity for desired traits. When practiced in a herd, inbreeding decreases the variation in the genes existing in a herd or population. Individual animals will have more gene pairs in the homozygous state. As this happens, detrimental recessive genes also begin to express themselves because of the increase in homozygosity. Therefore, it is important to avoid high levels of inbreeding so that expression of bad recessive genes can be minimized, while allowing more expression of the good ones. Inbreeding causes a decline in performance that is called **inbreeding depression**.

Inbreeding depression A loss or reduction in vigor, viability, or production that usually accompanies inbreeding.

Linebreeding Mating system in which the relationship of an individual is kept close to an outstanding ancestor by having the ancestor appear multiple times on both sides of the pedigree.

Linebreeding is a form of inbreeding in which the purpose is to concentrate the genes of an outstanding ancestor in the linebred individuals. Linebreeding may result in mild inbreeding if the common ancestor appears at least three to four generations back in the pedigree. However, the inbreeding can be intense with parent offspring matings or after several generations of linebreeding to the same common ancestor. The adoption of modern genetic evaluations has replaced the practice of linebreeding in the livestock species. However, linebred pedigrees are relatively common in many companion animal species, especially in those bred for show ring type.

Figure 6–10
Historically, inbreeding has been practiced to fix the traits associated with breeds such as color and markings, horns, and production traits to produce animals with distinctive characteristics. Compare these distinctly different beef breeds: the Angus and the Brahman.

(Photos courtesy of Christy Collins, Inc. Used with permission.)

Outbreeding is the process of mating less closely related individuals when compared to the average of the population. This can be applied to animals in the population as well as animals as far out as another breed. The effect of this is directly opposite to that of inbreeding. This procedure produces individuals that have more heterozygous gene pairs. This increase in heterozygosity increases the vigor in the animals, which is termed **heterosis**, or hybrid vigor. Heterosis is defined as the superiority of an outbred individual relative to the average performance of the parent populations. Traits that are lowly heritable often show high levels of heterosis. Reproductive traits are a good example of a lowly heritable trait that shows high levels of heterosis. Moderately heritable traits show moderate levels of heterosis, such as the growth traits. Highly heritable traits show little heterosis. The amount of heterosis that is used can either be increased or decreased by the system of mating used.

Crossbreeding, mating animals from different breeds, is a means of taking advantage of outbreeding. Each breed is generally more homozygous than the average of the population. By mating individuals from different breeds, a breeder can take advantage of the homozygocity of the parents to ensure heterozygocity in the offspring. The success of a crossbreeding program depends on the quality of the animals used in the system and whether or not their genetics complement each other. Therefore, it is essential to use breeds that complement each other well to strengthen the good traits and decrease expression of the bad ones. Reproductive traits benefit from crossbreeding systems. On average, crossbred females have more offspring (litter-bearing species) and have better mothering characteristics than the average of the two breeds used to produce them. Many times, breeders produce crossbred females and then mate them to a purebred sire of a third breed that excels in non-maternal traits such as feedlot performance or carcass characteristics to take full advantage of the heterosis in both the offspring and the dam, as well as the strengths of each of the breeds. Elaborate methods of controlled crossbreeding have been developed to capitalize on the advantages breeds can offer in outcrossing. In general, crossbred individuals tend to be more vigorous, fertile, and healthy, and grow faster than the average of parental stock that make up the cross.

Several different methods can be used to evaluate how much genetic contribution an animal will have in any breeding scheme. Methods are being applied to evaluate parents and determine an estimate of their genetic merit. This information can be used to get an idea of the additive genetic merit of an individual, and in selecting animals that have the opportunity to produce offspring that excel in the evaluated traits. These predictions of genetic merit are based on records of the individual's own performance as well as the performance of all relatives. Relatives that are more closely related to the animal being evaluated are more beneficial because they are more likely to contain similar genetic makeup. However, all related animals are useful because they share at least some common genes. Breeding values are covered in more detail in the next chapter.

BIOTECHNOLOGY AND GENETIC ENGINEERING

Genetics is an area of science that is contributing greatly to the overall advancements being made in **biotechnology**. In fact, the advances made in recombinant DNA technology, often called *genetic engineering*, have made it the most recognizable form of biotechnology being practiced today. It is common for people to think of biotechnology and genetic engineering as synonymous terms and not realize there are other areas of biotechnology.

Molecular biology has made it possible to identify the specific genes that control various characteristics. Worldwide, scientists are working to identify all of the

Outbreeding The process of mating less closely related individuals when compared to the average of the population.

Heterosis The superiority of an outbred individual relative to the average performance of the parent populations included in the cross.

Crossbreeding Mating animals of diverse genetic backgrounds (breeds) within a species.

Biotechnology A set of powerful tools that employ living organisms (or parts of organisms) to make or modify products, improve plants or animals, or develop microorganisms for specific uses.

genes of humans and animals, as well as their actual DNA sequences. This mapping of the genome is one of the finest examples of shared information and cooperation in the history of science. Scientists in laboratories scattered to the corners of the earth communicate, contribute information to shared databases, and work together to untangle the mysteries of the genetic code. Once genes are located on the chromosome and the functions they control are identified, then more precise animal breeding practices can be employed. For example, a trait like meat tenderness, which cannot be measured directly on potential parents, may be influenced by a few genes with large effects and DNA markers could be used to identify those individuals that possess the favorable alleles associated with meat tenderness. Although conventional selection on performance characteristics would still be used, it could be enhanced through the inclusion of genetic markers obtained through DNA analysis. This is referred to as **marker-assisted selection**. Marker-assisted selection is currently being employed through several efforts in different types of livestock. For example, genomic information has been incorporated into predictions of genetic merit in dairy cattle since 2009. The American Angus Association now includes genomic information in its predictions of genetic merit. Various suppliers of swine and poultry breeding stock routinely include genomic information to enhance genetic improvement in their lines. In addition, inserting the genes from one animal into another can create new combinations of genes. This can even be done between species. This process of genetic modification creates a **transgenic** animal. These concepts are explored further in a later chapter.

The benefits of this new form of genetic manipulation over conventional forms are multiple. In traditional breeding practices, many of the genes passed to the next generation are unknown. More individual genes and markers are being identified rapidly in all types of livestock that will allow precision breeding, which will ensure that good genes are passed on and undesirable ones excluded. Outcomes will be easier to predict. In transgenic animals, even less guesswork will be involved because the exact genetic information being transferred to create a transgenic animal will be known. The speed of genetic improvement will be increased because the genetics of a set of potential breeding animals can be mapped long before they even reach puberty. In traditional breeding schemes, identifying the genetics of an individual often has to wait for the birth and development of its offspring.

As exciting as the potentials are for improving livestock for production purposes, the area of greatest promise for gene manipulation and recombinant DNA technology is in a slightly different area. Genes can be inserted from animals of the same species. However, they can also be inserted from any species into another. Human genes can be inserted into bacteria or other species of animals. Fish genes can be inserted into pigs, and so on. Although several potential benefits can be envisioned from this procedure, one area holds incredible promise. Animals, microorganisms, and plants can be genetically manipulated to produce substances they otherwise could not produce. For example, bacteria now produce human insulin that is identical to the insulin produced by the human body. Prior to the commercial availability of this insulin, diabetics depended on the insulin of pigs and cattle, which was harvested as a slaughter by-product. Although life saving, this insulin was slightly different from that produced by humans. Now insulin-dependent diabetics can use the same insulin their bodies refuse to produce for them. Already, goats, sheep, and cows have been genetically manipulated to produce foreign proteins in their milk that have value in treating diseases. Most of these are protein products. The animals that produce these compounds are simply milked and the compound is purified. In this way, these transgenic animals can produce large quantities of therapeutic agents that are otherwise not available or are too expensive to produce. Many more of these applications are

Marker-assisted selection Selection for specific alleles using markers such as linked DNA sequences.

Transgenic An animal or plant that has had DNA from an external source inserted into its genetic code.

expected in the very near future. Transgenic chickens will probably be producing a range of therapeutic medicinals in their eggs in the near future.

Gene mapping and, subsequently, improved selection, combined with the use of transgenics for specific genes, will provide benefits in other areas as well. Specific gene therapies will be developed for diseases in animals and humans. Obviously, these are being developed with humans as the highest priority. Scientists working in this field confidently predict the availability of several dozen such gene therapies within the decade. Animals can be genetically manipulated to produce strains that will serve as models for the study of various human diseases. It is also likely that animals can be transgenically altered to produce organs that do not trigger rejection reactions for transplant into humans. Animals will be selected through the use of mapping technology to be resistant to specific diseases, reducing or eliminating the need for vaccines, antibiotics, chemicals, and other means of disease control and prevention. Biotechnology is explored in greater detail in a subsequent chapter.

SUMMARY AND CONCLUSION

Genetics is the study of how DNA codes for the biochemical reactions of life. From a practical perspective, it is important to understand how to direct the genetics of the next generation so the genetic material of the animals produced causes them to have characteristics that are considered economically important. Cells in the body reproduce by two processes. Mitosis is the process used for the growth and maintenance of body tissue. Meiosis is the other process, which differs from mitosis in that the genetic material of an individual is halved before the cell reproduces itself. This process leads to a recombination of genetic material, half from each parent, when sperm and egg unite. Humans have been manipulating the genetic codes of some species for millennia. The organized effort of animal breeding began in the 18th century with the work of an English stockman named Robert Bakewell. Modern animal-breeding techniques have led us to organized efforts that help us manipulate the genetic code. These techniques include breeding relatives through inbreeding and linebreeding to fix certain genetic types, and outbreeding and crossbreeding to maximize heterozygosity. The tools of modern molecular biology are revolutionizing the science of genetics. What used to take generations to accomplish is now possible in one generation. In addition, animals, microorganisms, and plants are being genetically altered to provide a wide range of medicinal products for our benefit. This evolving area of science is perhaps the most promising area of scientific discovery being pursued today.

STUDY QUESTIONS

1. Define the term *gene*.
2. Draw a DNA molecule with four base pairs.
3. List the two types of nitrogen bases in a DNA molecule.
4. What kind of bond holds these bases together?
5. Describe what is meant by supercoiling of DNA.
6. What is the variation in chromosome numbers when more than one full set is present in an individual?
7. Down syndrome is an example of what type of chromosomal variation?
8. What is the process that takes place within the nucleus of a cell whereby a copy of a DNA molecule is formed from another?
9. What is an allele?
10. What is the difference between an animal that is homozygous for a gene and one that is heterozygous?
11. Describe the relationship between a gamete and a somatic cell with regard to the number of chromosomes in each.
12. What is the entire genetic composition of an individual referred to as?
13. List the two types of sex chromosomes.
14. Each somatic cell contains _____ autosomes, whereas the same cell contains _____ sex chromosomes.
15. Each gamete contains _____ autosomes and _____ sex chromosomes.

16. Describe in general terms the process of mitosis.
17. Describe in general terms the outcomes of meiosis.
18. Compare/contrast dominant and recessive alleles.
19. What is the physical appearance of an animal known as?
20. Describe an example of codominance and an example of incomplete dominance.
21. The blood types of humans serve as a good example of what kind of allelic situation?
22. Explain the concept of sex-linked inheritance with relation to the X and Y chromosomes.
23. When the sex of an individual determines how a gene is expressed in the phenotype, this is known as a _____ trait.
24. Milk production is an example of what kind of trait?
25. Define *population genetics*.
26. What does the term *gene frequency* describe?
27. What are four methods by which gene frequencies are changed in a population? Briefly describe each.
28. Compare natural selection with artificial selection.
29. What kind of gene action takes place in qualitative versus quantitative traits? Name an example trait for each type.
30. What is the major nongenetic source of variation discussed in this chapter? Give three examples.
31. Define *heritability*. What is the range for heritability values?
32. A trait that is lowly/highly (circle one) heritable for a given trait allows more genetic change for that trait from one generation to the next.
33. Give examples of high, moderate, and lowly heritable traits.
34. Describe the systems of mating discussed in this chapter.
35. What is biotechnology? Genetic engineering? How are they related?
36. Describe some of the potential benefits to humans of the manipulation of the genetic code.

REFERENCES

Author's Note: For the second, third, and fifth editions, Dr. David S. Buchanan, Professor, Animal Science, formerly of Oklahoma State University and now of North Dakota State University, reviewed this chapter. In addition, Dr. Buchanan contributed new material to the chapter with each review. For the fourth and fifth editions, Dr. Tony Seykora, Professor, Dairy Genetics, University of Minnesota, reviewed this chapter. Dr. Seykora contributed new material. The author gratefully acknowledges these contributions.

Alcamo, I. E. 1996. *DNA technology: The awesome skill.* Dubuque, IA: Wm. C. Brown.

Bourdon, R. M. 2000. *Understanding animal breeding.* 2nd ed. Upper Saddle River, NJ: Prentice Hall.

Buchanan, D. S. 2011. Professor of Animal Science, North Dakota State University, Fargo, ND. Personal communication.

Buchanan, D. S., A. C. Clutter, S. L. Northcutt, and D. Pomp. 1993. *Animal breeding: Principles and applications.* 4th ed. Stillwater: Oklahoma State University.

Fowler, M. 1989. *Medicine and surgery of South American camelids.* 3rd ed. Ames: Iowa State University Press.

Hartl, D. L. 1994. *Genetics.* 3rd ed. Boston: Jones and Bartlett.

Klug, W. S., M. R. Cummings and C. A. Spencer. 2008. *Concepts of genetics.* 8th ed. Upper Saddle River, NJ: Prentice Hall.

Lee, T. F. 1993. *Gene future.* New York: Plenum Press.

Mertens, T. T., and R. L. Hammersmith. 2001. *Genetics laboratory investigations.* Upper Saddle River, NJ: Prentice Hall.

Stufflebeam, C. E. 1983. *Principles of animal agriculture.* Upper Saddle River, NJ: Prentice-Hall.

Taylor, R. E. 1992. *Scientific farm animal production.* 4th ed. New York: Macmillan.

Van Vleck, D. L., J. E. Pollack, and B. E. A. Oltenacu. 1987. *Genetics for the animal sciences.* New York: W. H. Freeman.

7

Animal Breeding

Key Terms

Accuracy

Across-breed EPD

Animal breeding

Breed

Breeding soundness examination

Breeding value

Contemporary group

Expected progeny difference (EPD)

F_1

Feed efficiency

Generation interval

Genetic correlation

Heritability

Maternal effect

Parent average

Percentile

Phenotypic value

Porcine stress syndrome

Possible change

Predicted transmitting ability

Predicted transmitting ability net merit dollars

Quality grade

Rate of gain

Reliability

Single-trait selection

Sire summary

Type production index

Ultrasonic scan measures

INTRODUCTION

Animal breeding is the application of genetic principles to improve the efficiency of production of farm animals. It is a field that has contributed enormously to animal agriculture. By applying the principles of animal breeding, the productivity of all the food-producing species has increased. Much of that progress occurred in the last half of the 20th century because of the understanding of the nature of genetic variation, including at the molecular level, the increased application of the tools of the animal breeder to herds and flocks and the advent of sufficient computing power to deal with the complex mathematical models that are necessary to most fully identify superior individuals. Scientists have made remarkable progress in providing the tools to make improvements logically and systematically in the major food-producing species. For many reasons, animal breeding work on horses, goats, and the companion species has not achieved the same level of understanding. The primary reason is economic justification. It is hard to justify the same level of research directed to a species that is of lesser economic importance. Most of this research has been done at the land grant universities of the United States. Their mission and limited resources have dictated that the research be aimed in the direction that will net the greater good.

Learning Objectives

After you have studied this chapter, you should be able to:

- Define *animal breeding* and explain its contributions to animal science.
- Describe the general principles of animal breeding as it applies to beef cattle.
- Define *heritability* and *genetic correlations*.
- Explain how to use EPDs in beef cattle breeding.
- Describe the uses and benefits of a beef cattle sire summary.
- Describe the general principles of animal breeding as it applies to dairy cattle.
- Explain why associations among traits are so important to dairy cattle selection.
- Identify goals on traits of emphasis in dairy cattle selection.
- Describe the DHI system and explain its use in dairy cattle selection.
- List the ways in which swine genetic improvement is similar to and different from the other major species.
- Describe the difference in the way breeds influence the swine industry compared to the other industries.
- Describe the general principles of animal breeding as it applies to sheep.

Animal breeding The use of biometry and genetics to improve farm animal production.

Animal breeding is a field that is changing, just as all science is changing. The tools of genetic engineering, such as marker-assisted selection and transgenics are enhancing the work of animal breeders, enabling genetic progress to occur much more rapidly. It is an exciting time in the history of genetic improvement as the tools of the molecular biologist are combined with the tools of the quantitative geneticist.

This chapter is divided into sections based on species. Each section discusses the tools and goals of animal breeding as directed at that species. Only beef cattle, dairy cattle, swine, and sheep are included because these are the species for which the techniques and applications are the most advanced and useful. The chicken is the only major exception to this statement. However, the application of animal breeding principles to the poultry industry is almost completely in the hands of the major breeding companies that dominate that industry. On a commercial basis, virtually no producer is involved in making breeding decisions. For this reason, poultry is excluded. The poultry breeder employs the same techniques that are discussed for other species and the progress during the last 50 years has been nothing short of astonishing.

BEEF CATTLE GENETIC IMPROVEMENT

The beef cow-calf producer is in business to produce beef as efficiently as possible. Modern breeding requires selecting for a balance of production performance (such as rate of gain) and end product merit (such as tenderness) to meet consumer expectations for eating satisfaction. Bull selection is a primary area in which producers can make directional change in their herd genetics. A wealth of performance information is available for what appears to be an endless list of traits.

The major areas of economic importance include reproductive efficiency, mature size, calf growth, maternal performance, and carcass traits. The level of production must be matched with available feed resources and the production environment. The design of the herd is not an easy task because very rarely is a successful breeding program designed around selection for a single trait. Fortunately, studies in animal breeding have quantified the genetic variation in beef cattle traits, so that beef cattle producers may use this information in producing better beef through designed breeding programs.

The following sections address key areas of genetic improvement in the beef cattle industry. Animal breeding principles are related to specific beef examples and current genetic selection tools are discussed.

Heritability

An understanding of the principles of heritability and genetic correlations for beef cattle traits is needed to better use the variety of selection tools and **breed** trait information that is available. Differences in traits measured in animal populations are the sum of genetic and environmental factors associated with those traits. **Heritability** indicates the proportion of the differences between individuals that is genetic. Heritability is not the same in every herd. It can vary between herds and within a herd if the management or the system of mating changes. Much research has been directed toward the study of heritability for various traits in beef cattle. Average heritability estimates from many studies for beef cattle are shown in Table 7–1. In general, reproductive traits tend to have low heritability (<0.20), growth traits tend

Breed Animals with common ancestry. They have distinguishable characteristics, and when mated with others of the breed, produce offspring with the same characteristics.

Heritability A measure of the amount of phenotypic variation that is due to additive gene effects. The proportion of differences between individuals that is genetic.

Table 7–1
HERITABILITY ESTIMATES FOR BEEF CATTLE

Trait	h^2
Birth weight	0.35
Weaning weight	0.30
Weaning score	0.25
Feedlot gain	0.45
Carcass grade	0.40
Fat thickness	0.33
Rib eye area	0.58
Marbling	0.42
Retail product %	0.30
Calving interval	0.08
Gestation length	0.35
Pasture gain	0.30
Yearling weight	0.40
Feed efficiency	0.38
Dressing %	0.38
Tenderness	0.55
Cancer eye	0.30

Source: Adapted from Cundiff, L.V. and K.E. Gregory. 1977. Beef Cattle Breeding. USDA Ag. Inf. Bull. 286 and Lasley, J.F. 1978. Genetics of Livestock Improvement. Prentice-Hall.

to have moderate heritability (0.20–0.40), and carcass traits tend to have fairly high heritability (>0.40).

Probably the most practical use of heritability is that it indicates the ease with which we can make genetic improvement through selection. As we can see from the published estimates of heritability in Table 7–1, it is much easier to show selection progress for growth and carcass traits than for reproductive traits. This has led some beef cattle producers to decide that reproductive traits should not be included in a selection program. However, this idea overlooks the fact that reproduction is the most important factor in the efficiency of most beef enterprises. The importance of traits associated with reproduction makes up for the low heritability, so reproduction should be considered for most selection programs.

Also, heritability indicates the proportion of the superiority in an individual or in a group of individuals that can be passed on to the next generation. This property is used to estimate breeding value. **Breeding value** is the value of an individual as a parent. The actual breeding value of an individual is never known, but it can be estimated from the performance of the individual and its relatives. Common information on relatives includes progeny, sire, dam, and sibling records.

Breeding value The worth of an individual as a parent.

Genetic Correlations

Very rarely are successful breeding programs based on **single-trait selection;** therefore, it is important to understand the genetic relationship between traits of interest. **Genetic correlation** refers to a situation in which the same or many of the same genes control two traits. The magnitude of genetic correlations may vary between −1 and +1. A genetic correlation of 0 indicates that different genes influence the two traits; thus the traits are uncorrelated. If the sign of the genetic correlation is positive, then the breeding values of the animals for the two traits tend to vary together. The reverse is true for a negative correlation.

Single-trait selection Selection for only one trait or characteristic.

Genetic correlation The situation in which the same or many of the same genes control two traits.

The absolute value of the correlation indicates the strength of the association between the two traits. When a genetic correlation exists between two traits, it means that the correlation does not equal 0. Rarely does this mean that the correlation is perfect at +1 or −1. For example, a genetic correlation of 0.10 is positive, but the magnitude of the correlation does not imply a strong genetic association between the two traits.

Knowledge of the magnitude of the genetic correlation between various traits is useful in a selection program. For example, **feed efficiency** is a difficult and expensive trait to measure. **Rate of gain** is a relatively easy and inexpensive trait to measure. A favorable genetic correlation exists between rate of gain and feed efficiency. Selection of sires can be directed toward rate of gain, which is easily measured. If the rate of gain is improved through selection, some improvement is expected in feed efficiency due to the favorable genetic relationship between the two traits. Genetic correlations are not always favorable. For example, selection for increased yearling weight has an adverse effect on calving difficulty. The fact that the genetic correlations are not perfect gives breeders the opportunity to try to identify sires that are exceptions to the unfavorable correlation.

Table 7–2 shows genetic correlations between growth and carcass traits. Some of these relationships may be beneficial if they are considered in a complete breeding program. As you can see, genetic correlations are seldom perfect. For example, many of the genes that control birth weight also control carcass weight in the same direction, as indicated by the positive genetic correlation of 0.60 in Table 7–2. Remember that the relationship is not perfect. Genetic correlations indicate what is likely to happen to one trait when selection is practiced for another trait.

To design the genetics of the beef animal for a particular production level, selection objectives must balance many traits of economic importance. Continued interest in carcass merit will result in an increase in multiple-trait selection practices in breeding programs. This makes information on the genetic correlations between carcass and other traits even more important.

Performance Information

To make genetic change in a desired direction, cow-calf producers have to know the current performance level of their herd. Through knowledge of beef cattle traits and their heritabilities, producers can use available selection tools to design a breeding program. The program should be designed with performance items in the plan

Feed efficiency Product (gain, milk, eggs, and so on) per unit of feed.

Rate of gain Pounds of gain per day over a specified period.

Table 7–2
GENETIC CORRELATIONS BETWEEN GROWTH AND CARCASS TRAITS

Trait	ADG^W	ADG^F	CAR	FAT	REA	MAR	SHR[1]
Birth weight (BW)	0.28	0.61	0.60	0.27	0.31	0.31	−0.01
ADG to weaning (ADG^W)		0.49	0.73	0.04	0.49	0.31	−0.05
ADG feedlot (ADG^F)			0.89	0.05	0.34	0.15	0.06
Carcass weight (CAR)				0.08	0.44	0.25	0.00
Fat thickness (FAT)					−0.44	0.16	0.26
Rib eye area (REA)						−0.14	−0.28
Marbling (MAR)							−0.25

[1]SHR 5 Warner-Bratzler shear.
Source: Adapted from Benyshek, 1988.

that address breeding, calving, weaning, yearling, carcass, and maternal breeding objectives.

Performance programs come in many forms. Core programs begin at the ranch. Seedstock and commercial cow-calf producers have different needs. Seedstock producers sell breeding animals. Commercial cow-calf producers market calves to be finished for market. Also, herd size can influence the degree of detail that a producer is willing or able to assemble. Keep in mind that meaningful cow-calf records may be handwritten or computerized (Figure 7–1). The challenge is to choose performance records that are useful in making management decisions.

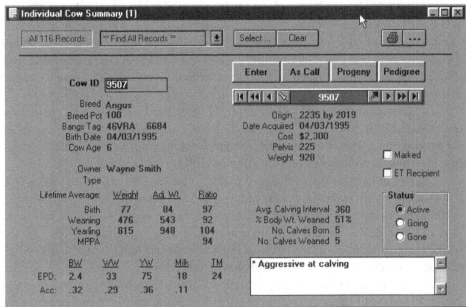

(a)

(b)

Figure 7–1 (a) Cow summary report and (b) calf data entry form. (Source: Cow Sense Herd Management Software, Midwest MicroSystems L.L.C. Used with permission.)

Seedstock breeders work closely with breed associations to develop extensive on-farm performance programs. Data collection and compilation are accomplished through strong ties between breeders and association personnel. Records across the country and, in some breeds, internationally, are used to generate genetic values for animals within a breed. Additional supplements to on-farm performance programs may include, but are not limited to, feedlot and carcass data collection programs and bull evaluation center data.

Commercial producers need an effective performance program that encourages the culling of inferior animals and selection of herd replacement breeding stock. Very rarely are effective selection programs based on single traits. Sire selection is the area in which commercial herds can place the greatest selection pressure. Commercial producers may rely on their seedstock "partners" to remove some of the guesswork in their bull selection and assist them in the use of specialized selection tools such as expected progeny differences (EPDs), discussed later in this chapter. Commercial cow herd and calf crop records are the nuts and bolts that assist producers in choosing the necessary bull power. Currently, a greater percentage of commercial and seedstock producers are forming stronger links to better understand performance progress and genetic tools from conception to carcass.

Sometimes commercial producers think they need EPDs on their crossbred cows to use EPDs. This is not true. The choice of sires has a tremendous impact on the genetic improvement of the herd. The producer does not need to have registered cows, or straightbred cows of one breed, to use EPDs as a sire selection tool.

A good understanding of the herd performance level for reproductive, growth, and maternal merit, and even carcass merit, is the first priority. Calving and weaning percentages, pregnancy percentage, pounds weaned per exposed females, calf death loss, and average mature cow size are examples of decision-making tools. The sire selections are then made using EPDs to move the herd genetically in the desired direction. Throughout history, geneticists have studied methods for use in identifying superior individuals in beef cattle populations. Sire selection has tremendous value to the beef cow-calf operation. Choices of herd sires not only have an impact on the resulting calf crops, but also affect the performance of the cow herd if daughters of the sires are kept as replacement heifers. Ideally, beef producers like to select sires of desirable genetic merit for genetic improvement in economically important traits. Selection of desirable genetics to match with a cow herd is a challenging task. Fortunately, the concept of breeding value provides beef producers an avenue to make useful selection decisions. The background on breeding value estimation leads to a better understanding of the merit of EPDs.

Genetic Evaluation, Breeding Value, and Expected Progeny Difference

Breeding value is used as an estimate of the transmitting ability of an animal. Breeding value, or genetic merit, is calculated from information on an individual's performance and the performance of progeny, sibs, parents, grandparents, and so on. The information comes from purebred breeders who report data to the national herd improvement program for their breeds. The combined information from all contributors provides a national database for the breed. A mathematical model called an animal model (AM) is used to predict breeding values. These values are then used to calculate the expected progeny difference.

Expected progeny difference (EPD) A prediction of the difference between the performance of an individual's progeny compared to all contemporaries for the progeny.

Half of the breeding value is equal to the **expected progeny difference.** The word *difference* implies a comparison. Thus EPDs let us compare or rank the superiority of individual animals. EPDs provide a prediction of future progeny performance of one individual compared to another individual within a breed for a specific trait. The EPDs are reported in plus or minus values in the units of measurement for the trait. For example, birth, weaning, and yearling weight EPDs are reported in pounds. In contrast, fat thickness EPDs are reported in inches.

Each individual member of a breed can have EPD values calculated for it. Age, sex of calf, or status as a parent are not limiting factors. Even a newborn calf can be assigned EPDs. It is possible to compare any two members of a breed, regardless of location. However, EPD values may be used to directly compare only those animals within a breed. The EPD values for a Hereford bull may not be compared against the EPDs for an Angus or Limousin bull.

Preferential mating of certain individuals does not bias the results. A genetically superior bull can be mated only to genetically superior cows and his EPD will not be inflated. This is accomplished by adjusting for the EPDs of the cows to which he is mated. Also, any genetic change within a breed for a particular trait is accounted for by adjusting for genetic trend. Thus comparisons may be made across generations of cattle. Young bulls with no progeny may be directly compared with older sires that have progeny.

Maternal genetic values, such as milk EPD, may be computed for the maternally influenced trait—such as weaning weight. EPDs are comparable across herds because mathematical models used to calculate EPDs account for differences in environment and management.

National Cattle Evaluations   The first national sire summary was published in 1971 by a beef breed association. For the first time, bulls within a breed could be compared across herds, across regions of the United States, and across generations. All of the major beef breed associations today conduct national cattle evaluations (NCEs) and compute EPDs as a service to their breeders. These values are published and generally made available at least once a year.

Contemporary Group   In the collection of beef cattle performance information, breed associations recognize that contemporary group definition is critical. A **contemporary group** is a group in which animals of a given sex and age, having similar treatment, are given an equal opportunity to perform. The basis of sound performance testing relies on correct identification of contemporary groups. Accuracy in estimation of genetic differences within a group of animals depends on the accuracy of grouping.

Contemporary group A group in which animals of a given sex and age, having similar treatment, are given an equal opportunity to perform.

Growth Trait EPDs

EPD values are most useful when two individuals are compared directly. For example, consider the following birth weight EPD example of two sires. Assume both sires are from the same breed, and the EPDs have equal accuracies:

	Sire A	*Sire B*
Birth weight EPD, lbs	+5	−2

The expected difference in the progeny of Sire A and Sire B for birth weight is 7 lbs. Sire A has an EPD of +5 and Sire B has an EPD of −2. On the average, we should expect the calves of Sire A to be 7 lbs heavier at birth than calves of Sire B, if all calves are managed the same and have dams of similar genetic merit. The predicted performance difference is 7 lbs. Because EPDs only allow the prediction of performance differences, not actual performance, it is not possible to estimate the actual birth weight average for these calves.

The following is an example for weaning weight. It describes a weaning weight difference in the progeny of two bulls:

	Sire A	Sire B
Weaning weight EPD, lbs	+25	−10

The expected difference in the progeny of Sire A and Sire B for weaning weight is 35 lbs. Sire A has an EPD of +25 and Sire B has an EPD of −10. On the average, we should expect the calves of Sire A to be 35 lbs heavier at weaning than calves of Sire B, if all calves are exposed to the same environmental conditions and are out of cows of similar genetic merit.

An example for yearling weight follows. It describes a yearling weight difference in the progeny of two bulls:

	Sire A	Sire B
Yearling weight EPD, lbs	+50	+10

The expected difference in the progeny of Sire A and Sire B for yearling weight is 40 lbs. Sire A has an EPD of +50 and Sire B has an EPD of +10. On the average, we should expect the calves of Sire A to be 40 lbs heavier as yearlings than calves of Sire B, if all calves are managed in a uniform manner and have dams of similar genetic merit.

Breed Average EPD and Base Year

It is frequently said that an EPD is a comparison to an average bull. This, unfortunately, is not true. A zero EPD represents the average genetic merit of animals in the database at the time when sufficient information existed to calculate EPDs. Therefore, it represents a historic base point, or base year. Some breed associations now set the base year to a particular year. If the breed has made any genetic change for a trait, the average EPD for the trait will no longer be zero. Breed associations publish the average EPDs in the sire summaries made available to the public. Information printed in the summaries should be examined carefully before individual EPDs are studied.

Accuracy

Accuracy The measure of reliability associated with an EPD. If little or no information is available, accuracies may range as low as 0.01. A high accuracy would be 0.99.

Accuracy is the measure of reliability associated with an EPD. Each EPD value should have an accuracy assigned to it. Accuracy is expressed as a value between 0 and 1. A high accuracy (>0.7) means a higher degree of confidence may be placed on the EPD, and the EPD value is not expected to change much as further information is gathered. A low accuracy (<0.4) means that the EPD may change a great deal as additional information is gathered. Nonparent animals have lower accuracy values because no progeny information contributes to their EPD. From a practical standpoint, the EPDs are used to select bulls for use in the herd, and accuracies help determine how extensively to use them. Some sale catalogs do not list accuracies with the EPDs. For young animals with no progeny data, such as yearling bulls, accuracies are generally low. They improve as the animal has offspring to contribute to the data from which its EPDs are calculated.

Possible Change

Possible change The measure of the potential error associated with EPD values.

Possible change is the measure of the potential error associated with EPD values. Many sire summaries are starting to include these values. Possible change is expressed as "+" or "−" in the same units as the EPD. These values quantify the amount a certain EPD may deviate from the "true" progeny difference. Accuracy and possible change values share a relationship. As more information is accumulated, accuracy

increases and possible change diminishes. For a given accuracy, the "true" progeny differences of two thirds of all animals evaluated within a breed are expected to fall within the plus or minus possible change value. The following example illustrates this point:

Birth weight EPD = +2.0 lbs Accuracy = 0.90 Possible change = ±1.3 lbs

Of all of the animals with this EPD and accuracy, two thirds are expected to have "true" progeny differences between +0.7 and +3.3. These "true" differences have a much greater chance of falling toward the center of the range defined by the possible change value than falling close to the extremes.

Also, one third of the individuals in the evaluation may have their "true" progeny difference values fall outside the range of +0.7 and +3.3. This means that one sixth of the individuals may have "true" values less than +0.7, and one sixth of the individuals may have "true" values more than +3.3.

Sire Summaries

Sire summaries include a sampling of the available genetic material in each breed. Newly calculated and updated summaries for breeds that conduct national cattle evaluations are available online at least once a year and, in some cases, as frequently as weekly. Summaries include EPDs, accuracies, graphs of the average change in EPD for the particular breed, breed average EPDs, possible change values, and other useful materials. Descriptive material written at the beginning of each summary describes the format for reporting the EPDs.

Almost all sire summaries include birth weight, weaning weight, yearling weight, and milk EPDs (Figure 7–2). Many summaries currently include some characteristics that have a role in reproduction such as calving ease, gestation length,

Sire summary Genetic information published on sires available within a breed.

Sire Evaluation of Proven Sires

ANIMAL IDENTIFICATION	OWNER	GRPS PROG	DTRS PROG/DTR	BW EPD ACC	WW EPD ACC	YW EPD ACC	MILK EPD ACC	TOTAL MAT. EPD	STAY EPD ACC	HPG EPD ACC	MARB EPD ACC	REA EPD ACC	FAT EPD ACC
FORSTER LAKOTA 3100 REG.#: 405225 CATEGORY: A BIRTHDATE: 04/01/1993 SIRE: RED CENTURION C103 MATERNAL GRANDSIRE: LFS GALENA 132	FORSTER RED ANGUS ALTA GENETICS, INC. WBD	30 89	23 1.9	1.2 .82	30 .75	49 .72	26 .65	41	8 .63		-0.06 .22	0.03 .22	0.00 .19
FORSTER MAGNUM 6142 REG.#: 526563 CATEGORY: A BIRTHDATE: 03/30/1996 SIRE: RED BBC PRESIDIO 5Z MATERNAL GRANDSIRE: BUFCRK COPPERTOP1628	KINCHEN CATTLE CO FORSTER RED ANGUS	19 79	2 1.0	1.6 .80	17 .68	28 .58	22 .33	30	8 .32				
FORSTERS PAY DAY 376 REG.#: 192675 CATEGORY: A BIRTHDATE: 02/27/1986 SIRE: RAB ABE LINCOLN MATERNAL GRANDSIRE: ROCKY MT 19	FORSTER RED ANGUS REDLAND RED ANGUS BOOT JACK RANCHES	23 157	49 4.7	4.3 .85	31 .81	41 .80	1 .77	17	6 .75	6.3 .19	-0.04 P	0.03 P	-0.02 P
FRITZ MONU 2X 211 REG.#: 373666 CATEGORY: A BIRTHDATE: 02/07/1992 SIRE: LEACHMAN MONU 2X 8098 MATERNAL GRANDSIRE: RCN DYNAMO 614	KEITH & LINDA VANDE SANDT FRITZ RED ANGUS	13 29	14 1.8	-2.5 .71	21 .64	29 .62	15 .57	25	9 .55		0.17	-0.15	0.00
FTF DOUBLE CHIEFN601 REG.#: 130241 CATEGORY: A BIRTHDATE: 03/29/1961 SIRE: FTF DOUBLE CHIF L218 MATERNAL GRANDSIRE: FTF CHIEFTON 7068	GREER RANCH	59 210	93 4.7	-1.5 .88	18 .86	31 .85	20 .83	29	14 .83	22.0 .46	0.16 .34	-0.10 .33	0.00 .29
GENERAL VANGUARD REG.#: 289875 CATEGORY: A BIRTHDATE: 11/12/1987 SIRE: FFC VANGUARD 638F MATERNAL GRANDSIRE: CV GENERAL LEE	MCKELVEY RED ANGUS CATTLE RANCH	31 64	34 2.3	3.2 .81	32 .76	51 .74	8 .71	24	3 .71		-0.04 P	-0.07 P	0.01 P
GET-A-LONG LICORICE REG.#: 128766 CATEGORY: A BIRTHDATE: 04/10/1979 SIRE: RED SR IMAGE 200F MATERNAL GRANDSIRE: RED VALLEY REVOLUTION	KENNETH FRAZER DOUBLE FORK RANCH	167 610	236 5.0	4.4 .93	37 .91	51 .90	8 .89	27	14 .89	8.7 .22	-0.03 .28	0.04 .28	0.00 .24
GILCHRIST CHIEF W515 REG.#: 273997 CATEGORY: A BIRTHDATE: 02/13/1987 SIRE: JKG CHIEFTON L303 MATERNAL GRANDSIRE: FTF RED RITO M428	BUFFALO CREEK RED ANGUS J BAR K RANCH	121 257	96 3.1	-0.7 .89	28 .86	60 .85	16 .83	30	14 .82	6.5 .19	0.17 .61	-0.18 .59	-0.05 .51
GILCHRIST COYOTE B225 REG.#: 371018 CATEGORY: A BIRTHDATE: 03/22/1992 SIRE: BJR FIRE-MAN 0150 MATERNAL GRANDSIRE: JKG CHIEFTON L303	STAR G RANCH GILL RED ANGUS BLUE RIDGE LAND & CATTLE	76 185	55 1.4	2.4 .87	33 .82	50 .80	23 .76	39	3 .76		0.04 .24	-0.06 .23	-0.02 .21
GILCHRIST HOWLER 95 REG.#: 477961 CATEGORY: A BIRTHDATE: 02/25/1995 SIRE: GILCHRIST COYOTE B225 MATERNAL GRANDSIRE: 741 PANHANDLER 189	BRYLOR RANCH BLUE RIDGE LAND & CATTLE CODY E GRIFFIN	29 47	7 1.2	2.0 .77	20 .65	34 .60	15 .50	25	4 .49		0.02 .19	-0.03 .19	-0.01 .19
GLACIER ALPINE 658 REG.#: 514846 CATEGORY: A BIRTHDATE: 02/20/1996 SIRE: CREEK SIDE COPPER MATERNAL GRANDSIRE: LEACHMAN MONU 2X 8096	GRILL CATTLE CO GLACIER RED ANGUS	30 78	7 1.0	0.6 .78	20 .66	29 .64	17 .50	27	6 .48		0.29 P	-0.05 P	0.00 P
GLACIER ARROW 664 REG.#: 514799 CATEGORY: A BIRTHDATE: 02/21/1996 SIRE: GLACIER STATURE 318 MATERNAL GRANDSIRE: GLACIER NATIONAL	SCHULER-OLSEN RANCH GLACIER RED ANGUS	19 87	2 1.0	-1.8 .61	19 .69	52 .62	21 .35	31	7 .33	9.2 .23	-0.05 .51	-0.44 .48	0.00 .41
GLACIER CAMAS 752 REG.#: 557327 CATEGORY: A BIRTHDATE: 02/21/1997 SIRE: GLACIER SUPER WEIGHT MATERNAL GRANDSIRE: GLACIER DYNARISE	GARY SONSTEGARD GLACIER RED ANGUS	22 70	0 0.0	-0.3 .78	21 .66	34 .55	15 .27	26	5 .26		0.03 .26	-0.41 .25	0.00 .22
GLACIER CASCADE 464 REG.#: 440319 CATEGORY: A BIRTHDATE: 03/26/1994 SIRE: GLACIER NATIONAL MATERNAL GRANDSIRE: GLACIER SUPER WEIGHT	KOLLE RED ANGUS GLACIER RED ANGUS	26 70	8 1.7	-3.1 .78	17 .69	39 .62	24 .52	32	6 .51		0.05 .51	-0.36 .49	0.02 .44

Figure 7–2

Beef cattle sire summary. (Source: Red Angus Association of America, Denton, TX. Used with permission.)

heifer pregnancy, scrotal circumference, and stayability and carcass traits such as carcass weight, rib eye area, fat thickness, marbling score, and tenderness.

Maternal Trait EPDs

Maternal effects are an important consideration in evaluating beef cattle performance. Extensive studies have been conducted to quantify maternal effects for a variety of traits, particularly those measured during the preweaning growth period. In beef cattle, the dam makes at least two contributions to the offspring phenotypic value. **Phenotypic value** is the physical expression of the genetic makeup of an animal, such as a weaning weight. These contributions are the sample half of her genes passed directly to the offspring and the maternal effect she provides her calf. A **maternal effect** is defined as any environmental influence that the dam contributes to the phenotype of her offspring. The contribution of the dam is environmental with respect to the calf (mothering ability, milk production environment, and maternal instinct). The genetics of the dam allow her to create this environment for her calf. Maternal effects are important during the nursing period but have diminishing effects postweaning.

Phenotypic value A measure of individual performance for a specific trait.

Maternal effect Any environmental influence that the dam contributes to the phenotype of her offspring.

Milk EPD

Weaning weight is influenced by the genes for growth in the calf and the genes for milk (mothering ability) in the cow. There are separate EPD values for these two components. The weaning weight EPD evaluates genetic merit for growth and the milk EPD evaluates genetic merit for mothering ability. The milk EPD that results from the separation of weaning weight into growth and milk segments is, like any other EPD, fairly simple to use. It is the expected difference in weaning weight of calves out of daughters of a particular sire, due to differences in mothering ability. For example, consider the following two bulls:

	Sire A	Sire B
Milk EPD, lbs	+10	−6

Sire A has a milk EPD of +10; Sire B has a milk EPD of −6. The expected weaning weight difference, due to mothering ability alone, in calves out of daughters by the two bulls is 16 lbs. The 16 lbs are expressed in pounds of weaning weight, not pounds of milk.

Combined Maternal EPD

The combined maternal EPD (sometimes called maternal weaning weight) reflects both the milking ability transmitted to daughters and the direct weaning growth transmitted through daughters to their calves. Here is an examples:

	Weaning Weight EPD	Milk EPD	Weaning Weight Maternal Combined EPD
Bull A	+20	+12	+22
Bull B	+4	+6	+8

$$\text{Combined (Bull A)} = 1/2\,(20) + 12 = 22\text{ lbs}$$

$$\text{Combined (Bull B)} = 1/2\,(4) + 6 = 8\text{ lbs}$$

Bull A has a direct weaning weight EPD of +20 lbs, which expresses the ability of the bull to transmit weaning growth directly to his progeny. On the average, calves sired by Bull A should be 16 lbs heavier at weaning than calves sired by Bull B, assuming both bulls are mated to a comparable set of females and the calves are exposed to the same environmental conditions. The 16-lb difference in future progeny performance is due to genes for direct weaning growth.

The milk EPD for Bull A (+12) is the contribution to his daughter's calves solely through transmission of genes for mothering ability. Sire A has a milk EPD of +12; Sire B has a milk EPD of +6. The expected weaning weight difference, due to mothering ability alone, in calves out of daughters by the two bulls is +6 lbs.

The combined EPD for Bull A (+22) is computed by taking half the weaning weight EPD plus all of the milk EPD. The +22 lbs reflects both the milking ability transmitted to daughters and the direct weaning growth transmitted through the daughters to their calves. In a similar fashion, the combined EPD for Bull B is half times the weaning weight EPD plus the milk EPD, or +8 lbs. An average 14-lb difference between the combined EPDs for the two bulls (22−8=14) would be expected to be the difference in weaning weight of calves out of the daughters of the two bulls. The difference reflects the milking ability of the daughters and the direct weaning growth transmitted through daughters to their calves.

Carcass EPD

Carcass trait EPDs are an additional performance tool that is becoming more available each year. Many of these EPDs are generated from progeny carcass data for various sires within a breed. Generating EPDs for sires within a breed can be an expensive project because carcass data on close relatives, particularly progeny, must be captured. When collecting data on progeny of sires for genetic evaluation, it is most desirable to have at least 25 progeny per sire, although this may be difficult to achieve. For carcass trait EPDs, a simple comparison of two bulls within a breed is conducted, as shown in Table 7–3. Look at the difference in EPDs between the bulls. On the average, future calves out of Bull A will have 50-lb heavier carcass weights, 0.40 sq. in. larger rib eye areas, and 1% greater retail product percentage than calves sired by Bull B. Future offspring of Bull B will have a fourth higher marbling score than calves out of Bull A.

Ultrasonic scan measures can be used to evaluate carcass merit as well as actual measurements on carcasses. Some breeds present separate EPDs for ultrasonic measurements and for actual carcass measurements. The fact that these EPDs can differ can be disconcerting and, increasingly, these two sources of measurement are combined to form a single EPD for each of the measures of carcass merit.

Ultrasonic scan measures Measurements of body tissues taken with ultrasound waves.

Table 7–3
ANGUS CARCASS EPD EXAMPLE

EPD	Breed Average	Bull A	Bull B	Difference
Carcass weight, lbs	+5.95	40	−10	50
Marbling score	+.05	−.10	.15	.25
Rib eye area, sq. in.	+.12	.40	.00	.40
Fat thickness, in.	−.003	.00	.00	.00
% Retail product	+.10	.5	−.5	1%

Source: Dolezal, 1999. Used with permission.

Mature Size

Mature size is an important issue in the beef industry today. Size is composed of closely related measures of weight and height; however, the relationship among these traits is not clearly understood. Studies of mature size in beef cows have estimated lifetime growth curves for weight through maturity. Other reports have considered the influence of body size on the biological efficiency of cows.

Genetic prediction of mature size may allow beef cattle breeders to make a directional change in the mature size of their cow herd or to emphasize uniformity of cow size for a particular production environment. Studies of the genetic components of mature size have addressed weight and height at maturity separately by trait, rather than as a composite measure.

Mature weight and height are highly heritable traits. For example, heritability estimates in Angus cattle are 0.49 for weight and 0.87 for height in mature cows. Heritabilities of this magnitude indicate that selection for these traits would be effective. In other words, if beef producers wanted to make changes in the height and weight of the cow herd, they would select sires of replacement heifers using some guidelines for desirable size for the herd production environment. Also, it is important to consider that the genetic correlation between mature weight and height is strong and positive. Large genetic association between these two traits suggests that selection for increased height would be associated with increased cow weight. Some beef breeds have incorporated cow size data into a genetic evaluation for the creation of mature cow size EPDs. Ideally, selection would be in favor of smaller birth weights, larger weaning and yearling weights but smaller mature size. Bending the growth curve in this manner can be difficult but success in this endeavor would have a strong positive effect on overall production efficiency.

USE OF EPDS

Use of EPDs for Selection in Seedstock Herds

Purebred producers know that they need to use EPDs in their breeding programs. Competitors are using them and genetic change is happening. Care needs to be exercised when making selection decisions. Type fads have caused some problems in the past when single traits were emphasized. Similar, or worse, problems may arise if a single performance trait is emphasized. For example, if the members of one breed association begin to emphasize yearling weight and ignore all other characteristics, several concerns may result. Birth weight would be expected to increase, with the attendant calving difficulty. Mature size should also increase, perhaps to the point where the functionality of the cow herd would diminish. This could also lead to problems in reaching desirable **quality grade** at an acceptable weight. Each trait has a set of drawbacks, if changes are carried to an extreme. The availability of EPDs would make such extremes easier to reach, if breeders chose blindly to emphasize a single trait.

A more balanced selection program is certainly desirable. Some producers recommend choosing herd sires that have high yearling weight EPD, high milk EPD, and low birth weight EPD. Because these three characteristics are sufficiently different from one another, the difficulties from extreme changes in any one of them would be unlikely to result. Such a program, along with careful consideration of the various reproduction and carcass merit EPDs should result in a balanced program of improvement.

Quality grade Scale that indicates quality and value of the carcass such as *prime*, *choice*, and so on.

Purebred producers are not only the users of EPDs, but they also provide the data used in calculating EPDs. Producers are strongly encouraged to provide complete, accurate records on all calves born each year. Complete, accurate recordkeeping is the only way that useful EPDs can be calculated.

Use of EPDs for Selection in Commercial Herds

Commercial producers should make maximum use of available EPDs when considering purchases of breeding stock. Seedstock producers should be providing such information on all cattle that are for sale. Again, a balanced program of trait selection is desired.

A commercial producer has a first responsibility of choosing the appropriate breed, or breeds, for his or her program. Once breeds are chosen, examination of what is needed in replacement breeding stock is in order. Some recommendations for commercial scenarios are shown in Table 7–4.

Each of these recommendations should be followed with an awareness of the prevailing environmental conditions. Rougher conditions probably dictate avoidance of very high EPDs for growth or milk, and even more care to avoid high birth weights. Growth EPDs should be geared to the desires of the potential buyers. Again, traits for which there are no EPDs as yet can also be important. Traits associated with reproduction certainly fall into this category. Commercial producers should demand that bulls have passed a **breeding soundness examination.** The cow herd of the seller should be examined for regularity of calving.

EPDs within a breed are directly comparable between herds. Therefore, if a commercial producer has more than one source of breeding stock, he or she can compare the genetic merit of the different sources. Unfortunately, EPDs cannot be compared between breeds. A bull with a low birth weight EPD from a large mature size breed may sire calves that are heavier than those from a bull with a high birth weight EPD from a moderate sized breed. A low birth weight EPD does not guarantee a minimum of calving difficulty if the choice of breeds is incorrect.

Breeding soundness examination Physical examination to determine the readiness of an individual for breeding purposes.

Pedigree Estimated EPDs

After the first of each year, sale catalogs prepared for production sales and full of information on potential herd sires become available. Many sale catalogs contain EPDs for the bulls offered for sale. Data on some bulls appear in catalogs with limited

---

Table 7–4

RECOMMENDATIONS FOR EPDS FOR VARIOUS COMMERCIAL SCENARIOS

Use of Individual	Breed	Birth	Weaning	Yearling	Milk[1]
Terminal sire on mature cows	Large carcass	Not too high	High	High	Not relevant
Bull to use with heifers	Small to medium size	Low	Moderate	Moderate	Consider if keeping heifers
Sire replacement heifers	Medium size maternal	Low to moderate	Moderate to high	Moderate to high	Varies

[1]Selection decisions involving milk EPD should take into consideration the production environment and feed resources available for the cow herd.
Source: Buchanan et al., 1993, p. 84.

or no EPD information. This may be particularly true for young bulls that have not had their performance information included in the breed genetic evaluation. Bull buyers may use a quick and easy procedure to compute "pedigree EPD" values for young bulls with no EPDs. Pedigree EPDs can be computed provided there is access to EPDs on the animals in the pedigree of the young bull. By using the EPDs on animals in the young bull's pedigree and the knowledge of how breeding value is transmitted from generation to generation, pedigree EPDs can be computed.

Every calf has received a random sample of half of the sire's genes and a random sample of half of the dam's genes to combine into its genetic makeup. Parents of the calf have received their genetic makeup in the same fashion, with half of their genetic makeup contributed by each of their parents. By understanding this halving nature of inheritance, the EPDs on parents and grandparents in the pedigree of a young bull may be used to compute pedigree EPDs.

Some breed associations have an "interim EPD" program based on pedigree information to provide EPDs on young animals that have not had an opportunity to have their individual performance included in the most recent national cattle evaluation for the breed. Many sale catalogs may already provide the pedigree EPD for convenience.

Across-Breed EPDs

Currently, most EPDs are used only on a within-breed basis. They are calculated for the specific breed; therefore, the EPDs are only useful for direct comparisons of future progeny performance for cattle within that breed. The across-breed EPD concept (AB-EPD) has been actively investigated since the late 1980s. Commercial bull buyers using more than one breed of bull are particularly interested in having this EPD option. The methodology for accomplishing AB-EPDs on a national scale is not yet perfected. To compare cattle of different breeds, additional information is required. This information includes (1) mean breed differences in the environments of interest; (2) the base year, or zero EPD point, for the breeds of interest; and (3) the expected effects of heterosis (or hybrid vigor) for matings between the breeds of interest. Breed comparison data from the U.S. Meat and Animal Research Center are the best resources available to date. Breed adjustments to make across-breed EPD comparisons are computed annually at this research station.

EPDs and Crossbreeding

Planning a crossbreeding system first relies on the choices of breeds, followed by the use of within-breed EPDs as selection tools for performance traits. To assist beef producers in their choices of breeds, studies have tried to group or categorize breeds into general biological types. Perhaps the most famous and extensive of these studies involves the Germ Plasm Evaluation study conducted at the U.S. Meat and Animal Research Center (USMARC) at Clay Center, Nebraska. Table 7–5 lists 25 different sire breed groups that were evaluated in calves out of Hereford and Angus dams or calves out of the two-breed cross (F_1) dams. The breed groups illustrate relative differences (X = lowest, XXXXXX = highest) in growth rate and mature size, lean-to-fat ratio, age at puberty, and milk production. Increasing numbers of Xs indicate relatively higher performance levels and older age at puberty.

F_1 Two-breed cross animals.

Table 7–5
BREEDS GROUPED INTO BIOLOGICAL TYPES FOR FOUR CRITERIA[1]

Breed Group	Growth Rate and Mature size	Lean-to-Fat Ratio	Age at Puberty	Milk Production
Jersey (J)	X	X	X	XXXXX
Longhorn (Lh)	X	XXX	XXX	XX
Hereford-Angus (HAx)	XXX	XX	XXX	XX
Red Poll (R)	XX	XX	XX	XXX
Devon (D)	XX	XX	XXX	XX
Shorthorn (Sh)	XXX	XX	XXX	XXX
Galloway (Gw)	XX	XXX	XXX	XX
South Devon (Sd)	XXX	XXX	XX	XXX
Tarentaise (T)	XXX	XXX	XX	XXX
Pinzgauer (P)	XXX	XXX	XX	XXX
Brangus (Bn)	XXX	XX	XXXX	XX
Santa Gert. (Sg)	XXX	XX	XXXX	XX
Sahiwal (Sw)	XX	XXX	XXXXX	XXX
Brahman (Bm)	XXXX	XXX	XXXXX	XXX
Nellore (N)	XXXX	XXX	XXXXX	XXX
Braunvieh (B)	XXXX	XXXX	XX	XXXX
Gelbvieh (G)	XXXX	XXXX	XX	XXXX
Holstein (Ho)	XXXX	XXXX	XX	XXXXX
Simmental (S)	XXXXX	XXXX	XXX	XXXX
Maine Anjou (M)	XXXXX	XXXX	XXX	XXX
Salers (Sa)	XXXXX	XXXX	XXX	XXX
Piedmontese (Pm)	XXX	XXXXXX	XX	XX
Limousin (L)	XXX	XXXXX	XXXX	X
Charolais (C)	XXXXX	XXXXX	XXXX	X
Chianina (Ci)	XXXXX	XXXXX	XXXX	X

[1]Increasing number of Xs indicates relatively higher values.
Source: Cundiff et al., Beef Improvement Research Federation Symposium, 1993, p. 130.

DAIRY CATTLE GENETIC IMPROVEMENT

Dairy producers have been leaders in genetic improvement. Many commonly known techniques for evaluating genetic merit have been derived and tested initially on dairy cattle records. One advantage the dairy industry has is the focus on a limited number of economically important traits. Traditionally, milk yield has been the primary driver in trait emphasis for profitability. Yet very rarely are effective breeding programs based on a single trait. Dairy producers are challenged to balance traits of economic importance to address some of the following goals:

- Achieve profitable milk yield levels.
- Monitor milk composition.
- Generate profitable replacement animals that are productive under the stress of high production levels.
- Sustain and improve cow longevity in the herd.

The following sections address key areas of genetic improvement in the dairy cattle industry. Animal breeding principles are related to specific dairy examples and current genetic selection tools are discussed.

Heritability Estimates

An understanding of the heritability and genetic correlations for dairy cattle traits is necessary to take advantage of the variety of selection tools and breed trait information available. Studies in animal breeding have quantified the genetic variation in dairy production, so producers may use this information to be more profitable through designed breeding programs. Although much emphasis is placed on milk yield and its impact on profitability, it is important to review the heritabilities of other commonly known dairy production traits. As discussed earlier, the most practical use of heritability is that it indicates how easily we can make genetic improvement through selection. However, one should not overlook more lowly heritable traits, such as the reproductive complex. These traits are highly influenced by environment and management but significant differences between individuals can still exist.

Table 7–6 presents heritability estimates for dairy production parameters compiled from various research reports. In general, most reproductive traits tend to have low heritability (<0.20); yield traits tend to be moderately heritable (0.20–0.40); and composition traits and weights tend to have fairly high heritabilities (>0.40). Keeping in mind the earlier discussion, and viewing the heritabilities, one can see that it is relatively easy to change mature weight or wither height through selection. To improve reproductive efficiency or longevity, the dairy cattle breeder must take advantage of all the genetic tools available.

Associations Among Traits

Genetic correlation refers to a situation in which the same or many of the same genes control two traits. Table 7–7 presents phenotypic and genetic correlations between milk yield and other production characteristics. Phenotypic correlations are

Table 7–6
HERITABILITY OF VARIOUS TRAITS IN DAIRY CATTLE

Trait	Heritability
Milk yield	0.30
Milk fat yield	0.30
Protein yield	0.30
Total solids yield	0.25
Milk fat %	0.50
Protein %	0.50
Persistency	0.40
Peak milk yield	0.30
Milking rate	0.40
Gestation length	0.40
Birth weight	0.40
Mature weight	0.50
Wither height	0.50
Conception rate	0.05
Reproductive efficiency	0.05
Calving interval	0.10
Productive life length	0.08
Feed efficiency	0.35
Mastitis resistance	0.10
Overall type score	0.20
Dairy character score	0.20
White coat color (Holsteins)	0.90

Source: Wilcox, 1992, p. 3. Used with permission.

Table 7–7
GENETIC CORRELATIONS BETWEEN MILK YIELD AND OTHER TRAITS

Trait	Correlation with Milk Yield	
	Phenotypic	Genetic
Fat yield	0.69	0.45
Protein yield	0.9	0.81
Fat %	−0.35	−0.35
Protein %	−0.35	−0.30
Type score	0.29	0.00
Stature	0.11	−0.01
Strength	0.12	0.07
Dairy character	0.50	0.68
Foot angle	0.00	−0.24
Rear legs (set to hock)	0.02	0.14
Pelvic angle	0.04	0.19
Fore udder attachment	−0.09	−0.47
Rear udder height	0.12	−0.13
Rear udder width	0.16	0.09
Udder depth (distance from floor of udder to ground)	−0.27	−0.64
Medial Suspensory ligament	0.14	0.12
Front teat placement	0.02	−0.12
Productive life length	0.15	0.08
Mastitis susceptibility (somatic cell score)	−0.10	0.20

Source: Adapted from Buchanan et al., 1993, p. 96. Updated according to Cole *et al.*, 2010.

correlations between two traits that producers actually measure or see; thus a combination of genetics and environment plays a role in expression of the trait, such as weight or height. Genetic correlations are more difficult to visualize.

Knowledge of the magnitude of the genetic correlation between various traits is useful in a selection program. The magnitude of genetic correlations may vary between −1 and +1. A genetic correlation of 0 indicates that different genes influence the two traits; thus, the traits are uncorrelated. For example, selection based on milk yield has little or no effect on front teat placement (Table 7–7).

The absolute value of the correlation indicates the strength of the association between the two traits. When a genetic correlation exists between two traits, it means that the correlation does not equal 0. Rarely does this mean that the correlation is perfect at +1 or −1. For example, a genetic correlation of 0.20 between mastitis susceptibility and milk yield is positive, but the magnitude of the correlation does not imply a strong genetic association between the two traits. Therefore, selection based on milk yield does not significantly increase the susceptibility to mastitis.

The sign (+/−) of the genetic correlation indicates the relationship between traits (i.e., how selection for one affects the other). If the sign of the genetic correlation is positive, then the breeding values of the animals for the two traits tend to vary together. The reverse is true for a negative correlation. Therefore, if selection is for increased performance in one trait, performance in the other trait will likely decrease. For example, the percentage traits for composition (fat % and protein %) tend to be negatively associated with milk yield. However, yield traits (fat and protein) tend to be highly correlated in a positive direction with milk yield, both phenotypically and genetically.

Consideration of the relationship between traits can be very beneficial if they are considered in a complete breeding program. Again, the tabular values reveal that genetic correlations are seldom perfect. For example, many of the genes that control dairy character also control milk yield in the same direction, as indicated by the positive genetic correlation of 0.68 in Table 7–7. The relationship is not perfect. The fact that genetic correlations are not perfect provides breeders with the opportunity to try to identify sires that are exceptions to the unfavorable correlation. Again, genetic correlations give us an indication of what is likely to happen to one trait when selection is practiced for another trait. The magnitude of the correlation suggests how closely traits will vary together.

Goal Setting and Trait Emphasis

The genetic improvement program for every dairy herd must have goals to design the cow herd with the genetics for making a profit. Milk yield and composition are important economic considerations. Within-herd genetics and production performance must be evaluated and scrutinized through effective recordkeeping. Also, access to genetically superior animals outside the herd through the use of artificial insemination is critical. Before deciding whether selection should be practiced for a particular trait, consider the following:

• Can the trait of interest be accurately measured?
• What is the heritability for the trait? Is genetic progress through selection possible?
• Will selection for this trait contribute to income (directly or indirectly)?

Most producers begin planning a well-founded breeding program through basic use of: (1) Dairy Herd Improvement Association (DHI) records and (2) semen purchase of bulls with genetic superiority for economically important traits.

Trait emphasis should be balanced with respect to the heritability of the trait, genetic correlations among traits, the reliability of the information, and economic importance of the trait. This is no small task considering there are national genetic evaluations for about 30 traits (Figure 7–3). U.S. dairy geneticists have attempted to simplify selection decisions for dairy farmers by properly weighting all the traits into the Net Merit Dollar Index (NM$). Similar indexes have been developed by breed associations, such as the Total Performance Index (TPI) by the Holstein Association. The traits in these indexes are properly weighted for the average or most typical dairy producer to maximize profit on a commercial dairy. Individual dairies may want to change emphases depending on their management systems and goals. Low-input grazing herds put more emphasis on reproductive traits and feet and legs and less emphasis on milk production. Also, smaller cows tend to make more efficient grazers than large cows.

Producers who sell breeding stock put more emphasis on fancy type traits. The so-called eye appeal of the animal seems to influence price in the sales ring much more than the animal's genetics for milk production. For dairy producers with aspirations of developing a great show cow, most emphasis needs to be placed on final score type, stature, dairy form, and the udder traits. Dairy producers must be careful in selecting their goals in that the genetics of a show animal is quite different from the genetics needed to produce milk most efficiently.

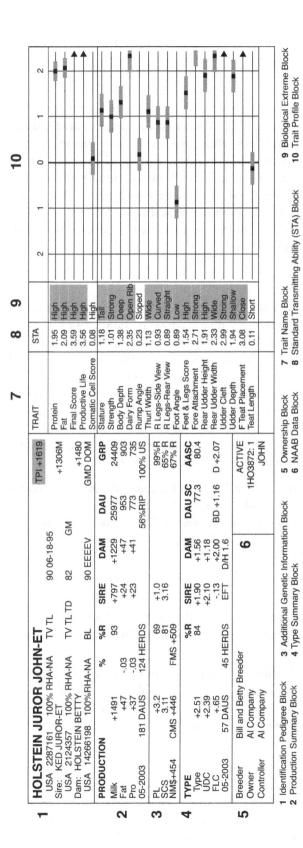

1 HOLSTEIN JUROR JOHN-ET
USA 2287161 100% RHA-NA TV TL 90 06-18-95
Sire: KED JUROR-ET
USA 2124357 100% RHA-NA TV TL TD 82 GM
Dam: HOLSTEIN BETTY
USA 14266198 100%RHA-NA BL 90 EEEEV
TPI +1619
+1306M
+1480
GMD DOM

2 PRODUCTION

	%	%R	SIRE	DAM	DAU	GRP
Milk	+1491	93	+797	+1229	25977	24409
Fat	+47	-.03	+24	+47	953	903
Pro	+37	-.03	+23	+41	773	735
05-2003	181 DAUS		124 HERDS		56%RIP	100% US

3

		%R			
PL	+3.2	69	+1.0		99%R
SCS	3.11	81	3.16		65% R
NM$ +454	CMS +446		FMS +509		67% R

4 TYPE

		%R	SIRE	DAM	DAU SC	AASC
Type	+2.51	84	+1.90	+1.56	77.3	80.4
UDC	+2.39		+2.10	+1.18		
FLC	+.65		-.13	+2.00	BD +1.16	D +2.07
05-2003	57 DAUS		45 HERDS	EFT	D/H 1.6	

5
Breeder Bill and Betty Breeder
Owner AI Company
Controller AI Company

6
ACTIVE
1HO3872: 1
JOHN

7 8 9

TRAIT	STA	
Protein	1.95	High
Fat	2.09	High
Final Score	3.59	High
Productive Life	3.56	High
Somatic Cell Score	0.08	High
Stature	1.18	Tall
Strength	1.01	Strong
Body Depth	1.38	Deep
Dairy Form	2.35	Open Rib
Rump Angle	0.23	Sloped
Thurl Width	1.13	Wide
R Legs-Side View	0.93	Curved
R Legs-Rear View	0.89	Straight
Foot Angle	0.89	Low
Feet & Legs Score	1.54	High
Fore Attachment	2.71	Strong
Rear Udder Height	1.91	High
Rear Udder Width	2.33	Wide
Udder Cleft	2.99	Strong
Udder Depth	1.94	Shallow
F Teat Placement	3.08	Close
Teat Length	0.11	Short

10

1 Identification Pedigree Block
2 Production Summary Block
3 Additional Genetic Information Block
4 Type Summary Block
5 Ownership Block
6 NAAB Data Block
7 Trait Name Block
8 Standard Transmitting Ability (STA) Block
9 Biological Extreme Block
10 Trait Profile Block

Figure 7-3
How to read Holstein sire information. (Source: Holstein Foundation. Used with permission.)

GENETIC EVALUATION PROCEDURES

DHI System

Much of the genetic improvement in milk production in the United States is attributable in part to good use of performance records through the Dairy Herd Improvement (DHI) system. Data obtained monthly through the DHI production testing and management system provide producers with detailed reports on the current status of their herd. These records are also compiled nationally through the U.S. Department of Agriculture (USDA) to calculate genetic evaluations for sires.

The DHI system of genetic evaluation consists of comparing sire daughters with contemporaries in the same herd. Superior sires are chosen based on their ability to pass specific traits to their offspring. Initially, young bulls are chosen based on superior pedigree value. These genetics are then randomly mated to cows across various locations for production of daughters. These daughters' records are compared with their contemporaries to allow the calculation of estimated genetic transmitting ability of the bull.

Animal Model

The USDA-DHI Animal Model Genetic Evaluation compiles lactation yield information for milk, fat, protein, somatic cell score, productive life, and pedigree or relationships among animals. For a cow's lactation record, sources of variation such as management group, genetic merit, permanent environment, and herd by sire interactions are considered. Specific effects of age, length of lactation, and milkings per day are adjusted prior to analysis. The animal model procedure produces predictions of the breeding (genetic) value of an animal. Breeding value is defined as the value of an individual as a parent. Parents transfer a random sample of the genes to their offspring. Breeding value gives an estimate of the transmitting ability of the parent. Some basic values generated from the evaluation are as follows:

Predicted transmitting ability Half the breeding value.

PTA—One-half the breeding value is equal to the **predicted transmitting ability** (PTA). The PTA implies a comparison. Thus, PTAs allow us to compare or rank the superiority of individual animals. PTAs provide a prediction of future progeny performance of one individual compared to another individual within a breed for a specific trait.

Reliability A measure of accuracy in dairy records.

REL—**Reliability** (%R) is the measure of accuracy, or the amount of information in an evaluation.

Parent average The average PTA of the parents of a dairy cow.

PA—**Parent average** (PA) is the average PTA of the sire and dam of the individual in question. If a parent is unknown, an unknown-parent group effect is used.

Predicted transmitting ability net merit dollars An economic index that measures relative lifetime profit of a dairy cow.

PTANM$—**Predicted transmitting ability net merit dollars** (PTANM$) is an economic index. PTANM$ combines evaluations for milk, fat, protein, somatic cell score, productive life, udder composite, feet and leg composite, size, daughter pregnancy rate, calving ease, and stillbirth rate. It is a measure of relative lifetime profit.

Producers benefit from the extensive herd summary reports provided by DHI. Herd analysis and management reports include production, reproduction, genetics, udder health, and feed cost information. Figure 7–4 illustrates the identification and genetic summary portion of a sample DHI report. This report is useful in verifying the number of replacement and producing animals in the operation. As one might expect, the usefulness of DHI records is enhanced by a higher percentage of identified animals.

Identification and Genetic Summary

Age group	Number animals	Average age	NUM. identified by		Number ID. changes	NO. animals with PTA$/PA$	Average PTA$ / PA$	
			Sire	Dam			Animal	Sire
0-12	62	6	62	62		58	+108	+187
13+	66	18	66	66		61	+97	+163
Replacements	128	12	128	128		119	+103	+175
1st lact	34	23	34	30	2	34	+84	+140
2nd lact	30	36	28	26		28	+73	+122
3+ lacts	58	59	51	44		49	+52	+87
All lacts	122	43	113	100	2		+68	+114
% Identified (producing females)			93	82				

Herd PTA$ option	Genetic profile of service sires		
MFP	Proven A.I. sires	A.I. young sires	All other sires
% of herd bred to	75	20	5
Number of bulls used	5	12	3
Average PTA$ or PA$	+200	+216	+10
AV. percentile rank (net merit)	83	90	0

Figure 7–4
Sample DHI report. (Source: Dairy Records Management Systems. Used with permission.)

The PTA$ and PA values are presented for cows within the herd, as well as their sires. Values are calculated using the USDA Animal Model Genetic Evaluation procedure. PTA$ in this report is the economic value of the PTAs for milk, fat, and protein. An increase in cow and sire PTA$ from younger to older cows is an indication of within-herd genetic progress.

Sire Selection

With sire selection playing an important role in genetic improvement, dairy producers spend a great deal of time studying bull proofs given in sire summaries. Figure 7–3 shows a sample data summary for a Holstein sire. Perhaps the best application of genetic evaluations involves the comparison among sires. An example comparison of data on two Holstein sires from a summary is shown in Table 7–8.

The TPI value is a **total performance index**. This multiple trait approach calculated by the Holstein Association combines PTAs (protein, fat, type), udder composite, feet and legs composite, somatic cell score, productive life, daughter pregnancy rate, dairy form, daughter calving ease, and daughter stillbirth rate. It provides a ranking of sires on their ability to transmit a balance of traits. Net merit dollars (NM$) is the economic index calculated by the USDA as an index of relative lifetime profit.

Table 7–8 shows that yield comparisons between the two sires favor the future offspring of Superior Brett over Average Jake. For example, if daughters of these bulls are housed in the same herd as contemporaries and are managed alike, the expected difference in milk, fat, and protein yield would be 495, 37, and 8, respectively, in favor of Superior Brett. However, protein percentage would tend to favor Average Jake, illustrating a negative association between these two traits in this example. From an economic standpoint, Sire Brett is still on top with respect to NM$ and TPI values. In this example, the reliabilities (%R) are similar for both bulls, indicating similar accuracies. If the %R values were largely different, decisions on how extensively to use a young sire (low %R) would be needed. A low accuracy bull is not bad; he is

Total performance index Index used by the Holstein Association to rank sires on their ability to transmit a balance of traits.

Table 7–8
COMPARISON OF DATA ON TWO HOLSTEIN SIRES

	Superior Brett	Average Jake	Difference
TPI™	+1618	+1430	+188
PTA			
M (milk)	+1850	+1355	+495
F (fat)	+88	+51	+37
P (protein)	+55	+47	+8
PTA%			
F (fat %)	+0.09	+0.09	0
P (protein %)	−0.01	+0.06	−0.07
% R (reliability of PTAM and PTAF)	78%	80%	−2%
PTA			
NM$ (net merit dollars)	+470 (69%R)	+407 (65%R)	+63
SCS (somatic cell score)	+3.40 (57%R)	+3.10 (57%R)	+0.30
PL (productive life)	+1.1 (42%R)	+0.2 (40%R)	+0.9
T (type—final score)	+1.58 (75%R)	+1.30 (72%R)	+0.28
%DBH (difficult births in heifers)	9% (71%R)	7% (72%R)	+2%

Source: Dolezal, 1999. Used with permission. Modified to August 2000 base change.

part of the new genetic information for the breed. Reliability values are expected to increase as more daughter records contribute to the bull's proof.

The somatic cell score (SCS) PTA is a tool that allows producers to select bulls based on their ability to sire daughters with lower rates of mastitis. Somatic cells are body cells. When found in milk, they indicate damage to the udder that is caused by mastitis. Research indicates that single-trait emphasis for higher milk yield is associated with increased incidence of mastitis. This is not a perfect relationship. Not all high production sires have associated rates of mastitis in daughters. Heritabilities used by the USDA are 0.10 for SCS and 0.30 for milk production. This suggests that genetic change to reduce mastitis is slow. In the previous example, the SCS of Sires Brett and Jake's daughters are expected to differ on the average by 0.3 ($3.40 - 3.10 = 0.3$). The PTASCS should be viewed as a selection tool, rather than as a sole selection criterion, to optimize total economic merit.

To continue to increase the genetic potential of the herd, follow a few basic rules:

- Use an index such as net merit dollars to weight properly the production and non-production traits to maximize total economic merit.
- Use 7 to 10 sires per herd per year.
- Select sires from the top 10% based on an index such as NM$ or TPI.
- Use elite genomically tested young sires on at least a portion of the herd.
- Use sires with 70% reliability or higher.
- Consider calving-ease bulls for heifers.
- After sires have been selected, individually mate animals to lower average inbreeding in offspring.

SWINE GENETIC IMPROVEMENT

Generation interval The average age of parents when their offspring are born.

Genetic improvement programs are a primary focal point for today's swine industry. The high reproductive rate and short **generation interval** in swine allow rapid genetic progress for economically important traits. In recent years,

the swine industry has followed some of the patterns set by commercial poultry production. Much of the pork produced today originates from corporate swine production systems, which are vertically integrated from conception to consumer. This leads to an interesting structure for modern pork production, which contains seedstock breeders, commercial swine producers, and corporate production units.

The National Swine Improvement Federation (NSIF) and National Pork Producers Council (NPPC) are key organizations for documentation on swine genetic resources. The NSIF and NPPC, as well as other agencies, have historically sponsored "Guidelines for Uniform Swine Improvement Programs." Seedstock and commercial swine producers, corporate operations, researchers, and extension personnel utilize this publication. The guidelines give details on the use of uniform procedures for measuring and recording swine performance data.

The NPPC is a member organization of NSIF. The NPPC's mission is to make pork production successful and profitable from the production segment to the ultimate consumer. This council works closely with producers, researchers, and extension personnel, and has swine industry ties.

Performance Information

Efficient pork production relies on objective data collection for economically important traits, breeding value estimation, and planned selection decisions. Key areas include the reproductive complex, growth rate and efficiency, and carcass traits. With the high reproductive rate in swine, extensive evaluation of female reproduction is critical. Data include birth records, litter size (number farrowed alive and dead), farrowing ease scores, litter weight at weaning, and reproductive soundness. On the male side, reproductive soundness data are collected on boars for libido, mounting, mating ability, and semen evaluation. Herd reproductive measures include pigs per sow per year; pregnancy, farrowing, and weaning rate percentages; live pigs per litter; and mated female to service boar ratio.

Growth rate and feed efficiency are evaluated extensively in the swine production system. Economically important measures include days to 250 lbs, average daily gain (ADG), and feed efficiency. Body composition and carcass merit are important to producers as well as to the ultimate consumer eating experience. Data collected include backfat thickness (live), carcass fat depth, loin eye area, pounds of lean pork, and loin muscle color, firmness, and marbling.

Visual appraisal is important in swine breeding programs as it is in many other species. For swine, feet and leg soundness along with underline soundness may be scored; these areas affect production and reproduction success.

Porcine stress syndrome (PSS) is tracked in swine populations. This condition has genetic control at a single locus and is identified as a homozygous-recessive genotype. Pigs under stressful conditions exhibit blotchy skin color and heavy breathing, and they can die from this condition. Phenotypic differences between normal and PSS pigs are that PSS individuals appear more muscular and shorter bodied. The ham area may appear more rounded and circular, along with prominent loins and rumps. Fortunately, the PSS animals can be identified by a blood test or Halothane anesthesia test. Those individuals with the condition should be culled.

Porcine stress syndrome Genetic defect in which pigs are heavily muscled but have poor carcass quality and may die when subjected to stress.

Genetic Parameters

Heritability indicates the proportion of the superiority in an individual or in a group of individuals that can be passed on to the next generation. This property is used

Table 7–9
HERITABILITY ESTIMATES OF TRAITS IN SWINE

Trait	Heritability, %
Pigs born alive	10
Pigs weaned	10
Litter birth weight	30
Individual birth weight	20
Adjusted 21-day litter weight	15
Feed efficiency	30
Days to 230 lbs	35
Average daily gain	40
Average daily feed intake	24
Dressing percent	30
Backfat probe	40
Loin muscle area	47
Carcass lean percent	48
Age at puberty	32
Ovulation rate	39
Rebreeding interval	23

to estimate breeding value. The actual breeding value of an individual is never known. It can be estimated from the performance of the individual and its relatives. Common information on relatives includes progeny, sire, and dam records. Table 7–9 pre-sents heritability estimates and correlations for some economically important traits. Growth and carcass measures are moderately to highly heritable. The magnitude of these estimates indicates that selection for these traits will be effective. The heritability estimates for traits like pigs born alive and pigs weaned are lower and will be more difficult to make progress through selection.

Breeding Value and Expected Progeny Difference

Parents transfer a random sample of their genes to their offspring. Breeding value gives an estimate of the transmitting ability of the parent. Half of the breeding value is equal to the expected progeny difference (EPD). The word *difference* implies a comparison. Thus EPDs let us compare or rank the superiority of individual animals. These concepts were explored in the beef cattle improvement section. The same principles and assumptions apply for swine genetic evaluations.

Swine Breeds

Unlike the beef industry, fewer swine breeds have had a large impact on commercial swine production. Within these breeds, extensive evaluation of superior individuals has taken place. Specialized sire and dam lines have been developed using these evaluations. Subsequent commercial crossbreeding systems are designed for efficient pork production. Today's swine industry is strongly focused on genetic evaluation of performance data among and within breeds. For example, the NPPC has been instrumental in leading and supporting genetic evaluation programs. Examples include

the Terminal Sire Line National Genetic Evaluation and the Maternal Line National Genetic Evaluation Programs.

An interesting angle to the swine industry is that many times the actual breed composition of a particular breeding line is not known. This approach was patterned similarly to commercial poultry production. Commercial units rely on the seedstock producer choices or corporate genetic selections to set the genetics of their animals. Private companies employ geneticists to carefully evaluate all production aspects of their base genetics. Hybrid boars and sows are developed with protected rights to the actual genetic makeup of breeds and individuals within breeds.

The swine industry capitalizes on the advantages of heterosis, particularly maternal heterosis benefits for reproduction. Crossbred sows are used in rotational crossbreeding systems, as well as the maternal side of the terminal cross programs. Research on hybrid boars has indicated that these sires have increased libido, structural soundness, and improved conception rates. Market offspring produced may express 100% of the individual heterosis, as long as the breeds are different for sire and dam lines in the crosses.

Selection index application is very common in the swine breeding programs. Index approach may be directed toward maternal, paternal, or general improvement strategies. Index equations allow the simultaneous evaluation of two or more traits. Traits are weighted based on their economic value and the overall selection objectives for the breeding population. The index accounts for economic value, but also heritability, genetic and phenotypic correlations, and the phenotypic variation for the respective traits. Specific indexes are designed for maternal lines, emphasizing reproductive performance as expressed in litter size and 21-day litter weight. Additional production traits may be included. On the sire, or paternal side, post-weaning traits are important, as well as days to 250 lbs and backfat thickness. Feed conversion emphasis is included in the index through genetic correlations between the other traits.

Many times, maternal and paternal lines developed through index selection are combined into a terminal crossbreeding system in which distinct lines are crossed to produce market pigs. No replacements are generated from this system. In contrast, a general selection index is used in more rotational crossbreeding systems. Equal value is given to reproductive and production traits, since individuals in this system must serve as a sire and a dam. A rotational system generates its own replacements.

Breeds from other countries have been studied to determine if specialized genetics would benefit commercial hog production. Perhaps the most well-known quest is that of the Chinese breeds of swine. These breeds are of great interest because of their high reproductive rate (7–17 pigs born alive) as well as early puberty advantages. However, limiting factors associated with these breeds are low growth rate, poor conformation, and excessive fat deposition. Four main breeds are Meishan, Fengjing, Jiaxing Black, and Erhualian. Future developments in pig genome research may identify specific genetic material that these breeds may contribute to future reproductive advances.

Stages

A well-known performance resource in swine genetic evaluation is *STAGES* (Swine Testing and Genetic Evaluation System). This system evaluates the genetic superiority of swine using a statistical methodology similar to that of the beef and dairy industries. The U.S. swine breed associations use the program, which was developed jointly by Purdue University and USMARC. STAGES incorporates

Figure 7–5

Genetic trend for Yorkshire sow productivity index (SPI).

(Source: Purdue University, 2007.)

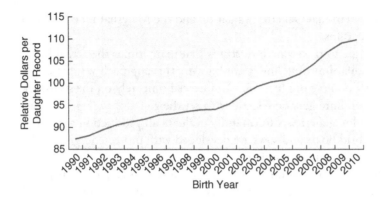

performance information on individuals, progeny, and collateral relatives, as well as the use of relationships among these animals, to generate breeding values (and ultimately within-herd EPDs). For example, postweaning and reproduction analyses are conducted on a within-herd basis. Breeders rely on performance information collected from on-farm programs, national breed tests, and progeny tests to generate within-herd EPDs for animals.

Also, a STAGES national evaluation is run for specific herds to generate across-herd EPDs. Across-herd genetic evaluations to compare animals in different herds within a breed are used to identify the best genetic material nationally. Also, centrally tested boars have been evaluated nationally by this approach. For selection decisions, the seedstock breeders use these data in conjunction with their within-herd evaluation of breeding prospects. Commercial producers rely heavily on the progress of their seedstock suppliers to capture the value of these genetic evaluations.

An example of another index is the sow productivity index (SPI), used to select litters with future replacement gilt candidates. The index includes EPDs with reproductive emphasis. Weighting factors are placed on the EPDs for number of pigs born alive, litter weight, and number weaned relative to the economic value for the trait. Figure 7–5 illustrates the genetic change that has taken place in the Yorkshire breed for SPI (including reproductive traits only).

Figure 7–6 shows the genetic trend lines for days to 250 lbs. In this case, negative EPD values are more desirable, so the change over time is in a negative direction. Thus, the time it takes an animal to reach 250 lbs has been shortened genetically.

Figure 7–6

Genetic trend for days to 250 lbs in Yorkshire swine.

(Source: Purdue University, 2007.)

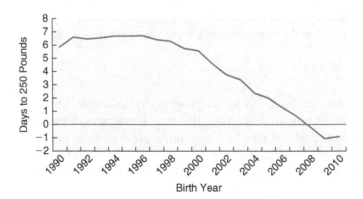

SHEEP GENETIC IMPROVEMENT

The sheep producer is in the business of producing two products, lambs and wool, as efficiently as possible. The major areas of economic importance to the sheep producer are lamb growth, prolificacy, and, in some areas, wool quality and quantity. However, the tools are not the same for sheep breeding and genetic improvement as they are for the other major meat breeds. EPDs have only been available for sheep since 1986 and are not yet as useful as they are for the other species. In addition, artificial insemination is rarely used in the sheep industry. This makes gaining genetic progress through the widespread use of superior sires less of an influence on the industry. The following sections discuss the key areas of sheep breeding and genetic improvement available to the sheep producer.

Breed and Breed Types

To understand sheep genetic improvement and breeding systems, it is first necessary to understand something of the genetic diversity of sheep breeds. Breeds of sheep available in the United States can range from fine-wool breeds, to long-wool breeds, to hair breeds. These breeds can range in mature size from 100 lbs to over 400 lbs, and average from one lamb per ewe per year to over three lambs per ewe per year. Some breeds lamb year-round; most lamb only in the spring of the year. With this degree of genetic diversity available to the sheep producer, selection of the breeds utilized in a commercial operation is crucial to the success and profitability of the operation. The appropriate choice depends on the geographic location, feed conditions, weather conditions, and goals of the operation.

For simplification and ease of understanding, the breeds are grouped together and classified. They can be classified by face color (black face versus white face) or by wool type (fine wool versus long wool versus hair). However, the most common classification is by use, based on the major function of the breed in common mating systems: ewe breed, dual-purpose breed, and ram breed (Figure 7–7).

Ewe Breeds   Ewe breeds are generally the fine-wool, white-faced breeds and those that were developed from crosses of the fine-wool breeds (Rambouillet, Merino) with long-wool breeds (Lincoln, Border Leicester), or the highly prolific breeds (Finnsheep, Romanov). The breed most widely seen in commercial flocks in the United States is the Rambouillet or Rambouillet cross; the term most generally used for these range ewes is the Western ewe or Western White-face ewe.

(a)

(b)

(c)

Figure 7–7
Sheep breeds are often classified by use of the breed. The pictured breeds of sheep are examples of the different breed classes: (a) ewe breed, Rambouillet; (b) ram breed, Shropshire; and (c) dual-purpose breed, Corriedale.

Ram Breeds   Ram breeds are the meat-type breeds used primarily as terminal sires on the ewe breeds or dual-purpose breed to increase lamb gain and carcass quality for market lamb production. The ram breeds are noted for size, fast growth, and carcass quality. The two most widely used ram breeds in the United States are the Suffolk and Hampshire breeds, with the Dorset, Shropshire, Oxford, and Southdown breeds used in some instances.

Dual-Purpose Breeds   The breeds classified as dual purpose are those that can be used as either ewe breeds or ram breeds, depending on the environment and production goals of the operation. These are breeds that are not only noted for milk production, mothering ability, and twinning rate, but also exhibit some of the characteristics noted in the ram breeds such as better growth rate and carcass quality. Examples of dual-purpose breeds are the Dorset, Columbia, and Corriedale.

Selection

Heritability   An understanding of the heritability of important traits (low, moderate, high) in sheep production is needed to better understand the use of selection and mating systems in the sheep operation. Simply stated, the heritability of a trait describes how easily genetic improvement can be made. The variation in a trait is made up of genetic and environmental components. Heritability is the proportion of difference among animals for a trait (e.g., milk production) due to genetic difference, rather than environmental factors. This is important because geneticists are interested in the portion that is transmissible from parent to offspring. Strictly defined, heritability is the ratio of additive genetic variance to total phenotypic variance. This is important to genetic improvement because breeding value depends heavily on additive genetic variance. If variation does not exist, then progress through selection cannot be made.

Average heritability estimates for various traits are shown in Table 7–10. In general, reproductive traits tend to be low in heritability (<0.20), growth traits tend to be moderately heritable ($0.20–0.40$), and carcass and fleece traits tend to show high levels of heritability (>0.40). The most practical way to understand the use of heritability is in the selection process. The higher the heritability of a trait, the quicker improvements can be made through selection for that trait. Reproductive traits such as prolificacy are lowly heritable and, therefore, sheep breeders see very little progress when selecting for twinning rate. That is why other methods are used to increase twinning rate in the ewe flock. However, the carcass traits have very high heritabilities and selection progress can be noted from one generation to the next very quickly when selecting for the carcass traits. The growth traits are moderate in heritability and selection for these traits will show good genetic improvement from generation to generation.

Selection for growth traits.   Growth traits are of economic importance to sheep operations. Because growth traits show moderate levels of heritability, selection programs that emphasize growth traits can show good genetic improvement from generation to generation. Selection for growth is most important in the ram breeds. These individuals are the predominant sires used for commercial market lamb production and their main contribution to the lamb crop is growth rate and carcass merit. Increased growth rate allows producers to market lambs at an earlier age or at heavier weights. In the sheep industry, the most important growth trait is weaning weight.

Weaning weights are influenced by not only growth rate of the lamb, but age of the ewe, type of birth, and method of rearing of the lamb. Selection for growth

Table 7-10
HERITABILITIES OF VARIOUS TRAITS

	Percent		Percent
Reproductive Traits		**Carcass Traits**	
Ewe fertility	5[1]	Carcass weight	35
Prolificacy[2]	10	Weight of trimmed retail cuts	45
Scrotal circumference	35	Percent trimmed retail cuts	40
Age at puberty	25	Loin eye area	50
Lamb survival	5	12th rib fat thickness	30
Ewe productivity[3]	20	Dressing percent	10
Growth Traits		**Fleece Traits**	
Birth weight	15	Grease fleece weight	35
60-day weight	20	Clean fleece weight	25
90-day weight	25	Yield (%)	40
120-day weight	30	Staple length	55
240-day weight	40	Fiber diameter	40
Preweaning gain: birth–60 days	20	Crimp	45
Postweaning gain: 60–120 days	40	Color	45
Dairy Traits			
Milk yield	30		
Fat (%)	30		
Protein (%)	30		
Fat yield	35		
Protein yield	45		

[1]May increase to 10% in ewe lambs and in ewes bred in spring.
[2]Lambs born per ewe lambing.
[3]Pounds of lamb weaned per ewe exposed.
Source: *Sheep Production Handbook*, 1996, p. BRD-61. Used with permission.

rate simply by using lamb weaning weight may not be effective unless some of these common nongenetic factors are adjusted for. Weaning weights should be adjusted for age of lamb, sex, type of birth, method of rearing the lamb, and age of the dam. These adjustments and an example of the calculations are shown in Table 7–11.

National Sheep Improvement Program (NSIP)

Expected progeny differences are widely used in the beef, dairy, and swine industries, but are just in the infancy stages in the sheep industry. The National Sheep Improvement Program (NSIP), initiated in 1986, was designed to provide both the purebred producer and the commercial producer with a performance recording and genetic evaluation program. The NSIP evaluates maternal traits, growth traits, wool traits, and is developing carcass traits.

The NSIP uses the standard set of adjustment factors shown in Table 7–11 for the adjustment of weaning weights. In most breeds, the genetic evaluations are done on a within-flock basis until the database grows large enough to have sufficient ties to have across-flock genetic evaluations. Across-flock ties occur when related individuals are in two or more flocks. Genetic ties normally occur through the rams rather than the ewes because of the high number of progeny per ram and the movement of rams or sons of rams from flock to flock. The breed associations using across-flock genetic evaluations through NSIP are the Polypay, Suffolk, Columbia, Dorset, Hampshire, Katahdin, Romney, Rambouillet, and Targhee breeds.

Table 7–11

MULTIPLICATIVE ADJUSTMENT FACTORS FOR ADJUSTING LAMB PREWEANING AND WEANING WEIGHTS TO A COMMON AGE OF DAM, LAMB SEX, AND LAMB TYPE OF BIRTH-REARING

Sex	Ewe Age	Type of Birth-Rearing					
		1–1	2–1	2–2	3–1	3–2	3–3
Ewe	1	1.13	1.29	1.38	1.40	1.51	1.80
	2 or over 6	1.08	1.19	1.29	1.28	1.38	1.54
	3–6	1.00	1.10	1.19	1.18	1.27	1.36
Ram	1	1.02	1.15	1.21	1.23	1.31	1.53
	2 or over 6	0.98	1.08	1.17	1.16	1.25	1.38
	3–6	0.91	1.00	1.08	1.07	1.15	1.23
Wether	1	1.10	1.25	1.33	1.36	1.45	1.72
	2 or over 6	1.05	1.16	1.26	1.25	1.35	1.50
	3–6	.98	1.08	1.16	1.15	1.24	1.33

Adjustment factors are from the Report of the NSIP Technical Committee, 1986. Weights are adjusted to a single ewe lamb from a 3- to 6-year-old ewe equivalent. Adjustment factors are to be used on preweaning and weaning weights taken at approximately 30, 60, 90, or 120 days of age. Before applying adjustment factors, actual weight must be adjusted to the same age for each lamb using one of the following two equations:

1. If birth weight is available:

$$\text{Age adjusted wt.} = \left[\frac{\text{actual wt.} - \text{birth wt.}}{\text{age when weighed}} \times \text{adjustment age(days)} \right] + \text{birth wt.}$$

2. If birth weight is not available:

$$\text{Age adjusted wt.} = \frac{\text{actual weight}}{\text{age when weighed}} \times \text{adjustment age(days)}$$

Final adjusted weight is given by multiplying the age adjusted weight by the appropriate adjustment factor. Example: A ewe lamb born as a triplet and reared as a single from a 7-year-old ewe weighed 7 lbs at birth and 66 lbs at weaning when 93 days of age. What is her adjusted 90-day weight?

$$\text{Age adjusted wt.} = \left[\frac{66 - 7}{93} \times 90 \right] + 7 = 64 \text{ lbs}$$

Final adjusted 90 day wt. = 64 × 1.28 = 82 lbs

Lamb born in litters of greater than three should use the triplet adjustment factors. Lambs born as singles and reared as twins should use the twin–twin (2–2) adjustment factors and lambs born as singles or twins and reared as triplets should use the triplet–triplet (3–3) adjustment factors.

Source: *Sheep Production Handbook*, 1996, p. BRD-63. Used with permission.

Heterosis in Sheep Breeding

All of the meat-producing species rely on crossbreeding to improve productivity. However, the sheep industry has used crossbreeding systems very effectively for decades. Crossbreeding systems in sheep involve mating ewes and rams of different breed or breed crosses to produce offspring that are superior (due to heterosis) in performance to that of either of the parent stock. Systematic crossbreeding systems are advantageous because they utilize heterosis.

Heterosis, or hybrid vigor, for a trait is defined as the superiority of the crossbred individual relative to the average performance of the purebreds included in the

Table 7-12
AVERAGE HETEROSIS EFFECTS IN THE CROSSBRED LAMB[1]

Trait	Level of Heterosis (%)
Birth weight	3.2
Weaning weight	5.0
Preweaning daily gain	5.3
Postweaning daily gain	6.6
Yearling weight	5.2
Conception rate	2.6
Prolificacy of the dam[2]	2.8
Survival: birth to weaning	9.8
Carcass traits	approximately 0
Lambs born per ewe exposed[1]	5.3
Lambs reared per ewe exposed[1]	15.2
Weight of lamb weaned per ewe exposed[2]	17.8

[1]From the review by Nitter, G. 1978. Breed utilization for meat production in sheep. *Animal Breeding Abstracts* 46: 131–143.
[2]Purebred ewes mated to a different breed of ram to produce crossbred lambs.
Source: *Sheep Production Handbook*, 1996, p. BRD-28. Used with permission.

cross. In general, crossbred individuals tend to be more vigorous, fertile, healthier, and grow faster than the average of parental stock that make up the cross. Traits that are lowly heritable show high levels of heterosis. Reproductive traits are a good example of a lowly heritable trait that shows high levels of heterosis. Moderately heritable traits show moderate levels of heterosis, such as the growth traits. Highly heritable traits such as fleece and carcass traits show little hybrid vigor. Average heterosis effects for the crossbred lamb and crossbred ewe are shown in Tables 7–12 and 7–13, respectively. The total effect of heterosis on the crossbred lamb is 17.8%; the effect of heterosis on the crossbred ewe is 18%. These advantages make it imperative for the sheep producer to use crossbreeding systems to improve the economic efficiency of the commercial sheep operation.

Table 7-13
AVERAGE HETEROSIS EFFECTS IN THE CROSSBRED EWE[1]

Trait	Level of Heterosis (%)
Fertility	8.7
Prolificacy	3.2
Body weight	5.0
Fleece weight	5.0
Lamb birth weight	5.1
Lamb weaning weight	6.3
Lamb survival: Birth to weaning	2.7
Lambs born per ewe exposed	11.5
Lambs reared per ewe exposed	14.7
Weight of lamb weaned per ewe exposed	18.0

[1]From the review by Nitter, G. 1978. Breed utilization for meat production in sheep. *Animal Breeding Abstracts* 46: 131–143.
Source: *Sheep Production Handbook*, 1996, p. BRD-29. Used with permission.

SUMMARY AND CONCLUSION

Animal breeding is a discipline that takes the principles of genetics and applies them to practical selection and management systems. The goal is to produce the best animals for the conditions in which they will be produced. The cow-calf producer is in the business of producing beef as efficiently as possible. The techniques used and the selections made for breedings must balance production performance and end-product merit. EPDs are a tool to assist in this process. A wealth of information is available to use. The challenge is to identify the combinations of genetics and environment that is most profitable and competitive. Similar tools are readily available to the dairy producer. Extensive data collected through the DHI system has allowed rapid genetic progress to be made in economically important traits. Availability of PTAs provides a challenge for producers to evaluate the economic importance of each trait and to keep current with new technologies. A well-known performance resource for swine breeders to use in selection is the Swine Testing and Evaluation System. This system evaluates the genetic superiority of swine using mixed-model technology similar to that of the beef and dairy industries. Sheep producers have a similar program in place called NSIP. However, this is a new program compared to the other species. It is less developed because there are fewer sheep and fewer participating sheep producers. Sheep producers use selection and crossbreeding but have less information with which to work.

STUDY QUESTIONS

1. Define animal breeding. Why is animal breeding more important as a discipline now than it was 50 years ago? Have all species of livestock benefited from animal breeding research? Why or why not?
2. Speculate on ways in which biotechnology and genetic engineering will make animal breeding a more useful science.
3. What are the major areas of economic importance in beef cattle breeding?
4. Define *heritability*. Describe the difference in heritability among growth traits, reproductive traits, and carcass traits in beef cattle.
5. Why is understanding genetic correlations important in beef cattle breeding? Describe such a relationship between two traits.
6. Why is it important for a beef cattle producer to know the performance of his or her herd? What are some types of performance programs? How do breed associations help?
7. What is an EPD? Define it in relation to breeding value. For what traits can EPDs be calculated? What animals within a breed can have EPDs calculated?
8. What is a contemporary group? Why is this important?
9. What does it mean for EPDs within a breed to be standardized? What is a base year?
10. Define and explain the value of *accuracy* and *possible change*.
11. What is a maternal effect in beef cattle? What are its components? What is milk EPD? What is weaning weight EPD? What is combined maternal EPD?
12. Describe the difference in the use of EPDs in the selection of seedstock herd compared to selection in a commercial herd.
13. In what situation might it be advantageous to calculate estimated EPDs from pedigree information? What would you expect the accuracy of such EPDs to be?
14. Speculate on the value of across-breed EPDs. What are the problems in calculating these values?
15. Name some major goals for dairy cattle genetic improvement. How much more or less complicated does the use of heritability estimates seem in dairy cattle compared to beef cattle? Is the definition of heritability the same?
16. What are some traits that a producer could expect his herd to make rapid improvement in through the application of sound animal-breeding techniques? Little progress?
17. What does it mean when we say that "genetic correlations are seldom perfect"?
18. Describe the value of DHI in dairy cattle breeding programs.
19. What are some traits that are difficult to measure and include with susceptible accuracy in breeding programs?
20. Define these terms: *predicted transmitting ability, reliability, parent average, predicted transmitting ability dollars,* and *percentile ranking.*

21. What is a somatic cell score (SCS)? Does available information suggest that the SCS is influenced much by genetics?

22. How does the short generation interval in the pig give swine breeders an advantage in making genetic progress?

23. What do NSIF and NPPC contribute to swine breeding excellence?

24. Based on the information provided, what are the areas of emphasis in swine breeding? How does visual appraisal contribute?

25. What is PSS? Why should individuals with this condition be culled?

26. What has been the influence of swine breeds on the swine production industry? What is their relationship to hybrid boar and sow breeding lines developed by commercial companies?

27. What is a selection index?

28. Presuming genetic engineering becomes widespread in livestock breeding, what genes would you select from the Chinese pig to contribute to a synthetic sow line? Boar line?

29. What is STAGES? What is its value? What is a sow productivity index and what is its value?

30. In the sheep section of this chapter, more emphasis was placed on breeds than in the other sections of this chapter. Why?

31. Describe the importance of capitalizing on heterosis in sheep breeding. Integrate a discussion of ewe breeds, ram breeds, and dual-purpose breeds into your answer.

REFERENCES

Author's Note: For previous editions Dr. Sally Dolezal, Dr. Daniel Waldner, Dr. Gerald Q. Fitch, Dr. David Buchanan, and Dr. John L. Evans of Oklahoma State University contributed to this chapter. Starting with the second edition, Dr. Tony Seykora of the University of Minnesota has reviewed the chapter and contributed new material. For the fifth edition, Dr. David Buchanan, North Dakota State University, reviewed and revised the chapter. The author gratefully acknowledges these contributions.

Beef Improvement Federation. 1996. *Guidelines.* 7th ed. Colby, KS: Beef Improvement Federation. http://www.beefimprovement.org.

Benyshek, L. L. 1988. Evaluating and reporting carcass traits. Proceedings of the Beef Improvement Federation 1988 Annual Convention, Albuquerque, NM.

Buchanan, D. S., A. C. Clutter, S. L. Northcutt, and D. Pomp. 1993. *Animal breeding: Principles and applications.* 4th ed. Stillwater: Oklahoma State University.

Cole, J. B., P. M. VanRaden and Multi-State Project S-1040. 2010. Net merit as a measure of lifetime profit: 2010 revision. AIPL Research Report NM$4 (12-09). Found at www.aipl.arsusda.gov/reference/nmcalc-2010.htm

Cundiff, L. V., and K. E. Gregory. 1977. *Beef cattle breeding.* USDA Ag. Inf. Bull. 286.

Cundiff, L. V., F. Szabo, K. E. Gregory, R. M. Koch, M. E. Dideman, and J. D. Crouse. 1993. Breed comparisons in the germplasm evaluation program at MARC. Proceedings of the Beef Improvement Federation Research Symposium and Annual Meeting, May 1993, Asheville, NC.

DHIA. 1997. DHI-202 Herd Summary. Fact Sheet A-1. Columbus, OH: Dairy Herd Improvement Association.

Dickinson, F. N. 1985. *Genetic improvement of dairy cattle.* National Cooperative Dairy Herd Improvement Program Handbook, Fact Sheet 1–7.

Freeman, A. E. 1992. Integrating genetic evaluations into a breeding plan. In *Large dairy herd management.* Champaign, IL: Management Services, American Dairy Science Association.

Gregory, K. E., L. V. Cundiff, and R. M. Koch. 1999. *Composite breeds to use heterosis and breed differences to improve efficiency of beef production.* U.S. Department of Agriculture, Agricultural Research Service. Technical Bulletin 1875, pp. 1–175.

Guidelines for Uniform Beef Improvement Programs. Beef Improvement Federation. Ed. W. D. Hohenboken. 8th ed. 2002. pp. 1–161. (www.beefimprovement.org)

Kuehn, L. A., L. D. Van Vleck, R. M. Thallman, and L. V. Cundiff. 2007. Across breed EPD tables for the year 2007 adjusted to breed differences for birth year of 2005. Proceedings of the 2007 Beef Improvement Federation 39th Annual Meeting. Accessed online August 9, 2007, at http://bifconference.com/bif2007/Symposium/074_Across_Breed_EPD.pdf.

Lamberson, W. R., and E. R. Cleveland. 1988. Genetic parameters and their use in swine breeding. Swine Genetics Fact Sheet Number 3, NSIF-F33. Raleigh, NC: National Swine Improvement Federation.

Lasley, J. F. 1978. *Genetics of livestock improvement.* Upper Saddle River, NJ: Prentice-Hall.

National Swine Improvement Federation. 1998. *Guidelines for uniform swine improvement programs.* Asheville, NC: http://mark.ansi.ncsu.edu/nsif/.

Northcutt, S. L., and D. S. Buchanan. 1993a. *Expected progeny difference: Part I, Background on breeding value estimation.* OSU Fact Sheet. F-3159. Stillwater: Oklahoma State University.

Northcutt, S. L., and D. S. Buchanan. 1993b. *Expected progeny difference: Part II, Growth trait EPDs.* OSU Fact Sheet. F-3160. Stillwater: Oklahoma State University.

Northcutt, S. L., and D. S. Buchanan. 1993c. *Expected progeny difference: Part III, Maternal trait EPDs.* OSU Fact Sheet. F-3161. Stillwater: Oklahoma State University.

Northcutt, S. L., and D. S. Buchanan. 1993d. *Expected progeny difference: Part IV, Use of EPDs.* OSU Fact Sheet. F-3162. Stillwater: Oklahoma State University.

Purdue University. 2011. *Swine testing and evaluation system (STAGES).* West Lafayette, IN: Purdue University. http://www.sspro.com/stages/index.aspx.

Rothschild, M. F., and G. S. Plastow. 1999. *Current advances in pig genomics and industry applications.* U.S. Genome Mapping Coordination Program. Ames, IA. http://www.genome.iastate.edu/~max/rev98/.

Rothschild, M. F., and A. Ruvinsky. 1998. *The genetics of the pig.* Wallingford, UK: CAB International. http://ansc.une.edu.au/genpub/genpig.html.

Sheep production handbook. 2002. Denver, CO: American Sheep Industry Association, Inc.

Sire summaries supplement (SSS). 1998. Brattleboro, VT: Holstein Association.

USDA-DHIA. *Factors for standardizing 305-day lactation records for age and month of calving.* Columbus, OH: USDA-DHIA.

White, J. M. 1989. Characteristics of good dairy cattle. In *Guide to genetics.* Brattleboro, VT: Holstein Association.

Wiggans, G. R., and P. M. VanRaden. 1989. *USDA-DHIA animal model genetic evaluations.* Nat. Coop. Dairy Herd Imp. Prog. Fact Sheet H-2. Ames, IA.

Wilcox, C. J. 1992. Genetics: Basic concepts. In *Large dairy herd management.* Champaign, IL: Management Services, American Dairy Science Association.

Woodward, B. W., L. V. Cundiff, D. L. Notter, and D. L. Van Vleck. 1999. Understanding and using across breed expected progeny differences (EPDs). In *Beef Cattle Handbook.* Beef Cattle Resource Committee of the North Central Land Grant Universities. Accessed online August 3, 2007. http://www.iowabeefcenter.org/pdfs/bch/01310.pdf.

8

Animal Reproduction

Key Terms

Ampullary-isthmic junction
Artificial vagina (AV)
Atresia
Blastocyst
Broad ligament
Colostrum
Corpus luteum (CL)
Donor
Dystocia
Embryo transfer
Epididymis
Episodic
Estrous cycle
Estrus
Flow cytometer
Flushing
Follicle-stimulating hormone
Folliculogenesis
Freemartin
Gametes
Generation interval
Gonads
Hypothalamus
In vitro

Libido
Lordosis
Luteinizing hormone
Luteolysis
Monoestrus
Morula
Oocyte
Ovulation
Parturition
Passive immunity
Pituitary gland
Placenta
Polyestrus
Postpartum
Postpartum interval
Pregnancy disease
Progesterone
Prostaglandin
Puberty
Recipients
Secondary sex characteristics
Semen
Testosterone
Zygote

Learning Objectives

After you have studied this chapter, you should be able to:

- Describe how the endocrine system drives the production of gametes.
- Identify the various anatomical features of female and male reproductive systems.
- Compare and contrast the functions of the male and female gonads.
- State how conception, pregnancy, and parturition occur.
- Discuss the considerable influence of the environment on reproductive function.
- Describe the uses and advantages of the technologies recently employed in animal reproduction.

INTRODUCTION

Reproduction is required for propagation and continuation of a species, and as such, is an essential process in all species. Producers of domestic animals are particularly concerned with reproduction, as the production of young is the primary determinant of income for most livestock species. Even dairy producers, who generate the majority of their income through milk sales, require reproduction to occur to initiate lactation. In fact, increases in reproductive efficiency are considered to have a much greater impact on profitability than does progress in general production methods. A 3% improvement in birthrate would result in an additional 1 million beef calves born per year, 3.2 million pigs born per year, and

3.7 million gallons of milk produced per year. Considering these numbers, efforts to increase reproductive efficiency in domestic animal species are typically well rewarded financially. Likewise, selection against poor reproductive efficiency is similarly rewarding.

Reproduction in all animals, both male and female, requires tremendous coordination between the hypothalamus, the pituitary gland, and the gonads. Because these individual endocrine glands behave in concert with one another, they are often referred to as a single entity, the hypothalamo-pituitary-gonadal axis, which acts to coordinate and carry out the processes involved with germ cell development and maintenance, fertilization, pregnancy, and **parturition**, the process of giving birth. These processes, although critical to produce offspring, are active only during certain phases of the life cycle. These phases are typically age dependent. In addition, many other factors come into play, including season (day length), presence of the opposite gender, and level of nutrition. Knowing which factors affect reproductive function and determining how to minimize the negative effects of those factors are critical to successful reproduction.

At the basis of the reproductive system is the **gonad**. The female gonad is the *ovary* and the male gonad is the *testis*. The gonads have two primary functions: steroidogenesis, or the production of the sex steroids, and gametogenesis, or the production of **gametes**. Both of these functions are hormonally controlled and require absolute coordination for proper activity to be expressed. The hormones responsible for proper function of the gonads are produced by the brain (hypothalamus) and **pituitary gland**. Because the gonad is directly responsive to the action of the hypothalamus, environmental factors including nutritional status, length of daylight, and emotions have a profound influence on reproductive function. Some reproductive terms and other information of general value about some species are listed in Table 8–1.

Parturition Process of giving birth.

Gonads Sex organs; testis in male, ovary in female.

Gametes Mature sperm in the male and the egg or ova in the female; the reproductive cells.

Pituitary gland Gland sitting directly below the hypothalamus.

PUBERTY

Puberty Transitional state through which animals progress from an immature reproductive and hormonal state to a mature state.

Before an animal of either sex is capable of reproduction, it must go through the process of **puberty**. The signals for puberty differ by species, but the most important factors influencing the onset of puberty are age and weight. However, nutritional stress, season of the year, and other factors can also affect the onset of puberty. Puberty is simply the process of maturing from a nonfunctional endocrine and physiological reproductive state into a state of functional gamete and hormone production. After puberty, an animal is said to be *reproductively competent*. Puberty is associated with the **secondary sex characteristics** commonly associated with each sex. The transition through puberty is characterized by inconsistent reproductive competency.

Secondary sex characteristics Characteristics that differentiate the sexes from each other; occur most profoundly during and after puberty.

Examples of secondary sex characteristics in males include such things as humps on the necks of bulls, beards on men, increased musculature in the male of most species, and changes in the sound of vocalization (for instance, the voice change in boys that happens at puberty). For females this includes the many characteristics lumped together that we refer to as femininity: added body fat that creates curves where once angles were visible, mammary development, smoother hair coats, and so on. Behavioral characteristics such as "marking" territory (both sexes) or aggression in males are also part of the complex.

Table 8–1

REPRODUCTIVE TERMS BY SPECIES

	Cats	Cattle	Dogs	Goats	Horses	Chickens	Sheep	Swine
Mature male	Tom	Bull	Dog	Buck	Stallion	Cock[1]	Ram	Boar
Mature female	Queen	Cow	Bitch	Doe	Mare	Hen	Ewe	Sow
Young male	—	Bullock	Puppy dog	Buck kid	Colt	Chick[2]	Ram lamb	Boar[3]
Young female	—	Heifer	Puppy bitch	Doe kid	Filly	Chick[2]	Ewe lamb	Gilt[3]
Newborn	Kitten	Calf	Pup	Kid	Foal	Chick[2]	Lamb	Pig
Unsexed male	Gib	Steer	Castrate	Wether	Gelding	Capon	Wether	Barrow
Groups	Bevy	Herd	Pack	Band	Herd	Flock	Flock	Herd, drove, or sounder
Genus	Felis	Bos	Canis	Capra	Equus	Gallus[4]	Ovis	Sus
Act of parturition	Littering	Calving	Whelping	Kidding	Foaling	NA	Lambing	Farrowing
Duration of heat	6–7 days	14 hrs	2–21 days (6–12 avg)	42 hrs	6 days	NA	30–35 hrs	2–3 days
Length of estrous cycle (average; range)	18; 14–21 days	12; 18–24 days	3 1/2–13 months; (6 months avg)	21; 15–24 days	21; 16–30 days	NA	16; 14–20 days	21; 18–24 days
Time of ovulation in (days) relation to heat	Stimulated by mating	10–14 hrs after end of estrus	Usually 1–3 days after first acceptance of male	Near end of estrus	1–2 days before end of estrus	NA	1 hr before end of estrus	18–60 hrs after estrus begins
Gestation period (average; range) (days)	63; 62–64	281; 274–291	63; 58–68	151; 140–160	336; 310–350	21-day incubation	150; 140–160	113; 111–115
Age at puberty (months)	4–18 (much breed variability)	8–14	5–24	4–8	10–12	4–6	4–8	5–7

[1]Called a tom in turkeys.
[2]Called a poult in turkeys, a gosling in geese, and a duckling in ducks.
[3]Shoat refers to a young pig of either sex under one year of age.
[4]Genus for chicken.

ENDOCRINOLOGY

Hypothalamus Area of the brain responsible for many homeostatic functions.

Episodic The pulsatile manner in which the gonadotropic hormones are secreted by the anterior pituitary gland. Controlled by the pulse-generating center of the brain.

Luteinizing hormone Gonadotropic hormone primarily responsible for providing the signal to disrupt the mature follicle in females, and the production of testosterone by the Leydig cells of the testes in the male.

Follicle-stimulating hormone Gonadotropic hormone responsible for growth, development, and maintenance of follicles in females, and the production of sperm in males.

Testosterone Male steroid sex hormone.

Atresia The degeneration of follicles that do not make it to the mature stage, otherwise known as the Graafian stage.

Ovulation Release of the ova or egg from the ovary.

The endocrine functions involved in reproduction are initiated by the **hypothalamus**, a small area of the brain, which plays a critical role in the body's ability to adapt to the environment. The hypothalamus releases a hormone called *gonadotropin-releasing hormone* (GnRH). Release of this hormone is the first step in a cascade of hormonal events that must proceed in a coordinated manner to result in successful action by the gonads. Interestingly, GnRH is released in a pulsatile manner, causing all of the hormones and actions to be **episodic** (Figure 8–1). This action maintains a high degree of sensitivity in the system. The stimulation for GnRH release is controlled by a center referred to as the *pulse-generating center*. This center is under control of various parts of the brain and, in fact, integrates the many environmental signals to produce a driving force in the endocrine cascade.

GnRH travels a short distance to the anterior pituitary gland, which sits directly below the hypothalamus. The anterior pituitary gland, in turn, responds to GnRH by releasing two other hormones: **luteinizing hormone** (LH) and **follicle-stimulating hormone** (FSH). These two hormones enter the bloodstream and travel to the gonads of both males and females. Again, these hormones are released into the bloodstream in a pulsatile manner so that the gonads are only exposed to high levels of the gonadotropins (LH and FSH) intermittently.

Testosterone, the primary male hormone, is produced by the testes. In the male, release of LH is the signal to the testes to produce testosterone. If LH is not present, testosterone is not produced in adequate quantities for expression of the secondary sex characteristics associated with males. FSH in males is required for the production of sperm, the male gamete.

In the female, FSH is responsible for growth and maintenance of the developing follicle that is destined to produce the ova, which is the female gamete. Without adequate FSH support, the follicle undergoes death in a process referred to as **atresia**. As the follicle grows and develops, it produces estrogen (Figure 8–2). The increased level of estrogen causes a surge of LH to be released from the pituitary gland. This surge of LH initiates the breakdown of the follicle wall, thereby releasing the ova from the ovary and making it available for fertilization (Figure 8–3). This release of the ova from the ovary is called **ovulation**.

Figure 8–1

Episodic release of the hormones of reproduction in response to the release of gonadotropin-releasing hormone (GnRH).
LH = luteinizing hormone; FSH = follicle-stimulating hormone. (Source: Senger, 2003, p. 216. Used with permission.)

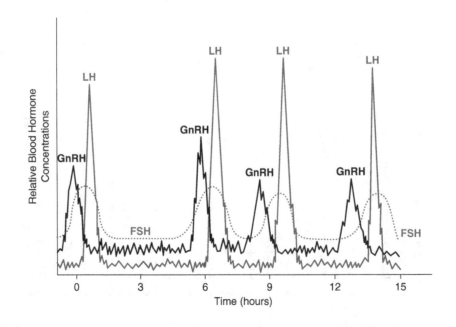

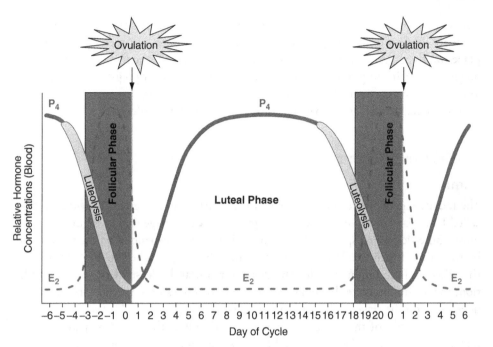

Figure 8–2
Phases of the estrous cycle.
P = progesterone;
E = estrogen. (Source: Senger, 2003, p. 148. Used with permission.)

After ovulation, the follicle is transformed into a **corpus luteum (CL)**. This structure's primary responsibility is to produce the hormone **progesterone**, which is required to support pregnancy. Progesterone inhibits LH and FSH release, prevents behavioral **estrus**, and decreases the motility of the muscles in the uterus. In some species (goat, rabbit, and sow), the CL is required throughout gestation to maintain

Corpus luteum (CL) Ovarian structure responsible for the production of progesterone for the support of pregnancy.

Progesterone Female sex steroid produced by the corpus luteum or the placenta.

Estrus The period when a female is receptive to mating. Synonymous with *heat*.

Figure 8–3
Illustration of the ovary.
(Source: Senger, 2003, p. 25. Used with permission.)

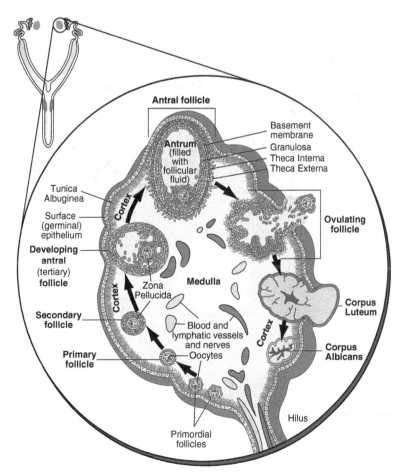

a successful pregnancy. In other species (cow, mare, and ewe), the CL provides adequate progesterone during early pregnancy, but becomes unnecessary because the **placenta**, the organ that surrounds the fetus and attaches to the female uterus during pregnancy, begins to produce enough progesterone to support pregnancy sufficiently. The placenta is the organ through which oxygen and nutrients are passed to the fetus from the female and waste is passed from the fetus to the female.

Placenta The organ that surrounds the fetus and unites it to the female while it develops in the uterus.

ANATOMY

Female

The female reproductive tract consists of the ovaries (female gonad), oviducts (also called Fallopian tubes), uterus, cervix, vagina, and external genitalia (Figure 8–4). In most domestic animal species, the reproductive tract is suspended below the rectum by the broad ligament. The ovaries occur in pairs, are attached to the ligament at the hilus, and are responsible for the development, and release of the ova. In addition, the ovaries produce the female sex steroid hormones progesterone and estrogen, depending on the stage of the reproductive cycle.

Oocyte The gamete from the female.

The ovaries of the newborn female contain all of the **oocytes** (gametes) the female will ever have. The functional oocytes are sequestered in primordial follicles before birth, which remain in a quiescent state until recruited into a growing pool that enter folliculogenesis, the growth and development of the primordial follicle in the ovary, during the monthly **estrous cycle** of the female. During folliculogenesis, follicles will continue to develop or die through atresia. The few follicles that survive to sufficient size produce the high levels of estrogen required to result in the surge of LH that ultimately causes the release of the ova from the follicle. It is not yet clear

Estrous cycle The time from one estrus (heat) to the next.

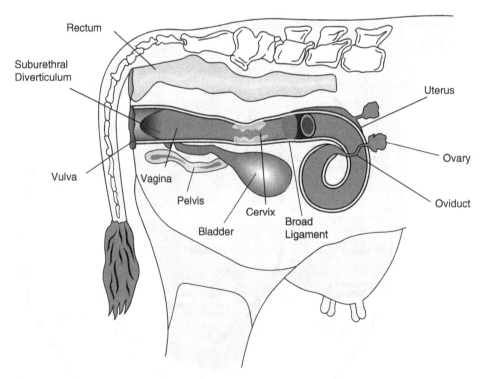

Figure 8–4

Female reproductive tract. (Source: Oklahoma State University. Used with permission.)

how the follicle that survives to ovulation is chosen among the 100 or so that begin to grow each month.

The ovum is released from the follicle and is "captured" by the *infundibulum*, a funnel-shaped structure at the end of the oviduct that surrounds the ovary. The thin membrane directs the ovum into the oviduct, preventing it from entering the abdominal cavity. The upper portion of the oviduct is the ampulla, and it connects with the isthmus, the lower portion of the oviduct. The isthmus connects the oviduct with the uterine horn. The area where the ampulla and isthmus connect, the ampullary-isthmic junction, is considered the site of fertilization. The oviduct is glandular, providing nutrients and a transport medium in the secretions. The eggs remain in the oviduct for approximately 3 to 6 days, depending on the species.

Species differ greatly in the type of uterus configuration present, as indicated in Figure 8–5. The primary difference between types of uteri is the presence of uterine horns. The uterus functions to provide a passageway for sperm cells from the cervix to the oviducts, to provide glandular secretions to nourish the embryo prior to development of the placenta, to provide a proper environment for the development of the fetus, to provide nutrients and eliminate waste products for the developing fetus through the placental–uterus junction, and to expel the fetus during parturition. The uterus is a very muscular organ, and contractions aid in the expulsion of the fetus. However, this contractility of the uterus must be suppressed to allow the embryo to implant to the wall of the uterus for a successful pregnancy. After ovulation, the development of a functional CL ensures that adequate progesterone is produced and secreted. Progesterone suppresses the contractility of the uterus, which allows the embryo to implant.

The uterus is connected to the cervix, which acts as a gatekeeper from the vagina into the uterus. The cervix has five primary functions:

1. To act as a passageway for sperm cells.
2. To act as a storage reservoir for sperm cells. In this way there can be a more consistent release of sperm into the uterus. This increases the chances that viable sperm will be present at the same time the ova is prepared for fertilization.

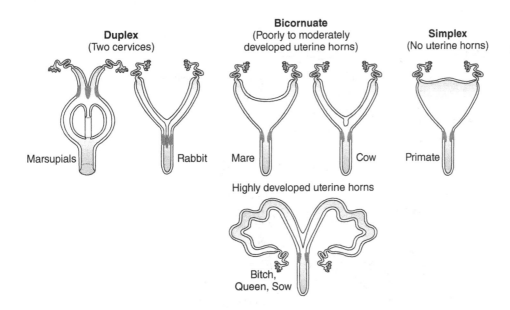

Duplex (Two cervices)   **Bicornuate** (Poorly to moderately developed uterine horns)   **Simplex** (No uterine horns)

Marsupials   Rabbit   Mare   Cow   Primate

Highly developed uterine horns

Bitch, Queen, Sow

Figure 8–5

Types of uteri. (Source: Senger, 2003, p. 30. Used with permission.)

3. To act as the primary barrier between the external and internal environments.
4. To provide lubrication.
5. To act as a passageway for the fetus at parturition.

The cervix, a very thick-walled, sphincter-like organ, has a canal with many crypts and folds through which the sperm must travel (except for the mare and sow in which the sperm is deposited directly into the uterus). This canal becomes occluded, or shut off, from the vagina by viscous secretions that are produced under the influence of high progesterone. The viscous secretions are referred to as *cervical seal* or *cervical plug*. Its function is to prevent the entrance of any contaminants when the embryo or fetus may be present. In fact, if the cervical seal is broken during pregnancy, spontaneous abortion generally follows. Under the influence of high estrogen, the cervix produces copious amounts of mucus to lubricate the vagina. This secretion also aids in preventing microorganisms from gaining entrance to the uterus by flushing the contaminants out.

The vagina serves a dual function, first, as the copulatory organ in most species, and second, it serves as a birth canal to expel the fetus. Unlike the uterus, the vagina is not a muscular organ. The vagina connects the cervix with the vulva, or the outside anatomical feature of the female. The vulva consists of two labia (inner and outer), which, under normal circumstances, provide a closure protecting the female reproductive tract against entry by microorganisms.

Male

The primary structures of the male reproductive tract are the testes, penis, duct system, and accessory sex glands (Figure 8–6). The testes, which are analogous to the ovary in the female, are responsible for both gamete (sperm) production and production of the male sex steroids. Because the production of sperm is very temperature dependent, occurring at temperatures 4–6°C cooler than normal body temperature, the body has developed several mechanisms to maintain proper temperature control. The testes begin development in the abdominal cavity but descend from the abdomen to the scrotum, usually during fetal development, through the inguinal canal. Infrequently, one or both of the testes may not descend and instead remain in the abdomen in a condition referred to as *cryptorchidism*. Because testosterone production can occur at body temperatures, a bilateral cryptorchid (neither

Figure 8–6

Male reproductive tract.

(Source: Oklahoma State University. Used with permission.)

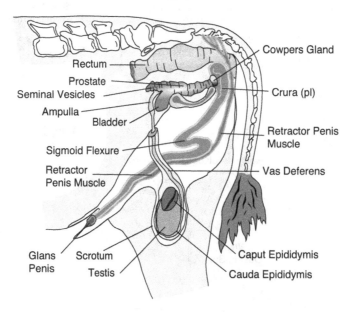

testis descended) male will exhibit secondary sex characteristics of a normal male. However, sperm production requires cooler temperatures, so the affected male is generally infertile. With unilateral cryptorchidism (one descended testis), the descended testis is fertile and often compensates for the lack of sperm production by the undescended testis. Therefore, the males are typically fertile. The condition appears to be hereditary, and, therefore, cryptorchid males should not be used for reproductive purposes.

The testes are suspended by the spermatic cord into the scrotum. The scrotum protects the testes and allows quick cooling for the testes to maintain proper temperature. The scrotum contains many thermosensors, which determine the outside temperature and cause several reactions, including scrotal sweating to dissipate the heat. In addition, neural connections from the scrotal thermosensors to the brain can affect the respiration of the male during heat stress. The increased respiration rate again dissipates the heat, thereby lowering testis temperature. The spermatic cord also connects the testis to the abdominal cavity through the inguinal canal. The spermatic cord contains the blood supply to the testes, neural connections, and a muscle that is capable of raising and lowering the testes. When the testes become cold, the external cremaster muscle raises the testes closer to the body to warm them. The cremaster muscle works in concert with the tunica dartos muscle, a smooth muscle layer underneath the skin of the scrotum. The tunica dartos muscle is capable of holding the testes close to the body for sustained periods of time. When the testes become too warm, the external cremaster muscle and tunica dartos muscle relax, thereby allowing the testes to descend. In bulls and rams, the scrotum may become very pendulous during hot summer days. This is an example of how the body tries to compensate for environmental conditions to maintain processes such as sperm production. Another unique feature for temperature control is a specialized vascular system called the *pampiniform plexus,* a network of veins surrounding convoluted segments of the testicular artery, which acts as a countercurrent heat exchange that cools arterial blood as it travels from the body to the testes, and warms the blood traveling from the testes to the body. If the body is not able to disperse enough heat and the testes become too warm, sperm production may halt and pregnancy rates can be depressed.

The testes are responsible for sperm and testosterone production. Testosterone is responsible for the secondary sex characteristics in males. In contrast to females, which have limited ova production, the male has tremendous gamete production potential. Sperm is produced continuously, as opposed to females, who are born with the total number of gametes they will ever have. Sperm are produced by seminiferous tubules within the testis capsule, and are then transported through the **epididymis** for further development and storage. Sperm collected from the head of the epididymis are typically immature and nonfertile. However, offspring have resulted from fertilization of eggs with sperm collected from the tail of the epididymis. Prior to ejaculation, the sperm travel from the epididymis through the ductus deferens to the urethra. The ductus deferens (vas deferens) can be cut in a procedure called a *vasectomy.* This almost certainly results in sterility but leaves sexual function intact. It is occasionally used to produce a male called a *teaser* to aid in estrus detection. The sperm in the ductus deferens are suspended in a fluid from the testes. However, several other organs add fluid to the sperm to make up the final product, **semen**. Boars and stallions produce gelatinous fractions that act to seal the cervix after breeding to prevent loss of semen back through the cervix. The seminal vesicles, prostate gland, and bulbourethral glands (Cowper's gland) all produce secretions that increase the volume of the semen, add nutrients to the semen, and aid in coagulation of the semen after ejaculation.

Epididymis Duct connecting the testis with the ductus deferens. Responsible for sperm storage, transport, and maturation. It consists of a head, a body, and a tail.

Semen Fluid from the male that contains sperm from the testis and secretions from several other reproductive organs.

The penis is the organ that deposits the semen in the vagina or cervix, depending on the species. The penis can be either vascular (stallions) or fibroelastic (bulls, boars, rams). The vascular penis enlarges during sexual excitement by retaining blood in specialized erectile tissue. The increased blood volume under high pressure causes erection. Following ejaculation, the blood is allowed to leave the organ, thereby decreasing blood pressure and volume in the penis.

With the exception of the stallion, the common farm animal species have a fibroelastic penis that exists in an S-shaped configuration inside the body until erection. During sexual excitement, the muscles responsible for retaining the penis in the sigmoidal flexure relax, allowing the penis to extend through the sheath. There is minimal increase in diameter of this type of penis. One modification of the penis is noted with the boar. The glans penis (the end of the penis) of the boar is corkscrew-shaped, such that it engages into the analogous corkscrew-shaped cervix of the sow. Therefore, the boar deposits the semen in the cervix rather than the vagina.

Because the penis is such a vascular organ, trauma can cause severe hemorrhaging. It is a fairly common injury for bulls to suffer a "broken penis," in which the penis is bent or kicked while extended. The blood from the penis leaks out and pools in the surrounding tissue. Many times the damage is irreparable and prevents the bull from ever mating naturally again. Semen can still be collected using an electroejaculator, which is explained later.

PREGNANCY

Successful timing of ovulation and mating should result in pregnancy. During estrus, the female becomes receptive to the male, thereby encouraging copulation (the physical mating). The ova, recently released from the ovary and traveling down the oviduct, becomes fertilized in the ampullary-isthmic junction of the oviduct. The window of opportunity for fertilization is very narrow. If fertilization has not occurred within approximately 12 hours, the oocyte begins to degenerate, and the chance for successful fertilization decreases drastically. Fortunately, sperm travels to the ampulla very rapidly, as soon as several minutes after ejaculation. In addition, the cervix and uterus have numerous crypts and crevices that hold sperm. Thus sperm deposited for several hours or even days before ovulation have an opportunity to reach the oocyte.

Zygote Cell resulting from the fusion of the sperm and oocyte.

Morula Early-stage embryo, after cell division multiplies cell numbers in the zygote.

Blastocyst More differentiated embryo consisting of an inner cell mass, blastocoele, and a trophoblast.

Prostaglandin A group of fatty acid hormones, one of which is prostaglandin $F_{2\alpha}$, which breaks down the corpus luteum allowing the female to return to estrus.

Once the oocyte is fertilized, it becomes a one-celled embryo called a **zygote**. Cell division begins soon after fertilization and the zygote becomes a multicelled **morula** embryo. Further development transforms the morula embryo into a **blastocyst**. The blastocyst embryo is free-floating as it moves down the oviduct toward the uterine horns and body of the uterus. The day of implantation varies by species, but generally occurs between 14 and 40 days in farm animals. The blastocyst continues to develop, and cellular partitions become evident. The inner cell mass is the initial fetus, and the trophoblast partition develops into the placenta (Figure 8–7).

Relatively high levels of progesterone are required for maintenance of the pregnancy, and the CL supplies the progesterone during the early phases of pregnancy in all species. However, for pregnancy to be maintained, degradation of the CL must be prevented. The pregnancy must first be recognized by the female. If pregnancy is not recognized in time, the CL degrades, thereby removing the source of progesterone required to support the pregnancy. In the cow, ewe, and mare, the nonpregnant uterus produces **prostaglandin** $F_{2\alpha}$ ($PGF_{2\alpha}$), which travels to the

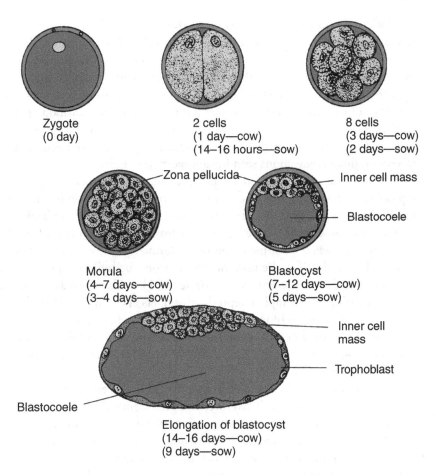

Figure 8–7
Specific cleavage stages at given times after fertilization in the cow (281-day gestation) and the sow (114-day gestation). (Source: Bearden and Fuquay, 1997, p. 91. Used with permission.)

Zygote
(0 day)

2 cells
(1 day—cow)
(14–16 hours—sow)

8 cells
(3 days—cow)
(2 days—sow)

Zona pellucida

Inner cell mass

Blastocoele

Morula
(4–7 days—cow)
(3–4 days—sow)

Blastocyst
(7–12 days—cow)
(5 days—sow)

Inner cell mass

Trophoblast

Blastocoele

Elongation of blastocyst
(14–16 days—cow)
(9 days—sow)

ovary and causes **luteolysis,** or breakdown of the CL. The blastocyst of the species, however, produces proteins that block the production and release of $PGF_{2\alpha}$, thereby preventing luteolysis.

The trophoblastic cells of the blastocyst give rise to the various layers of the placenta. The fetal membranes are made up of the amnion, the chorion, the allantois, and the yolk sac (Figure 8–8). The amnion surrounds and cushions the fetus in

Luteolysis Breakdown or degeneration of the corpus luteum. Occurs at the end of the luteal phase of the estrous cycle if pregnancy is not detected.

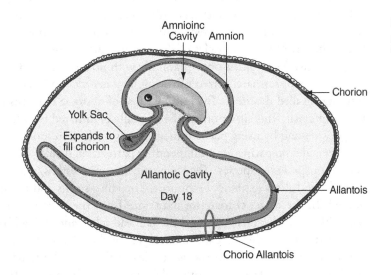

Figure 8–8
Fetus with placenta. (Source: Geisert, 1999.)

Amnioinc
Cavity

Amnion

Chorion

Yolk Sac

Expands to
fill chorion

Allantoic Cavity

Day 18

Allantois

Chorio Allantois

amniotic fluid. In case of severe trauma, this amniotic fluid protects the fetus. The allantochorion, a fusion of the allantois and chorion, is in contact with the endometrium of the uterus. The yolk sac provides nutrients to the developing embryo/fetus. In some species such as birds, the yolk sac is prominent. In others, the yolk sac develops early but degenerates early in the pregnancy. In total, the placenta regulates the exchange of oxygen, nutrients, waste, and in some species, antibodies, between the mother and fetus. The actual connection between the uterus and placenta to facilitate these exchanges varies greatly by species, from a very diffuse connection as in the sow, to very localized connections seen in ruminants.

When more than one fetus is present, the membranes of the multiple fetuses typically fuse together. This is a normal occurrence and has no bearing on development, except in the cow. In cattle, the blood supplies for the multiple membranes fuse as well, allowing hormones to transfer from one fetus to the other. If the twins are of the same sex, development continues normally. However, if the twin combination is a bull and heifer, the male hormones from the bull disrupt the development of the female. For this reason, about 10 out of 11 heifers born as a twin with a bull are sterile owing to incomplete reproductive tracts, a condition called freemartinism. A relatively inexpensive blood test has been developed to determine whether a newborn heifer is normal or a **freemartin**. The incidence of multiple births in beef cattle is relatively low but is about 6% in dairy cattle and has been increasing with higher milk production levels.

As a rule of thumb, approximately two-thirds of fetal growth occurs in the last trimester of the pregnancy. Therefore, energetic demands of the female are greatest during this period and can create special nutritional requirements, which must be met. For example, ewes carrying more than a single fetus are susceptible to a condition called **pregnancy disease** in which the female is not capable of providing, or is not provided, enough nutrients to support the high demand of the fetuses. Likewise, cows and horses must be fed adequately such that energy reserves are appropriate at birthing. If not, the female is faced with high nutrient demands to support lactation without the necessary resources to draw on. Typically, these females are late to return to estrus, and subsequent breeding is delayed.

Parturition

Parturition, the process of giving birth, is the culmination of pregnancy. Parturition is initiated by hormones secreted by the offspring. It is also possible to induce parturition using a cortisol-type drug such as dexamethasone. As the young move up the pelvic cavity and begin to push against the cervix, a neural connection from the cervix to the brain stimulates the release of oxytocin from the posterior pituitary gland. Oxytocin travels to the muscles of the uterus, causing contractions that aid in expelling the fetus. Most births occur naturally with no assistance. However, malpresentations and inappropriately sized offspring may necessitate intervention. Difficulty in birthing is called **dystocia**. The leading cause of dystocia is a fetus that is too large for the birth canal. This situation can be virtually eliminated by selecting for low-birth-weight sires and by using pelvic dimensions as a selection tool in the females.

Females preparing for an impending parturition display behavioral changes that vary from species to species. They generally become restless, may separate from other animals, and show extreme discomfort. The vulva swells and the udder becomes engorged. In the mare, **colostrum** may ooze from the teats in the few days prior to parturition. The ligaments around the tailhead relax, and the tail becomes relaxed.

Birth is preceded by expulsion of part of the allantochorion (referred to as the *waterbag*), which usually breaks as it releases fluid. As the fetus moves through the pelvic cavity, the placenta becomes detached from the uterus. This leads to a loss of

Freemartin Condition in cattle in which a female calf is born as a twin with a bull calf and as a result is infertile.

Pregnancy disease Also referred to as *pregnancy toxemia*. A form of ketosis in females that occurs in late pregnancy because the female cannot eat enough of the feed she is provided or is not provided enough feed. Usually occurs in cases of multiple fetuses; common in sheep.

Dystocia Birthing difficulty.

Colostrum First milk given by the female after birth of the young.

connection for oxygen and nutrients to the fetus. Therefore, it is essential that labor progresses fairly rapidly to ensure that the young has adequate oxygen. In cows, mares, ewes, and does, the position of the fetus is normally front feet first, with the head lying between the two front legs. In pigs, either head- or tail-first presentation is normal.

The last phase of parturition is expulsion of the fetal membranes. This typically happens within a reasonable period of time after birth. In some circumstances, the placenta does not pass, resulting in a condition called *retained placenta*. Retained placenta in cattle used to be removed manually by a veterinarian, and the cow would be treated with antibiotics to prevent infection. However, the current dogma is to allow the placenta to slough off on its own, even up to a week after parturition. In horses, however, a retained placenta results in a serious health problem and should be treated as an emergency.

Following parturition, some species lick their young to clean and invigorate it, as well as to develop an identification bond with it. Others do not clean their young. Most farm animal species are relatively precocious and able to stand within minutes of birth. It is critical for the young to nurse as soon as possible after birth to obtain the antibodies contained in the milk. Colostrum, or first milk, differs from normal milk in that it is higher in protein, vitamin, mineral, and antibody concentrations. The antibodies, which are large protein molecules capable of fighting disease, are passively transferred to the young by being absorbed from the digestive tract. This confers **passive immunity** to the young. However, the gut begins to close to passage by the antibodies soon after birth. Therefore, if the young has not nursed soon after birth, it is incapable of taking advantage of the immunity of its mother. Many producers keep frozen colostrum in the event that a calf, lamb, or foal is born and has not nursed within 2 to 3 hours of birth. The frozen colostrum can be thawed and fed to the young through a tube placed in its stomach. Because the antibodies in the colostrum reflect the immunity of the mother, the more diseases the mother has been exposed to or vaccinated against, the more antibodies the young will gain. Therefore, it is better to collect colostrum from older, rather than young, animals.

Passive immunity Immunity conferred to an animal through preformed antibodies it receives from an outside source.

The period between parturition and the onset of estrous activity is referred to as the **postpartum** period or **postpartum interval**. Management during this period is particularly important in cattle, which must become pregnant again within 80 days after calving to maintain the desired 12-month calving interval. In seasonal breeders, such as sheep and goats, this period has a much lower importance because season (actually, day length) has an overriding suppressive effect on reproduction. The females do not exhibit estrous activity until several months after parturition, regardless of other environmental factors. The postpartum interval is greatly affected by poor nutrition and by the presence and suckling of offspring. In combination, these two factors severely limit the onset of estrus. In swine, the suckling effect is so strong that producers wean the young early to stimulate the onset of estrus in a timely fashion. Beef cattle producers are now experimenting with short-term weaning to stimulate the onset of estrous activity, combined with increased feed intake to decrease the postpartum interval. Dairy cattle producers have a more difficult time managing the postpartum interval because the cows must continue producing high volumes of milk.

Postpartum After parturition.

Postpartum interval Period of time from parturition to first estrus in the female.

ENVIRONMENTAL INFLUENCES ON REPRODUCTION

Many environmental conditions can have profound influences on reproductive function. The nutritional status of an animal greatly affects a female's ability to become pregnant, and it also influences a male's ability to exhibit the **libido** (sexual drive)

Libido Sexual drive.

and necessary sperm production to impregnate females. The nutritional effect can be divided into two categories:

1. Nutritional status: The long-term energy, protein, vitamin, and mineral regimen the animal has been exposed to; often reflected by how much body fat the animal is carrying.
2. Nutritional balance of an animal: The day-to-day consumption of proper nutrients in the proper amounts to support reproduction.

All nutrient groups can affect reproduction in animals; however, the primary nutritional limitation is energy. As a female loses body condition, or fat, her ability to become pregnant is limited. All species have a body condition level below which a female will not conceive. However, obesity can also become a limiting factor in reproductive function. Separation of nutritional status and nutritional balance is important, particularly in breeding females. For example, cows with questionable energy reserves (fat content) may be encouraged to ovulate and exhibit estrus by increasing energy intake for a short period prior to and during the breeding season. This process, called **flushing**, is commonly used in sheep, swine, and goats to increase ovulation rate.

Stress has a significant negative influence on fertility, although the mechanisms are not entirely understood. As increased knowledge of animal behavior is gained, increasing reproductivity by decreasing stress becomes an important concept for producers to adopt. Mixing unfamiliar animals together during the breeding season can present enough stress to decrease the incidence of estrus and reduce conception rates, particularly when combined with other environmental factors.

Many species exhibit a very strong reproductive response to the length of day. This is not limited to the female. In sheep, the weight of the testes in the ram fluctuates throughout the year, being greatest in the fall during the breeding season, and the least in the nonbreeding season. However, the most significant effect of season is on the estrus of females during the breeding season and the lack of estrous cycles during the nonbreeding season. The mare is an example of a long-day seasonal breeder, so named because estrus is observed as days are becoming longer. Sheep, deer, elk, and goats are short-day breeders and onset of estrus is observed in the fall, as days become shorter. The exact mechanisms for seasonality are not known. However, the amount of sunlight present during the day is detected by the brain and transmitted to the pulse generator in the hypothalamus, which turns on the release of GnRH to start the endocrine cascade. Likewise, in the nonbreeding season, the pulse generator is shut down, and the ovary does not receive the gonadotropic support from the anterior pituitary gland for adequate development and maintenance of the follicles. Because seasonal breeders respond to length of light during the day, reproductive function can be manipulated by using artificial light to simulate the changing seasons. Therefore, it is possible to have ewes lambing in the fall, rather than the spring, and have mares foaling in late summer, rather than the spring. In addition, some breeds of season-breeding species are much less affected by day length than are other species. For example, most whiteface breeds of sheep have longer breeding seasons than those of blackface breeds. Also, the closer to the equator one goes, the less seasonal the species become because of a more consistent day length throughout the year. Although cows are not recognized as being seasonal breeders, there is increasing evidence that fertility is higher at certain times of the year.

Species such as the sheep, goat, and mare can be described as being seasonally **polyestrus** because they exhibit more than one estrous cycle during a breeding season. However, some species such as the dog are seasonally **monoestrus** because they exhibit only one estrus during the breeding season.

Flushing Feeding extra feed to stimulate estrus and ovulation rates.

Polyestrus Exhibiting more than one estrous cycle.

Monoestrus Exhibiting only one estrous cycle; for example, the bitch is seasonally monoestrus.

Figure 8–9
USDA-Agricultural Research Service-developed techniques for turkey semen (shown here) have been used to increase populations of endangered species such as the bald eagle and whooping crane. (Photo by Keith Weller. Courtesy USDA-Agricultural Research Service.)

TECHNOLOGY AND REPRODUCTION

Artificial Insemination

Artificial insemination (AI) was one of the first biotechnologies employed in the livestock industry to improve the reproduction and genetics of farm animals. In 1899, Russian scientist E. I. Ivanoff initiated efforts to establish AI as a practical procedure and was the first to develop methods as we know today. The first AI cooperatives were established in 1938 with significant growth of AI industry occurring through the 1940s. Today, inexpensive techniques have been developed, and artificial insemination (AI) is now a common procedure in many species and is used, to some degree, in virtually all species (Figure 8–9). For example, in dairy cattle, approximately 80% of the calves born result from artificial insemination. This procedure allows dairy producers to use semen from proven sires to improve herd genetics. Artificial insemination is used on nearly 100% of the commercially grown turkeys because modern large-breasted turkey males are incapable of mating naturally. Several horse breed associations have recently changed registration rules so producers can take better advantage of this technology.

Successful insemination requires the acquisition of high-quality semen from a male, the detection of estrus in the female, and the ability to deposit the semen properly in the reproductive tract of the female. Semen is usually collected by stimulating the male to ejaculate into an **artificial vagina (AV)**, which has a receptacle to receive the sample (Figure 8–10). Another method of collecting semen in bulls, rams, and boars is to use an electroejaculator. The use of an electroejaculator is often preferred with males who refuse or are incapable of mounting a female naturally because of injury or age. This instrument consists of an electrical prod placed in the rectum of the male. The electrical current stimulates contraction of muscles causing sperm

Artificial vagina (AV)
Device used to collect semen from a male. Following erection, the penis is directed into the artificial vagina and the male ejaculates, capturing the ejaculate in a reservoir of the AV.

Figure 8–10
Photo vof an artificial vagina.

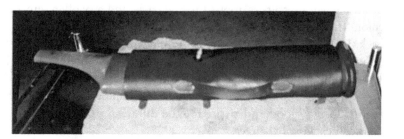

Table 8–2
CHARACTERISTICS OF SEMEN FROM FARM ANIMALS

Characteristics	Cattle	Goats	Horses	Sheep	Swine
Volume of ejaculate (ml)	2–10	.2–2.5	20–300	.5–2.0	150–500
Sperm concentration (10^9/mL)	.3–2.0	1–5	.03–.8	–5	.02–.35
Motile sperm (%)	70	80	70	75	60
Ejaculates/week	4	20	3	20	3
Motile sperm (AI)	10	60	100	120	1,200
Females inseminated/ejaculate (AI)	350	25	60	20	20

Source: Compiled from Bearden and Fuquay, 1997, Cole and Garrett, 1980, and Cupps, 1991.

to be expelled. With either method of collection, the sample is generally extended with a solution that contains proteins and buffers, and frozen in liquid nitrogen (for bulls and rams), or cooled sufficiently to prolong the life of the sperm (for boars and stallions). Frozen semen can be stored indefinitely. In fact, bull semen collected and frozen in the 1950s still retains enough fertile sperm to result in acceptable pregnancy rates. Characteristics of semen from various farm animal species are presented in Table 8–2.

In the late 1980s, a breakthrough in semen-sexing technology led to the development of a flow cytometer capable of differentiating and separating X- and Y-chromosome-bearing sperm in amounts suitable for AI. This technology is based on the ability to accurately differentiate the 2.8–4.2% difference in DNA content between the X and Y chromosome. In 1992, the first sex-selected calf was produced utilizing in vitro fertilization. Further advances in flow cytometry allowed for the first sex-selected calf to be born by means of AI in 1997. In 2003, the commercialization of this technology led to the availability of sexed semen for many different species worldwide.

Detection of estrus is one of the most difficult tasks in successful artificial insemination. Placement of the semen in the reproductive tract of the female must be coordinated with the timing of ovulation of the egg from the follicle on the ovary to ensure that fertilization can occur while the sperm is still alive and in the proper location. Fortunately, many species present specific behavioral activities that are characteristic of estrus. In the cow, a female allows other females, and males, to mount her approximately 12 hours prior to ovulation. Therefore, when a cow is standing to be mounted, she will be ready to be artificially inseminated in approximately 12 hours. The difference in timing between artificial and natural breeding is to accommodate for the placement of the semen. In natural breeding in the cow, semen is deposited in the vagina, and sperm must traverse through the cervix before entering the uterus. In artificial insemination, the sperm is deposited directly into the uterus, thereby bypassing the cervix. Mares have a characteristic "winking" of the vulva following urination when in estrus. Sows exhibit **lordosis**, a steadfast posture when pressure is applied to the back, and a swollen vulva that turns red in color. Therefore, to detect estrus in the sow, all one must do is press heavily on the back. If the sow walks away, she is not in estrus. If the sow not only stands but also refuses to move when pressure is applied, she is likely in estrus. The ewe presents a particular problem. Ewes do not exhibit overt signs of estrus and, therefore, are very difficult to identify for breeding. The female dog sloughs the lining of the uterus, losing blood and tissue for the duration of estrus. Cats typically exhibit marked behavioral changes.

Lordosis Posture assumed by females in estrus such that they resist pressure applied to the back.

Estrous Synchronization

To combat the problem of estrous detection, and to minimize the labor involved in artificial insemination in cattle, drugs have been developed to synchronize estrous cycles in females. In this manner, several females can be given the proper drugs to provide a tight estrous synchrony so animals come into estrus in a narrow window and can be bred at the same time. There are three basic approaches to synchronizing estrus.

One approach is to give injections of prostaglandin $F_{2\alpha}$ ($PGF_{2\alpha}$) during the luteal phase causing regression of the corpus luteum. (Federal law restricts this drug to use by or on the order of a licensed veterinarian, and it is not for human use. Women of childbearing age, asthmatics, and persons with bronchial and other respiratory problems should exercise extreme caution when handling this product.) $PGF_{2\alpha}$ is a hormone naturally produced and released by the uterus when pregnancy is not recognized by the dam. The regression of the CL removes the inhibitory effect of progesterone on the release of LH and FSH allowing the levels of LH and FSH to increase dramatically, permitting the development of the follicles for ovulation. Therefore, females with a functional CL ovulate approximately 72 hours after the injection of $PGF_{2\alpha}$. If there was no functional CL present, the cow may be given another injection approximately 11 days after the first. The second injection is usually effective in evoking estrus.

A second method of estrous synchronization is the use of progesterone, which can be fed orally or administered as a vaginal insert. EAZI-BREED™ CIDR® Cattle Inserts contain 1.38 grams of progesterone in elastic rubber molded over a nylon spine and are administered intravaginally. Melengestrol acetate (MGA), a medicated feed additive (feed additives are limited to use exactly as labeled; use of the product in any fashion other than as labeled is illegal), is a synthetic progestin (progesterone-like in action) used primarily for the suppression of estrus in feedlot heifers. The actions of the progesterone block the release of LH and FSH, thereby interrupting the estrous cycle of the female. Upon removal of the implant, the inhibitory effects of progesterone are removed, and the female exhibits estrus.

Another popular method incorporates the use of GnRH (federal law restricts this drug to use by or on the order of a licensed veterinarian) into the synchronization regime to time not only estrus, but ovulation as well. The use of GnRH is popular with dairy cattle producers.

Embryo Transfer

Embryo transfer (ET) is the process of collecting fertilized embryos from one female (donor) and placing them in another (**recipient**) for further development (Figure 8–11). This technology became available to livestock producers in the 1970s. The value of embryo transfer is that it allows for the production of many more offspring from genetically superior females. ET is similar to, but less extensive than, the increased breeding potential from males using artificial insemination. Although used to some extent in several species, it has been most widely used in the cattle industry. There is less incentive for ET use with swine because they are litter producers and have a much shorter **generation interval**. With sheep and goats, there is less incentive for ET use because it is more difficult to make the procedure cost effective. The following discussion focuses on the cow for that reason.

The process of embryo transfer begins with the superovulation of the female. Superovulation is the process of administering exogenous FSH such that the ovary receives the gonadotropic support so more than the normal number of follicles reach the preovulatory stage. In fact, the FSH prevents follicles that would normally

Embryo transfer The process of transferring fertilized embryos from one female to another female.

Recipients Females used to carry the embryos of a donor animal throughout gestation.

Generation interval The average age of animals within a species when they bear their first offspring.

Figure 8–11

The dairy cow (upper right) is the genetic mother of the 10 calves. She was super-ovulated, and the embryos were recovered from her uterus 1 week after concep-tion. After 3 to 10 hours of culture in vitro, the embryos were transferred to the uteri of the 10 recipient cows (left) for gestation to term. (Photo courtesy of George E. Seidel, Jr., Colorado State University.)

undergo atresia from dying. Therefore, the FSH does not increase the number of eggs being produced, it just keeps the follicles in a productive and developing state, therefore resulting in more ovulating, fertilizable eggs. As the donor cow is being superovulated, the cows being used to receive the embryos—the recipients—receive hormone injections to synchronize their estrous cycles with that of the donor cow. The synchronization of the recipient's estrous cycle with the donor is critical to the success of the procedure. Multiple inseminations of the donor cow are timed so that the majority, if not all, of the eggs will be fertilized.

The embryos stay in the donor cow for about seven days, which is the most viable stage for transfer,and are then flushed out of the oviducts, as they have not yet implanted. The embryos are identified under a microscope and placed, one by one, into a recipient female. If all goes well, the embryo develops into a fetus in the recipient, who produces a calf that carries the genetics of the sire and the donor female. Commercial embryo transfer companies boast greater than 60% pregnancy rates with good-quality embryos. In addition, if more embryos are collected than there are available recipients, it is possible to freeze the embryos indefinitely. The producer thereby has more flexibility in planning calvings, can hold on to frozen embryos to determine the quality of full siblings, and can maximize the use of recipients. Embryo transfer greatly increases the genetic impact that a cow can have on a herd by increasing the number of offspring born each year.

"In Vitro" Fertilization

Although embryo transfer is used extensively across the United States in cattle, it does have disadvantages. For example, ET can only be performed when a cow is open. Therefore, it is necessary to keep a superior cow nonpregnant for long periods to complete the procedure of superovulation, breeding, and flushing of the embryos. Second, some cows do not respond to the hormones as expected. When the ovaries are understimulated, no eggs are produced. When they are overstimulated, too many eggs are often produced and all may be nonfertile.

Recent technology allows the collection of the eggs directly from the ovary, before the follicles have fully developed. These ova are then fertilized **in vitro** and allowed to develop to stages appropriate for placement into recipients. This method has many advantages, including these:

* Collection of ova during pregnancy
* Use of different sires on the ova from each collection
* Frequent collections, as often as weekly

There are some drawbacks to collecting eggs directly from the ovary. The technology is not perfected. In addition, it is relatively expensive and time-consuming. However, in vitro pregnancy rates are approaching the success observed with embryo transfer. Increased pregnancy rates will be expected with advances in the technology and when more people become proficient at the procedure.

In vitro In a test tube or other environment outside the body.

REPRODUCTION IN POULTRY AND BIRDS

Hen

The goal of reproducing young is the same in poultry as in mammalian species. However, the method varies in that the young are not carried inside the body. Rather, the eggs are laid outside the body where they are incubated until the young are ready to emerge (hatch) from the shell. Figure 8–12 shows the reproductive tract of the hen. The discussion focuses on the hen; however, the process is similar for other avian species.

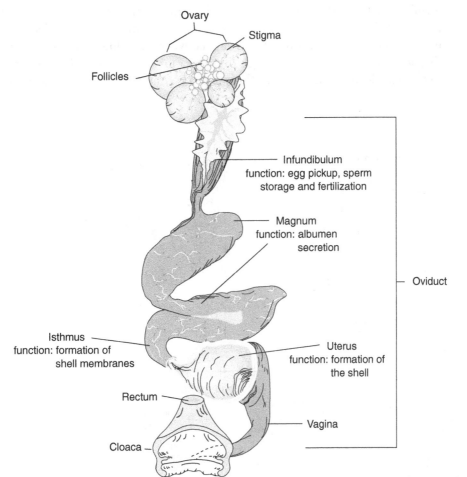

Figure 8–12

Avian reproductive tract. The avian oviduct is adapted into different sections: infundibulum, magnum, isthmus, uterus, and vagina. Although these parts have the same names as parts of the mammalian reproductive tract, their functions are quite different. (Source: Adapted from Geisert, 1999.)

Poultry females (hens) have only one functional ovary, unlike mammals, which have two. Only the left ovary in the hen is functional. When a female chick hatches, approximately 4,000 ova are attached to the ovary, each enclosed in a follicle. The follicle contains the blood vessels that will nourish the egg when it is time for it to mature. The ova begin maturing at sexual maturity. Each mature ovum is successively released from its follicle by rupture of the follicle wall. This release from the follicle is called *ovulation*. The rupture occurs along a line called the *stigma*. The ovum (yolk) moves into the oviduct where the additional parts of the egg are added.

In the oviduct, the egg moves from region to region where very specific steps in egg formation occur (Figure 8–13). The first section of the oviduct, the infundibulum, captures the yolk from the body cavity after ovulation. In the infundibulum, fertilization occurs if sperm are present. Sperm can remain viable for up to several weeks in some species. The total time the yolk spends in the infundibulum is 30 minutes or less. The yolk moves into the second portion of the oviduct, the magnum. The yolk stays in the magnum for 2 to 3 hours, during which time the thick portion of the albumen, or white, of the egg is added. The albumen is deposited around the yolk. In the next portion of the oviduct, the isthmus, the shell membranes are added. During the 1.5 hours that the egg is in the isthmus, it takes up water and mineral salts and the inner and outer membranes of the shell are added. Calcification of the shell occurs in the uterus, or shell gland, which is the next portion of the oviduct. In addition, the remainder of the albumen is added in the uterus. Early in the 18 to 20 hours the egg is in the uterus, it undergoes *plumping*, a process of adding water and minerals to the egg through the previously formed membranes. Once the plumping process is over, the calcification of the shell takes place and shell pigment is added. After the shell formation is complete, the egg moves from the uterus, through the vagina, where the bloom or cuticle is added, through the shell and then through the cloaca for oviposition, which is expulsion to the outside of the hen's body. This process is commonly referred to as laying the

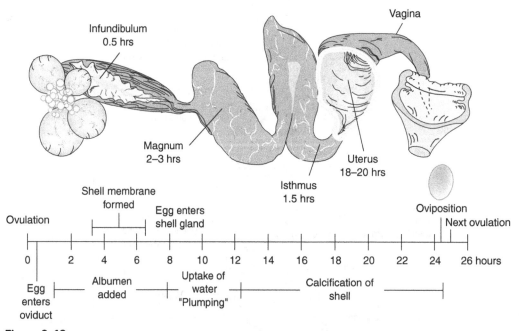

Figure 8–13

Steps in egg production. (Source: Adapted from Geisert, 1999.)

egg. The total time from ovulation to the laying of the egg is slightly more than 24 hours. Approximately 30 minutes after the egg is laid, another ovulation occurs and the process is repeated. Fertile eggs may be incubated by the hen or collected for artificial incubation. In the case of the vast majority of eggs laid by chickens, the eggs are not fertile and are processed as a food source.

Cock

Figure 8–14 shows the reproductive organs in the male bird. Hens lay eggs in the absence of males, and it is not necessary for sperm to be present in the female's reproductive tract for an egg to form. For this reason, no males are found with chickens in commercial laying houses.

However, if reproduction of the species is desired, sperm must be present in the infundibulum during the process of egg formation. As observed for the hen, there are substantial differences in the reproductive tract of male birds as compared to that of mammals. The differences begin with the testes, which are found inside the body cavity rather than outside it. The sperm cells move from the testes into the vas deferens, which leads to the cloaca and terminates in small papillae found in the wall of the cloaca. The male bird has a phallus, but it is rudimentary compared to that of the mammalian species. During copulation, the sperm are transferred from the papillae to the phallus and deposited in the oviduct via the cloaca of the female.

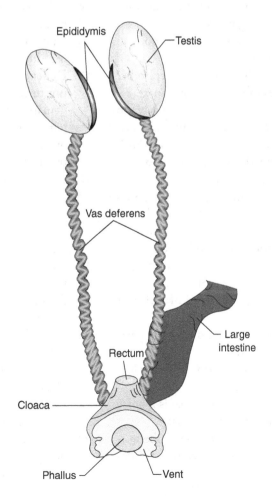

Figure 8–14
Reproductive organs in the male avian. (Source: Adapted from Geisert, 1999.)

SUMMARY AND CONCLUSION

Maintaining reproductive function is central to the success of livestock enterprises that rely on the production of young. The success of reproduction relies on absolute coordination among many systems of the body. Environmental factors may radically influence the expression of reproductive behavior, release of critical hormones, success of implantation of the embryo, and maintenance of pregnancy. Only when environmental factors are most favorable are animals able to express reproductive success fully.

Many tools of modern technology are improving our ability to manage the reproductive process. However, producers must also work diligently to increase the genetic potential for high reproductive function. A conflict can arise for the producer because of the advent of some of the emerging technologies. For example, it is not in the long-term best interest of the producer or the industry to use embryo transfer on a "good" cow that is not capable of maintaining a pregnancy. Likewise, using a stallion with a low sperm count may eventually decrease the fertility of numerous offspring, a defect that may take generations to correct. Opportunities for increasing production through advances in reproductive technology are tremendous. However, producers wishing to pursue this strategy have the responsibility to use it wisely.

STUDY QUESTIONS

1. Why is reproduction so important to the producers of domestic livestock?
2. Describe the interplay among the many factors that affect animal reproductive function.
3. What are gonads? What are their main categories of function? What does the brain have to do with the proper function of the gonads?
4. What is puberty, and what does it have to do with secondary sex characteristics?
5. What does it mean for a hormone to be episodic? What are two examples of episodic hormones?
6. What is the hypothalamus? What does it have to do with reproduction? What is the anterior pituitary? What does it have to do with reproduction?
7. Make a table. Down the side of the table, list each of the hormones that has a function in reproduction of the female. Across the top, make categories for origin, target, and function. Fill in the table.
8. Make a table. Down the side, list each of the hormones that has a function in reproduction of the male. Across the top, make categories for origin, target, and function. Fill in the table.
9. Describe the different types of uteri of different species of animals.
10. List and briefly discuss the functions of the parts of the female reproductive tract.
11. List and briefly discuss the functions of the parts of the male reproductive tract.
12. What is the difference in the type of penis a horse has compared to that of a bull and a boar?
13. Why is it so important for the testicles to be outside the body cavity? Discuss temperature regulation of the testes.
14. What is cryptorchidism, and what are its consequences to fertility?
15. Why would it not be good for a bull to produce a gelatinous fraction in his semen like the boar and stallion do?
16. What can be the consequences of a male animal getting kicked during mating? What is the likely outcome of this? Is there any way to still retain the breeding services of the male, especially a bull?
17. Depending on the species, it is possible for mating to take place as much as 2 to 3 days before ovulation and a pregnancy still ensue. However, a natural service that takes place 2 to 3 days after ovulation will not result in a pregnancy. What is the difference?
18. Describe the role of the CL in pregnancy. Do you think it would be possible for a physical mishap to cause a disruption of the CL and therefore terminate a pregnancy? Can you think of what such a mishap might be?
19. Describe the role of the placenta. What happens to the placenta in multiple births? In what species does this cause a problem? What is the problem and what is it called?
20. Describe the reproductive and environmental interaction that leads to pregnancy disease, especially in sheep.
21. What are the steps in parturition?
22. Describe the value of colostrum to baby animals. Why must it be consumed soon after birth?
23. What is important about the management of the postpartum period in livestock? What are the major factors that affect it?

24. Describe the difference between nutritional status and nutritional balance. What effect does each have on reproduction?

25. What effect does stress have on reproduction in livestock? Do you think this could mean that handling systems for managing open females should be designed with stress reduction in mind?

26. What effect does season of the year have on reproduction? Is this more of an issue with some species than with others? If yes, which species?

27. What is the value of artificial insemination to a breeding program? How is semen collected for use in artificial insemination? How long will it last if properly processed, frozen, and stored? What are the challenges to successful AI?

28. What are some of the signs that various species display during estrus?

29. What is the value of estrous synchronization? Describe the three methods of estrous synchronization discussed in the text.

30. What is the value of embryo transfer? Can it be used on all the common livestock species? On what species is it most commonly practiced? Why?

31. Describe the procedure for embryo transfer in cattle.

32. What are the differences and similarities between embryo transfer and in vitro fertilization?

33. What is the caution that producers must exercise in order to protect the long-term integrity of the genetic pool of livestock if they use technology to enhance reproduction?

REFERENCES

Author's note: This chapter was prepared in part by Dr. T. L. Beckett, California Polytechnic State University, San Luis Obispo, California. For the 5th edition, Dr. Daniel R. Stein, Oklahoma State University, reviewed and contributed new material to this chapter.

Bearden, H. J., and J. W. Fuquay. 1997. *Applied animal reproduction.* 4th ed. Upper Saddle River, NJ: Prentice Hall.

Bearden, H. J., J. W. Fuquay, and S. T. Willard. 2003. *Applied animal reproduction.* 6th ed. Upper Saddle River, NJ: Prentice Hall.

Bone, J. F. 1999. *Animal anatomy and physiology.* 3rd ed. Upper Saddle River, NJ: Prentice Hall.

Cole, H. H., and W. N. Garrett, eds. 1980. *Animal agriculture: The biology, husbandry, and use of domestic animals.* 2nd ed. New York: W. H. Freeman.

Cupps, P. T. 1991. *Reproduction in domestic animals.* 4th ed. San Diego: Academic Press.

Frandson, R. D., and T. L. Spurgeon. 1992. *Anatomy and physiology of farm animals.* 5th ed. Philadelphia: Lea and Febiger.

Geisert, R. D. 1999. *Learning reproduction in farm animals.* A multimedia CD-ROM. Stillwater: Oklahoma State University.

Senger, P. L. 1997. *Pathways to pregnancy and parturition.* Pullman, WA: Current Conceptions, Inc.

Senger, P. L. 2005. *Pathways to pregnancy and parturition.* 2nd revised edition. Pullman, WA: Current Conceptions.

part three
The Animal Industries

9

Beef Cattle

Learning Objectives

After you have studied this chapter, you should be able to:

- Explain the place of beef cattle in U.S. agriculture.
- Discuss the reasons why the United States has such a large beef industry.
- Give a brief history of the cattle industry in the United States.
- Describe the beef industry structure.
- Give an accurate accounting of where the beef industry is physically located in the United States and explain why each region has the portion of the beef industry it does.
- Discuss the role of genetics in the present and future of the beef industry.
- Explain the breeds revolution in the U.S. beef industry, including the outcomes and ultimate implications to the industry.
- Outline the basis of managing beef cattle for reproductive efficiency.
- Describe the feed supply of beef cattle. Explain the purpose of beef cattle in the United States and other countries.
- Discuss common health challenges to beef cattle.
- Outline and discuss nutritional benefits of beef to humans.
- Discuss trends in the beef cattle industry, including factors that will influence the industry in the future.

Key Terms

AI stud
Beef cycle
Breed
Breeding soundness exam
Breeds revolution
British breeds
Composite breed
Estrous cycle
Estrus
Eutrophication
Expected progeny difference (EPD)

Feedlot
Finishing phase
Forage
Grain-fed beef
Heritability
Least-cost ration
Net calf crop
Performance testing
Seed stock
Stocker calf

SCIENTIFIC CLASSIFICATION OF CATTLE

Phylum:	Chordata
Subphylum:	Vertebrata
Class:	Mammalia
Order:	Artiodactyla
Suborder:	Ruminata
Family:	Bovidae
Genus:	*Bos*
Species:	*taurus; indicus*

THE PLACE OF THE BEEF CATTLE INDUSTRY IN U.S. AGRICULTURE

The beef industry is the single largest money-generating commodity in all of agriculture in recent times (Figure 9–1). The gross annual income from beef in the United States has averaged approximately $45 billion in recent years. About half of the value of the cash receipts from U.S. agriculture in any given year is generated from animal agriculture. On average, beef accounts for approximately 39% of animal agriculture's share of total farm cash receipts (Figure 9–2). Another way to look at the importance of beef is to consider that cattle and calves rank in the top five commodities for 40 of the 50 states. Thirteen states

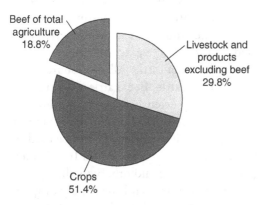

Figure 9–1
Beef farm cash receipts as a percentage of U.S. farm cash receipts, 2000–2009. Source: USDA-NASS, 2011a.

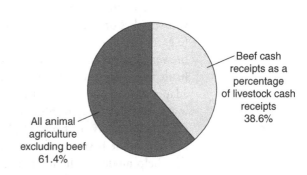

Figure 9–2
Beef yearly farm cash receipts as a percentage of total animal agriculture's cash receipts, 2000–2009. Source: USDA-NASS, 2011a.

record more than $1 billion each in gross income from marketing of cattle each year. An additional 13 states exceed $0.5 billion. There are approximately 740,000 beef cattle operations in the United States. Although we have only 4.5% of the world's population, the United States raises 7% of the world's cattle and produces nearly 19% of the world's beef and veal. By any standard, the beef industry is a major industry in the United States, and the United States is a major beef producer and consumer.

PURPOSE OF THE U.S. BEEF CATTLE INDUSTRY

The purpose of the beef cattle industry in the United States is to make use of resources that would otherwise go to waste, predominantly grass. As a ruminant, beef cattle convert grass that humans cannot use into high-quality food, by-products, and work we can use. This roughage conversion is cattle's chief contribution to human welfare (Figure 9–3). Much of the land of the United States is best suited to grass production. The 48 contiguous states have approximately 1,029 million acres of agricultural land, 57% of which is grazing land. The grazed land includes the vast expanses of dry lands in the American West, additional acreages that are unsuited to cultivation because of topography or some other reason, the swampy lands of

Figure 9–3
The purpose of the beef cattle industry is to make use of resources, predominantly grass, that would otherwise go to waste.
(Photo courtesy of USDA-Natural Resources Conservation Service.)

the coasts, croplands currently used as pasture, forest that is grazed, and the high elevations found in the mountainous regions. In addition to these grazing resources, vast supplies of waste material from the agronomic crops of the nation's agriculture (e.g., cornstalks and wheat straw) and food by-products (e.g., corn cannery waste, brewer's grains, and sugar beet pulp) are also fed to beef cattle. All are resources difficult to use for productive purposes if not for beef cattle. Beef cattle are a rugged, adaptable domestic species that can be managed very extensively to harvest grass at low cost. Thus, they fulfill a unique niche in resource utilization for the benefit of our whole society. In times of plentiful grain production, beef cattle can be used to help make the best use of the abundance from agronomic production. In this way, they help moderate the fluctuations in grain prices that could otherwise disrupt agronomic practices and endanger the agricultural economy and the supply of grain for human consumption. Cattle are actually modest consumers of grain. This modest use of grain increases palatability of the product, improves efficiency, and helps provide for year-round production, thus avoiding great differences in the seasonal availability of beef.

Cattle are used extensively around the world by a wide variety of people for their grass conversion ability. With 1.38 billion head distributed globally, cattle are arguably the most important of all the domestic livestock species.

HISTORICAL PERSPECTIVE

The word *cattle* once meant all domestic species. It is derived from the Latin word *capitale,* meaning "wealth" or "property." Today, the word is used only in relation to *Bovidae.* Cattle were probably domesticated by 6500 B.C.; however, such milestones are hard to determine with certainty. Cattle spread with humans as we populated the globe, and they have had a wider range of uses by more people than any other domestic species.

Figure 9–4 gives a historical look at cattle numbers in the United States. The number of beef cattle in the United States has historically fluctuated in a predictable manner; this fluctuation is described as the **beef cycle**. Because of economic factors and the biological factors unique to beef production, beef cycles have tended to be approximately 5 years of expansion followed by approximately 5 years of reduction. The cycle

Beef cycle Historic fluctuations in beef cattle numbers that occur over roughly 10-year periods.

Figure 9–4
Historic cattle inventory in the United States. Source: USDA-NASS, 2011b.

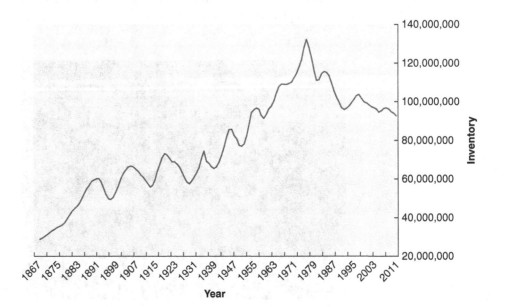

since the mid-1990s has not followed predictable patterns causing many industry leaders to speculate that a fundamental change in beef industry structure may be occurring.

Christopher Columbus was the first cattle producer of the Western Hemisphere. He brought cattle to the West Indies on his second voyage in 1493. Cortez brought cattle to Mexico in 1519. Cattle were distributed across the American West as a part of the Spanish mission culture established at the beginning of the 17th century. Spanish Longhorn cattle were used to stock the missions. In 1609, English settlers brought cattle to New England. These cattle were primarily work animals and milk producers. As the settlement of the continent proceeded, the grasslands became beef-producing areas.

By the middle of the 19th century, beef cattle in the West were being improved with newly imported Shorthorns. After the Civil War, many of the Texas Longhorns were rounded up and shipped east to feed the growing population. As Longhorn blood became increasingly scarce in the cattle population, the Shorthorns failed to meet the rigors of range life and Herefords came to dominate the Western beef industry. This breed transformation was hastened by the devastating winter weather of 1886, which killed much of the Western beef herd. Angus were later crossed on the Herefords resulting in black calves with white faces, which became known as *black baldies*. The black baldy is still very much a part of the beef cattle industry. Having learned the hard way that quality cattle needed better care than previously thought, the Western beef industry underwent a two-decade period when greatly improved husbandry practices strengthened the region's position as a major cattle-producing area. Quality cattle were reared and fattened on grass to meet the growing meat needs of an increasingly prosperous nation.

After World War II, the next major shift in the U.S. cattle industry occurred. Cattle had been fattened for many years as secondary enterprise operations on farms in grain-producing areas. These were small operations with only a few cattle. This situation was destined to change. Technological and industrial innovation led to phenomenal increases in agricultural output. Huge grain surpluses developed in areas of the country so far removed from markets that shipping costs made realizing a profit impossible. Enterprising cattle and grain producers began feeding surplus grain to increasing numbers of cattle. Although grain-fed beef was more expensive, consumers quickly developed a taste for its improved flavor and tenderness. A marketing revolution took place in which chain grocery stores began offering self-service meat counters with a wider variety of meat products readily available. Demand for the new **grain-fed beef** grew. The United States had ample pasture and grasslands available for the production of the feeder calves needed by this industry segment. A new industry segment developed that involved concentrating large numbers of cattle and feeding them grain in a **finishing phase** just prior to slaughter. This industry developed first in California and Arizona in the 1950s, and then in the Plains states of Colorado, Texas, Oklahoma, Kansas, and Nebraska in the early 1960s. Thus was born the beef feedlot industry. During the 1970s, this phase became the driving force in the U.S. beef cattle industry. Major meat processors moved to the feedlot area.

With the development of beef feedlots, the beef industry increased in importance as a money generator in American agriculture. Beef cow numbers first exceeded dairy cow numbers in 1954, advancing the notion of beef as king in U.S. agriculture. The feedlot industry became dissatisfied with the type of cattle available. Small-statured animals with light adult weights fattened well on grass but finished too rapidly on grain and did not grow to the size the industry felt made optimal use of the finishing phase. They also grew slowly. The industry needed cattle that would grow faster to heavier weights and produce less waste fat on grain diets. These needs ushered in an era often referred to as the **breeds revolution** in the beef industry.

Grain-fed beef Meat from cattle that have undergone a significant grain feeding.

Finishing phase Grain-feeding period just prior to slaughter.

Breeds revolution Period of great expansion in numbers of breeds of beef cattle.

Figure 9–5
An example of the kind of genetics brought into the United States during the beef breeds revolution.

Beginning in 1965 with the opening of the first major quarantine station for cattle in Canada, previously prohibited cattle breeds could be legally imported into North America. Over the next 25 years, the number of beef breeds in the United States increased to more than 70 (Figure 9–5). Cattle feeding changed to accommodate the type of cattle the new breeds provided. The rest of the country increasingly shifted its production style and techniques to accommodate the demand of the consumer for grain-fed beef. Total cattle numbers peaked in 1975 with 132 million head (cattle, calves, beef, and dairy). The current smaller cattle herd produces more meat in a year than was produced when cattle numbers were at their peak. Genetics, nutrition, management, and shifts in the demands of packers have all contributed to this phenomenon.

Average annual per capita supplies (and consumption) of beef declined from 1976 until the early 1990s. Part of the decrease was a result of closer trimming (less fat content) of retail cuts. However, quality issues also plagued the industry with the change in the cattle, and consumers ate less beef and larger amounts of lower-cost alternatives, predominantly poultry. Since the early 1990s, the yearly fluctuations in per capita beef consumption appear to have been related primarily to availability. However, consumers also respond to reasons that do not pertain to price when making their purchases, including convenience, product safety, and health and nutritional information. All of these factors present challenges to the beef industry.

STRUCTURE OF THE BEEF INDUSTRY

Number, size, location, and major activity of the firms in an industry are the elements we refer to as the "structure of the industry." Beef cattle production differs from most other kinds of livestock production because it is divided into more phases. Animals change ownership when moving from one phase to the next. Thus, the same animal tends to be owned by several people. There is also a distinct regionality to the beef industry—different regions of the country tend to specialize in a single, or perhaps two, phases. The major segments of the beef cattle industry are seed stock producers, commercial cow-calf producers, yearling or stocker operators, and feedlot finishing operations. Figure 9–6 shows the general flow of animals through the various structure segments.

Seed stock Brood stock intended for future production.

Seed stock production (Figure 9–7) is the only segment that doesn't produce animals whose primary use is for meat consumption. The vast majority of animals produced from this segment will ultimately be slaughtered for food, but only for salvage

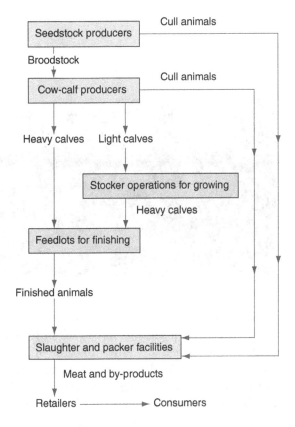

Figure 9–6
The movement of animals through the segments of the beef industry.

value at the end of a productive life. The primary goal of this industry segment is to produce breeding stock. Stock may be purebred or bred in controlled crossbreeding programs that produce the parent generation of cattle for commercial calf producers. The product of greatest demand from this segment is bulls. Usually these bulls are purebred animals whose pedigrees and qualitative information, such as **expected progeny difference (EPDs)**, make selections easier and the results of the matings more predictable. Commercial cow-calf producers rely on these breeders for quality sires to pasture mate with their herds of commercial cows. The very best purebred seed stock producers will produce cattle of high enough quality that they can sell seed stock to other purebred breeders and help improve the overall quality of the breed.

Expected progeny difference (EPD) A prediction of the difference between the performance of an individual's progeny compared to all contemporaries for the progeny.

Figure 9–7
Beef seed stock producers provide breeding stock to other seed stock producers and cow-calf producers.
(Photo courtesy of American Hereford Association. Used with permission.)

Figure 9-8

Commercial cow-calf producers produce calves that are sold at weaning to feedlots or stocker operators. (Photo by Charlie Rahm. Courtesy USDA-Natural Resources Conservation Service.)

AI stud Company that markets semen from high-quality males.

If the quality is high enough, they will also be able to market semen and embryos. These elite breeders are also able to sell or lease bulls to **AI** (artificial insemination) **studs** that sell semen to a variety of cattle breeders. Cull females may be marketed as commercial cows. A substandard female by purebred standards can usually be a superior commercial cow as long as she is not suffering soundness problems. Controlled crossbreeding programs produce quality crossbred heifers to sell to cow-calf producers to become brood stock. These programs allow cow-calf producers to produce controlled crossbred offspring without having to own herds of different breeds.

Commercial cow-calf producers (Figure 9–8) represent the first phase of producing animals whose primary use is for the table. The product from this segment is 6- to 10-month-old, 300- to 700-lb calves that are usually sold at weaning to either a feedlot or a **stocker calf** operator. Cow-calf producers generally produce crossbred calves bred for slaughter.

Stocker calf Weaned calf being grown prior to placement in a feedlot for finishing.

Their goals are to produce the heaviest calves possible with the least cost. Margins are tight for these producers, and costs must be kept to a minimum. Cow-calf operations typically plan to have a spring or fall calving season. This is usually dictated by the type of feed available in the given region and other costs associated with rearing calves. Most of the U.S. cow herd calves in the spring. When the calves are ready to wean, the cow-calf producer has several options. The easiest option is simply to market the calves and begin making plans for next year's calf crop. Heavier calves with rapid growth potential are usually placed directly in a feedlot. Lighter calves are often purchased by a stocker operator to grow before they are placed in the feedlot. However, if the producer has feed or access to feed, he or she may choose to wean the calves and grow them to heavier weights before selling them. In this way, a cow-calf operator may also be a stocker operator.

Yearling or stocker operators (Figure 9–9) are in the business of growing calves to heavier weights on low-priced forage before the calves enter the feedlot. They typically purchase calves from cow-calf producers and grow them during a specific season and then ship them to feedlots. The improved potential for growth exhibited in today's cattle and the increased milk production of the cows have resulted in heavier calves at weaning. These heavier calves can go directly into the feedlot at weaning. However, in years of high grain prices, a percentage of these calves are also grazed in the stocker phase. Common feed resources on which this phase depends are regional, but include small-grain pasture, cool-season grasses, summer pastures, summer range, crop residues, standing prairie hay, hay, or silage.

Figure 9–9

Yearling or stocker operators grow calves to heavier weights on low-priced forage. The calves then enter the feedlot. (Photo by Bob Nichols. Courtesy USDA-Natural Resources Conservation Service.)

The feedlot phase (Figure 9–10) is referred to as the *finishing phase* of the industry. Here 600- to 850-lb cattle are finished to market weight and condition. Both steers and heifers are fed in feedlots. Feedlots vary in size and location. Small operations may feed only a few head on the farm of origin as a way for farmers to diversify and use their equipment and labor when they can't otherwise use them in the farming operation. Others are huge operations that concentrate tens or even hundreds of thousands of cattle in highly specialized operations that do nothing but finish cattle for slaughter. The vast majority of the slaughter cattle in the United States are fed on grain in feedlots before they are sent to slaughter. The amount of time an animal spends in the feedlot varies but is typically 120–150 days. Modern feedlot management is highly dependent on automation and mechanization to keep the cattle appropriately cared for. Cattle have such different genetic potential that it makes predicting an exact weight at slaughter difficult. They may range from 900–1,400 lbs at slaughter. Cattle feedlots and meatpacking plants that process the carcasses have both increased in size and decreased in number during the past 35 years. This is a trend that is expected to continue.

It is important to know that the beef industry has these parts. However, do not conclude that the various phases are cleanly and neatly divided. Nothing could be

Figure 9–10

In feedlots, cattle are finished for market. (Photo by Jeff Vanuga. Courtesy USDA-Natural Resources Conservation Service.)

further from the truth. There is a growing trend for owners to retain the ownership of their cattle through one or more phases. A Tennessee cow-calf operator may stock his or her own calves after weaning and then ship them to a custom feedlot that will feed those cattle for a fee. A Texas Panhandle feedlot operator may purchase calves from Mississippi cow-calf producers and put them in a custom grazing program on an Oklahoma wheat pasture and then select from them when he chooses to fill the pens of his feedlot. Such arrangements are destined to become more commonplace in the beef industry.

GEOGRAPHIC LOCATION OF BEEF CATTLE IN THE UNITED STATES

Cow-calf production is found in every state. Figure 9–11 shows the actual numbers of beef and dairy cows found in the individual states. Dairy cows are included in the figure because they also contribute to beef supplies. The area in which beef cows are found generally depends on the availability of low-cost forage and roughage. In the Plains states, western states, and southwestern states, vast acreages of land grow grass but don't receive enough rainfall to grow crops. The use of beef cows on this land offers the best opportunity for the land to be productive. In Figure 9–11, notice the large number of cows in Montana, South Dakota, Nebraska, Kansas, Texas, and Oklahoma as examples. Other areas with significant cow populations can be found in the grain-producing areas of the country. A significant by-product of grain production is crop residues, including low-quality residues such as straw and cornstalks. The mature beef cow uses these low-quality, high-volume feeds better than any

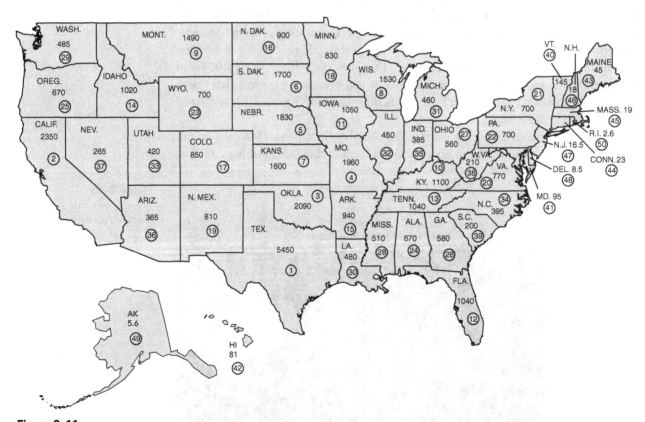

Figure 9–11

Distribution of total U.S. cows and heifers that have calved (beef and dairy) × 1,000 (circled numbers indicate state rank).

Source: USDA-NASS, 2011b.

Table 9–1
CATTLE MARKETED (× 1,000) ANNUALLY IN THE UNITED STATES, 2010

State	Marketed: 1,000 + Capacity Feed Lot
Texas	5,500
Kansas	5,083
Nebraska	4,810
Colorado	2,000
Iowa	976
California	612
Oklahoma	777
South Dakota	501
Idaho	435
Arizona	294
Washington	402
Other states	686
United States	22,078

Source: USDA-NASS, 2011b.

other livestock species. Much of the crop residue is found in the Corn Belt, which contributes to large number of cows in Iowa and Missouri, for example. The southeastern region of the country has an abundance of grazing land and the advantages of mild winters and good rainfall that produce significant year-round grazing conditions. Year-round grazing is possible in the coastal areas (look at Florida) owing to mild climate, and also in the upper East South Central states of Tennessee and Kentucky because of their use of cool-season grasses.

Stocker operations are drawn to the same things that cow-calf operations are, except that the quality of the feed needs to be better. Thus, the same areas that have cows and calves tend to have stocker calves also. The winter **small-grain** areas like Kansas, Texas, and Oklahoma generally import calves for winter grazing from areas that have lower-quality winter feed, such as Grain Belt states. The higher-quality winter wheat is an ideal feed for the stocker calf. Because there is so much wheat pasture, calves from other regions are shipped in to take advantage of the abundance. Many go to such states as Kansas to graze summer ranges before being sent to the feed yard.

Small grains Grains such as oats, wheat, and barley.

The finishing of cattle in feedlots is one of the most important segments of the cattle industry. Cattle are finished for slaughter in many regions. As previously mentioned, secondary enterprise operations on farms in grain-producing areas have long fed cattle. However, the majority of cattle feeding is done in relatively few states (Table 9–1). Texas, Kansas, Nebraska, and Colorado account for nearly 80% of the finished cattle in the United States.

Figure 9–12 shows all cattle and calves by state to give an overall picture of where beef animals are located.

GENETICS AND BREEDING PROGRAMS

The fundamentals of genetics and breeding are discussed in Chapters 6 and 7. See those chapters for more detailed information on these topics. In simplest terms, two factors affect all of the economic traits in cattle. These factors are the environment to which the animal is exposed (feeding, climate, and so on) and the genetics of the

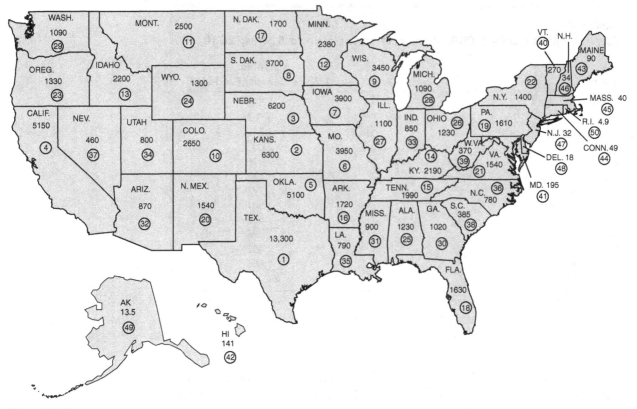

Figure 9–12
All cattle and calves × 1,000 for 2011 (circled numbers indicate state rank).
Source: Based on USDA-NASS, 2011b.

Heritability A measure of the amount of phenotypic variation that is due to additive gene effects.

animal. **Heritability** is the difference in individuals that is related to genetic makeup. Obviously, this is the portion of the difference that can be passed on to the next generation. The pace of progress made in a herd to improve the genetic potential of the offspring depends on how heritable the trait is. Table 9–2 shows heritability estimates of some economically important traits in beef cattle. It is easy to see why selection helps in making faster progress for some traits than others.

Table 9–2
HERITABILITY ESTIMATES OF SOME ECONOMICALLY IMPORTANT TRAITS IN BEEF CATTLE

Trait	Approximate Heritability
Calving interval	0.10
Birth weight	0.40
Weaning weight	0.30
Cow maternal ability	0.40
Feedlot gain	0.45
Efficiency of gain	0.40
Carcass traits:	
Carcass grade	0.30
Ribeye area	0.70
Tenderness	0.60

Source: Agricultural Information Bulletin No. 286 USDA, A.R.S.

For those traits in which genetic progress can be made, a wide range of tools is available. Such practices as **performance testing,** sire summaries, and EPDs if purebred seed stock is used are examples of means by which the selection and breeding program of a herd can be enhanced. It is especially important to use all genetic tools available in selecting for the more lowly heritable traits. Again, seed stock producers and commercial cow-calf producers vary tremendously in the tools they select and the degree to which they use the tools of choice.

For most commercial producers of meat animals, some system of crossbreeding could benefit the bottom line of the operation. Along with other advantages, cows produced by good systematic crossbreeding programs have longer productive lives, healthier calves, and better calving rates. Their calves have greater survivability, and they grow faster and to heavier weights. For a period after the breeds revolution, the nation's cow herd was more mixed up than it was crossbred. The effective use of crossbreeding programs requires that a crossbreeding scheme be implemented and then followed. Figure 9–13 shows an example of one of several effective crossbreeding schemes for beef cattle. A caution: Crossbreeding is not a substitute for the other elements of herd management such as disease control, parasite control, and nutrition. However, it costs as much to deworm, feed, and vaccinate a genetically inferior brood cow as it does to perform those same functions for a genetically superior cow. The superior genetic program will produce better returns on the other costs.

Performance testing
Evaluating an individual in terms of performance such as weight gain or milk production.

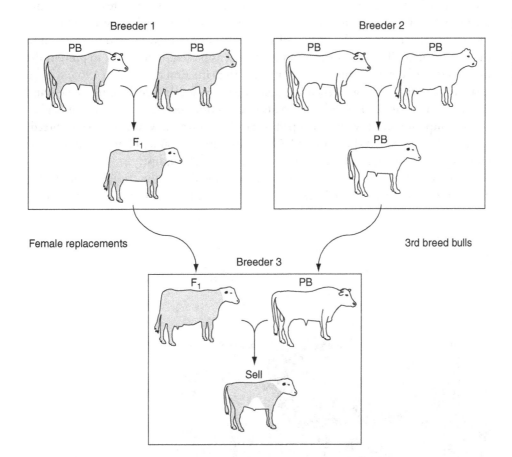

Figure 9–13
Terminal crossbreeding system. (Source: Northcutt and Buchanan, 1992. Used with permission.)

The cattle from Breeder 1 are termed F_1 hybrids and are the product of the mating of a purebred bull and a purebred cow from different breeds. Breeder 2 is producing purebreds of a 3rd breed. Breeder 3 is producing a calf that is 1/4 breed 1, 1/4 breed 2, and 1/2 breed 3. Those calves are all fed for slaughter, hence the term terminal cross.

Breeds

Breed Animals that have been selected for certain characteristics and that breed true for those characteristics.

Breeds, by definition, are animals that have been selected for a more uniform set of characteristics than their species shows as a whole. Survival of domestic species has depended on the animals becoming adapted to a specific set of conditions imposed by natural and human-made environments. Because humans occupy vastly different environments on this planet and impose a wide variety of conditions on livestock within those environments, it is only logical that many different genetic combinations of our favorite domestic livestock would be developed. Depending on the reference used, somewhere between 300 and 1,000 breeds and strains of cattle are recognized in the world. Most of those are found in small numbers in isolated geographic regions. Only a few of that number have ever been widely established in other areas of the world. Cattle are not indigenous to North America, so it is clear that our cattle must represent breeds that have managed to travel and become established beyond the confines of where they were developed.

Breed history was fairly simple in the United States until 1965. First there was the Texas Longhorn, which descended from the Spanish Longhorns (Figure 9–14). Shorthorns were imported to upgrade the Longhorns and effectively supplanted them. Herefords were imported and used to increase the hardiness of the Shorthorns and effectively supplanted them. Angus were then used to crossbreed with the Herefords and both became established as breeds in their own right. Brahman cattle were brought in for their superior abilities to handle heat, disease, and insects in certain parts of the country. Some **composite breeds**, Brangus and Santa Gertrudis, were developed. The Charolais entered the country just prior to World War II, and a few others found their way here in small numbers. All told, approximately 20 breeds were available until the mid-1960s. It is probable that additional breeds would have found their way into the United States if not for strict import restrictions placed on livestock to prevent the introduction of diseases from other countries. This situation changed in 1965, when a quarantine station was established by Canada on Grosse Isle. Cattle of many new and exotic breeds from Europe and other parts of the world soon began arriving and additional composite breeds were developed. From 1965 until now, the number of breeds has been in flux. Somewhere around 70 are currently available. However, only a few currently have any significant influence on the U.S. cattle industry.

Composite breed A breed developed from two or more previously established breeds.

The development of the feedlot industry was the major stimulus for the increase in the number of breeds because it needed cattle that could be fed to heavier

Figure 9–14

The Texas Longhorn, which descended from the Spanish Longhorn, dominated the beef cattle industry in the United States until after the Civil War. (Photo Courtesy Dr. J. Robert Kropp.)

Figure 9–15
Cows and calves in the same herd showing diverse genetics. Cattle that are more mixed up than crossbred contribute to quality and management problems. (Photo by Gary Kramer. Courtesy USDA-Natural Resources Conservation Service.)

weights and produce a leaner carcass. However, the cow-calf sector also recognized the need to increase its profits and faster-growing cattle were one of the elements needed to accomplish this. Using new and different breeds was an easy and effective way to do so.

Several dozen breeds were ultimately imported, although many proved of marginal value. However, the importations did change the face of the American cattle industry. The **British breeds** made room for the breeds that proved useful, and all established breeds were selected to be more like the imports in some traits. Unfortunately, fixing one problem invariably creates others. The U.S. cow herd became quite diverse in its genetic base (Figure 9–15). This caused problems with beef quality in the retail outlet and problems of management. In response to these concerns, the genetic base of the U.S. cow herd is again narrowing. Figure 9–16 shows that the Angus breed greatly exceeds all other breeds in annual registrations. Because they dominate the

British breeds Hereford, Angus, and Shorthorn. Breeds that originated in England.

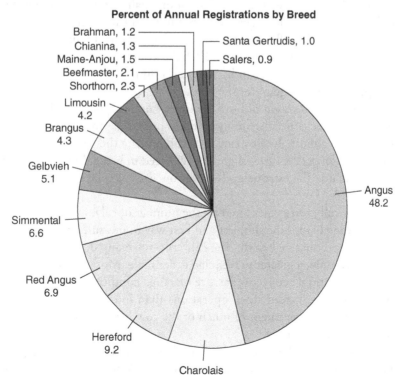

Percent of Annual Registrations by Breed

Brahman, 1.2
Chianina, 1.3
Maine-Anjou, 1.5
Beefmaster, 2.1
Shorthorn, 2.3
Limousin 4.2
Brangus 4.3
Gelbvieh 5.1
Simmental 6.6
Red Angus 6.9
Hereford 9.2
Charolais 9.5
Santa Gertrudis, 1.0
Salers, 0.9
Angus 48.2

Figure 9–16
Percent of total registrations by breed. Almost as many Angus cattle are registered yearly as the next 14 breeds combined.

seed stock sector, Angus are providing the highest number of bulls for the commercial cow-calf producers. Commercial producers are returning to high percentage and straight-bred British breeds, with some British crossbreeding, for their commercial cow herds. The calves will probably be more consistent but at the expense of the benefits of crossbreeding.

REPRODUCTIVE MANAGEMENT IN BEEF CATTLE

Chapter 8 is devoted to reproductive physiology. Refer to it for the fundamentals of male and female reproductive anatomy, physiology, and function.

The goal of breeding herds of beef cattle is to produce and raise one calf per year from each of the reproductively mature females in the herd. Attainment of such a goal would give an operation a 100% calf crop for the year. The calf must be born within a 12-month interval and at the right time of the year to make best use of the operation's resources (mostly feed) and generate the most profit for the herd. This is a deceptively easy thing to say and not nearly so easy to accomplish. Each cow in the herd must be safely in calf within 85 days of calving, or the 12-month calving interval cannot be maintained. Good management skills are essential if this goal is to be reached. The cow must recover from calving, start her heat cycle, and conceive. She must do all of this while raising the calf she just bore. There is tremendous overlap among good reproductive management, good animal health management, and good nutritional management. Nothing on a functional animal unit occurs in a vacuum. Everything is related. Unfortunately, many producers underestimate the magnitude of the problems with the reproductive efficiency of their herds.

Replacement heifers must be managed so they can be mated to calve at 2 years of age. To do this, they must be mated at 15 months of age and need to be at least 65% of their adult weight at the time of breeding. Some producers find this difficult to do and opt for calving heifers first at 30–36 months. This works if the producer is running both spring and fall calving herds. If not, then the only alternative is to calve them at 3 years of age. The loss of a calf or a half calf in these systems makes it more difficult for the female to generate a profit in her early lifetime.

Diseases that affect reproductive efficiency directly include brucellosis (Bang's disease), vibriosis, leptospirosis, IBR/BVD complex, and trichomoniasis. Control of these and other diseases can be easily accomplished by developing and following a complete health program for the herd.

The normal season of birth for cattle can be year-round. However, for management purposes, either the spring or fall is preferred. The decision as to which season to choose is almost always made to accommodate the best use of the available feeds. The gestation period varies slightly from breed to breed, but 280–283 days is considered standard. The **estrous cycle** for a cow is 19–21 days and the duration of **estrus** (heat) is 13–17 hours.

Estrous cycle Time from one estrus to the next.

Estrus Period of sexual receptivity in the female.

Net calf crop as measured by the number of calves weaned/number of cows in the breeding herd is the simplest and best way to measure the effectiveness of a herd's mating/reproductive health. The calf crop for many of the nation's herds is about 90%. Certainly, a greater percentage is desirable. Most of the nation's beef cows are mated by natural service in pasture or range conditions. Artificial insemination is more common in seed stock operations than in commercial herds. The extensive nature of the management of much of the cow herd is a detriment to using artificial insemination effectively.

Bulls should be evaluated before they are used in a breeding program for both genetic contribution and breeding soundness. A bull with poor genetics can do tremendous damage to the profitability of an operation. A bull produces many more calves in a lifetime than does any single cow. In addition, his presence in a herd can last for generations through replacement females chosen from his daughters. Thus, bull genetic evaluation is more important than that of any single female for the herd and should receive emphasis by the breeder. It is also important to know whether or not the bull is fertile and can produce offspring. The major factors that should be evaluated in a **breeding soundness exam** include testicular development, physical ability to breed females, semen quality, and libido. Breeding soundness should be determined sufficiently before the breeding season to allow replacement bulls to be acquired if need be.

Good records are essential to managing reproductive issues in the cow herd. Because management practices and standards vary with conditions across the country, cattle breeders are encouraged to contact their local extension service or the state extension specialists for help in setting up a record keeping program for their area.

NUTRITION IN BEEF CATTLE

Chapters 3, 4, and 5 give detailed information relating to nutrition, feeds, and feeding and are recommended for more detailed information than is provided in this section.

Cattle are ruminants. The feeding niche they occupy is as forage and roughage users. Thus, the nutrition and feeding of cattle in most of the production stages revolves around maximizing the use of forages.

The breeding herd is always managed to take maximum benefit from forages and roughages. If supplemental feeds are fed, they are used to further extend the use of forage by supplementing missing nutrients. Mineral supplements are needed in all parts of the country. Individual mineral deficiencies specific to a region occur in the various geographic areas of the country and don't usually cause a problem in other areas. Salt, calcium, and phosphorus are likely to be needed everywhere. Protein supplementation is often needed when such feeds as late-season pasture, low-quality hays, crop by-products, and other waste by-products are used. Energy may be supplemented during droughts, the winter months, as a boost for 2-year-old heifers too thin to rebreed, for replacement heifers, and at other critical times in the production cycle.

Stocker cattle feeding programs also depend on forages. However, the plane of nutrition has to be higher for stocker cattle than for brood cows. More energy and/or protein supplementation is usually necessary, and higher quality forages are needed. Although stocker programs vary somewhat from region to region, they generally fall into two categories. The first is to full-feed calves a complete mixed ration based on forage as a low-cost energy source. The second is to graze calves or give them harvested forages free choice and then feed additional energy and protein as a mixed supplement. Table 9–3 gives examples of supplements for grazing stocker calves. The stocker phase is also an excellent time to take advantage of the growth-enhancing implants and feed additives.

Feedlots are specialized finishing operations. High-quality feeds are needed to bring cattle to a suitable slaughter end point in as little time as possible. Several general types of feed programs are typically used during the 120–150 days a finishing beef animal is usually in a feedlot. A receiving ration is fed for the first week or two after arrival at the feedlot. Hay and a supplement may be fed or perhaps a complete milled ration. As quickly as possible, cattle are switched to high-energy feeds designed to optimize gain and, therefore, returns on the finishing cattle. Any number of rations are used with success. Table 9–4 shows examples of some typical beef cattle finishing diets. Most such rations are formulated with the use of **least-cost ration** formulation programs.

Breeding soundness exam Examination to determine the physical capacity of an individual to breed.

Least-cost ration A ration formulated to meet the animal's nutritional needs at the lowest cost from the feeds available.

Table 9–3
SUPPLEMENT FOR STOCKER CALVES GRAZING LATE SUMMER OR EARLY FALL PASTURES

	Composition, % (As Fed Basis)	
Ingredient	Oklahoma Gold	Oklahoma SuperGold
Cottonseed	86.0	17.0
Soybean meal	—	15.0
Wheat middlings	7.0	56.0
Molasses (pellet binder)	4.0	4.0
Vitamin and mineral premix	3.0	3.0
Feed additive	Variable	Variable
Crude protein, % as fed	38.0	25.0
Feeding rate, lbs per day	1.0	2.5

Table 9–4
TYPICAL BEEF CATTLE FINISHING DIETS

	Diet Type		
Ingredient	Processed Corn and Dry Roughage	Whole Corn and Corn Silage (% of DM)	Dry-Rolled Corn and Wet Corn Gluten Feed
Roughages			
Sudan grass hay	4	—	8
Alfalfa hay	6	—	—
Corn silage	—	10	—
Grain and grain by-products			
Steam-flaked corn	74.5	—	—
Dry-rolled corn	—	—	52.5
Whole shelled corn	—	71	—
Wet corn gluten feed	—	—	35
Liquid feeds			
Molasses	5	—	—
Condensed distiller solubles	—	4	—
Fat	3	—	—
Supplement[1]	7.5	15	4.5

[1]Supplement supplies calcium and phosphorus sources, urea and/or natural protein, trace minerals, vitamins, and feed additives.
Source: Galyean and Duff, 1998, p. 276. Used with permission.

Seed stock producers use similar feeds and feeding programs to the other segments. However, they are more likely to use higher levels of supplementation at all phases of production than the other sectors. Animals that demonstrate their full genetic potential fetch higher prices. Because seed stock producers command a higher price for their product than the other sectors, they can afford to invest more in feed.

CHALLENGES TO BEEF CATTLE HEALTH

Maintaining a healthy herd is one goal of a productive beef cattle operation. Preventing health problems is often easier and more successful than treating unhealthy or diseased animals. Essential components of a herd health program include adequate nutrition and good sanitation, as well as solid vaccination and parasite control regimens. Despite diligent efforts at preventing diseases, health problems will still occur. Some of the most common diseases that may seriously affect the health of beef cattle are described below. Many other diseases affect beef cattle but are beyond the scope of this book.

Calf diarrhea (scours)

Diarrhea, or scours, is common in newborn calves. If severe, it can quickly result in life-threatening dehydration. Less severe but more persistent diarrhea can lead to emaciation because of malnutrition. Calf diarrhea has several causes, including infectious agents (such as bacteria, viruses, and protozoa), as well as noninfectious causes. Often, more than one of these causes is present at the same time. Infectious agents can be shed in the feces of sick calves and lead to infection and disease in other calves within the herd. Calves that don't receive adequate colostrum, or first milk, from their dams are more susceptible to developing diarrhea that is often severe enough to be fatal. Prevention is the best approach to decrease losses associated with calf diarrhea. Isolating sick calves, practicing good hygiene, providing quality nutrition to calves and their dams and ensuring calves receive adequate colostrum are good steps to help prevent calf scours.

Bovine respiratory disease

Respiratory disease, commonly resulting in pneumonia (inflammation of the lung) (Figure 9–17) is one of the most economically important diseases affecting the cattle industry. The causes of bovine respiratory disease are numerous and include infectious agents (viruses and bacteria) as well as environmental factors, such as weaning, transport, crowding, and poor ventilation. The factors that cause respiratory illness interact in complex ways, which makes bovine pneumonia difficult to prevent or control. Cattle of many ages and stages of life are at risk for respiratory disease. Beef cattle are at highest risk for developing pneumonia when they are introduced into feedlots in which large numbers of calves are mixed together. Being from a variety of backgrounds and locations, some of these animals may carry respiratory infections, whereas others are more susceptible to diseases. Add in the stress of transport and crowding, and the stage is set for shipping fever pneumonia, which can affect up to 35% of cattle in some feedlot situations. Prevention is the key to decreasing losses. This includes measures to decrease environmental stressors and to limit the mixing

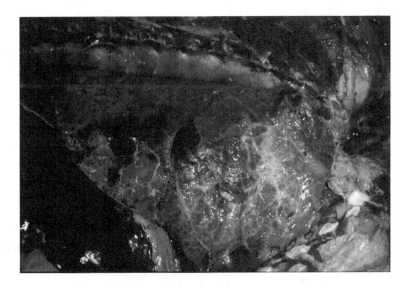

Figure 9–17
Shown is the lung of a feedlot steer that died of severe shipping fever pneumonia. Notice that almost all of the lung is severely damaged and rendered nonfunctional due to overwhelming bacterial infection. (Photo by Dr. Rodger Panciera. Courtesy Oklahoma Center for Veterinary Health Services.)

in the feedlot of new animals or animals from a variety of sources with established groups of cattle. Diligent monitoring for signs of illness among feedlot calves is essential for the early detection and treatment of pneumonia, which gives the best chance of successful therapy.

Blackleg

Blackleg is a noncontagious bacterial disease that is nearly 100% fatal in affected cattle, but it is readily prevented by vaccination with *Clostridium chauvoei* bacterin, which protects against the causative bacteria. Beef cattle between 6 months and 2 years, especially fast-growing calves on a high plane of nutrition, are the ones most commonly affected by blackleg. In many cases, cattle are found dead without any previous indication of illness. In other instances, sudden, severe lameness (due to muscle damage) may be followed by death within 12 to 24 hours. Treatment of affected cattle is rarely successful; however, in cases of a herd outbreak, vaccination accompanied by antibiotic treatment may help decrease losses within the herd. Vaccination of calves between 2 and 6 months of age is an inexpensive and effective means of prevention.

Bloat

Bloat is the excessive accumulation of gas within the rumen. If bloat is not relieved and becomes severe, it can cause compression of the heart and lungs and lead to the death of the animal. Bloat can be separated into two distinct categories: frothy bloat and free-gas bloat. Frothy bloat occurs most commonly in animals grazing lush pastures and is partially due to the rapid digestion of protein-rich feedstuffs that leads to foam formation in the rumen. Gas trapped in this foam cannot be eructated or belched as normal free gas would be. Rapid, severe distension of the rumen may result. Frothy bloat may also occur in feedlot cattle eating a high-grain diet. Free-gas bloat may be due to the consumption of high-concentrate feed by animals not adapted to eating a grain-rich diet. This leads to a rapid drop in rumen pH and decreased rumen motility, which interferes with normal gas eructation and causes rumen distension. Blockage of the esophagus can also cause free-gas bloat by interfering with the normal belching of gas from the rumen. The risk of bloat can be decreased by acclimating cattle to high-concentrate diets and including adequate roughage, allowing limited access to lush spring pastures, and possibly providing feed supplements that help control foam formation.

BEEF'S NUTRITIONAL BENEFITS TO HUMANS

A 3-oz serving of 90% lean, broiled, ground beef (hamburger) is 184 calories and provides the following proportion of the recommended daily dietary allowance for a 19- to 30-year-old man:

Protein	40%
Phosphorus	25%
Iron	29%
Riboflavin	11%
B_{12}	91%
Niacin	30%

Beef is a nutrient-dense food, which means it has lots of nutrition per calorie. Beef is a healthful food that can be part of the diet of virtually all people.

TRENDS AND FACTORS INFLUENCING THE BEEF INDUSTRY

The following sections represent some of the challenges, changes, and areas of focus for the cattle industry. The beef cattle industry's future may well depend on how well it meets these challenges.

Consumption

For many years, Americans ate more beef than any other protein source. However, annual per capita beef consumption in the United States declined from 1976 (one year after peak cattle numbers) until 1993 (Figure 9–18), while pork consumption stayed fairly stable and chicken and total poultry increased. Beef consumption remained stable from the early 1990s until the mid-2000s, when it again began to trend downward. Factors that influence demand for beef include:

* continued quality problems (taste and tenderness)
* gender and age (older people eat less beef and young men eat more beef than young women do). The population of the United States is aging.
* changes in the racial/ethnic mix of the population (different groups favor different proteins)
* concerns over food safety (beef products have been the subject of several high-profile product recalls)
* health concerns (calories, fat, and cholesterol)
* the relatively lower availability of convenient beef products (fresh products dominate the U.S. beef market, but consumers are increasingly buying convenient products)
* price and availability of beef (beef is expensive relative to other proteins—especially chicken)
* where you live (consumers in the Midwest eat more beef than consumers from other regions, and rural consumers eat more beef than those in urban and suburban areas)

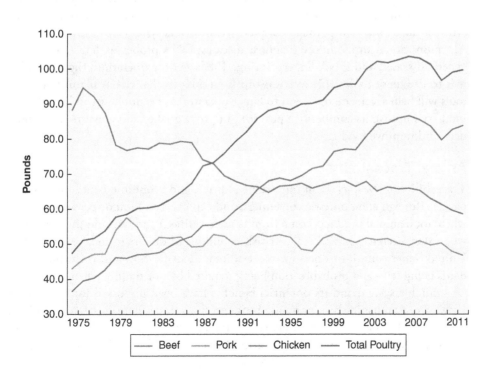

Figure 9–18

Beef per capita consumption compared to pork, chicken, and total poultry. Pounds retail weight.

Source: USDA-ERS, 2011b.

- gender (young men eat the most beef)
- income (low-income consumers eat more beef than middle- and high-income consumers)
- low-income consumers eat more ground beef
- middle-income consumers eat more stew beef
- high-income households eat more steak

Clearly, the beef industry must consider multiple factors if it is to protect its market share.

Exports/Globalization

The export market for beef looks bright for the long term. Exports have been increasing substantially since the early 1980s. The United States has been a net exporter of beef since 1992 on a value basis. Trade agreements, burgeoning human populations, and developing national economies are creating very favorable prospects for many agricultural exports from the United States. At this printing, approximately 10% of U.S. beef production is being exported. Although normal economic cycles, sporadic consumer concerns, trade disputes, and disease-related trade restrictions will surely affect year-to-year purchases, the overall trend is positive for the near future. However, this also brings about increased reliance on exports. All of this is also part of an increased influence of global companies in the industry.

Technology

Beef producers have not historically been progressive users of available technology. However, cost competitiveness will increasingly give the edge to those who adopt and appropriately use the ever-increasing array of products and technological innovations. There has been a relative explosion of technology-based tools made available in recent years: beef management phone applications, lower-cost sexed semen, designer embryos produced by recombinant DNA technology and multiplied through cloning, marker assisted selection, an expanded arsenal of drugs, growth enhancers and vaccines, radio frequency identification tags, computerized feed bunks, expanded use of video imaging and ultrasound to evaluate breeding stock, and many other tools. Other technologies are becoming more commonly used, such as embryo transfer and artificial insemination, perhaps coupled with estrous synchronization (fixed-time AI), monoclonal antibodies to diagnose diseases, DNA probes to detect and predict genetic diseases, and DNA fingerprinting. The larger the operation, the more likely it is to use these tools. This relationship is circular in that the availability of these tools will help accelerate the trend to larger operations. Technology can help the beef industry improve its competitive position, improve quality and consistency of products, and improve food safety.

Animal Traceability

Traceability of livestock is an important political and economic issue. Increasingly, packers, foreign and domestic consumers, and exporters and importers want to know where food animal products come from (source verified) and how old the animal was when slaughtered (age verified). At risk is billions of dollars in meat exports if the United States cannot or does not meet animal identification and traceability standards being set—and probably soon being required by our trading partners.

Such a system and its potential benefits have been discussed for many years. However, establishing a nationwide program for animal identification and disease traceability has been difficult. Between 2004 and 2010, the USDA tried to implement the National Animal Identification System (NAIS) as a voluntary program.

The perceived intrusion of NAIS as well as the equipment cost and labor involved in tagging animals proved to be problematic. The voluntary and unpopular NAIS program was discontinued and will be replaced by a new animal disease traceability framework. Regulations for identifying and tracking livestock are expected to be implemented by 2013. This new program for tracing animal disease is designed to be a flexible one, in which each state or tribal nation will define the details of animal identification so as to minimize the burden for producers but still meet a national standard. Visit www.usda.gov/traceability for current information about the animal disease traceability framework.

Food Safety

The food supply in the United States is arguably the safest in the world. Meat, specifically, is closely monitored by the government prior to purchase. Even so, safety of the food supply is a front burner issue with the consuming public. Examples of issues of concern to the public are feed additives and growth promotants, antibiotic use, and foodborne pathogens. The beef industry must contend with both safety of beef and the consumer's *perception* of safety. Foodborne illnesses are especially volatile and emotional issues with consumers. Beef is an extremely safe food. However, events in the news easily shape public perception. A relatively small number of unfortunate incidents have produced a general negative perception. Although a perfectly safe food supply is unachievable, all segments of the beef industry are working to reduce risks to consumers. All phases of the industry must do their part, or all phases of the industry will suffer the consequences. Products must be as safe as possible.

Many elements of the National Cattleman's Beef Association's Beef Quality Assurance program are designed to help producers ensure that domestic and international beef consumers enjoy ready access to a safe, wholesome, and healthy beef supply. Those guidelines can be accessed at http://www.bqa.org/.

Bovine Spongiform Encephalopathy (BSE)   BSE, commonly referred to as "mad cow disease," is a fatal disease in cattle first diagnosed in Great Britain in 1986. In March 1996, it was announced that a new variant of Creutzfeldt–Jakob disease (vCJD) in humans might be linked to BSE and humans were contracting the disease from the infected animals. The disease is a degenerative disease of the central nervous system for which there is no cure. Ultimately, the disease was confirmed in several countries, but it is believed that almost all victims contracted the disease while living or visiting Great Britain. The cost of BSE to the affected countries (Great Britain has been affected the most) includes inestimable emotional distress, loss of consumer confidence, billions of dollars in lost revenues and lost animals, and the deaths of more than 170 people. Because it appears that the minimum incubation time of vCJD is 7 years with as much as 25 years possible, the loss in human life is certain to rise. The good news is that reported cases in both cattle and humans have been steadily declining. Only 3 human cases were reported in 2010.

In December 2003, the USDA announced that a dairy cow in Washington state had tested positive for BSE. The cow had been imported from Canada. In June 2004, an enhanced BSE testing program was implemented by USDA. As of press time for this text, three total animals have tested positive for BSE in the United States. The most recent case, in Alabama in 2006, was determined to have been caused by a rare genetic abnormality.

The beef industry was affected by the discovery of a BSE-infected animal on U.S. soil. Although U.S. consumers reacted with little more than short-term concerns, export markets were damaged and there are now costs to the industry that were not there before. Consumer surveys indicate that the potential of BSE to affect beef

Figure 9–19
Finding low-cost and effective methods of dealing with waste from feedlots is an industry priority. (Photo courtesy of USDA.)

consumption dramatically is very real. It is not yet time to relegate this concern to history, but it is no longer the front-burner issue that it once was.

Environmental Concerns

The effect of agriculture (agronomy and animal) on the environment is a growing public concern. The animal industries are visible industries and considered major polluters. Manure and wastewater from concentrated animal feeding operations (CAFOs) have the potential to contribute pollutants such as nitrogen and phosphorus, organic matter, sediments, pathogens, heavy metals, hormones, antibiotics, and ammonia to the environment (Figure 9–19). Excess nutrients in water (i.e., nitrogen and phosphorus) can result in or contribute to low levels of dissolved oxygen (anoxia), **eutrophication**, toxic algal blooms and fish kills. Pathogens in manure can also create a food safety concern if manure is applied directly to crops at inappropriate times. In addition, pathogens of animal origin have been responsible for some shellfish bed closures. Nitrogen in the form of nitrate can contaminate drinking water supplies drawn from groundwater. Additional concerns over dust, climate change, greenhouse gases, carbon footprint, and more are gaining attention. Look for new and improved technologies to mitigate environmental problems associated with agriculture. These include new strategies and methods of reducing the loss of nutrients in manure to the environment. New feeding strategies are needed to reduce nutrient excretions, emissions, and odor from manure. Alternate uses for manure that add to profitability instead of subtracting from it are needed. Moreover, many agricultural practices are in place to enhance stewardship of the land and other natural resources. Healthy land produces healthy livestock (Figure 9–20).

Current environmental laws, regulations, policies, and guidance regarding CAFOs can be found at http://www.epa.gov/agriculture/anafolaw.html. Tougher waste disposal laws are inevitable and will add costs to production. Everyone involved understands that the air, soil, and water supply must be protected.

Organic and Natural Production

Partly in response to growing concerns over the environmental footprint of agriculture, some consumers are seeking products that they perceive come from more ecologically friendly and sustainable production systems. Many consumers are willing to pay a premium for organic or **natural** meat from animals produced free of antibiotics, growth enhancers, and feed additives, believing them healthier

Eutrophication Promotion of excess growth of one organism to the disadvantage of other organisms in the ecosystem.

Natural As defined by USDA, "a product containing no artificial ingredient or added color and is only minimally processed. Minimal processing means that the product was processed in a manner that does not fundamentally alter the product. The label must include a statement explaining the meaning of the term natural (such as 'no artificial ingredients; minimally processed')."

Figure 9–20
Cattle on a rotational grazing system in Rio Arriba County, New Mexico. Such systems optimize production while protecting and improving the land for future generations. (Photo by Jeff Vanuga. Courtesy of USDA-Natural Resources Conservation Service.)

to consume, better tasting, and lower in calories and fat. In large measure, this is what has made organic farming one of the fastest growing segments of U.S. agriculture. The term *natural* has proliferated in product naming and marketing. A good deal of niche marketing has already developed around such products and more products are expected. In response, over 2 million acres of rangeland and pastureland have been certified for organic livestock production by livestock producers, with more expected. The number of U.S. Certified Organic beef animals was approximately 64,000 in 2008 but has been steadily increasing. In addition, there is also a resurging interest in grass-fed beef. All of these options represent a way for the industry to practice product differentiation and gain market share in specific markets.

Biofuel Production

The rapid increase in U.S. domestic biofuels production, part of a national initiative to decrease dependence on imported oil by increasing the availability of cleaner, domestic alternatives to imported oil and gas, is affecting the animal industries because corn is the preferred grain in making fuel-grade ethanol and a preferred feed source for livestock feeding. Corn prices have increased substantially in response to new ethanol-plant demand. More acreage is being planted to produce corn, which has caused a reduction in the production of soybeans, sorghum, and other feed crops commonly used for cattle feeding. Grain prices and availability will always affect the amount of grain fed to livestock. Some of this may be mitigated by the increased availability of by-products from the biofuel production (distiller's grain). Nevertheless, overall reduction in animal production is predicted.

Many factors will ultimately influence just how much ethanol is produced and the overall effect on agriculture and its component industries. Useful feed-grade by-products are available from ethanol production. A bushel of corn produces 2.8 gallons of ethanol and 17–18 lbs of distillers' grains. Generally, by-product feeds are best used if they can be fed close to the point of production. This could cause more cattle to be fed in the ethanol-producing regions of the country, which is most likely to be centered in the Corn Belt, and fewer cattle to be fed in the western states. Alternative feed sources and decreased grain use are possible responses. For example, cattle can be kept on forage to heavier weights before being placed in feedlots. The price of crude oil is also a major factor in how many ethanol plants are built and how much ethanol is ultimately produced.

Industry Structure

Industry Consolidation   The number of U.S. beef cattle operations has been declining for decades. There are now less than ¾ million operations. This trend seems destined to continue. The remaining operations will continue to get bigger. This is true of all phases of the industry. The greatest concentration has occurred so far with feedlots and beef packers. However, cow herds are also slowly increasing in size. The seed stock sector is consolidating, which means fewer providers of genetic material. This follows the overall trend in agriculture. Bigger operations can make better use of machinery, equipment, and management because they can more easily achieve economy of scale. Even so, part-time operators, people who are retired, people looking to diversify, and hobbyists will probably always play a role in the cow-calf segment and serve to keep herd size smaller than it might otherwise be.

Industry Integration   One potential, highly probable, and desirable solution to many of the challenges to the beef industry is the increase in the amount of communication, cooperation, and coordination among beef industry segments. Terms like *alliance*, *vertical cooperation*, and *vertical coordination* describe these kinds of industry structures. These are variations of, and alternatives to, vertical integration. All are expanding further into the beef industry. Alliances of many types are being forged in this historically segmented industry, both horizontally and vertically. What remains to be seen is which ones work, how far the restructuring will go, and what effects the consumer and producer will observe.

ADDITIONAL TRENDS AND CONCERNS

Other factors and trends affecting the beef industry include:

- The farm/ranch population is aging, and there is a lack of desire on the part of much of the next generation to enter the industry. With this is coming a transfer of wealth and land. A prime competitor for land suited to grazing is for recreational use. As that land is sold, much of the value is transferred out of agriculture. Many are concerned about how this will affect the beef cattle industry.
- Increasing fuel and freight costs and their effect on production efficiency, operational expenses, and overall profitability.
- Increasing capital requirements to participate in the industry.
- Consumers increased reliance on emotion rather than science and facts for their buying decisions.
- Availability and a quality of workforce is far from assured.
- Decreased cow herd/supply, both in the United States and globally, is becoming a concern.

SUMMARY AND CONCLUSION

Beef cattle make use of resources that would otherwise go to waste. They convert grass into products and work that humans can use. The United States is a major beef producer and consumer. The gross annual income from beef in the United States is approximately $45 billion. Beef cattle production differs from most other kinds of livestock production because it is divided into several distinct phases, and cattle are generally owned by different people in each phase. There is also a distinct regionality to the beef industry. There is a growing trend for owners to retain the ownership of their cattle through one or more phases. Such arrangements are probably destined to become more commonplace in the beef industry as it reorganizes to remain competitive. The beef cattle industry is in a state of change. The beef cattle industry's future will depend on how well it meets current and future challenges.

Facts about Beef Cattle	
Birth weight:	Varies with breed and sex; 50–120 lbs
Mature weight:	Varies with breed, sex, and condition; male 1,400–3,000 lbs; female 900–1,800 lbs
Slaughter weight:	1,000–1,500 lbs
Weaning age:	5–8 months
Breeding age:	14–19 months (female)
Normal season of birth:	Year-round, spring and fall seasons preferred
Gestation:	280–283 days
Estrous cycle:	19–21 days
Duration of estrus (heat):	13–17 hours
Calving interval (months):	12 desirable
Normal calf crop:	90%
Names of various sex classes:	Calf, heifer, cow, bull, steer
Weight at weaning:	400–800 lbs
Type of digestive system:	Ruminant

STUDY QUESTIONS

1. Cattle and calves account for what percentage of the total cash receipts of animal agriculture? Describe the magnitude of this industry in other ways.

2. What is the purpose of the beef cattle industry in the United States? Describe it in terms of feed and use of resources.

3. How does the beef cycle describe cattle numbers in the United States?

4. When were the first cattle brought into the Western Hemisphere? Who brought them and what part of the continent were they on? Who was responsible for multiplying cattle across the American West?

5. How did surplus grain production after World War II lead to the modern practice of feedlot finishing beef animals?

6. How does the structure of the beef industry differ from that of other animal industries? What are the major segments of the beef cattle industry?

7. Why are cattle located where they are in the United States? Why do different regions specialize in different segments?

8. Approximately how many total head of cattle are there in the United States?

9. What are some of the tools available to help cattle producers make sound decisions about the genetics they use?

10. What influence did the development of the feedlot segment of the beef cattle industry have on beef breed availability?

11. What are the five most important breeds of beef cattle?

12. Briefly describe management for maximal reproductive efficiency.

13. Select one of the disease concerns discussed in the chapter and condense the discussion to four main points.

14. Briefly discuss nutrition in beef cattle for each class of animal.

15. What are some important nutrients that a 3-oz serving of cooked beef provides? What does "nutrient dense" mean?

16. What has been happening to the market share of beef compared to pork and chicken? What are the major factors affecting beef consumption?

17. What role will exports likely play in beef production in the future?

18. What role will technology play for the cattle industry in the future?

19. Why is it important to develop a system of animal traceability in the United States?

20. What are the food safety issues that concern people about beef?

21. Give a brief chronology of the BSE outbreak and its effects on the U.S. beef cattle industry.

22. How will environmental concern affect the cattle industry in the future?

23. What opportunities do you think the beef industry has to develop for natural and organic products for the market? Why?

24. Do you think the positives of biofuels outweigh the negatives? Why?

25. In the future, cattle operations will continue to grow larger. Why is this so?

26. Briefly discuss how and why vertical integration will affect the beef industry in the future.

REFERENCES

For the 5th edition, Melanie A. Breshears, DVM, PhD, Diplomate ACVP, assistant professor of veterinary pathobiology, Center for Veterinary Health Sciences, Oklahoma State University, contributed material to this chapter.

Ensminger, M. E. 1987. *Beef cattle science.* 6th ed. Danville, IL: Interstate.

Ensminger, M. E. 1991. *Animal science.* 9th ed. Danville, IL: Interstate.

FAO. 2011. *FAOSTAT statistics database: Agricultural production and production indices data.* http://apps.fao.org/.

Galyean, M. L., and G. C. Duff. 1998. Feeding growing-finishing beef cattle. In *Livestock feeds and feeding,* 4th ed., R. O. Kellems and D. C. Church, eds. Upper Saddle River, NJ: Prentice Hall.

Gill, D. R. 1992. Nutrition, health and management on newly arrived stressed stocker cattle. In *Oklahoma beef cattle manual,* 3rd ed. Stillwater, OK: Agricultural Experiment Station, Oklahoma State University.

Hibberd, C. A., K. Lusby, and D. Gill. 1992. Mechanics of formulating stocker cattle rations and supplements. In *Oklahoma beef cattle manual.* 3rd ed. Stillwater, OK: Agricultural Experiment Station, Oklahoma State University.

Johnson, M. Z., D. R. Stein, D. S. Buchanan, and S. Northcutt. 2008. Beef cattle breeding. In *Oklahoma beef cattle manual.* 6th ed. Stillwater, OK: Oklahoma State University.

Lalman, D., and D. Doye, eds. 2008. *Beef cattle manual.* 6th ed. Stillwater, OK: Agricultural Experiment Station, Oklahoma State University.

National Cattlemen's Beef Association. 2011. *Cattle and beef industry statistics.* http://www.beef.org.

NRC. 2000. *Nutrient requirements of beef cattle.* 7th ed. Washington, DC: National Academy Press.

Taylor, R. E. 1984. *Beef production and the beef industry: A beef producer's perspective.* Minneapolis, MN: Burgess.

Taylor, R. E., and T. G. Field, 2007. *Beef production and management decisions.* 5th ed. Upper Saddle River, NJ: Prentice Hall.

U.S. Department of Agriculture, Agricultural Research Service. 2010. USDA National Nutrient Database for Standard Reference, Release 23. Nutrient Data Laboratory Home Page, http://www.ars.usda.gov/nutrientdata

USDA-ERS. 2005. *Factors affecting U.S. beef consumption.* Accessed online May 2011. http://www.ers.usda.gov/publications/ldp/Oct05/ldpm13502/ldpm13502.pdf

USDA-NASS. 2011. *Quick stats: Agricultural statistics data base.* Accessed online June 2011. http://www.nass.usda.gov/QuickStats/.

Ward, Clement E. 2004. *Pork, beef, and poultry industry coordination.* Stillwater, OK: Oklahoma Cooperative Extension Service, AGEC-552.

Wileman, B. W., D. U. Thomson, C. D. Reinhardt, and D. G. Renter. 2009. *Analysis of modern technologies commonly used in beef cattle production: Conventional beef production versus nonconventional production meta-analysis.* Journal of Animal Science 87:3418–3426.

10
Dairy Cattle

Key Terms

Babcock Cream Test
Bovine somatotropin (BST)
Condensed milk
Diversified farm
Embryo transfer
Genetic markers
Gomer bull

Herd health
Mastitis
Milk
Pasteurization
Posilac
Silo
Somatic cell count

SCIENTIFIC CLASSIFICATION OF CATTLE

Phylum: Chordata
Subphylum: Vertebrata
Class: Mammalia
Order: Artiodactyla
Suborder: Ruminata
Family: Bovidae
Genus: *Bos*
Species: *taurus; indicus*

THE PLACE OF THE DAIRY CATTLE INDUSTRY IN U.S. AGRICULTURE

Dairy products provide nearly 11% of all yearly cash receipts from agriculture (Figure 10–1). This ranks dairy as third in animal industries behind beef and combined poultry and eggs. The annual cash receipts from dairy products in the United States is approximately $26 billion. Dairy products generally account for approximately 22% of animal agriculture's share of annual farm cash receipts (Figure 10–2). Dairy products rank in the top five commodities for 38 of the 50 states. Nine states exceed $1 billion in yearly cash receipts from farm **milk** sales to milk-processing plants and dealers. An additional six states exceed $0.5 billion. The United States produces approximately 15% of the world's cow's milk. Dairy cattle also produce beef (20–25% of U.S. total) from cull dairy cows and Holstein calves that are fed in commercial feedlots (Figure 10–3). Most veal comes from dairy

Learning Objectives

After you have studied this chapter, you should be able to:

- Explain the place of dairy cattle in U.S. agriculture.
- Explain the reasons for the size of the U.S. dairy industry.
- Give a brief history of the dairy industry in the United States.
- Describe the structure of the U.S. dairy industry.
- Give an accurate accounting of where the dairy industry is located geographically in the United States.
- Give a brief synopsis of DHIA and its functions.
- Identify and place in context the role of genetics in the dairy industry.
- Describe the general basis of managing dairy cattle for reproductive efficiency.
- Describe the feed supply of dairy cattle and explain how it affects dairy management.
- Describe the goals of a dairy herd health program and some common diseases that affect dairy cows.
- Discuss bovine somatotropin and its use in the dairy industry.
- Explain the nutritional benefits of milk to humans.
- Discuss trends in the dairy industry including factors that will influence the industry in the future.

Milk The normal secretion of the mammary glands of female mammals.

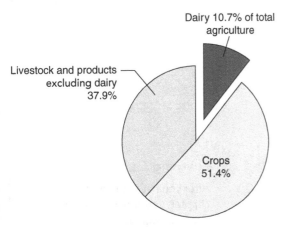

Dairy 10.7% of total agriculture

Livestock and products excluding dairy 37.9%

Crops 51.4%

Figure 10–1

Dairy products farm cash receipts as a percentage of total U.S. farm cash receipts, 2000–2009. Source: USDA-NASS, 2011b

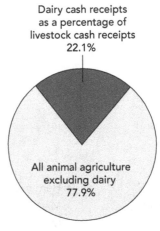

Dairy cash receipts as a percentage of livestock cash receipts 22.1%

All animal agriculture excluding dairy 77.9%

Figure 10–2

Dairy products yearly farm cash receipts as a percentage of total animal agriculture's cash receipts, 2000–2009. Source: USDA-NASS, 2011b.

Figure 10–3

In addition to milk, 20–25% of the beef consumed in the United States each year comes from cull dairy cows and dairy steers, like the animals shown, which are finished for beef.

calves fed all-milk diets and slaughtered when weighing a few hundred pounds. By any standards, the dairy industry is a major industry in the United States, and the United States is a major dairy product producer and consumer.

PURPOSE OF THE DAIRY CATTLE INDUSTRY IN THE UNITED STATES

The purpose of the dairy industry is to make use of resources that humans cannot use and to produce food that humans can use. As ruminants, most of the feed energy consumed by dairy cows is from forages. This forage conversion is their chief contribution to human welfare (Figure 10–4). In addition to forage, vast supplies of waste material from the agronomic crops of the nation's agriculture (e.g., cottonseed) and food by-products (e.g., soybean meal, bakery by-products, distiller's grains, and citrus pulp) are fed to dairy cattle. Table 10–1 compares relative percentages of feed nutrients converted to edible products by livestock species. The dairy cow's conversion of feed to food is the most efficient of all the domestic animals.

Figure 10–4
The purpose of the dairy industry in the United States is to make use of forage and convert it to milk. They also efficiently use leftovers from agronomic crops, such as cottonseed, and food by-products, such as bakery by-products, distiller's grains, and citrus pulp. (Photo by Tim McCabe USDA Natural Resources Conservation Service.)

Dairy cows have traditionally provided a means for farmers to add value to homegrown feeds. Farm-produced grain could provide more profit if fed to a cow and the milk sold than if the grain was sold. Dairying also provides a way for farmers to distribute labor needs across seasons in diversified operations. Fewer cows can be milked during the planting and growing season for crops, which allows time for the farmer to attend to the land. When the harvest is over, more cows can be milked to use available labor. In this way, dairy cattle help us maximize the use of available resources to the benefit of the whole society. In times of plentiful grain production, dairy cattle can be used to help us make best use of the abundance from agronomic production. In this way, they help to moderate the fluctuations in grain prices that could otherwise disrupt agronomic practices and endanger the agricultural economy and the supply of grain for human consumption.

Although cattle are milked around the world, most are multipurpose cows that produce milk, as well as meat and labor. Historically, only developed economies such as the United States have had a specialized dairy industry. This is changing. Modern dairies are becoming much more common around the world.

Table 10–1
RELATIVE PERCENTAGES OF FEED NUTRIENTS CONVERTED TO EDIBLE PRODUCTS BY ANIMAL SPECIES

Animal Product	Gross Energy Conversion (%)	Protein Gross Edible Conversion (%)
Milk	20–25	30–40
Chicken (broiler)	15–20	20–30
Eggs	15–25	30–40
Pork	15–20	10–15
Beef	4–5	5–8

Source: Voelker, 1978 and Smil, 2005.

HISTORICAL PERSPECTIVE

Until 1850 or so, the history of dairy cattle in the United States varied little from that of beef cattle because there were no specialized dairy breeds in the United States. The cows that were milked were simply the same animals used for all other purposes. Milk production was usually for the producer's own use or for local sale.

After the Civil War, the commercial milk-processing industry began developing and the dairy industry began evolving in earnest. The first cheese factory had actually been established in Oneida, New York, in 1851. However, several developments led to a rapid expansion of the fledgling industry. Gail Borden patented **condensed milk** in 1856 and established a condensery in 1857 in Burrville, Connecticut. The new product occupied less space and provided a use for surplus milk. Mechanical refrigeration was developed in 1861, which allowed for greater flexibility in shipping and storing fresh milk. In 1864, Louis Pasteur discovered the microbiological fundamentals that would lead to the process of **pasteurization**. Commercial pasteurizing machines were available in 1895. By the 1860s, there were specialty dairy centers near the larger Atlantic Coast cities. Cows that would support the industry were needed. Significant numbers of cows of various dairy breeds were imported, and between 1868 and 1880, breed associations were formed.

The refrigerated rail car was invented in 1871, which allowed shipment of products over greater distances. **Silos** were invented in 1875 at the University of Illinois, which allowed dairy farmers to store high-quality feed for the winter and gave dairying its year-round dimension. The cream separator was developed in 1878 by Dr. Gustav De Lavel. *Hoard's Dairyman* was first published in 1885, and by 1889 was recognized as the most important dairy journal in the country. Dr. S. M. Babcock introduced the test for milk fat (butterfat) that would bear his name, the **Babcock Cream Test**, in 1890. This test provided a basis for the pricing of milk. Testing for tuberculosis began in 1890, resulting in this widespread cattle disease being all but eradicated. The fledgling industry got its first university curriculum when the University of Wisconsin established a dairy program in 1891. The first testing and recordkeeping association was formed on August 12, 1905, in Newaygo County, Michigan. Many similar organizations were formed and, in 1927, the Dairy Herd Improvement Association was instituted by the American Dairy Science Association with a rules committee for milk production testing. The first milking machines were assembled in 1903 and were soon manufactured by D. H. Burrell Company in Little Falls, New York. Milk was soon sold in glass bottles. Paper milk cartons were introduced in 1950, followed by plastic milk containers in 1964.

Tank trucks were first used to transport milk in 1914. In the 1930s, bulk tank handling of milk on the farm began in California. Homogenized milk made its debut in 1919. Vitamin D fortification began in 1932. Artificial insemination began in dairy cattle in 1936 and was commercially available in 1939. After World War II, artificial insemination techniques caused the genetic improvement of dairy cows to take a giant leap. Antibiotics for animal use were developed in the 1940s and 1950s, which allowed for more efficient treatment of bacterial diseases in cattle.

During the early 1950s, the industry began restructuring. Operations got larger, which allowed for economies of scale. Milk production reached its peak in 1964 at 127 billion pounds. The all-time high number of dairy cows was reached in 1945 at 27.8 million. Numbers of cows and producers have been declining ever since. Production per cow has been increasing. Technological innovation and consumer demands are creating a very dynamic environment within the industry.

Condensed milk Milk with water removed and sugar added.

Pasteurization Controlled heating to destroy microorganisms.

Silo Structure in which silage is made and stored.

Babcock Cream Test Test for determining the fat content in milk.

STRUCTURE AND GEOGRAPHIC LOCATION OF THE DAIRY INDUSTRY

Dairying is among the least concentrated of all the major farm enterprises in the United States, with dairy cows found in every state in the union. In large part, this is because of the perishable nature of milk and the costs of shipping it over long distances. Thus, dairy cows tend to be found near the human population. Figure 10–5 gives a full break-out of milk cows by state and region. Among the 10 largest milk-producing states are the 6 most-populated states. An exception to this is Wisconsin, which has many more cows and produces much more milk than its population needs. However, Wisconsin has long had a strong milk manufacturing industry. Idaho is another state whose milk-producing rank (top 5) is quite different from its human population rank, at 39th. However, it ships much of its production to the West Coast states.

The dairy industry restructuring has consistently trended toward fewer operations (Figure 10–6) that have increasingly more cows per operation. As a result, in excess of 60% of the U.S. milk supply is produced in herds of 500 or more cows (Figure 10–7) and that percentage increases yearly. In addition, the activities of the dairy have been changing. They have become more specialized and more likely to be the sole farm activity. Dairy herds were traditionally self-contained family operations with as many cows as the family's resources would allow. The dairy was generally an integral part of a complete, **diversified farming** program. Crops of various sorts were grown on the farm, most of the dairy's feed needs were met on the farm, and

Diversified farm Farm with multiple income-generating enterprises.

Figure 10–5

Milk cows by state and total milk production by region. The number found within the state represents the number of dairy cows × 1,000. The number beside the region name represents the total milk produced in the region in millions of lbs of milk. All information represents averages for recent years. Source: USDA-NASS, 2011d.

Figure 10–6

Milk cow operations, 1980–2010. The trend since the 1950s has been to fewer total dairy cattle operations. At the same time, the average dairy has gotten larger. Source: USDA-NASS, 2011a.

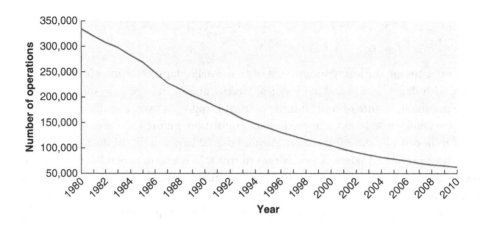

Figure 10–7

Percentage of U.S. milk production by size of operation. More of the cows are in larger herds, and fewer in smaller herds. This reflects the trend of small herds going out of the dairy business. As this is happening, fewer, larger herds are controlling a greater percentage of the cows. Source: USDA-NASS, 2011a.

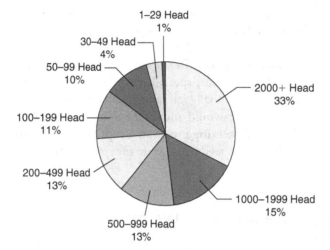

replacement animals were grown on the farm. The milk check came regularly, which helped meet the needs of the family and the cash flow for the remainder of the farming operation. In many ways, this epitomized the concept of "family farm" to much of the country. Much national farm policy has revolved around protecting this ideal. Although dispersed across the country, the dairy industry was historically centered in regions of the northeastern portion of the country.

The structure of the industry has reached a point at which the traditional dairy no longer predominates. Large-scale dairies with thousands of cows have increased. These large operations are able to expand by taking advantage of labor-saving technologies that small operations cannot afford. Operations of 100 cows or less still exist, but the definition of *small* and *large* are both changing as the overall average herd size increases. Production has shifted west to take advantage of mild dry climates and to accommodate an increasing human population. From the beginning, these new, larger western producers adopted business organizations and management strategies that reduced milk production costs resulting in a competitive edge. This further contributed to the westward shift in milk production, and it is still a driving factor. The top-10 dairy states are listed in Table 10–2. These 10 states produce approximately three-fourths of U.S. milk. California became the largest milk-producing state in 1994. Idaho surpassed New York in 2010 to become the third largest dairy state.

The dairy cow population declined to less than 10 million cows in 1990 (Figure 10–8) while the average amount of milk produced per cow has increased (Figure 10–9) and the total milk output from the nation's dairy industry has increased (Figure 10–10). The increase in milk per cow is compensating for the decrease in the number of cows.

Table 10–2
TOP-10 DAIRY STATES

Total Milk (lbs)		Total Cows (1,000 Head)	
California	40.39 bill.	California	1760
Wisconsin	26.04 bill.	Wisconsin	1260
Idaho	12.78 bill.	New York	610
New York	12.71 bill.	Idaho	550
Pennsylvania	10.73 bill.	Pennsylvania	540
Minnesota	9.10 bill.	Minnesota	470
Texas	8.83 bill.	Texas	410
Michigan	8.33 bill.	Michigan	354
New Mexico	7.88 bill.	New Mexico	318
Washington	5.90 bill.	Ohio	272

Source: USDA-NASS, 2011c.

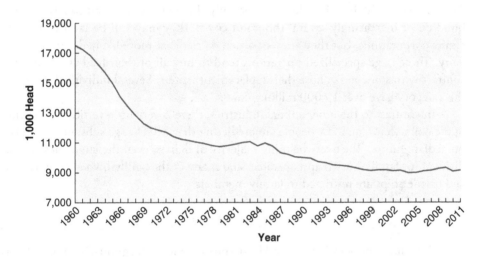

Figure 10–8
The number of dairy cows in the United States. The decrease in cows has not caused a decrease in total milk production because of an increase in average productivity of the remaining cows. Source: USDA-NASS, 2011a.

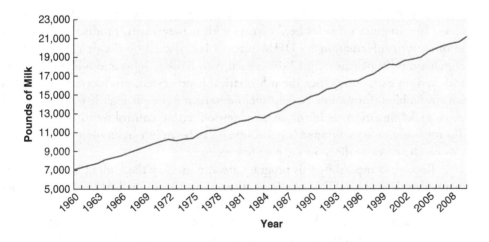

Figure 10–9
Rate of milk production per cow. Improved genetics, management, and use of technological innovations have caused a sustained trend of more milk per average cow. Source: USDA-NASS, 2011c.

Most U.S. dairies fall into one of two major categories. The first category consists of smaller herds of fewer than 200 cows, about as many as the average family could expect to handle and still do a good job. Most of the country's dairies remain in this category. A larger percentage of these dairies are located in the traditional dairy states than in the newly emerging dairy states. Dairies in California, New Mexico,

Figure 10–10
*Total milk production has
steadily increased in spite
of a trend for fewer cows.*
Source: USDA-NASS, 2011a.

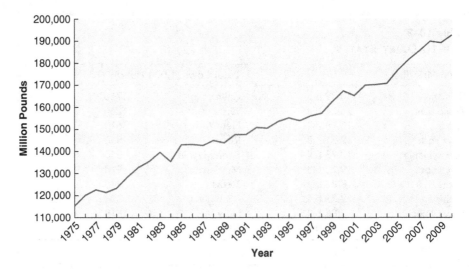

Arizona, Texas, Idaho, and Florida, especially the newer ones, tend to have several hundred or increasingly several thousand cows. They may still be family farms or family corporations, but they are specialized dairies that more likely do nothing but dairy. These large specialized operations tend to buy all of their feed and may even contract with someone to raise their replacement heifers. Several individual dairies in this category have over 15,000 milking cows.

In contrast to the other animal industries, there is very little vertical integration in the dairy sector, and few people are predicting that will change substantially in the immediate future. The overwhelming majority of dairies, even the large ones, are individual- or family-owned and operated, and many of the family-owned corporations and partnerships are restricted to family members.

DAIRY HERD IMPROVEMENT ASSOCIATION (DHIA)

The National Cooperative Dairy Herd Improvement Program (NCDHIP) was established in 1965. It is administered at the state and local levels by the Dairy Herd Improvement Association (DHIA) and collects and processes information on dairy cows. The program provides herd owners with management, production, and cost information. Information on DHIA records is collected on the dairy by a DHIA representative approximately 12 times each year. Milk weights and milk samples are collected on each cow. Once the information is processed, producers are provided with valuable information to help them determine the profitability of individual cows, make nutrition decisions, manage reproduction, control mastitis, and so on. The organization is mentioned here because it can be an integral tool in managing the cow for the needs outlined in the next few sections.

Records compiled by this program are also used by the United States Department of Agriculture (USDA) for sire evaluation purposes. The USDA sire summaries provide accurate estimates on the genetic merit of sires. This is accomplished by comparing daughters of individual sires with daughters of other sires in the same herds. Any producer using artificial insemination in a dairy benefits from this service.

GENETICS AND BREEDING PROGRAMS

The fundamentals of genetics and breeding are discussed in Chapters 7 and 6, which has a specific section on dairy cows. See those chapters for the fundamentals of dairy cattle breeding.

Table 10–3

GENETIC CHANGE IN SELECTED DAIRY PERFORMANCE TRAITS FOR DIFFERENT BREEDS FOR COWS BORN IN 1962 COMPARED TO 2008

	Breed					
	Ayrshire	Guernsey	Holstein	Jersey	Brown Swiss	Milking Shorthorn
Milk yield (lb)	4,976	6,548	7,794	7,410	5,943	5,139
Fat yield (lb)	172	240	265	247	207	184
Protein yield (lb)[1]	69	96	132	150	91	63
Somatic cell score[1]	+0.2	+0.1	+0.1	+0.4	+0.2	+0.1
Daughter pregnancy rate (%)	−4.9	−7.6	−6.7	−4.6	−7.3	−4.3

[1] 1986–2008.
Source: Interpreted from www.aipl.arsusda.gov, May 2007.

The dairy industry has made tremendous genetic progress in milk production (Table 10–3). Milk, fat, and protein have increased significantly for all of the breeds. Holstein cows born in 1962 averaged 14,319 lbs of milk on a mature equivalent basis, whereas those born in 2004 are averaging 26,219 lbs. About 60% of the increase is related to genetic progress and 40% of the increase to better management.

A disturbing statistic from Table 10–3 is the negative trend for daughter pregnancy rate (DPR). DPR is defined as the percentage of time that a cow would be expected to get pregnant during a three-week reproductive cycle during the breeding period of a lactation. Getting lactating cows pregnant has become one of the biggest challenges facing dairy farmers. Genetic evaluations for DPR were not officially published by the USDA until February 2003. It was often incorrectly argued that because the heritabilities of reproduction traits were only 1–5%, it would not be worthwhile to try to improve fertility genetically. Hopefully, with prudent use of these genetic evaluations for DPR now available, the negative trend for fertility can be reversed.

The USDA's Net Merit Index was modified in January 2010 to include traits known to be economically important and reflect more accurately the genetics that cows need for maximum lifetime net profit. Traits considered in the index, heritabilities, and genetic correlations are presented in Table 10–4. Interestingly, the current genetic correlation between milk and productive life is now only 0.08, contrasted with the 0.75 published from earlier work (Table 7–7). This means that in the past higher-producing cows stayed in the herd much longer than low-producing cows, but that strong relationship is no longer true today.

The relative index weights on the various traits in the Net Merit Index, the expected PTA gain/year and expected genetic trend per decade is reported in Table 10–5. All of the traits in the index are expected to change in a desirable direction. Even though no weight is put on PTA milk, milk is expected to increase 1,374 lbs over the next decade because of its positive genetic correlation with fat and protein. **Somatic cell** score should decrease. The −0.98 in body size composite correlates to a reduction in about 20 lbs in weight per cow over the ten year period. Smaller cows tend to require fewer lbs of feed per lb of milk produced. The downward trend in daughter pregnancy rate should be reversed and significant increases in calving ease should be noted.

Somatic cells Cells in the body other than gametes.

Table 10–4
HERITABILITIES AND GENETIC CORRELATIONS OF TRAITS CONSIDERED IN THE NET MERIT INDEX

	PTA Trait									
PTA Trait	Milk	Fat	Protein	PL	SCS	Size	Udder	Feet/ Legs	DPR	CA$[1]
Milk	**0.30***	0.45	0.81	0.08	0.20	−0.10	−0.20	−0.02	−0.32	0.15
Fat		**0.30**	0.60	0.08	0.15	−0.09	−0.20	0.02	−0.33	0.11
Protein			**0.30**	0.10	0.20	−0.10	−0.20	−0.02	−0.35	0.16
Productive life				**0.08**	−0.38	−0.16	0.30	0.19	0.51	0.40
Somatic cell score					**0.12**	−0.11	−0.33	−0.02	−0.30	−0.08
Size						**0.40**	0.26	0.22	−0.08	−0.24
Udder							**0.27**	0.10	0.03	0.06
Feet/legs composite								**0.15**	−0.04	−0.04
Daughter pregnancy rate									**0.04**	0.34
Calving ability dollars										**0.07**

[1]CA$ (Calving Ability Dollars) is a function of calving ease and stillbirth rate.
Source: aipl.arsusda.gov/reference/nmcalc-2010.htm

Table 10–5
RELATIVE NET MERIT INDEX WEIGHTS ON THE VARIOUS TRAITS AND EXPECTED GENETIC CHANGE FOR HOLSTEINS

PTA Trait	Relative Weight (%)	Expected PTA Gain/Year	Expected Genetic Trend/Decade
Milk (lb)	0	69	1,374
Fat (lb)	16	3.8	76
Protein (lb)	19	2.1	43
Productive life (mo)	22	0.50	10.0
Somatic cell score	−10	−0.022	−0.45
Size composite	−6	−0.05	−0.98
Udder composite	7	0.04	0.80
Feet/legs composite	4	0.04	0.80
Daughter pregnancy rate	11	0.17	3.5
Calving ability ($)	5	1.5	30

Breeds

Specialized dairy breeds were imported into the United States and breed associations were established between 1868 and 1880. The six dairy breeds used in the United States and their average DHIA performance levels are reported in Table 10–6. The most popular breed by far is the Holstein, accounting for almost 95% of the cows on DHIA test. Jersey is the second most popular breed with about 4% of the cows. The remaining four breeds account for only a very small percentage of the cows in the United States.

In general, the number of registered dairy cattle has been declining (Table 10–7). However, the past few years have seen substantial increases in Holsteins, Jerseys, and

Table 10–6
PRODUCTION LEVEL OF U.S. DAIRY BREEDS, 2010

Breed	No. of Cows	lbs Milk	% Fat	% Protein
Ayrshire	4,878	15,602	3.9	3.2
Brown Swiss	12,775	18,635	4.1	3.4
Guernsey	5,422	15,377	4.5	3.4
Holstein	3,776,761	23,187	3.6	3.1
Jersey	225,111	16,611	4.7	3.6
Milking Shorthorn	1,758	13,757	3.5	3.1

Source: DHI Report K3, USDA.

Table 10–7
REGISTRATION OF ANIMALS BY DAIRY BREED ASSOCIATIONS

Year	Ayrshire	Brown Swiss	Guernsey	Holstein	Jersey	Milking Shorthorn	Total
1950	24,236	22,721	94,901	184,246	67,309	28,290	421,703
1970	15,069	16,416	43,783	281,574	37,097	5,410	399,349
1980	10,977	12,871	20,907	353,949	60,975	4,924	464,603
1990	7,752	11,756	13,930	395,906	53,547	2,596	485,487
2000	6,046	10,648	6,151	317,567	63,776	2,595	406,783
2005	4,860	10,076	5,093	301,852	72,885	3,154	397,920
2010	4,131	10,658	4,810	339,908	90,362	2,760	452,629

Brown Swiss. Total registration of dairy cattle peaked in 1984 at 590,298 registrations. Holsteins have had the highest numbers of registered cattle in the United States since very early in the 20th century. However, Jerseys are increasing registrations at a faster rate than Holsteins.

Traditionally, there has been very little **crossbreeding** in dairy cattle in the United States. The major reason was because Holsteins produced so much more milk than the other breeds that heterosis was not large enough to justify crossbreeding. However, in recent years, dairy producers have shown interest in crossbreeding. Reasons for the increase in crossbreeding include the decreased fertility in purebreds, a shift in payment away from milk volume and toward payment for lbs of fat and protein, and dairy producers wanting a more trouble-free and healthier cow.

Crossbreeding Mating animals from different breeds within a species.

It is difficult to determine what percentage of the cows in the United States are crossbreds, but the number is increasing. Many of the crossbred cows are in low input herds that are not on the DHIA test. The most popular crossbreds are Jersey-Holstein (Figure 10–11).

There is growing interest in four additional breeds from Europe for crossbreeding purposes: Swedish Red and Norwegian Red (collectively referred to as Scandinavian Red), Normande, and Montbeliarde. These breeds have had well-organized genetic improvement programs and have selected both for production and fitness traits (including fertility) for many years. Table 10–8 shows a comparison of these crosses with Holsteins in seven California dairies. On average, the pure Holsteins produced more milk in the first lactation. However, the crossbreds had fewer stillbirths, better fertility, and were less apt to be culled.

Figure 10–11

It is difficult to determine what percentage of the U.S. dairy cows are cross-bred, but the number is increasing. (Photo courtesy Dr. Tony Seykora. Used with permission.)

Table 10–8

AVERAGE PRODUCTION OF FIRST LACTATION OF CROSSBREDS AND HOLSTEINS IN SEVEN CALIFORNIA DAIRIES

	Holstein	Normande—Holstein	Montbeliarde—Holstein	Scandinavian Red—Holstein
Number of cows	380	245	494	328
Milk (lbs.)	21,510	18,805	20,196	20,461
Fat (lbs.)	763	703	736	750
Protein (lbs.)	672	611	646	655
% of Holsteins for combine fat plus protein		92%	96%	98%
% stillbirths at first calving	14%	10%	6%	5%
Average days open	150	123	131	129
% culled in first 305 days	14%	7%	8%	7%

Source: *Journal of Dairy Science* 89:2799, 2805, 4944.

Crossbreeding studies are currently being conducted by several universities. Results may determine the extent of future crossbreeding in the U.S. dairy industry.

REPRODUCTIVE MANAGEMENT IN DAIRY CATTLE

Chapter 8 is devoted to reproductive physiology. Refer there for the fundamentals of male and female reproductive anatomy, physiology, and function. Likewise, see that chapter for a look at the specialized function of lactation. Be aware that reproductive performance is closely tied to other factors, especially nutrition and level of management.

Reproductive problems are especially troublesome in the dairy industry. Sterility and delayed breeding cost the dairy industry hundreds of millions of dollars each year. A cow must have a calf to produce milk, and, because milk production declines over time, it is desirable to have the cow calve with relative frequency to initiate a new cycle of milk production. Additionally, we need for the daughters of the herd to become the replacements for their dams. Their genetics should be better than that of their dams, and they are needed to replace cows that are culled. A realistic goal of breeding the dairy cow is to produce a calf at 13-month intervals. Because of the number of factors that influence the reproductive performance of a good dairy cow, this is a challenging goal. A cow must be pregnant within 115 days of calving or the 13-month calving interval cannot be maintained. The cow must recover from calving, start her heat cycle again, and conceive. She must do all of this while producing a sizable quantity of milk that is larger each year for the average cow. Good management is necessary for this to happen.

Nutrition is central to reproductive efficiency in dairy herds. A cow generally loses weight for the first few weeks after calving because it is impossible for her to eat enough to increase production during early lactation and maintain body weight. Thus, the body reacts by catabolizing stored tissue for energy and losing weight. This can create a problem because a dairy cow must maintain a certain body condition to begin preparing for heat cycles and impregnation. Thus, good nutrition is necessary for both maximal milk production and reproductive performance.

Because most dairy cattle in the United States are artificially inseminated, one of the challenges to a successful breeding program is heat detection. Use of **gomer bulls** or hormone-treated cull cows to help spot cows in estrus (heat) can help. Learning the physical and behavioral signs of a cow in heat is also essential. Remember that a cow only displays the signs of heat for 12 to 18 hours on a 19- to 21-day cycle, which presents a narrow window of opportunity for heat detection. Increasingly, dairy producers use hormone programs to help control and detect estrus by making it more predictable. Replacement heifers must be managed so they can be mated to calve at 2 years of age. To do this, they must be mated at 15 months of age and need to be at least 65% of their adult weight at the time of breeding. Dairy cows are freshened year-round. The gestation period varies slightly from breed to breed and ranges from 280 to 283 days.

Gomer bull Bull rendered incapable of mating naturally.

Diseases that affect reproductive efficiency directly include brucellosis (Bang's disease), campylobacteriosis, leptospirosis, IBR/BVD complex, and trichomoniasis. Control of these and other diseases can be accomplished easily by developing and following a complete health program for the herd. Use of AI, which eliminates the possibility of a bull spreading disease, makes disease management in a dairy much easier.

Good records are essential to managing reproductive issues in the dairy herd. A large number of programs exist to assist the producer in this regard. Both manual and computer programs are readily available. Most work as well as the person who is using them. Because management practices and standards vary with conditions across the country, cattle breeders are encouraged to contact their local extension service or their state extension specialists for help in setting up a recordkeeping program for their area. Many dairy producers use DHIA records in managing their breeding programs.

NUTRITION IN DAIRY CATTLE

Feed costs account for 45–65% of the costs of the dairy. Feeding is the single most important factor in the profitability of the dairy herd.

Dairy cattle are ruminants. They can use forages and roughages to produce a usable product for humans. The nutrition and feeding of dairy cattle is similar to that of beef cattle. Most of the production stages revolve around maximizing the use of forages as the feed base. However, higher-quality forages are required and dairy feeding has a greater dependence on concentrate feeds to supplement the forage. Chapters 3,

6, and 7 give detailed information relating to nutrition, feeds, and feeding. See those chapters for general nutrition information not provided in this section.

Managing the nutrition of dairy cattle is very dependent on the class of cattle to be fed. Different classes of dairy animals use different amounts of grain and other supplemental feeds to extend the use of forage by supplementing missing nutrients. The very young and the cow in production need the greatest amounts of supplementation of energy feeds. Mineral supplements critical in feeding the producing female include salt, calcium, and phosphorus. Additional individual mineral deficiencies occur in the various geographic regions of the country. Protein and energy feeds are often needed to keep heifers growing at an acceptable rate and to keep cows producing at optimal levels.

Baby calves destined to be producing cows are fed on a commercial calf milk replacer or on milk produced at the dairy. In some dairies, colostrum, milk being discarded because of antibiotic use on a cow, or otherwise-contaminated milk is used. It is economically advantageous to switch calves to dry concentrate feeds and forage as soon as possible to decrease costs of feed, labor, and housing. Calves are usually fed their liquid feed twice a day, although systems are available for free choice feeding. Calves are offered dry feed (Table 10–9) when they are only a few days old and weaned when their consumption is adequate.

Heifer-growing programs depend increasingly on maximizing the use of forages as the heifer gets larger and more able to use the forages effectively.

Table 10–9
EXAMPLES OF SOME CALF STARTERS

	Grain Starters[1]		
	1	2	3
Ingredients (air-dry basis)			
Corn (cracked or coarse ground) %	50	30	
Ear corn (coarse ground) %			50
Oats (rolled or crushed)	22	18	
Barley (rolled or coarse ground) %		20	21
Wheat bran %		8	
Soybean meal %	20	16	21
Molasses %	5	5	5
Dicalcium phosphate %	.5	.5	.5
Limestone %	1.5	1.5	1.5
TM salt and vitamins %	1	1	1
Composition (dry-matter basis)			
Crude protein %	18.1	18.0	18.4
TDN %	80.0	78.8	78.0
ADF %	7.0	6.9	9.1
Calcium %	.80	.80	.82
Phosphorus %	.48	.56	.47
Vitamin A, IU/lb	1,000	1,000	1,000
Vitamin D, IU/lb	150	150	150
Vitamin E, IU/lb	11	11	11

[1] Hay may be offered free choice with grain starters.
Source: Linn et al., 1988.

Because replacement heifers should ideally enter the milking herd at 24 months of age, the plane of nutrition must be good to keep them growing at an appropriate rate. However, different programs must be developed for the animals at different ages, weights, and seasons. Energy and/or protein supplementation is usually necessary. Higher-quality forages are also needed to keep animals gaining rapidly enough to enter the milking string at age 2. After 1 year of age, it may be possible to feed heifers good-quality forage and mineral supplements until just before calving.

Dairies generally rely on one of two systems of feeding the producing cows. Cows can be allowed to graze on high-quality pastures and then fed their concentrate ration at a different time, often in the milking parlor. This has been the traditional method of dairying in the United States and is still used by many small dairies. Increasingly, however, dairy cows are handled in a dry-lot system. Cows are kept in confinement facilities, usually consisting of a barn or loafing shed and a small lot, often concrete, where they are fed and watered. The cows are often grouped by production level and fed a complete, mixed ration (total mixed ration, or TMR) from bunks. In this way, a cow uses fewer nutrients in procuring her feed and can divert more to producing milk. There is also less waste of feed in these systems. Forage is still the basis of the ration; however, it is mixed with the energy, protein, mineral, and vitamin concentrate portions of the ration prior to feeding. Thus, each bite a cow takes is balanced for her needs. Cows are not fed in the milking parlor in this system. Most dairy rations are formulated with the use of least-cost ration formulation programs. Table 10–10 shows examples of complete, mixed rations for producing cows (Figure 10–12).

The following list shows the advantages and disadvantages of the TMR system. Cows should be grouped by production level to best take advantage of the complete ration system.

Advantages:

1. There is no parlor grain feeding.
   a. Reduced cost of parlor construction and maintenance of feeding equipment.
   b. Less dust and mess in the parlor.
   c. No delay in milking time waiting for cows to eat grain.
   d. More cows milked per person-hour and cows are in the parlor less time.
   e. Cows stand more quietly and defecate less during milking.

Figure 10–12
Total mixed rations can be fed in dry-lot systems. These diets have the advantage of providing balanced nutrition in every bite. (Photo by Scott Bauer. Courtesy USDA Agricultural Research Service.)

Table 10–10
EXAMPLE RATIONS FOR VARIOUS MILK PRODUCTION PHASES[1]

Item	Phase 1	Phase 2	Phase 3
Milk (lbs/day)	90	80	50
DM intake (lbs/day)[2]	49	51	38
Ration 1 lbs/day (as fed)			
Alf hay (88% DM), 20% CP	28	34	27
Corn-oats[3]	21	24	16
SMB-44%	5.0		
Dical-18% P	0.5	0.45	0.30
Salt, vitamins, TM	0.30	0.25	0.25
Weight change	−1.5	—	+0.5
Ration 2 (corn silage limit fed)			
Alf hay, 20% CP	19	34	23
Corn silage (35% DM)	25	25	25
Corn-oats	18	12	10
SMB-44%	7.5	0.3	–
Dical-18% P	0.45	0.50	0.3
Salt, vitamins, TM	0.30	0.25	0.25
Weight change	−1.2	—	+0.5
Ration 3 (hay limit fed)[4]			
Alf-grass hay, 16% CP	10	10	10
Corn silage	41	70	57
Corn-oats	16	11	6
SMB-44%	11.5	8.2	4.5
Dical-18% P	0.40	0.30	0.25
Limestone	0.40	0.30	0.15
Salt, vitamins, TM	0.30	0.25	0.25
Weight change	−1.4	+0.7	+0.5
Ration 4			
Alf-grass hay, 16% CP	23	32	24
Corn-oats	22	22	19
SMB-44%	8.5	3.5	1.1
Dical-18% P	0.45	0.40	0.25
Limestone	0.20		
Salt, vitamins, TM	0.30	0.25	0.25
Weight change	−1.9	—	+0.5

[1]1,350-lb cow, 3.8% fat test.
[2]Estimated average intake during the phase.
[3]85% corn–15% oats mix.
[4]Feed amounts may have to be limited during phases 2 and 3 to avoid over conditioning.
Source: Linn et al., 1988.

2. The dairy producer has more control over the total feeding program.
   a. Concentrates can be liberally fed to high producers without overfeeding the low producers. TMRs are often mixed and fed with greater accuracy than conventional feeding.
   b. Silage tends to mask the taste and dustiness of feed ingredients, which allows for the use of more economical but less palatable feeds in the diet.
   c. Cows eat many times a day. Feed intake is greater and nutrients are used better, especially urea. Overall feed efficiency often improves.
   d. Fewer cows have digestive upsets and go off-feed.
   e. Milk production per cow is often higher.

3. Labor is less for feeding the total herd.
   a. Equipment and rations for the lactating herd can be used for feeding dry cows, heifers, and calves from 2 months of age.
4. Cost of cow housing and feeding facilities is less.
   a. Feed bunks are simpler with no need for conveyers or augers.
   b. Less bunk space is needed, as little as 8 in. per cow.
   c. Free-stall numbers can be reduced.

Disadvantages:

5. Special equipment is needed.
   a. The equipment must have the capability to blend the ingredients thoroughly.
   b. The mixer, preferably mobile, must have the capability for accurate weighing.
   c. A crowd gate or training gate may be needed initially to get cows into the parlor.
6. Cows should be grouped by production levels.
   a. If not grouped, cows in late lactation tend to get too fat.
   b. Dry cows must be removed from the lactating herd.
   c. Grouping cows is more difficult in small herds.

Forages commonly used in dairy production include legumes such as alfalfa or lespedeza, small-grain forage such as oats or barley, corn or sorghum forage, and various grasses. These forages may be harvested by the cow (grazing), harvested mechanically and fed immediately (often called "green chop"), or harvested and stored as hay, silage, and haylage. Commonly used grains and by-products are corn, sorghum, small grains, soybean meal, and cottonseed meal. Many by-product feeds, such as brewer's grains, distiller's grains, beet pulp, and citrus feeds are used to feed dairy cows. These by-products tend to be used in the region of the country where they are produced.

HERD HEALTH

Maintaining herd health and preventing problems that commonly affect high-producing dairy cattle is essential for achieving efficient and profitable milk production. In order to produce large volumes of high-quality milk, dairy cattle must be systemically healthy, reproductively sound, and receive adequate nutritional support. Workable dairy **herd health programs** include a total approach to management, nutrition, medicine, and environmental control. The general principles of a comprehensive herd health program include (1) prevention rather than treatment; (2) planned health-related procedures and examinations; and (3) sound recordkeeping and record use in making herd management decisions.

Even with diligent efforts to prevent health problems, some diseases will still occur. A few of the common disorders that threaten the health of dairy cattle are described below. A significant number of other diseases may affect dairy cattle, but discussion of them is beyond the scope of this book.

Herd health program A comprehensive and herd-specific program of health management practices.

Mastitis

Mastitis (Figure 10–13) is an inflammation of the udder caused by a wide variety of bacteria or occasionally other types of infectious organisms that enter the udder from the outside environment. Mastitis decreases the quality as well as the quantity of milk produced, even when the disease is not severe enough to make the cow noticeably ill. Therefore, preventing mastitis and effectively treating affected cows (or culling untreatable animals) is essential in dairy herds. Poor milking practices, faulty milking machines, and unsanitary conditions (muddy pens, dirty bedding, etc.) increase the

Figure 10–13
The cut surface of an udder affected by mastitis. The glandular tissue is severely inflamed due to a bacterial infection. Notice the tan, cloudy fluid (pus) filling the gland sinus. (Photo by Dr. Rodger Panciera. Courtesy Oklahoma Center for Veterinary Health Services.)

Contagious Capable of being transmitted from animal to animal.

risk for mastitis. Some forms of mastitis are caused by bacteria that are **contagious** and are transmitted from cow to cow through unclean milking machines. For that reason, detection of infected animals, followed by their treatment or elimination is essential for preventing the spread of infection to additional animals. With diligent treatment and hygiene, these contagious types of mastitis can be controlled or even eradicated from the herd.

Milk fever (hypocalcemia)

Milk fever, also called parturient paresis, occurs most commonly in dairy cattle around the time of calving. These cows undergo a sudden loss of calcium when milk production begins, which interferes with normal nerve and muscle function. As a result, affected cows first go through a period of restlessness and muscle tremors before becoming unable to stand. If treatment with intravenous calcium supplementation is not given, the disease may progress to unconsciousness and death. Even though the response to appropriate treatment is usually immediate, prevention of milk fever through nutritional means, such as the adjustment of dietary cation-anion difference and dietary calcium during late pregnancy is often successful and is much preferred.

Displaced abomasum

The abomasum is the true stomach of ruminants. Due to its relatively loose attachments to other abdominal organs, it may become displaced following excess gas accumulation or other processes that affect its function or motility. Displacement of the abomasum happens most commonly in dairy cows within the first few weeks after calving. Symptoms can range from decreased food intake and mild abdominal pain to severe cases in which animals rapidly become weak, depressed, bloated, and dehydrated. These cows may die without rapid surgical correction. To decrease the risk of this potentially serious disease, high-grain rations should be introduced slowly and adequate roughage included in the diet to maintain normal function of the forestomachs and abomasum. Early detection of decreased appetite or other signs in affected cattle is important because early treatment is more likely to be successful and prevent progression to severe, life-threatening disease.

Johne's disease

Johne's disease is a contagious intestinal infection that can cause a significant decrease in milk yield and eventually lead to diarrhea, severe weight loss, and death

Figure 10–14
Johne's disease. A cow infected with M. avium subspecies paratuberculosis *that is in the late stages of disease. She has typical clinical signs such as weight loss, watery diarrhea, and general poor health.* (Photo by Peggy Greb. Courtesy USDA-Agricultural Research Service.)

in adult cattle (Figure 10–14). This disease is unique in that cattle usually become infected when they are young (<6 months) but do not develop signs of illness until they are older (2–6 years). Large numbers of the disease-causing bacteria are shed in the feces of infected animals. Exposed calves become infected and later begin shedding bacteria and will likely develop disease as adults. Many cattle with this infection have subclinical disease, meaning that signs of illness are not readily observable, especially in the early stages. Cattle with subclinical disease can easily go undetected and contaminate the environment with bacteria, which transmit infection to susceptible animals. For this reason, testing to aid in detection and culling of infected animals, as well as careful attention to sanitation, are essential for eliminating Johne's disease from dairy herds. Replacement animals should be purchased from farms free of the infection and should be tested before introduction to the herd. Since youngsters are most susceptible to infection, in herds positive for Johne's disease, calves should be removed from cows immediately after birth, fed pasteurized colostrum, and remain segregated from adult cattle until after 1 year of age. Offspring born to cows with signs of Johne's disease should be culled, since they may be infected before birth and then serve as a source of infection for the rest of the herd. No effective treatment is available for Johne's disease, so husbandry practices that allow early detection of the disease and limit the spread of infection are the primary means of control.

BOVINE SOMATOTROPIN (BST)

This section is included as a stand-alone section in this chapter because of the uniqueness of the topic to the dairy industry. However, the implications are broader and have both biological and social implications that deal with all of agriculture, medicine, and, indeed, anything biological that occurs on this planet.

Bovine somatotropin (BST) is a hormone produced naturally by cattle in the pituitary gland, which is an endocrine gland located at the base of the brain. The effects of BST have been known since the 1930s. Each species produces its own unique version of this hormone. BST accomplishes several things in the body, including regulation of growth in the young. Injections of BST increase milk production in dairy cows. In and of itself, that is not earth-shaking news. What makes BST unique is that developments in recombinant DNA technology make it possible to produce BST on a large-scale basis. This product is referred to as rBST.

Bovine somatotropin (BST) A hormone produced by the pituitary gland of the cow. Injections of BST increase milk production in most cows.

With any product that would be used on an animal, rBST required government approval. Herein lies the importance of rBST, which was the first such product to be approved for use in animals in the United States. As such, the process was long and painful. A tremendous amount of controversy surrounded the approval of BST, and its approval was a landmark accomplishment for the fledgling biotechnology industry. Most of the concern was raised by consumer watchdog organizations. It is important to understand that several consumer and medical groups had approved and endorsed the use of rBST. It had been in use in Europe and Mexico for some years before it was approved in the United States. Commercial use of rBST received approval in 1993 for use in 1994. Actual herd records indicate that producers using rBST are realizing from 5 to 15 lbs of increased milk production per day per cow. Individual cows generally improve milk production by 10–15%.

Milk from rBST-treated cows is safe for humans to consume and has no ill effects on human health. A small amount of naturally occurring BST has always been found in milk. There are three major reasons why rBST use in cows is safe. First, BST is a species-specific protein that is active only in cattle. Second, over 90% of the BST found in milk is destroyed during the pasteurization process. Third, any BST found in milk is digested in the human digestive system as is any other protein. Slightly elevated levels of insulin-like growth factor (IGF-1) can be found in milk from cows treated with rBST. This is not a cause for concern for these reasons: First, these levels are not above normal ranges for cows. Second, human milk has higher levels of IGF-1 and it has not caused any problems. Third, IGF-1 is not biologically active when ingested by humans and is digested by the human digestive system just as BST is. Fourth, the amount of IGF-1 in a serving of milk is insignificant compared to the amount produced in the human body daily. A multitude of studies have demonstrated that BST, whether natural or synthetic, has no effect on humans.

Posilac Commercially available BST.

Posilac (sterile sometribove zinc suspension) is the registered trade name of commercially available rBST. The generic name of this product is recombinant DNA-derived methionyl bovine somatotropin. Posilac is administered as an injection every 14 days, beginning in the 9th week after calving. rBST has to be injected because it is a protein that would be digested by the cow if fed to her. Hormones like estrogen and progesterone (birth control pills) are smaller and can be absorbed intact from the gut.

For over a decade rBST use appeared to be a nonissue with most consumers. However, consumers' general concerns over health and wellness as well as interest in organic and natural foods led some producers to begin producing certified rBST-free milk. The availability of the rBST-free products seems to have kindled concern among consumers and has led several retailers and milk cooperatives to announce they were no longer willing to sell milk produced with the help of rBST. This effectively eliminated the use of rBST in many herds. The controversy continues.

NUTRITIONAL BENEFITS OF MILK TO HUMANS

A 1-cup serving of 2% milk fat milk contains 125 calories and provides the following proportions of the recommended daily dietary allowance for a 19- to 30-year-old man:

Protein	14%
Phosphorus	32%
Calcium	37%
Zinc	11%
Riboflavin	35%
Thiamin	8%
B_{12}	54%

Milk is a very nutritious food. Recent trends in eating patterns have shown consumers decreasing their consumption of whole milk in favor of lower fat versions. The only thing that consumption of lower fat milk changes substantially is that the calories go down incrementally with decreasing fat content of the product, and this improves the nutrient density. Calcium is especially important in the average diet, and milk does an excellent job of providing it.

TRENDS AND FACTORS INFLUENCING THE DAIRY INDUSTRY

The dairy industry is a dynamic industry. Several factors are shaping the changes and direction of the industry. The following discussion is not all inclusive but does discuss some of the major issues and factors to watch.

Restructuring

Trends   Dairy production is shifting to larger operations and fewer dairy producers (total dairies shrank by over one-third in the 2000s), with a greater percentage of the cows in larger herds (see Figures 10–6, 10–7, and 10–15). Large dairies have significant cost advantages over small ones. The cost of adopting new technologies into a dairy will continue to cause the minimum economically feasible size of a dairy operation to increase. Bigger operations can make better use of machinery, equipment, and management because they can more easily achieve economy of size. Technological innovations and continued increases in the quantity of milk produced per cow will hasten this trend. Production will continue to shift, with the West benefitting the most from the shift. However, some traditional dairy states—such as Wisconsin, Michigan, Ohio, and New York—have increased their milk production in recent years. Much of this is due to increased milk production per cow. Dairy farms will increasingly become more specialized as they increase in size and reduce in number and more mega dairies with more than 10,000 cows will emerge in both new and traditional dairy states. Fewer farmers will raise their own feeds; they will buy all or part of it. More dairy farmers will rely on specialized heifer-rearing operations to rear their replacements. Confinement dry-lot housing and automation with concomitant reduction in labor requirements will continue.

Managers and Labor   Dairying will need increasingly knowledgeable managers and high-quality labor, especially as the average size of a dairy increases and as the technological innovations become more and more sophisticated. Family-owned dairies will increasingly hire non-family members to manage or at least to assume major responsibilities in their dairies.

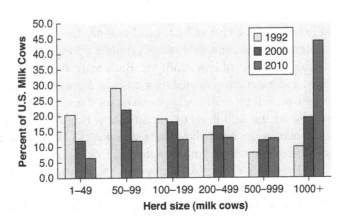

Figure 10–15
Milk production shifts to larger dairies. Source: USDA-NASS 2011.

Family Farms   Most dairy farms are family enterprises. This will quite probably continue to be the case. However, more family operations will become legal partnerships or will incorporate. Large, corporate commercial dairies will continue to increase.

Policy   The dairy industry has traditionally been the focus of a great deal of federal public policy and is heavily regulated. Increasingly, the argument is being made that U.S. dairy policy is too complex and a hindrance to market development, innovation in dairy product development, and development of export markets. Voices throughout the dairy industry have been calling for a dairy policy overhaul. Not all agree on what the new policies should look like, but most indicate reform is needed. As one of the author's colleagues stated, "Will we have supply-side management, or a continued messy and complicated government pricing program that is good for consumers but very bad for producers?"

Technology   Historically, dairy producers have been progressive users of available technology. Cost competitiveness will give the edge to those producers who adopt and appropriately use the ever-increasing array of products and technological innovations. Expected aids include improved vaccines, better diagnostic aids, lower-cost sexed semen, designer embryos produced by recombinant DNA technology, an expanded arsenal of drugs, better heat detection mechanisms, ways of controlling reproduction, and lactation curve extenders.

Genomics The study of how the genome (DNA) of any species is organized and expressed as traits.

Genomics has the potential to increase genetic progress in the dairy industry by 50% or more. The sequencing of the cattle genome in 2004 allowed the development of the Illumina BovineSNP50 BeadChip in 2007. A single-nucleotide polymorphism (SNP, pronounced *snip*) is a DNA sequence variation occurring when a single nucleotide—A, T, C, or G—differs between individuals or paired chromosomes in an individual. For example, two sequenced DNA fragments from different individuals, AAGCCTA to AAGCTTA, contain a difference in a single nucleotide. The Illumina BovineSNP50 BeadChip allowed for the testing of over 38,000 polymorphisms spread evenly across the 30 chromosomes. This proved a huge advantage over marker-assisted selection where only a limited number of **genetic markers** could be tested for at one time. Genomics and SNP technology became synonymous. This technology was quickly adopted by the industry with thousands of dairy cattle genotyped and official genomic evaluations released by USDA for Holstein, Jerseys, and Brown Swiss by 2009. By May 2011, over 90,000 Holsteins had been genotyped in the United States. Genomics allows more accurate predictions of the genetics of bulls, heifers, and cows by more accurately estimating the relationships between animals and estimating the SNP effects on production, health, and conformation traits. Genetic progress is enhanced by using elite AI bulls at a younger age with more confidence and more accurately identifying elite females to be super ovulated for replacement bulls and heifers. Genomics also helps to detect and eliminate undesirable recessive alleles from the population.

Genetic markers Biochemical labels used to identify specific alleles on a chromosome.

Embryo transfer Collecting the embryos from a female and transferring them to a surrogate for gestation.

The use of **embryo transfer** will continue to help make genetic progress in the dairy herds of the United States and around the world. Because elite females can be identified at younger ages through genomic testing, increasingly younger animals are serving as donors of elite embryos. Both male and female offspring are then genotyped and generations turned over quickly. Because embryo transfer is still relatively expensive, it is generally only practiced on females of the genetic caliber in demand by AI studs for bull dams or on elite show ring cows to produce offspring for that niche market. Increasingly, other technologies will be coupled with embryo transfer such as embryo sexing, embryo splitting, in vitro fertilization, and cloning.

There is increasing interest in the U.S. dairy industry in robotic milking systems. Although several factors seem to motivate producers to consider robotic milking, labor availability and costs head the list. Finding, keeping, and paying for quality

Table 10–11

U.S. FLUID MILK SALES BY PRODUCT (MILLIONS OF POUNDS)

Year	Whole Milk	Lower Fat Milk	Skim Milk	Flavored Whole Milk	Other Flavored Milk	Butter-Milk	Total Beverage Milk[1]	Total Cream Products[2]	Eggnog	Yogurt	Total All Products[1]
1970	41,363	6,082	2,368	1,144	611	1,130	52,698	778	61	169	54,928
1980	31,253	15,918	2,636	1,075	1,197	927	53,006	1,173	95	570	54,844
1990	21,333	24,509	5,702	691	1,657	879	54,771	1,776	123	1,055	57,725
2000	18,448	23,649	8,435	892	2,444	622	54,490	2,665	93	1,837	59,085
2005	16,760	23,882	7,984	753	3,549	512	53,865	3,661	130	3,058	60,714
2006	16,443	24,271	8,123	719	3,733	504	54,687	3,715	132	3,301	61,835
2007	15,736	24,698	8,203	661	3,707	508	54,606	3,842	122	3,476	62,047
2008	15,309	25,924	8,246	579	3,729	547	54,554	3,734	124	3,599	62,011
2009	15,021	26,380	8,231	570	3,628	580	55,067	3,727	128	3,832	62,753

[1]Includes miscellaneous fluid milk products, beginning 2003.
[2]Light and heavy cream, half and half, sour cream, sour cream dips in CA, and sour cream used in dips elsewhere.
Source: USDA-ERS, Livestock, Dairy and Poultry Outlook, June, 2011.

labor is a growing problem in the dairy industry. Robotic milking has potential as a solution. Robotic systems are also reported to reduce stress on dairy cows. Only available in the United States since 2000, they have been commercially available internationally since the early 1990s. One of the major benefits to producers who use certain types of robotic systems is that cows decide when they want to be milked, eliminating the need for the dairy farmer to structure the day around milking times.

Consumption

Trends Milk is consumed as a variety of products including fluid milk, cheese, ice cream, yogurt, cream, and many more. National consumption of several fluid milk products is shown in Table 10–11. Per capita fluid milk consumption has declined in the United States since the middle of the 20th century (Figure 10–16). This trend is probably destined to continue. Milk competes with other beverages for the consumer's dollar. Milk's market share is less than that of soft drinks and similar to that for coffee and beer. Even bottled water has cut into milk's market share. Industry groups identify several problems that contribute to the low market share, ranging from health concerns to taste preferences and packaging. Lower-fat milk products are more popular with consumers than whole milk (Figure 10–16).

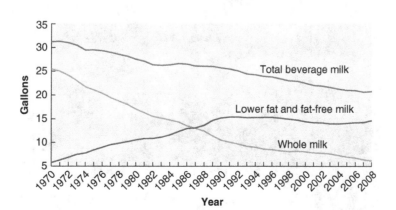

Figure 10–16
Whole, lower-fat, and total beverage milk per capita consumption, gallons, 1970–2008. Source: USDA-ERS. Food Availability (Per Capita) Data System (Release 23). http://www.ers. usda.gov/data/foodconsumption/.

Figure 10–17

Per capita cheese consumption. (Source: USDA-ERS, 2011b.)

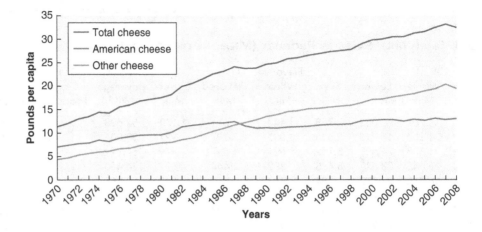

Cheese consumption (Figure 10–17) has increased dramatically. The amount of milk used to make cheese has been greater than fluid milk and cream use since the late 1980s and now accounts for over half of the end-product use of raw milk. Increased cheese consumption has provided for most of the growth in dairy product demand for decades. Factors contributing to increased cheese consumption include new cheese-containing products, wider availability of different kinds of cheese, demand for convenience foods, increased consumption of cheese-containing ethnic foods (especially Mexican and Italian foods), and cheese's ability to add rich flavor to a variety of foods. The increase in eating out and ordering in have also contributed to increased cheese consumption because it is a major ingredient in food manufacturing. Pizza and cheeseburgers both contribute significantly to overall cheese consumption (Figure 10–18).

Other products, such as yogurt, have enjoyed increasing popularity. In addition to traditional yogurt products, yogurt is now in cereals, fast-food desserts, toothpaste, makeup, and pet food. Better-for-you yogurts (Dannon's Activia, Yoplait's Yo-Plus, and many others) have become common in the U.S. marketplace.

Other changes are at work in U.S. dairy product consumption. Individual milk components such as individual proteins, skim solids, milk fat, and lactose are being marketed. As both at-home and away-from-home eating patterns change, the demand for dairy products is shifting from retail sales to restaurant and food processor use, which now account for the majority of dairy product use. These uses are especially important for cheese, butter, and cream. The growing diversity of the U.S.

Figure 10–18

Pizza has contributed significantly to increased cheese consumption. Other contributing factors include new cheese-containing products, availability of different kinds of cheese, increased consumption of cheese-containing ethnic foods (especially Mexican and Italian foods), demand for convenience foods, and cheese's many rich flavors.

(Photo by Scott Bauer. Courtesy USDA-Agricultural Research Service.)

consuming population is also a factor. Because of increased use of dairy products, per capita milk equivalent use is increasing modestly.

Nutrition and Health Consciousness   Milk consumption has been affected by its nutrient content and will continue to be so affected. As previously discussed, there has been a decline in whole-milk sales and an increase in reduced-fat milk sales. However, many consumers don't consider lower-fat milk products to be as palatable as whole milk. On the positive side, recent research studies have confirmed the positive role of calcium consumption in bone health, and milk is an excellent source of dietary calcium. Cheese already contributes over a quarter of the calcium in the U.S. diet. Other studies have suggested a positive role of milk consumption in a weight-loss diet and a positive role of milk consumption after exercise in muscle building. If these studies are confirmed, and the information becomes common knowledge, then milk consumption could get a boost with those relevant interest groups. Milk-based sports drinks, milk-based energy drinks, and cholesterol-cutting milk entered the marketplace in 2007. Several companies have subsequently introduced health-promoting products targeting specific user groups. More such products are under development. Milk and other dairy products are included in the dietary recommendations of all of the major health organizations. Based on the 2005 *Dietary Guidelines* and loss-adjusted food availability data from the USDA-ERS, Americans consume, on average, about 60% of the recommended daily amounts of milk and milk products (Wells and Buzby, 2008).

Organic Milk Production   Dairy has been one of the fastest growing segments of the organic foods industry. Reasons consumers give for preferring organic milk include environmental and animal rights concerns and health benefits. However, research has demonstrated no health benefits for organic milk over conventionally produced milk. In addition, organic milk is more expensive, selling for double the price of other milk in some parts of the country.

At this writing, the overall share that organic milk and milk products have of the market is approximately 3% and growing. The economic downturn of the late 2000s slowed the growth of organic dairy products. However, for the near future, growth of the organic milk segment is expected.

Food Safety

Consumer Concerns   Dairy products have an enviable record of safety. Certainly, dairy products are not immune from safety concerns, but the way milk must be handled and processed to keep it from perishing has also kept it from being a common source of food safety concerns. Bovine spongiform encephalopathy (BSE) should never become an issue in the U.S. dairy industry because milk is not a form of transmission of the disease.

Environmental Concerns   Waste disposal is an increasing concern to dairies. Concentrated animal feeding operations (CAFOs) are considered a significant source of ground- and surface-water pollution because of the high levels of nitrates and phosphorus, harmful bacteria, and salt found in manure. Many modern dairies fit this category of operation.

Most analysts predict the enactment of increasingly tougher waste disposal laws that will add costs to production. Individual states have enacted environmental regulations that go beyond federal requirements, and more are expected to do so. New, low-cost, effective means of animal waste disposal should help blunt the added costs that environmental stewardship will bring. Quality of the air, soil, and water supply is an important issue with consumers. Dairy producers will increasingly be concerned with nutrient management plans, carbon footprint, and other environmental issues in order to remain in business (Figure 10–19).

Figure 10–19

Many modern confinement dairies must consider ways to effectively and efficiently manage animal waste and control pollution. Shown here is a roofed, concrete-walled solid manure stacking facility basin and filter strip at a Michigan dairy.

(Photo by Lynn Betts, USDA-Natural Resources Conservation Service.)

Trade

Dairy product exports have been rising as world demand for food increases and new markets open. According to the U.S. Dairy Export Council, export volume amounted to nearly 13% of U.S. production in 2010—a sharp rise from previous years. However, increased dairy exports are expected to continue as dairy products and fast-food pizza and cheeseburgers become part of the diet in China, India, and various Southeast Asian nations. Access the latest export data from the U.S. Dairy Export Council at http://www.usdec.org/home.cfm?navItemNumber=82205.

INDUSTRY ORGANIZATIONS

American Dairy Science Association

http://www.adsa.org/

Dairy Management Inc.

10255 West Higgins Rd., Suite 900

http://www.dairyinfo.com/

Dairy Management, Inc., (DMI) is the domestic and international planning and management organization that works to increase demand for U.S.-produced dairy products abroad. DMI manages the **American Dairy Association**, the **National Dairy Council**, and the **U.S. Dairy Export Council**.

National Dairy FARM Program

http://www.nationaldairyfarm.com/

The National Dairy FARM Program: Farmers Assuring Responsible Management™ provides nationwide verification of dairy cow well-being. The organization's goal is to provide consistent and uniform animal practices and verify these practices on farm to reassure customers and consumers.

National DHIA

http://www.dhia.org/

National Milk Producers Federation

http://www.nmpf.org/

The National Milk Producers Federation (NMPF) is a farm commodity organization representing dairy marketing cooperatives in the United States. The NMPF provides a forum through which dairy farmers and their cooperatives formulate policy on national issues that affect milk production and marketing.

SUMMARY AND CONCLUSION

Dairy products provide approximately 11% of all yearly cash receipts from agriculture in the United States, amounting to approximately $26 billion. The purpose of the U.S. dairy industry is to provide high-quality food from resources that the human population cannot use, such as forage and by-products.

The dairy industry is dispersed across the country because it is generally more cost effective to produce milk near the human population that will consume it. Dairy cattle fill a niche in resource utilization, similar to other ruminants except that they require better feed, intensive management, and considerably more attention per animal. Milk is such a valued product that it makes the higher inputs worthwhile.

The dairy industry is restructuring. The West is becoming more important, operations are becoming larger, and technology is increasingly important in driving the industry. Because of the dairy industry's importance to U.S. agriculture and to human nutrition, an extensive network of resources and information is available to the dairy producer. Organizations like the DHIA help in providing information for making management decisions. Good information is available to dairy producers, but increasingly good managers are needed to make best use of the information.

Herd health is an especially important management tool for the dairy producer. Dairy cows produce a high-volume product. They must stay healthy to continue producing in an economical fashion. A program of total herd health can help. Trends and matters of importance to the dairy industry include continued restructuring, technological innovation, changing consumer preferences and demands, the fortunes of organic milk, and green concerns, such as environmental impacts and animal welfare.

Facts about Dairy Cattle

Birth weight:	Varies with breed and sex; 50–110 lbs
Mature weight:	Varies with breed, sex, and condition; female 900–1,600 lbs; male 1,400–3,000 lbs
Weaning age:	Commonly removed from cow at 1–2 days of age and fed milk or milk replacer for 4–8 weeks
Breeding age:	14–19 months (female)
Normal season of birth:	Year-round
Gestation:	280–283 days
Estrous cycle:	19–21 days
Duration of estrus:	12–18 hours
Calving interval (months):	11–15 (12 is preferable, but 13 is more realistic)
Normal calf crop:	70–80%
Names of various sex classes:	Calf, heifer, cow, bull, steer
Type of digestive system:	Ruminant

STUDY QUESTIONS

1. Dairy amounts to how much of the total cash receipts of animal agriculture? Describe the magnitude of this industry in other ways. In addition to milk and its products, what other major product does the dairy industry provide?

2. What is the primary purpose of the dairy industry in the United States? What are the resources it uses? What is the dairy's role in using homegrown feeds?

3. Study the section on the history of the dairy industry. Select five elements that you feel are the most important and justify your list.

4. How geographically concentrated is the dairy industry compared to the other animal industries? Why is this?

5. What are the major dairy areas in the United States? Include the states in each area. Where are the dairy areas in a state most likely to be found? Name the

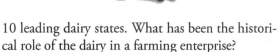

10 leading dairy states. What has been the historical role of the dairy in a farming enterprise?

6. How many dairy cattle are there in the United States? What is happening to the overall numbers? What is happening to dairy cow production per cow?

7. Describe the function and value of NCDHIP.

8. Name the major dairy breeds in the United States. Rank them on milk production and on popularity.

9. Why are reproductive problems such an issue in the dairy industry? What role does nutrition play in reproduction? How can DHIA records be used to help reproductive efficiency?

10. Why is feeding the most important variable that needs to be controlled if a dairy is to be profitable?

Why is good forage so important to dairy feeding and profitability?

11. Describe complete mixed ration feeding in dairy cattle. What are its advantages?

12. What are some common diseases that all dairy producers must understand and be able to prevent and respond to?

13. Describe the use of BST in dairy cattle. Does it work? Is it safe? Why or why not?

14. Describe the nutritional benefits of milk to the human diet. What nutrient is milk most famous for providing? After looking at the nutritional information, do you feel milk is being overlooked as an important source of other nutrients?

15. Describe the trends that are shaping the dairy industry in one sentence each.

REFERENCES

Beginning with the second edition, Dr. Tony Seykora, professor of animal science, University of Minnesota, has reviewed this chapter. In addition, Dr. Seykora contributed new material to the chapter. For the 5th edition, Melanie A. Breshears, DVM, PhD, Diplomate ACVP, assistant professor of veterinary pathobiology, Center for Veterinary Health Sciences, Oklahoma State University, contributed material to this chapter. The author gratefully acknowledges these contributions.

Aitchison, T. E. 1992. Dairy sire evaluations in the U.S.A. *The National Dairy Database (1992) Collection; Genetics Improvement.*

Blayney, D., M. Gehlhar, C. H. Bolling, K. Jones, S. Langley, M. A. Normile, and A. Somwaru. 2006. *U.S. dairy at a global crossroads.* USDA-ERS report number 28, November 2006. Accessed online at www.ers.usda.gov.

Drache, H. M. 1996. *History of U.S. agriculture and its relevance to today.* Danville, IL: Interstate.

Ensminger, M. E. 1980. *Dairy cattle science.* 2nd ed. Danville, IL: Interstate.

Ensminger, M. E. 1991. *Animal science.* 9th ed. Danville, IL: Interstate.

FAO. 2011. *FAOSTAT statistics database: Agricultural production and production indices data.* http://apps.fao.org/.

Linn, J. G., M. F. Hutjens, W. T. Howard, L. H. Kilmer, and D. E. Otterby. 1988. Feeding the dairy herd: Collection, feeding, and nutrition. *The National Dairy Database (1992) Collection; Genetics Improvement.*

McDonald, J. M., W. D. McBride, and E. J. O'Donoghue. 2007. Low costs drive production to large dairy farms. *Amber Waves.* USDA-ERS. Accessed online September 2007 at http://www.ers.usda.gov/AmberWaves/.

Miller, J. J., and D. P. Blayney. 2006. *Dairy backgrounder.* USDA-ERS, LDP-M-145-01. Accessed online July 2006. www.ers.usda.gov.

Murley, W. R., and G. M. Jones. 1985. Complete rations for dairy herds. *The National Dairy Database (1992) Collection; Feeding and Nutrition.*

Smil, V. 2001. *Feeding the world: A challenge for the twenty-first century.* Cambridge, Mass: MIT Press.

USDA-ARS. 2010. *USDA Summary of 2010 Herd Averages DHI Report K-3.* Accessed online March 2011. http://aipl.arsusda.gov/publish/dhi/current/hax.html.

USDA-ERS. 2011. *Livestock, dairy, and poultry outlook.* Accessed online. March 2011. http://www.ers.usda.gov/Briefing/Dairy/.

USDA-ERS. 2011a. *Farm income data.* Accessed online May 2011. http://www.ers.usda.gov/Data/FarmIncome/.

USDA-ERS. 2011b. *Food availability (per capita) data system Release 23.* http://www.ers.usda.gov/data/foodconsumption/.

USDA-NASS. 2010. *Overview of the United States Dairy Industry*. Sept. 2010.

USDA-NASS. 2011. *Dairy products annual summary*. April 2011. Washington, DC: National Agricultural Statistics Service, USDA.

USDA-NASS, 2011. 2011 Agricultural Statistics. Accessed online May 2011 at http://www.nass.usda.gov/Publications/Ag_Statistics/2007/index.asp.

USDA-NASS. 2011b. Briefing Room. Farm Income and Costs. Accessed online May 2011 at http://www.ers.usda.gov/Briefing/FarmIncome/.

USDA-NASS. 2011c. Milk production, 2011. Accessed online May 2011 at http://usda.mannlib.cornell.edu/MannUsda/viewDocumentInfo.do?documentID=1103.

USDA-NASS. 2011. Quick Stats: Agricultural Statistics Data Base. Accessed online March 2011 at http://www.nass.usda.gov/QuickStats/.

Weimer, M. R., and D. P. Blayney. 1994. *Landmarks in the U.S. dairy industry*. Agriculture Information Bulletin No. 694. Washington, DC: USDA-ERS.

Wells, H. F. and J. C. Buzby. 2008. Dietary assessment of major trends in U.S. food consumption, 1970–2005. USDA-ERS Economic Information Bulletin Number 33, March 2008.

🏚11

Poultry

Learning Objectives

After you have studied this chapter, you should be able to:

- Explain the place of poultry in U.S. agriculture.
- Describe the purpose and the value of the different poultry industry segments.
- Give a brief history of the poultry industry in the United States.
- Describe the poultry industry segments and structure.
- Give an accurate accounting of where the poultry industry is located in the United States.
- Quantify the role of genetics in the poultry industry.
- Explain the role of breeds in the U.S. poultry industry.
- Describe the major breeding programs for poultry.
- Give a basic outline for managing poultry to produce fertile eggs.
- Describe the feeding practices for different classes of poultry.
- Explain the concept of flock health management and give specifics regarding some common poultry diseases.
- Explain the nutritional benefits of various poultry products for humans.
- Discuss trends in the poultry industry including factors that will influence the industry in the future.

Key Terms

American Standard of Perfection
Avian
Bantam
Basic breeder
Blood spots
Breed
Broiler
Broiler duckling or fryer duckling
Brood
Brooder
Broodiness
Brooding
Candling
Chick
Class
Cock
Cockerel
Contract grower
Dead germs
Delmarva
Dirties
Economy of size
Fowl
Game birds
Gander
General combining ability
Hatching
Hen
Heritability
Heterosis
Inbred line

Inbreeding
Incrossbred hybrid
Incubator
Infertile
Layer
Laying
Litter
Mash
Mature duck or old duck
Mature goose or old goose
Molting
Omnivore
Outcrossing
Plumage
Poult
Poultry
Pullet
Quantitative traits
Roaster
Roaster duckling
Rooster
Setting
Sex-linked cross
Specific combining ability
Strain
Strain cross
Tom
Trapnest
Variety
Vertical integration
Young goose or gosling

SCIENTIFIC CLASSIFICATION OF POULTRY

Phylum:	Chordata
Subphylum:	Vertebrata
Class:	Aves

Order:	Galliformes
Suborder:	Galli
Family:	Phasinanidae (chicken); Meleagrididae (turkey)
Genus:	*Gallus* (chicken); *Meleagris* (turkey)
Species:	*domestica* (chicken); *galiopavo* (turkey)

THE PLACE OF POULTRY IN U.S. AGRICULTURE

Poultry is a term that includes a wide variety of domestic birds of several species, and it refers to them whether they are alive or dressed. However, the important commercial species are chickens and turkeys and, to a much lesser degree, ducks and geese. The poultry industry is large, with a combined gross annual income of almost $30 billion. The poultry industry has three major segments whose relative contributions to the total value of the poultry industry are shown in Figure 11–1. The poultry industry is responsible for over 11.6% of all U.S. farm cash receipts (Figure 11–2) and over 23% of animal agriculture's share of all U.S. farm cash receipts (Figure 11–3). The poultry sector is growing. It is the second-largest sector of animal agriculture.

Poultry Domestic birds raised for eggs and meat. However, this designation has some flexibility.

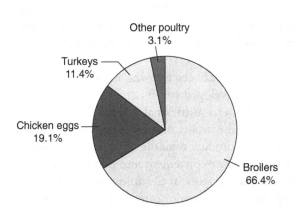

Figure 11–1
Relative contribution of poultry segments to total poultry industry value, 2000–2009. Source: USDA-NASS, 2011a

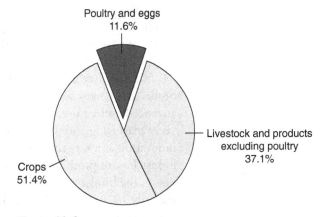

Figure 11–2
Poultry and eggs farm cash receipts as a percentage of total U.S. farm cash receipts, 2000–2009. Source: USDA-NASS, 2011a.

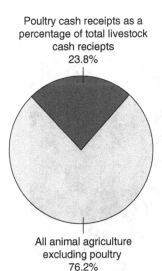

Figure 11–3
All poultry and eggs yearly farm cash receipts as a percentage of total animal agriculture's cash receipts, 2000–2009. Includes broilers, eggs, turkeys, ducks, and other poultry. Source: USDA-NASS, 2011a.

Figure 11–4

Broiler chickens such as these account for the largest share of the poultry industry. Broiler production has steadily increased in the United States since 1975. (Courtesy of USDA.)

Eleven states have in excess of $1 billion yearly in gross income from poultry. An additional nine have at least $0.5 billion. The poultry industry is in the top-five agricultural commodities for 28 states. The United States produces approximately 9% of the world's chicken eggs and 22% of the chicken meat, and it is the largest poultry meat-producing country in the world. The United States is second to China in chicken egg production, produces 50% of the world's turkey meat, and is the largest producer of turkeys in the world.

The poultry industry in the United States has been growing at a steady rate. The broiler and turkey sectors have aggressively developed and incorporated technology, advanced animal breeding techniques, advanced nutritional information, and very savvy marketing and product development. The broiler industry especially has seized innovation as a way to generate a lower-cost product than the other meat-producing industries can produce. It has made the product convenient and good to eat. In so doing, the broiler industry has been the success story of the animal industries since the early 1970s (Figure 11–4). The egg industry is a major contributor to the nation's food supply, providing more than 90 billion eggs annually. Of the domestic egg consumption, approximately 68% is consumed as fresh-shell eggs, and the remaining 32% is used in the manufacturing of products such as cakes, pies, pasta, and so on.

The duck segment of the poultry industry is the largest of the remaining segments (Figure 11–5). Ducks are raised primarily for meat. About 23 million ducks

Figure 11–5

Ducks comprise the largest segment of the poultry industry after broiler chickens, laying hens, and turkeys. Duck can often be found on the menu in upscale restaurants but is readily available for everyday dining. (Photo courtesy Culver Duck Farms.)

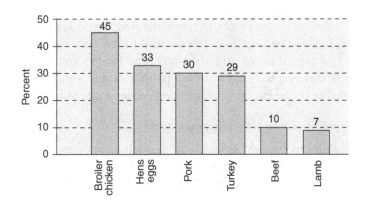

Figure 11–6
The graceful and beautiful swan is a poultry species kept almost exclusively for ornamental reasons.

are slaughtered annually in the United States to produce approximately 50,000 metric tons of meat. Most are produced under confinement on specialized duck farms in a few commercially important duck-production areas. However, many farms still raise a few ducks primarily for family use or for local sale. Geese are raised in practically all parts of the United States, although they are almost exclusively a hobbyist or farm flock species. Some are marketed commercially.

Game birds and other **exotic fowl** are usually kept either for exhibition or ornamental reasons or for meat production (Figure 11–6). Game birds are also kept for release and subsequent hunting. Demand for the meat is seasonal and is associated loosely with the Thanksgiving and Christmas holidays. This is probably because these holidays fall within the traditional hunting seasons. Many families have traditions of game dinners during the holiday seasons. The market for meat is generally local consumers or specialty processors, much of it for the hotel and restaurant trade.

Game birds Fowl for which there is an established hunting season. Also refers to fighting chickens.

Exotic fowl Nonindigenous, nonlivestock species often kept for ornamental reasons.

PURPOSE OF THE POULTRY INDUSTRY IN THE UNITED STATES

The primary purpose of the poultry industry in the United States is to produce inexpensive sources of protein for human consumption. The industry takes grain and by-products and produces meat and eggs very efficiently. These products are among the best buys in the marketplace today for high-quality protein. Poultry are monogastric and very efficient converters of grain to meat (Figure 11–7). Because they are

Figure 11–7
Product protein output as a percentage of feed protein.
(Source: Compiled from several sources from the *Proceedings of the 8th World Conference on Animal Production*, Seoul, Korea, 1998.)

Product	Percent
Broiler chicken	45
Hens eggs	33
Pork	30
Turkey	29
Beef	10
Lamb	7

monogastric, poultry require high-energy feeds to be produced economically. Feed costs are a high fixed cost, so economical production depends on reducing labor demands and reducing time to market as a means of more efficient production. This is done with expensive confinement facilities and full feeding of high-energy rations.

Poultry are quite useful worldwide. Increasingly, U.S.-style confinement facilities are being built around the world for their production. In poor countries, poultry are often fed on wastes and allowed to range freely and forage for themselves. Left to their own devices, they eat a variety of feedstuffs from insects to seeds, even small rodents and reptiles. Worldwide, chicken-meat production surpassed beef production in 1999 and amounts to over 73% of pork production and is gaining. Combined poultry-meat production equals over 32% of the world's total meat production. If the weight of the world's egg production is added to the previously mentioned poultry meats, then poultry accounts for approximately 1.5 times as much high-quality protein product as pork and nearly 2.5 times as much as beef.

Although not large in terms of economic value, poultry hobbyists comprise a large and dedicated group of individuals who deserve acknowledgment. Their interests range from fancy (exhibition) chickens to game birds. Poultry keepers have a wide variety of species from which to choose, and virtually all are hardy and easy to raise. Space requirements and feed bills can be kept to a minimum. Products can be harvested from the poultry for household use or sold to help defray costs. Pigeons can be raced. The ornamental species can grace a property or a body of water. Children in the family can be taught biology and responsibility, and they can learn to enjoy the animals and, by extension, other species as well. Without hobbyists, many breeds of poultry would effectively disappear because they have no place in the commercial industry.

In addition, several industrial uses of poultry give a somewhat different dimension to the purpose of the poultry industry and are worth mentioning. Fertile eggs are used in the preparation of vaccines for other animals and humans. Endocrine glands are used in making biological products. Eggs are used in the making of pharmaceuticals, and in paints, varnishes, adhesives, and printer's ink. Photography, book binding, wine clarification, leather tanning, and textile dyeing make use of eggs. Feathers are used in millinery goods, pillows, cushions, mattresses, dusters, and insulation material. The **chick** has also been a very important research animal. The chick is much more sensitive to the lack of several substances in the diet than are most other available species. Also, chicks are cheap and readily available, and large numbers of them can be hatched at the same time so as to provide accuracy and repeatability in research work.

Chick A young chicken or game bird of either sex from 1 day to about 5 to 6 weeks of age.

HISTORICAL PERSPECTIVE

Domestication

Domestic chickens were known in India over 3,400 years ago, and they were present in Egypt and China by 1400 B.C. DNA testing has demonstrated conclusively that modern chickens descended from the Red Jungle fowl *Gallus gallus,* which is native to Thailand and still found in the wild today. Gaming has been proposed and generally accepted as the primary motivation for the first domestication of the chicken. Cockfighting has been a favored pastime of many ancient civilizations and is considered to be the largest spectator sport in the world today.

Early Use in the United States

Columbus brought chickens along with a selection of other animals to this hemisphere on his second voyage in 1493. In 1607, the chicken was introduced to the North American continent by the settlers of the Jamestown Colony. The practice of

Figure 11–8
Small flocks of chickens were commonly kept in this country from colonial times until the middle of the 20th century as an integral part of the sustenance for the family. The primary product was eggs. The meat was reserved for special occasions and considered a luxury. During the mid-1920s, meat production from chickens reached significant levels and the broiler industry was born. It has been growing ever since. (Photographer Arthur Rothstein. Courtesy of USDA.)

small-flock keeping persisted until the middle of the 20th century (Figure 11–8). The flock provided meat and eggs for the family, and the extra was sold to provide cash to buy household staples. The practice began fading when agriculture began restructuring in the 1950s. In 1840, the first census of poultry was taken in the United States, providing a means of tracking the industry. In 1844, the incubator was patented, although it would not be until 1892 that the first long-distance express shipment of baby chicks would take place. This marked the beginning of the commercial hatchery industry. Commercial hatcheries got another boost in 1918 when the U.S. Post Office allowed chicks to be shipped by mail. The entire industry received another important device in 1923 when Ira Petersime developed the electrically heated incubator, providing a way for chicks to be hatched other than under **hens**. After 1960, virtually all chicks have been hatched in incubators and then shipped to producers.

Eggs

In 1872, a commodity exchange for the trading of cash eggs was chartered. In 1874, chicken wire, which made flocks easier to manage, was first introduced. In 1878, the first commercial egg-drying operation was established, giving eggs new uses and storage potential beyond the traditional spring–summer–fall **laying** season. In 1889, artificial light was first used to stimulate egg production in the winter months. This allowed producers to extend the season of lay beyond the traditional season. By 1899, frozen eggs were marketed, and the following year the first egg-breaking operation was established. In 1909, the electric candler, which allowed intact eggs to be inspected for deformities, was developed. This had positive **hatching** and egg-marketing implications. The USDA issued the first tentative classes, standards, and grades of eggs in 1923, and in 1934 legal standards for eggs were introduced, providing uniformity for marketing. The egg-producing industry took a major leap in 1929 when **layers** were kept in **individual cages** at the Ohio Agricultural Experiment Station. In that same year, **pelleting** of poultry feed began, which reduced waste and helped ensure that each animal received a balanced diet. In 1931, laying cages were first given general publicity and lights were kept on chicken hens all night at the Ohio Agricultural Experiment Station as a means of stimulating egg production. In 1932, forced **molting** started in Washington state, which improved egg quality and provided an important management tool for egg production.

Hen A mature female chicken or turkey.

Laying Technically, the expulsion of an egg (i.e., "That hen over there is *laying*."). However, commonly used to refer to hens in egg production (i.e., "Barn twelve is a *laying* hen barn.").

Hatching The process of a chick leaving the egg and emerging into the world. Birth for fowl.

Layer A hen in the physiological state of producing eggs regularly.

Individual cage Small pens perhaps 8 to 12 in. wide and 18 in. long designed to hold one or more hens.

Pelleting A method of processing feed in which the feed is first ground and then forced through a die to give it a shape.

Molting The shedding of feathers by chickens.

Genetics

Throughout the world, chickens evolved into different types to fit varied environments. For centuries, travelers took poultry with them. Poultry are small and easy to transport and could be eaten if food became scarce along the way. Keeping small flocks on ships, especially on long voyages, was common practice in previous centuries. In this country, existing breeds and developed breeds were used across the many environments the landscape offered. Poultry show divisions at county fairs helped ensure that breeds flourished and were kept in pure strains.

In 1828, the first Single Comb White Leghorns were imported into the United States. They would ultimately become the most important egg-producing breed in the United States. Breeding programs involving red chickens began in 1830 near Narragansett Bay, Rhode Island. The dual-purpose Rhode Island Red was one of the outcomes of these programs (Figure 11–9). Later, the New Hampshire Red was developed from the Rhode Island Red. In 1840, birds from China began entering the United States. In 1873, the American Poultry Association, the nation's first livestock organization, was formed. In 1874, they issued the American Standard of Excellence for poultry, known today as the ***American Standard of Perfection***. It has been updated and issued continuously since the first edition. The book provided a uniform set of breed standards for poultry breeders. In 1869, the first **trapnest** patent, which allowed a hen and her egg to be paired, was granted. Research had a valuable new tool. In 1870, the toe punch and a system of numbering based on the number and placement of toe punches were introduced for identification in breeding programs. In 1928, the first **sex-linked crosses** were advertised. In 1935, artificial insemination of poultry was introduced and the first successful **incrossbred-hybrid** chickens were produced for egg production. This led to an extremely important event in poultry breeding that occurred in 1940. Hy-Line Poultry Farms in Des Moines, Iowa, marketed its first Hy-Line layers. These birds were developed by applying inbred-hybrid corn-breeding principles to egg production. This was the effective beginning of the deemphasis of breeds, which were replaced by the use of lines and strains of birds in commercial poultry production. This is still common practice today.

Chicks

The problem of hatching large numbers of chicks had been dealt with by the development of the incubator, but there was still the problem of rearing large numbers of

American Standard of Perfection A standard published in book form by the American Poultry Association. It lists the recognized breeds and varieties of poultry and their characteristics.

Trapnest A nest that traps a hen while she is on the nest so that her production and egg quality can be recorded.

Sex-linked cross Sex-linked chicks can be sexed at birth by their color. Males are one color and females are another color.

Incrossbred hybrid Chickens developed by crossing inbred lines within the same breed. This technique is generally used to produce laying hens.

Figure 11–9
Breeding programs near Narragansett Bay, Rhode Island, resulted in the dual-purpose Rhode Island Red (pictured) and later the New Hampshire Red. (Courtesy of Watt Publishing Company)

chicks without the help of a hen. In 1903, the Cornell gasoline **brooder** was developed at Cornell University. Large numbers of chicks could be kept warm and could grow in the brooder. It was later replaced by the much safer oil brooder.

Integration

In 1895, the commercial feed industry began in Chicago. This was the important first step of overall integration of the poultry industry. In 1918, the first USDA federal–state grading programs for poultry were established. During the 1920s, poultry production began on an industrial scale. In the early days, live poultry were transported from areas of production to areas of consumption. An outbreak of **fowl** plague at the New York Central railroad yards stimulated the New York Poultry Commission Association to organize an inspection program, which led to the establishment of the USDA's Poultry Inspection Service in 1926. In 1928, the live poultry inspection expanded to include dressed poultry and edible products. The **Delmarva** region of the United States began to be the center of commercial broiler production. The USDA recognized this activity as different from traditional farm rearing of birds and in 1934 began reporting commercial broilers separately. The production of broiler meat by the broiler industry since 1940 is shown in Figure 11–10. At this time, the chicken was Sunday dinner rather than everyday fare. In 1940, mechanical poultry dressing was initiated, giving the meat-producing sector a giant boost. Improvements in diets, equipment, genetics, flock health, and processing came at a steady pace. Costs of production are estimated to have been cut in half from 1940 to 1960, and the industry spread across the Midwest. Prices declined and chicken became everyday food. The profit margin decreased for producers, who had to increase the size of their flocks to make a living. They soon began depending on the feed producer as their source of credit. As this practice grew, the feed dealers began to depend on the commercial feed manufacturers as their source of credit. To protect themselves financially, the feed suppliers and manufacturers began to acquire hatcheries and processors. Integration was born in the poultry industry. Consolidation began, and more **vertical integration** occurred, producing an industry that today is completely vertically integrated.

In 1956, Colonel Harland Sanders began franchise operations of Kentucky Fried Chicken, which ultimately led to new life for chicken consumption. This was the same year that integration and contracting began in the egg business. By 1962, corporate egg farms had become a viable part of the poultry industry. In a span of just a few years, poultry production was composed of large integrated farms that contracted with individual producers to produce eggs, broilers, and turkeys. The companies supplied the animals, feed, **litter**, fuel, and medication, and the

Brooder A device with controlled heat and light used to warm chicks from the day of hatch to approximately 5 weeks of age. The heat is usually contained in a large reflector or hover under which the birds congregate.

Fowl Any bird, but generally refers to the larger ones. In this context, it refers to poultry species only.

Delmarva Geographic region comprised of Delaware, Maryland, and Virginia.

Vertical integration A form of contract production in which all stages of production are owned by one entity, corporation, or individual.

Litter Material such as wood shavings, straw, or sawdust used to bed the floor of a poultry house.

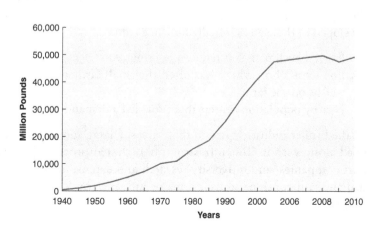

Figure 11–10
Production of broiler meat by the broiler industry.
Source: Based on USDA, Meat Animals Production, Disposition & Income, 1998, and USDA-NASS, 2011b.

Contract grower
Producers of poultry and eggs who contract with an organization, usually integrated, to raise a product for a price determined through the contractual arrangement.

contract growers provided housing and labor. By 1970, it was estimated that vertical integration involved 95% of the nation's broilers, 85% of the turkeys, and 30% of the table eggs. In 1972, a vaccine for Marek's disease was approved, reducing some of the risk for concentrating large numbers of poultry in single sites. In 1981, combined cash receipts for poultry first exceeded those from hogs and in 1997 surpassed dairy. Today, per capita consumption of chicken and poultry is still increasing. This is because of the poultry industry's ability to contain costs and provide products at lower prices relative to alternatives, and its aggressive development of convenient and further-processed products. The modern mechanized poultry farm as we know it emerged in the late 1950s. The integrated poultry industry we know today emerged between 1955 and 1975. Integration brings all phases of the operation under centralized control. From 1975 until the present, tremendous consolidation occurred. Today, there is a relatively small number of integrated super companies.

STRUCTURE AND GEOGRAPHIC LOCATION OF THE POULTRY INDUSTRY

Vertical integration provides the structural framework of the commercial poultry industry.

The U.S. Broiler Industry

Broiler A chicken of either sex produced and used for meat purposes. Generally slaughtered at 6 weeks of age or younger. The term *fryer* is often used interchangeably.

Roaster A young meat chicken, generally 12 to 16 weeks old weighing 4 to 6 lbs.

Game hen A standard meat-type chicken packaged at a smaller size. Also called Rock Cornish game hen or Cornish game hen to reflect the influence of the Cornish breed in most of the chickens sold this way.

Economy of size A relatively simple concept revolving around the maximization of the use of equipment, labor, and other costly items.

Brood A group of baby chickens. As a verb it refers to the growing of baby chicks.

Meat chickens are marketed primarily as **broilers**, **roasters**, or **game hens**. All come from what is referred to as the broiler industry. Modern broiler production is concentrated in a relatively few large farms with large investments in facilities. In 1959, the average number of broilers raised per farm was 34,000 birds. Today, several farms in the United States have more than 1 million birds per site. **Economies of size** favor large operations. In addition, gains in production efficiencies have allowed producers to rear more than six **broods** per house per year, so more birds can be grown in the same space. Before 1940, the broiler chicken was marketed at 16 weeks of age. Today, the broiler chicken is being reared to heavier weights and marketed at less than half that age.

The broiler industry is a highly integrated corporate industry rather than an industry of independent producers. A typical integrated broiler company owns or controls everything it needs but the consumer. All segments are either owned or controlled by the parent company. Well over 90% of the commercial broilers in the United States are grown under contract to an integrated broiler firm (Figure 11–11). A large percentage of what is left is grown on integrator-owned farms. Much of the product is sold with the producer's name on the label.

The broiler industry is centered in the southern and southeastern states, with the top 10 states remaining fairly constant (Figure 11–12). The industry located and developed in these areas initially for three reasons:

1. Favorable climate that reduced housing costs
2. Low-cost labor, which was often the small farmer who worked off the farm as well as on the farm
3. Nearby population centers that provided a demand for the product.

As the broiler industry grew in these areas, a large supporting infrastructure developed along with it. This infrastructure included processing plants, technical support companies, and university research and extension groups. This infrastructure had and will continue to have a major influence on keeping the industry centered in this area.

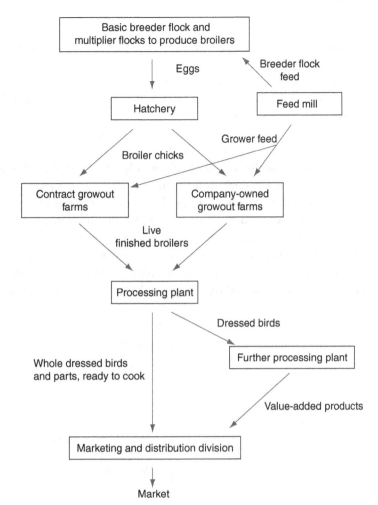

Figure 11–11
Structure of a typical integrated broiler company.
Source: Adapted from Taylor and Field, 1998.

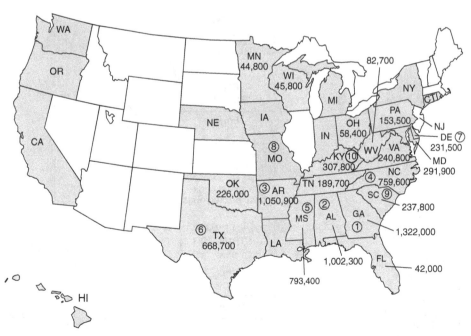

Figure 11–12
The production of broilers by state, number raised (× 1,000), 2009. Circled numbers indicate the ranking for the top-10 production states. Source: USDA-NASS, 2011c.

The U.S. Egg Industry

Egg production is also accomplished in large units that require large capital investments. Environmentally controlled housing and computer technology are common. Most eggs produced in commercial egg operations are never touched by human hands from the point of production until they are taken from their container to be used. The egg-producing industry is concentrated and integrated for many of the same reasons as the broiler industry. Most production is integrated from hatchery to marketing of the eggs (Figure 11–13).

Geographically, the poultry egg industry is distributed in a pattern much like that of the human population (Figure 11–14). Population is not the only factor that determines where layers are located, however. If that were so, then the distribution would perfectly mirror the human population, and it doesn't. However, egg production is more dispersed across the country than broiler production. There are several reasons for this, with these two being very important: (1) Eggs require less processing than broilers, which allows more flexibility in moving and marketing the product; and (2) locally produced fresh eggs can be promoted and sold at a premium.

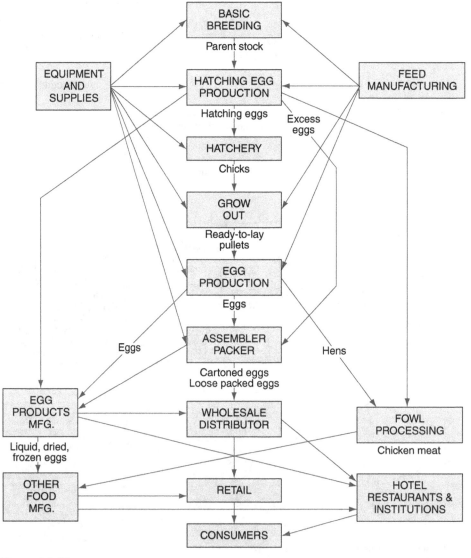

Figure 11–13

The integrated egg-producing operation. (Source: Schrader et al., 1978.)

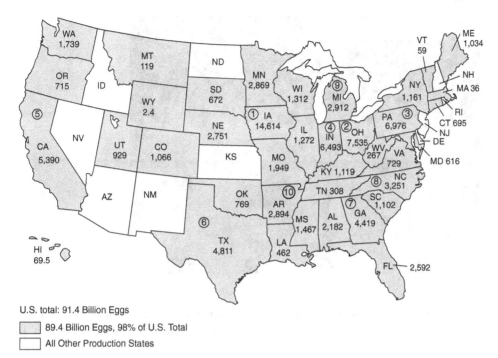

Figure 11–14

Egg production by state, in millions, in 2009. Circled numbers indicate ranking for the top-10 production states. Source: USDA-NASS, 2011c.

The average number of laying hens and **pullets** in the United States is about 340 million birds. Total U.S. egg production is about 92 billion eggs. The number of laying hens and eggs increased until the early 1970s and then remained relatively constant, with some declines noted in the mid-1970s until the late 1980s. Since the late 1980s, egg production in the United States has generally increased (Figure 11–15). The number of eggs per layer has increased from 227 per hen in 1973 to 269 per hen in 2011, with an approximate increase of one egg per hen per year.

Pullet A young female chicken.

The U.S. Turkey Industry

Most turkey production units grow from 50,000 to 75,000 birds and have approximately three and a half grow-out cycles per year (Figure 11–16). Large facilities often have a single **brooding** complex that serves multiple grow-out facilities.

Brooding The act of raising young poultry under environmentally controlled conditions during the first few weeks of life.

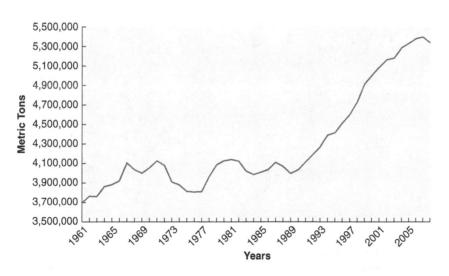

Figure 11–15

Egg production in the United States, 1961–2008. Source: FAOSTAT, 2011.

Figure 11–16

Turkeys in a 10,000-bird building in Benton, Arkansas. Manure and wood chips used for bedding are composted and used as fertilizer on nearby pastures. Turkey production is the third-largest segment of the poultry industry behind broilers and layers. (Photo by Jeff Vaughn courtesy of USDA-Natural Resources Conservation Service.)

Because turkeys are no longer produced just for seasonal consumption, turkey production is year-round. Virtually all turkeys are produced on contract to an integrator.

Turkey hens are marketed between 14 and 16 weeks of age and from 14–18 lbs. **Toms** are marketed between 17 and 20 weeks of age and from 26–32 lbs. Some variation exists based on whether the birds will be processed or sold whole and ready to cook. About 70% is further processed. Toms are preferred for further processing because of their larger weights as compared to hens. However, since only about a sixth of all turkey production is processed for the whole body market, many hens are also further processed. The remainder is processed and marketed as value-added products.

It is hard to see the same patterns in the turkey-producing industry as can be seen in the broiler industry (Figure 11–17). The reasons why particular states produce substantial amounts of turkey are varied. Virginia and South Carolina no doubt benefit from overlap from North Carolina, which is a top producer. Some

Tom A male turkey. Also called a *gobbler*.

Poult Baby turkeys. Once sex can be determined, they are called young toms (males) or young hens (females).

Figure 11–17

Turkey-producing states, in thousands, in 2010. Source: USDA-NASS, 2011c.

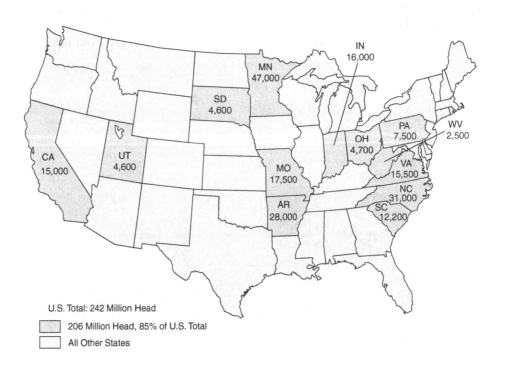

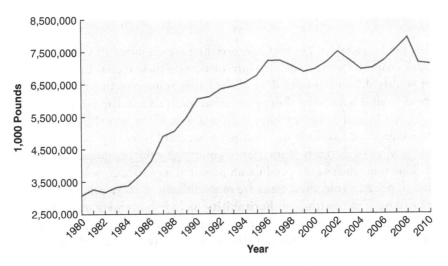

Figure 11–18
U.S. turkey meat production 1980–2010. Source: USDA-NASS, 2011b.

states are located near consumer centers. Arkansas benefits from the corporate structure already in place for broilers and layers. Some states benefit from being located near Arkansas. California has geographic isolation and population centers. The turkey industry has seen the same kinds of consolidation as the rest of the poultry industry. Nearly 8 billion pounds of turkey meat are produced in the United States each year on a live-weight basis. This requires approximately 270 million head of birds. Production of turkey underwent rapid increases during the 1980s and much of the 1990s. It has experienced more variable, but generally increasing, production since (Figure 11–18).

The U.S. Duck, Goose, and Other Poultry Industries

Table 11–1 gives statistics about several of the smaller poultry industries found in the United States. As can be seen from the table, none of these are large industries.

Table 11–1
MISCELLANEOUS POULTRY INVENTORY

Ducks		Geese		Pigeons or Squab	
Top 5 States	Inventory	Top 5 States	Inventory	Top 5 States	Inventory
Indiana	1,538,664	Texas	14,054	California	170,473
California	802,076	Minnesota	12,774	Pennsylvania	38,445
Pennsylvania	458,430	South Dakota	10,818	Washington	26,180
Wisconsin	413,598	Wisconsin	8,737	Minnesota	24,217
New York	204,552	Michigan	8,708	New York	21,394
U.S. Total	3,984,982	U.S. Total	177,812	U.S. Total	531,489

Pheasants		Quail	
Top 5 States	Inventory	Top 5 States	Inventory
South Dakota	450,713	Georgia	2,991,860
Wisconsin	433,795	North Carolina	1,513,994
Pennsylvania	424,251	Alabama	1,458,393
Michigan	338,446	Texas	1,435,992
Minnesota	311,481	South Carolina	923,757
U.S. Total	3,773,593	U.S. Total	10,611,067

Source: 2007 Census of Agriculture.

GENETICS AND BREEDING PROGRAMS

Quantitative traits Traits inherited through the action of many genes. Most of the economically important traits are quantitative such as growth and carcass characteristics and egg production traits. Qualitative traits are those inherited through the action of a single pair of genes.

Heritability A measure of the amount of phenotypic variation that is related to additive gene effects.

Heterosis The superiority of an outbred individual relative to the average performance of the parent populations included in the cross.

Inbreeding Mating individuals more closely related than the average of the population.

Inbred line An established line of chickens created by intensive inbreeding. They are usually mated to other inbred lines to produce commercial varieties.

Basic breeder Produces parent stock used for multiplication of poultry, either by outcrossing, inbreeding, or other methods. Also referred to as *primary breeder*.

Outcrossing The practice of mating unrelated breeds or strains in poultry. Used extensively in broiler production and to a lesser degree in other poultry.

Strain cross Mating different strains of the same breed and variety. Generally the strains have been inbred to some degree and selected for different strengths to get increased production in the offspring.

General combining ability A term that describes a strain that contributes positively to the genetic makeup of offspring resulting from mating it with several different strains.

The fundamentals of genetics and breeding are discussed in Chapters 6 and 7. See those chapters for more detailed information on these topics. Breeding and selection of poultry differs from breeding of the larger animals in three major ways: (1) It is more flexible because of short generation intervals and large numbers of offspring; (2) it has been the industry most subjected to modern animal breeding and selection techniques and has made the most progress; and (3) fewer people make all the decisions. Most of the traits of interest in poultry genetics are **quantitative traits**. These include traits such as egg production potential, egg size, growth rate, conformation, and so on. As a rule, these traits are more difficult to make progress in than are simpler traits. Traits with high **heritability** include body weight, feed consumption, egg weight, age at sexual maturity, egg shape, and egg color. Total egg production and feed efficiency are lower in heritability. Fertility and hatchability are very low in heritability.

Heterosis is very easy to demonstrate in poultry. Data from the 1950s indicate that heterosis can increase egg production by over 20 eggs per year. Other traits showing favorable heterosis include egg weight, body weight, and age at reproductive maturity (days to first egg). Many poultry-breeding systems specifically target heterosis because of its benefits. The hybrids must be produced from pure strains, which can be continually improved to produce ever better heterosis results.

The most important traits that laying hen breeding programs target are rearing mortality, laying mortality, age at 50% production, feed per weight of eggs produced, egg weight, percentage of large and extra-large eggs, body weight, several egg quality measurements, and shell quality. Meat-producing chickens must be selected for rate of growth, conformation, feed efficiency, structural soundness (fast-growing broilers often have leg problems), disease resistance, and skin and feather color. The parent stock of the broilers needs good reproductive characteristics so the eggs that will produce the broilers can be produced economically.

Poultry breeding programs make use of most of the animal breeder's tools in producing quality birds for production. **Inbreeding** is frequently used to produce strains of birds to use later by being crossed with a different **inbred line** for some specific purpose. These inbred lines are frequently only used by **basic breeders**. **Outcrossing** is the term used in poultry for crossbreeding. Outcrossing is also practiced through a variation called **strain crossing**, a process in which the inbred lines within the same breed might be used. When a specific strain usually contributes positively to a cross, it is said to have **general combining ability**. Other strains generally contribute only when crossed with other specific strains, referred to as **specific combining ability**. Some strains are known to contribute to crossing more positively if always used as the male parent, and others when used as the female parent. Once good combinations are discovered, the pure lines are maintained and used to produce the crosses, which may be three- or four-way crosses involving different breeds and/or strains.

Poultry breeding is handled in an extremely controlled manner. The actual number of individuals who direct breeding programs is considerably fewer than 100. This helps produce uniformity in the product. Companies invest large sums in breeding facilities, animals, labor, recordkeeping, and statistical analysis. For all practical purposes, all commercial poultry today are crosses of breeds, strains, or inbred lines.

BREEDS, VARIETIES, AND STRAINS OF POULTRY

Generally speaking, chickens are one of two types: meat type or egg type. However, this generalization is too simple to explain poultry fully. Chickens exist in many colors, sizes, and shapes and in more than 350 combinations of these traits. Additional species have also been developed with different characteristics. To identify and classify the species, they are designated by **class**, **breed**, **variety**, and **strain**.

A class is a group of breeds originating in the same geographic area. Names are taken from the region where the breeds originated. Examples include Asiatic, Mediterranean, American, and English. A breed possesses a specific set of physical features, such as body shape or type, skin color, number of toes, and feathered or nonfeathered shanks. Individuals within a breed, when mated to other individuals of the breed, pass these features to their offspring in a uniform way. Varieties are subdivisions of breeds. Varieties are based on such characteristics as feather color, comb type, and presence of a beard and muffs. For example, the Plymouth Rock is a breed that has several color varieties including Barred, White, Buff, and Partridge. Their body shape and physical features are essentially identical, but each color is a separate variety. Strains are families or breeding populations that are more nearly alike than the breed or variety they are a subdivision of. They may also be the products of systematic crossbreeding. However, a strain shows a closer relationship than that for others within the breed or variety. Today, the commercial poultry industry is based primarily on strains and strain crosses.

There are no effective breed registry associations for poultry that function in the same way as do the larger livestock breed associations. The American Poultry Association maintains a standard for recognized breeds and promotes exhibition of poultry. It publishes the *American Standard of Perfection*, which is a compilation of the breed standards. In this sense, the American Poultry Association functions as a breed registry. This book contains descriptions and information about more than 500 recognized breeds and varieties of chickens, **bantams**, ducks, geese, guinea fowl, and turkeys. Size, shape, color, and physical features are described and illustrated. The terms *purebred* and *registered* are not used in poultry. Instead, poultry that meet the breed and variety descriptions found in the *American Standard of Perfection* are referred to as "standard bred." Some chicken and duck breeds have miniature versions (a fifth to a quarter the size of the large bird). Some breeds also only exist in the miniature forms. These small forms are referred to as *bantams* (the term *bantam* is an adjective). Thus, there are bantam Leghorns and bantam Old English Game chickens.

Chicken Breeds in Modern Production

Relatively few of the breeds of poultry have any real place in the modern commercial poultry industry. Synthetic lines (strains) of poultry have gradually replaced the breeds in commercial poultry operations. They were developed originally from crossing pure breeds or even crossing within a breed by selecting from highly inbred lines within breeds. A brief discussion follows of breeds and varieties of chickens that are either still in use or were used to develop modern synthetic lines.

The Single Comb White Leghorn is one of several varieties of Leghorns (Figure 11–19). Many synthetic strains have been developed from this variety, and it is the most numerous breed in the United States today. Virtually all commercial white egg-producing flocks are strains of Leghorns. They are strictly egg type.

The Single Comb Rhode Island Red and Barred Plymouth Rock are used most often to produce sex-linked color differences in day-old chicks. In this way, chicks can be sexed easily and rapidly. Many commercial brown-egg layers are the result

Specific combining ability When a strain only contributes positively to a cross when mated with certain, specific other lines.

Class In poultry, a group of breeds originating in the same geographic area. Names are taken from the region where the breeds originated.

Breed Birds having a common origin with specific characteristics, such as body shape, that distinguishes them from other groups within the same species and breeds that produce offspring with the same characteristics. In poultry, a breed may include several varieties different only in color or comb type.

Variety A subdivision of a breed distinguished by color, pattern, comb, or some other physical characteristic.

Strain Families or breeding populations within a breed. They have been more rigorously selected for some trait or set of traits than the average of the breed.

Bantam Fowl that are miniatures of full-sized breeds. Some are distinct breeds, usually a fourth to a fifth the weight of standard birds. Considered ornamental.

Figure 11–19
Strains and strain crosses of the Single Comb White Leghorn are the most popular laying hen in the United States. (Photo by Stephen Ausmus courtesy USDA-Agricultural Research Service.)

Rooster A mature male chicken. Also referred to as a *cock*.

of crossing Rhode Island **roosters** with Barred Plymouth Rock hens. This cross is a good producer of large brown eggs.

The New Hampshire and White Plymouth Rock were, and still are, used to develop many of the synthetic lines of meat-type chickens. Most commercial meat-producing crosses have one or the other of both of these breeds somewhere on the female side.

The Cornish is an excellent meat-producing chicken, but it has poor reproductive characteristics. It is a very important part of the commercial meat-producing industry because of its growth rates and carcass characteristics. Cornish males are crossed with females that are crosses of Barred Plymouth Rock, White Plymouth Rock, New Hampshire, or synthetic lines. It is safe to say that virtually all the commercial broilers in the United States contain some Cornish blood (Figure 11–20).

There is some concern today that the genetic base of poultry species is too narrow. The counterargument is that most breeds have no place in commercial production. The American Livestock Breeds Conservancy is an organization that works to preserve endangered breeds of livestock and is a source of interesting information on minor breeds of all livestock species.

Figure 11–20
Cornish (pictured) males are crossed with females that are crosses of Barred Plymouth Rock, White Plymouth Rock, New Hampshire, or synthetic lines to produce meat birds. It is safe to say that virtually all the commercial broilers in the United States contain some Cornish blood. (Courtesy of Watt Publishing Company.)

Turkey Breeds

The modern turkey is a descendant of the wild turkeys native to North and Central America and is North America's major species contribution to the livestock industry (Figure 11–21). The *American Standard of Perfection* lists eight varieties of turkeys: Bronze, Narragansett, White Holland, Black, Slate, Bourbon Red, Beltsville Small White, and Royal Palm. All were developed in the United States except the White Holland. For all practical purposes, the term *breed* now refers to color and size types. The term *variety* now means different commercial brands offered for sale by poultry-breeding companies. Probably around 50 commercial turkey varieties are available from breeders and hatcheries in the United States. Large White, Medium White, Small White, and Bronze are generally offered. Because of the processing industry and the emphasis on size, the Large Whites have come to dominate. The white color varieties are the most popular because they withstand hot summer sun better than the colored varieties do. They are also easier to prepare for market because of the absence of dark pin feathers, which can leave a carcass looking dirty. The same is true for the other poultry species.

Duck and Goose Breeds

The Mallard is the most popular duck in the United States. The White Pekin duck, native to China, was brought to the United States in 1873. It is the major duck of commercial importance in the United States because it reaches market weight earlier than the other breeds, is a fairly good egg producer, and has white feathers. Pekins are also generally free of **broodiness**. The Rouen, a colored duck, is a popular farm flock breed. Although slower growing than the Pekin, it reaches the same weight under farm flock feeding and foraging. Its slower growth and colored **plumage** make it undesirable for commercial production. The Muscovy is also used in farm flocks because it is a good forager and the hens are good setters. It originated in Brazil and is the only one of the major breeds not originally developed from the wild Mallard. Meat production is generally the primary criterion in breed selection. Egg production for propagation and brooding tendency, and the white plumage that produces an attractive dressed carcass, are other characteristics that should be considered. There is growing hobbyist interest in bantam ducks such as White and Gray Calls, Black East Indias, Wood Ducks, Mandarins, and Teal ducks. Many poultry shows offer classes for these ducks.

Broodiness When a hen stops laying eggs and prepares to sit on eggs to incubate them. Once the eggs hatch, the hen cares for them. Such hens are referred to as being *broody*.

Plumage The total body feathering of poultry.

Figure 11–21
The wild turkeys of North and Central America were the wild progenitors of the domestic turkey.

The domestic goose, which was bred in ancient Egypt, China, and India, is said to have been in the United States since early colonial days. Most of the breed information and other references are obscure and difficult to authenticate. Most breeds arrived here via Europe, where they are much more popular. The White Emden (first believed brought to the United States in 1821) and Toulouse are the two most popular goose breeds. The African (said to be especially valuable in cross-breeding), Pilgrim, and White Chinese (said to be the best laying) are also raised in significant numbers.

REPRODUCTIVE MANAGEMENT IN POULTRY

In general, the management of poultry species for reproduction is very much alike for all poultry species. It is also similar in hobby and large commercial operations. When eggs fail to hatch properly, the reason may be the management of the breeder flock, the incubation procedures, or any step between the breeder flock and final hatch.

Breeder Flock Management

Proper management of the breeder flock is essential if healthy chicks are to be hatched. The breeder flock should be reared using proper management practices, and then selected to be healthy and free of **defects** that can interfere with proper mating and egg production. They should be genetically superior and free of deformities and flaws that would interfere with normal eating, drinking, and maintenance of social stature in the flock. Males should be aggressive and willing to breed. Females should be selected for good egg-laying traits.

Defect Unacceptable deviation from perfection. Most defects are inherited.

Mating Systems

To produce hatching eggs, poultry can be mated by using one of the following mating systems:

1. Mass mating. Several males are allowed to run with a flock of females. This method is a practical means of obtaining the maximum number of hatching eggs.
2. Pen mating. One male is mated with a small flock of females. This system is used to keep track of ancestry.
3. Stud mating. One female is mated with one male. The females can be removed, and another female is then put with the male. Hens can be successively mated to different males. More females can be mated to a superior male.
4. Artificial insemination. This system is commonly used in turkey production and less so in other species. Birds of quite different sizes can be mated.

The breeder flock needs proper nesting facilities and ample, clean nesting material. This helps prevent damage such as breaking and contamination of the shells with dirt and manure, which spreads disease and reduces hatching. Excellent management including sanitation, vaccination programs, and pest control is essential. High-quality diets formulated for breeder birds should be fed.

Selection and Care of Eggs

Frequent collection of eggs—a minimum of once a day with more frequent collection if daily temperatures reach 85°F—is important. Commercial hatcheries frequently collect five or more times a day. Eggs laid on the floor should not be used because they spread disease. Nest eggs that are dirty should also be discarded. Hatching eggs cannot be washed because it removes the protective sealing substance from the shell, allowing bacteria to enter the egg. Oversized, undersized, and abnormally shaped eggs should be discarded because hatching is poor. Likewise, cracked eggs and eggs with thin shells should be discarded. Commercial operations fumigate eggs prior to **setting** to reduce the bacteria on the shells and increase hatchability.

Egg Storage

Eggs should be placed in incubators as soon as it is convenient. Eggs held before incubation should be stored near 60°F and 75% humidity. Temperatures below 40°F reduce hatchability. The cool temperature delays embryonic growth until incubation begins, and the high humidity prevents moisture loss. Storage for less than 10 days is acceptable. After that time, hatch progressively declines to near zero for eggs stored for 3 weeks. Eggs that are not incubated within 3 or 4 days should be turned daily to prevent the yolk from touching the shell and injuring the embryo. Storage should be with the small end down and slanted at an angle of 30–45°. When eggs are to be placed in an incubator, they should be warmed slowly at first. Warming too rapidly causes moisture to condense on the shell, which may lead to mold and bacterial growth.

Setting Placing eggs to incubate. A setting hen is a broody hen incubating eggs.

Incubators

Eggs are incubated in devices aptly named **incubators**. They come in many shapes and sizes and with capacities from a dozen up to several thousand eggs. Table 11–2 shows **incubation** periods and incubation operation characteristics. Proper care must be given to relative humidity, temperature fluctuations, ventilation, and other factors to ensure a good hatch. Eggs must be regularly turned to prevent the embryos from sticking to the sides of the shells. Generally, eggs are not turned for the last 3 days before hatching because the embryos are moving into hatching position and should not be disturbed. After hatching, chicks are allowed to dry and fluff up before being moved to a brooder with feed and water.

Incubator A machine that provides the environmental conditions to encourage embryonic development in fertile eggs.

Incubation The process of sitting on eggs by a hen to warm them with body heat so that the eggs develop into young. Can also be done artificially in an incubator.

Testing for Fertility

Eggs in incubators can be tested for fertility by **candling** them at 4–7 days of incubation. Infertile eggs can be discarded and the space used for additional eggs. Candling does not harm the young embryos. Candlers can be purchased or made by placing a light bulb and fixture inside a cardboard box. Cutting a 1/2- to 3/4-in hole in the top or side of the box allows a narrow beam of light to escape. The internal features of the egg can be seen by placing it against the hole. A darkened room makes testing easier. Eggs with white shells are easier to candle and can be tested earlier than dark-shelled eggs. **Infertile** refers to an unfertilized egg or an egg that started developing but died before growth could be detected. **Dead germs** are embryos that died after growing large enough to be seen when candled. Both can be detected at this stage. An infertile egg looks clear except for a shadow from the yolk. In a live embryo, large blood vessels can be seen spreading out from the embryo. A dead germ can be determined by the presence of a blood ring around the embryo, which is caused by blood

Candling Inspection of the inside of an intact egg with a light to detect defects. Also, incubating eggs can be tested for dead germs and infertile eggs.

Infertile An egg that is unfertilized or in which the embryo dies.

Dead germs Embryos that have died.

Table 11–2
INCUBATION TIMES FOR SELECTED POULTRY SPECIES[1]

Item	Chicken	Turkey	Duck	Goose	Swan	Guinea	Quail
Incubation time (days)	21	28	28	28–32	35–40	26–28	17–24
Temperature (°F)	100	99	100	99	99	100	100

[1]Different incubators have different recommendations for temperature. There are also appropriate ranges for humidity and oxygen content of the air. For small incubators, follow the manufacturer's recommendations. Large commercial incubators are managed by skilled technicians and vary with the type and design.

moving away from the dead embryo. A second test can be made after 14–16 days of incubation. If the embryo is living, only one or two small light spaces filled with blood vessels can be seen. The chick may even be observed moving inside the shell.

NUTRITION IN POULTRY

Chapters 3, 4, and 5 deal with the intricacies of nutrition and feedstuffs in a much more detailed manner than this section. See those chapters for information on digestive anatomy, nutrition, feeds, and feeding. Poultry feeding has changed more than the feeding of any other species with the advent of modern production systems. The primary reason for this is that most of the poultry is produced in large units where maximum technology is used. Poultry nutrition is also more critical, complicated, and thus a greater challenge to the producer because poultry have more rapid digestion, higher metabolic rates, faster respiration and circulation, and higher body temperature (107°F). Poultry are more active, more sensitive to environmental influences, grow more rapidly, and mature at earlier ages. Egg production is an all-or-none phenomenon. However, we probably know more about poultry nutrition than the nutrition of any other species. Economic production depends on economical rations.

Avian Pertaining to poultry and/or fowl.

Omnivore An animal that eats both plant and animal matter.

Poultry species are monogastric and have a specialized **avian** tract. As **omnivores**, they seek a variety of plant and animal foods if left to scavenge. They have paired ceca, which will develop and digest some fiber if they are fed forages. The cecum is especially developed in geese. However, for the most part, modern production systems do not make use of this capacity. Poultry and swine generally compete for the same feedstuffs: concentrated feeds such as grains, soybean meal, and high-quality by-product feeds.

Feed is the largest cost in the production of the poultry species. Optimum growth and maximum growth are usually close to the same thing for growing animals. Thus, the nutrition and feeding of the meat producers revolves around optimizing growth. This is the best feeding strategy because the faster an animal reaches market, the smaller the percentage of total lifetime feed used for body maintenance. In addition, the faster an animal reaches market, the fewer days it requires housing, labor, and so on. Thus, the fixed costs of production are reduced. Egg-producing animals are usually high enough producers that they find it difficult to overeat. For laying animals, the nutrition of the animal is quickly reflected in the size, quality, and number of eggs.

Mash Finely ground and uniformly mixed feeds. Animals cannot separate feed ingredients; thus each bite provides all the nutrients in the diet.

Feeding practices in poultry operations across the country tend to be fairly uniform. The industry is so integrated that very consistent technology and methods of production are employed. Feedstuffs vary somewhat, and thus rations are different. Commercial poultry rations are formulated with the use of least-cost ration formulation programs that factor in the cost of nutrients from the available feeds and calculate the lowest cost, balanced diet. Poultry species are fed almost exclusively on complete mixed diets that are offered in **mash** or pelleted form. A high percentage of poultry rations is pelleted because there is less waste. Table 11–3 gives examples of rations for different classes of poultry based on corn and soybean meal. These feeds are the most commonly used energy and protein feeds in poultry rations. However, regional differences exist. Lower-cost diets can sometimes be formulated using regionally available feedstuffs. Different rations are mixed for optimum performance of the birds at their particular stage of production. All species need good-quality clean water provided free choice and adequate watering space.

Table 11–3
EXAMPLE RATIONS FOR DIFFERENT CLASSES OF POULTRY

Ingredient	Broiler Starter	Turkey Starter	Chicken Layer	Quail Grower	Duck Finisher
	PERCENTAGE OF COMPLETE RATION				
Yellow corn, #2 dent	56.46	47.75	60.50	71.85	77.25
Soybean meal (48% protein)	27.33	38.83	21.50	18.7	16.13
Meat and bonemeal (50% protein)	7.0	—	5.09	5.00	5.0
Meat meal (56% protein)	—	9.50	—	—	—
Bakery by-product	6.00	—	—	—	—
Alfalfa meal	—	—	—	2.00	—
Animal-vegetable fat	1.82	0.31	3.00	—	—
D,L-Methionine	0.17	0.24	0.11	0.15	0.16
L-Lysine HCl	—	0.23	—	0.41	—
Dicalcium phosphate	0.13	1.54	0.49	0.70	0.15
Ground limestone	0.49	0.81	8.66	0.74	0.86
Iodized salt	0.10	0.09	0.20	0.25	0.25
Sodium bicarbonate	0.20	0.20	0.20	—	—
Vitamin-mineral premix and feed additives	0.3	0.50	0.25	0.20	0.20
	Feed Analysis				
% Protein	22.50	28.00	18.00	18.0	17.0
Metabolizable energy (kcal/lb)	1,425	1,280	1,320	1,380	1,426
% Calcium	0.95	1.45	3.80	0.95	0.35
% Available phosphorus	0.48	0.83	0.45	0.45	0.35
% Lysine	1.21	1.80	0.94	1.2	0.80
% Methionine + cystine	0.92	1.10	0.71	0.70	0.70

Source: Recommendations from multiple sources.

FLOCK HEALTH MANAGEMENT

Many diseases affect chickens, turkeys, and other types of poultry. Because of the concentrated nature of poultry production, a single virulent disease can cause millions of dead animals and millions in economic losses. Luckily, some of the more devastating diseases that affect poultry have been eradicated from the United States. Still others have been controlled with the use of vaccines (Figure 11–22) and parasite control regimes. Nevertheless, poultry farmers must stay constantly on their guard against disease. Biosecurity measures are routinely practiced to minimize the risk of disease transmission from sources outside the production unit and reduce the transmission of diseases between groups of birds on the same farm. Some of the health threats that most commonly affect poultry are described below.

CHALLENGES TO POULTRY HEALTH

Rickets

Abnormal bone development, referred to as rickets, may be seen in young growing birds as a result of dietary calcium or phosphorus deficiency or as a result of inadequate vitamin D intake. Rickets is seen most commonly in young, growing birds but

Figure 11–22
Technicians vaccinate chicks subcutaneously. Vaccination is an important part of flock health management. (Photo courtesy USDA.)

Osteoporosis Disease in which bones are thinned, with decreased bone mass and strength.

laying hens may also be affected by similar mineral deficiencies. Older birds develop **osteoporosis**, which leads to a disease called cage layer fatigue. When young birds are affected, they will have stiff gaits, enlarged joints, and stunted growth. Laying hens with calcium deficiency will produce thin-shelled eggs with low hatchability, followed by decreased egg production. In severe cases, paralysis and death may result. Immediate dietary calcium supplementation may be effective in treating paralysis and preventing death in affected birds. Adequate mineral balance in rations and supplements is essential in preventing rickets in growing birds.

Fowl cholera

Fowl cholera is a bacterial infection caused by *Pasteurella multocida* that may cause disease in both chickens and turkeys. Young turkeys may be severely affected and die rapidly, even before showing signs of illness. Signs of sickness in birds that don't die suddenly can be quite varied and include weight loss, decreased appetite, lameness, depression, mucoid discharge from the mouth, difficulty breathing, diarrhea, and darkened wattles. Swollen joints and lameness may also be seen in birds that are sick for longer periods. Early **antibiotic** treatment may be helpful in controlling the disease in affected flocks. Good management—including vaccination, depopulation and disinfection between broods, and proper disposal of dead birds—is useful as a means of prevention.

Antibiotic A drug used to treat infection caused by bacteria or other microorganisms.

Mycoplasmosis

Several species of Mycoplasma bacterial organisms may cause infections in poultry that result in various types of disease. *Mycoplasma gallisepticum* causes chronic respiratory disease in chickens and infectious sinusitis in turkeys. Infection is typically transmitted from bird to bird, but may also be passed on in the egg to infect chicks or be spread from flock to flock by contaminated shoes, clothing or equipment. Affected birds may sneeze and have nasal discharge and difficulty breathing. Weight gains are decreased, and birds raised for meat may be condemned if **airsacculitis** is present at processing. In laying birds, egg production is decreased. Prevention of infection in disease-free flocks, as well as eradication of the infection from breeding stock so that bacteria are not transmitted to chicks, are the most effective means of controlling this disease. In circumstances where flocks are infected and depopulation is not a suitable strategy, antibiotics may be used to decrease disease but are not effective in completely clearing the infection.

Airsacculitis Inflammation of the air sacs, often due to infection with a disease-causing microorganism.

NUTRITIONAL BENEFITS OF POULTRY TO HUMANS

Table 11–4 presents the proportions of the recommended daily dietary allowance provided by eggs and chicken. Eggs have a very high nutrient density, which simply means that we get a large amount of essential nutrients in relation to the calories consumed. Eggs contain all essential amino acids needed by humans, many needed minerals, and all required vitamins except vitamin C. The protein in poultry meat is also of high quality, contains all of the essential amino acids, and is easily digested. The fat content of *uncooked product* is lower than that of many other meat products. Poultry meat is also a good source of vitamins and minerals.

TRENDS AND FACTORS INFLUENCING THE POULTRY INDUSTRY

Turkey Consumption and Production

Turkey production was previously shown in Figure 11–18. Per capita consumption appears to be stable at approximately 17 lbs (carcass weight equivalent), where it has been since 1990. Therefore, continued increase in production will probably depend on overall population increases and increased exports.

Broiler Consumption and Production

Broiler meat production continues to expand, although the rapid increases stalled in the mid 2000s (Figure 11–10). Per capita consumption of broiler meat steadily increased until 2006, when it stalled for the first time since 1975 and subsequently experienced further declines (Figure 11–23). It is expected to recover and continue to increase. Increasing exports will also play a role in U.S. broiler production.

Cost Advantages   Broiler meat has advantages in production costs over competing meats. The industry has produced increased amounts of chicken and, at the same time, lowered the price to consumers. Most market analysts suggest that this is a major reason why chicken has taken market share from beef. However, more is at work than simple price. If price was the only issue, then consumers would be expected to buy more total pounds because they could purchase chicken for less cost per pound.

Table 11–4
PERCENTAGE OF DAILY NUTRIENTS PROVIDED BY POULTRY PRODUCTS[1]

Nutrient	100 grams Cooked Skinless Chicken (%)	2 Large Eggs (%)
Protein	55	22
Phosphorus	33	25
Iron	13	15
Zinc	9	10
Riboflavin	9	39
Vitamin A	1	17
Thiamin	6	6
B_{12}	14	46
Niacin	86	0. 4
Folate	1	11
Calories (actual)	165	155

[1]Calculated on the recommended daily dietary allowance for a 19- to 30-year-old man.
Source: USDA, 2011.

Figure 11–23
Per capita meat consumption, 1975–2011. Source: Based on USDA-ERS, 2011b.

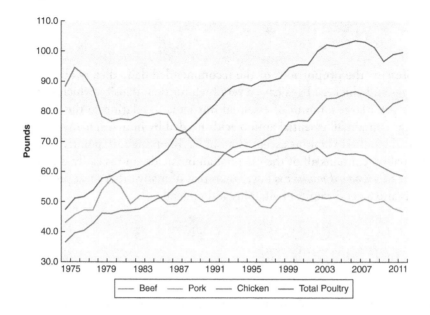

Shelf life The length of time fresh-dressed, iced, packed poultry can be held without freezing.

This would not explain how the product has managed to also gain an increasing percentage of the total yearly consumer expenditures for chicken, beef, and pork, which chicken has done largely at the expense of beef.

Convenient/Value-Added Products   Changes in social values, lifestyles, and demographic trends have caused an explosion in the convenience food market. Consumers with more disposable income but less time to prepare food are willing to pay for foods that they perceive are high in quality and in eating satisfaction, are healthy, and convenient. The poultry industry has outdone the beef and pork industries in developing value-added products and has maintained an aggressive posture in this regard. They consider themselves in the food business, not the meat-production business. A look at the advertising material of integrated poultry companies finds all the bases covered with phrases such as *simple and delicious, quality home meal replacements, affordable yet simple-to-prepare entrees, variety and appeal for kids, portable foods for grab-and-go convenience, dinner that's quick and easy,* and always the word *new: New flavors! New textures! New forms! New products!* These people are excited about chicken. Perhaps the best statement of all to illustrate the focus of these companies is "We convert chicken into customer satisfaction and loyalty." The poultry industry will continue to focus on price, packaging, **shelf life**, convenience, and taste. As long as they do these things, the industry will continue to grow.

Fast Food   Chicken is also a very important fast food. Harland Sanders probably had no inkling of the influence he would have on the poultry industry when he opened his first restaurant. However, before he died, the colonel witnessed multiple generations of Americans who had grown up deciding on "extra-crispy" or "original recipe." Kentucky Fried Chicken was the catalyst that revolutionized the fast-food industry where chicken is concerned. Fast-food chicken is available in virtually every fast-food restaurant and even in gas stations.

Nutrition and Health Consciousness   Nutrition and health consciousness will continue to play a role in food choices. The early 1980s has been dubbed the beginning of the health-conscious era, although eating habits had been changing before that time. Poultry products are good food. They are nutritious, are often leaner than alternative meats, and have gained the status of a health-conscious food. Poultry products found a place on the plate of the fat-conscious consumer. A look at poultry consumption trends clearly shows products that increased share of per capita consumption during the same

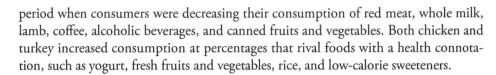

period when consumers were decreasing their consumption of red meat, whole milk, lamb, coffee, alcoholic beverages, and canned fruits and vegetables. Both chicken and turkey increased consumption at percentages that rival foods with a health connotation, such as yogurt, fresh fruits and vegetables, rice, and low-calorie sweeteners.

Egg Consumption

The high point for per capita egg consumption in the United States was in 1945 at 405 eggs per capita but began declining. Egg consumption declined somewhat because of health consciousness. However, changes in eating habits were probably a more important factor. People either skip breakfast or choose a noncooked breakfast from a glass or a package because of busy lifestyles. Foods that can be held in the hand and eaten on the go are popular. A sunny-side-up egg isn't very good hand food. Another problem is that eggs are not traditionally eaten at meals other than breakfast. Also, there aren't many further-processed, convenient products that feature eggs. The low mark in consumption was in 1991 with 233 eggs. However, egg consumption stabilized in the 1990s and increased in the new century. People on low-carbohydrate diets find the egg a very versatile and easy food to include in their diets. In addition, the egg is an important ingredient in many processed foods that are popular with consumers. The combined use of eggs in processed foods and a changing of attitudes about the nutritional value of the egg in the diet seem to be driving a consumption comeback for the egg. Per capita consumption of eggs in the United States is shown in Figure 11–24.

A changing ethnic mix in the U.S. population is also a driving force in the per capita consumption of eggs. The Mexican American population in the United States uses a greater percentage of shell eggs than their share of the population. As that population increases, it influences per capita egg consumption.

Cholesterol The health concerns about cholesterol have been a mainstream consumer issue for over 30 years. Early recommendations of some health-care professionals to reduce dietary cholesterol were based on the presumption that the level of circulating blood plasma cholesterol was directly tied to the quantity of cholesterol in the diet. Many scientists cautioned over and over that the link had not been established. Regardless of those cautions, eggs gained the status of a problem food because of their cholesterol content. A growing body of evidence has accumulated showing that dietary levels of cholesterol have very little to do with the plasma levels of cholesterol. Other factors such as total fat content of the diet, exercise, heredity, and several others are much more important. Based on research studies carried out for the past 50 years, it appears that the average plasma response of a normal, healthy person to a 100 mg/day change in dietary cholesterol intake is a 2.5 mg/dL change in plasma

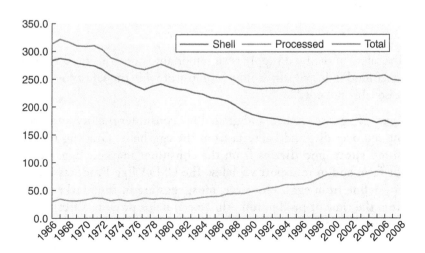

Figure 11–24
Per capita egg consumption in the United States.
Source: USDA-ERS, 2011b.

cholesterol levels. Approximately 15–20% of the population is somewhat more sensitive to dietary cholesterol, probably because of genetic factors. What all of this means is that reducing dietary cholesterol intake from 400 mg/day to 300 mg/day results in a plasma cholesterol reduction of 3.2 mg/dL in cholesterol-sensitive individuals, and as little as 1.6 mg/dL in cholesterol-insensitive individuals. Clearly, other factors are more important. New studies have shown that egg eating has no effect on the small dense LDL-3 through LDL-7 particles that cause the greatest threat for cardiovascular disease. This is good news for egg producers and egg eaters!

All-Natural and Organic Production

The increasing interest by consumers in natural products has prompted companies to begin producing and marketing poultry products to meet the demand. A central issue is the exact definition of what *natural* means on a food label. The USDA, producers, and several consumer groups have been trying to come to a commonly accepted and meaningful definition.

Organic products are no longer simply a lifestyle choice for a small share of consumers. They are now being consumed at least occasionally by a majority of Americans. Reasons given for this include concerns about growth hormones and antibiotic use in conventional livestock, the environment, and humane care of livestock. Organic poultry and egg markets in the United States are expanding rapidly with products readily available in traditional and natural food supermarkets in addition to the more traditional venues for organic products such as farmers' markets and health food stores. Price comparisons between organic and conventional products show significant organic price premiums for both broilers and eggs. Organic production has increased so rapidly that it prompted the USDA-ERS to begin reporting monthly organic and conventional prices (http://www.ers.usda.gov/data/organicprices/).

Both the organic market and the organic production industry in the poultry sector are immature and developing. Consumer demand will dictate that development and in turn influence production, processing, and marketing of organic poultry meat and eggs. In the short term, the future of the organic poultry sector is one of growth as it struggles to meet growing consumer demand.

Other interesting trends in egg production are developing in an effort to meet consumer demand such as vegetarian, cage-free, free-range, fertile, in-shell pasteurized, and nutrient-enhanced specialty eggs. Even blue-green eggs produced by the Araucana breed native to South America are available. All are produced with specific consumers in mind. Production costs are inevitably higher on specialty eggs, making them more expensive than generic shell eggs. Which, if any, will become significant parts of the industry remains to be seen.

Food Safety Concerns

The safety of the food supply is an important issue. This industry must do what the other food industries are doing—it must provide the safest food supply that can be reasonably provided.

Blood spots Small spots of blood found inside an egg, probably caused by blood vessels breaking in the ovary or oviduct during egg formation.

Dirties Eggs with dirt, fecal material, or other material on the shell.

Eggs Eggs are washed and graded for consumer quality and protection. Washing removes dirt and bacteria from the eggshells. Grading removes any cracks, **blood spots**, and **dirties** from the consumer market. Eggs are refrigerated on the farm and in transport vehicles. The USDA Egg Products Inspection Act does not define fresh eggs. However, most eggs are in the market within 1 to 7 days from the time of production. This speed helps provide a fresh, safe food product (Figure 11–25).

Figure 11–25
Eggs are washed and graded for consumer quality and protection. (Photo courtesy of Dr. Joe G. Berry, Department of Animal Science, Oklahoma State University. Used with permission.)

Eggs and salmonella The inside of an egg was considered almost sterile until eggs contaminated with *Salmonella enteritidis* were found. It was discovered that *Salmonella enteritidis* could silently infect the ovaries of healthy-appearing hens and contaminate the eggs before the shells are formed. The number of affected eggs is generally small. The likelihood of finding an infected egg is about 0.005%. Even then, the numbers of microorganisms in a properly handled and refrigerated egg are so small that they cannot easily cause illness in a healthy person. However, when eggs are not kept properly refrigerated or cooked properly or perhaps eaten raw, problems can easily occur. This is especially true if an infected raw egg is used in a food that is not cooked and to further compound the problem is not then properly refrigerated. Whereas healthy adults and children are at risk for egg-associated salmonellosis, the elderly, infants, and persons with impaired immune systems are at increased risk for serious illness because a relatively small number of bacteria can cause severe illness. Most of the deaths caused by *Salmonella enteritidis* have occurred among the elderly in nursing homes. Egg-containing foods prepared for high-risk persons should be thoroughly cooked and promptly served. A significant outbreak of egg-associated salmonellosis in 2010 sickened over 1,900 people and prompted a recall of over a half billion eggs. Salmonellosis is still a problem.

Poultry Meat Poultry meat has not been unduly tainted by the food borne illness scares associated with ground beef. Much of this has to do with the fact that poultry meat is rarely sold as a ground product. Also, much of it is further processed and subject to strict quality control. The Hazard Analysis and Critical Control Points (HACCP) system helps all meat industries provide safer products.

Integration and Consolidation

All phases of poultry production are and will continue to become more specialized, larger, concentrated on fewer farms, and more vertically integrated. More consolidation is inevitable, especially of the smaller companies. More integrators may opt to own the production units rather than to contract. Confinement rearing is here to stay (Figure 11–26).

Technological Innovation and Standardization

The poultry industry has made the most dramatic advancements in both biology and technical aspects of any of the livestock industries. Since 1925, the time for broilers to reach market has gone from 15 to 6 weeks or less. The amount of feed required

Figure 11–26
The poultry industry is highly concentrated and dependent on confinement housing. All phases of poultry production are and will continue to become more specialized, larger, concentrated on fewer farms, and more vertically integrated.
(Photo courtesy Culver Duck Farms.)

has been cut in half. It now takes less than 2 lbs of feed to produce 1 lb of meat. The number of eggs per hen has more than doubled. Much of this progress is related to the industry's willingness to take better advantage of modernization and technological innovation. It will continue to do so. Biotechnology will allow us to increase production and efficiency of all poultry segments. Mechanization will become a larger part of labor-saving (cost-saving) strategies.

Waste Disposal

Poultry farms will face tougher and tougher laws regarding litter and dead bird disposal. A new set of rules pertaining to CAFOs were signed into effect in 2008. The rule as well as explanatory material can be accessed at http://cfpub.epa.gov/npdes/afo/cafofinalrule.cfm. This rule updated those last updated in 2003. Additional regulations are sure to follow. Current environmental laws, regulations, policies, and guidance regarding CAFOs can be accessed through the U.S. Environmental Protection Agency.

One very exciting area of research has been in the area of nutritional effects on the content of poultry litter. Enzyme-modified diets have helped chickens digest more of the phosphorous in their feed, which allows for less phosphorous to be added to poultry diets. As a result of this and other nutrient management strategies, it is possible to reduce the phosphorous content of poultry litter by approximately a fourth. Other discoveries will continue to bring improvements and lessen the environmental footprint of the poultry industry.

Biotechnology

The products of biotechnology that will most help poultry producers are in the areas of disease prevention and treatment. In addition, such tools as marker-assisted selection will help further the genetic progress. Transgenic strains of poultry species to produce specific substances in the egg will be developed. This will make it possible to have poultry species contribute to human welfare in new and exciting ways (Figure 11–27).

Animal Welfare

The layer industry has long been under attack from animal rights proponents who object to the practice of caging layer hens rather than allowing them to range freely. In 2002, as an answer to those concerns, the United Egg Producers (UEP) put in place

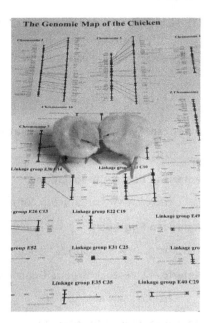

Figure 11–27

Chicks atop a picture of the genetic map of the chicken. The chicken genome has 39 pairs of chromosomes, whereas the human genome contains 23 pairs. Once the molecular geneticists have completed unraveling the "mystery genes" in the code, many production enhancements and transgenic applications will be found.

(Photograph by Peggy Greb. Courtesy of USDA-Agricultural Research Service.)

welfare guidelines. Eggs produced from caged hens under the guidelines are referred to as *United Egg Producers Certified.* The program is billed as "the way U.S. egg farmers assure retailers, foodservice professionals, and consumers that their eggs originate from farms that follow responsible, science-based modern production methods in the care of their egg-laying flocks." Information on the program and its guidelines can be found at http://www.uepcertified.com/. (Similar guidelines have been developed for meat production by the National Chicken Council, http://www.nationalchickencouncil. com/aboutIndustry/detail.cfm?id=19). Several restaurant chains put their own guidelines in place for producers from whom they buy eggs. However, animal rights groups have mounted a series of campaigns against caged layer production and state ballot measures directed at various animals have become more common. U.S. city councils have passed resolutions urging their citizens not to buy eggs produced by caged hens. Major restaurant chains, food retailers, and food processors have announced policies on purchasing eggs from cage-free suppliers. The volume of cage-free eggs produced in the United States seems certain to increase. In recognition of this trend, the UEP adopted welfare guidelines for cage-free production systems in late 2007.

Avian Influenza (Bird Flu)

Avian influenza H5N1 has been causing a great deal of concern in the United States and around the world. Millions of birds have died, and so have well over 300 people in 2004–2006. Trade disruptions cost countries billions of dollars.

Two types of avian influenza (AI) are identified as H5N1. One is low pathogenic (LPAI), and the other is highly pathogenic (HPAI). The subtype HPAI H5N1, often referred to as "Asian" H5N1, is the type currently causing worldwide concern. LPAI H5N1, "North American" H5N1, is of less concern.

HPAI spreads rapidly and is often fatal to chickens and turkeys. In countries where HPAI H5N1 has struck, millions of birds have died. HPAI H5N1 has not been detected in the United States. However, other strains of HPAI have been detected and eradicated three times in the United States: in 1924, 1983, and 2004. No significant human illness resulted from these outbreaks.

HPAI H5N1 has also infected people, most of whom have had direct contact with infected birds. Although many people who have contracted HPAI H5N1 have died, many have no more than the symptoms of the common cold. Concerns about

HPAI H5N1 revolve around the fear that the virus may mutate into a form that can pass easily from human to human. Such a mutation could create a virus capable of causing a worldwide pandemic. The threat from avian influenza has not yet passed.

INDUSTRY ORGANIZATIONS

American Association of Avian Pathologists

http://www.aaap.info/

American Bantam Association

http://www.bantamclub.com/

American Egg Board

http://www.aeb.org/

American Livestock Breeds Conservancy

http://www.albc-usa.org

American Poultry Association

http://www.amerpoultryassn.com/

International Waterfowl Breeder's Association (IWBA)

http://www.iwba.org/

National Turkey Federation (NTF)

http://www.eatturkey.com/about.html

United Egg Producers

http://www.unitedegg.org/

World's Poultry Science Association

http://www.wpsa.com/

SUMMARY AND CONCLUSION

The poultry industry is a large and thriving business based on meat- and egg-producing chickens and turkeys for meat production. A large contingent of hobby producers also use a number of other species such as ducks, geese, pigeons, and peafowl in addition to chickens and turkeys. The combined gross annual income of the poultry segments amounts to almost $30 billion. The primary purpose of the poultry industry in the United States is to produce inexpensive sources of protein for human consumption. It takes grain and by-products and produces meat and eggs very efficiently. These products are among the best buys available in the marketplace today for high-quality protein. Vertical integration provides the structural framework of the commercial poultry industry. Breeding and selection of poultry differs from breeding of the larger animals in three major ways: (1) it is more flexible because of short generation intervals and large numbers of offspring; (2) it has been the industry most subjected to modern animal breeding and selection techniques and has made the most progress; and (3) fewer people make all of the decisions. Generally speaking, chickens are one of two types: meat type or egg type, and they come in many colors, sizes, shapes, and combinations of these traits, designated by class, breed, variety, and strain. The management of the different poultry species for reproduction is very similar for all species. It is also of little matter if the birds are reared as a hobby or in a large commercial operation. When eggs fail to hatch properly, the reason may be the management of the breeder flock, the incubation procedures, or any step between the breeder flock and final hatch. Poultry feeding has changed more than the feeding of any other species with the advent of modern production systems. The primary reason for this change is that most of the poultry is produced in large units where maximum technology is used. Poultry nutrition is also more critical, complicated, and thus a greater challenge to the producer than the nutrition of other farm species. Eggs have recently increased in consumer demand. Turkey production has stabilized. Broiler meat continues to increase in its share of the consumer's dollar and per capita consumption.

FACTS ABOUT POULTRY

There are four major classes of chickens:

American Class:	Plymouth Rock, Wyandotte, Rhode Island Red, New Hampshire, Jersey Black Giant, Rhode Island White, Java, Dominique, and Holland
Mediterranean Class:	Leghorn, Minorca, Ancora, Blue Andalusian, Buttercup, and Spanish
English Class:	Cornish, Australop, Orpington, Dorking, Sussex, and Red Cap
Asiatic Class:	Brahma, Cochin, and Langshans
Egg production takes 24.5 to 25.5 hours in the oviduct:	Infundibulum where fertilization occurs (15 min); magnum where white is laid down (3 hrs); isthmus where the two shell membranes are formed ($1^1/_4$ hrs); uterus where eggshell is formed (20–21 hrs); vagina during laying (less than 1 min)
Average number of eggs/hen/yr:	1937 = 120–130; 2010s = 260+
Hen/cock ratio:	Light breeds 15–20/cock, general-purpose breeds 10–15/cock, and heavy breeds 8–12/cock
Incubation and hatching:	Eggs incubated for 21 days at 98.6–100.4°F and turned 1–2 times daily
U.S. egg weight classes (oz/doz):	Jumbo (30), Extra Large (27), Large (24), Medium (21), Small (18), and Peewee (15)
U.S. grades of egg:	AA, A, B, depending on quality factors such as shell, air cell, white, and yolk
Names of various sex classes:	Rooster or **cock**, hen, capon, cockerel, pullet
Market classes of poultry:	Cornish game hen, broiler or fryer, roaster, capon, stag, hen or stewing chicken, cock or old rooster
Market classes of duck and goose:	**Broiler duckling** or **fryer duckling, roaster duckling, mature duck** or **old duck, young goose** or **gosling, mature goose** or **old goose, gander**
Comb:	The fleshy protuberance on top of the head of a fowl. The types of combs include: (1) buttercup, (2) cushion, (3) pea, (4) rose, (5) silkie, (6) single, (7) strawberry, and (8) V-shaped

Cock A rooster aged 1 year or older.

Cockerel A rooster less than 1 year old.

Broiler duckling or fryer duckling A young duck usually under 8 weeks of age of either sex. It must have a soft bill and weigh from 3 to 6½ lbs.

Roaster duckling A young duck of either sex usually under 16 weeks of age. The bill must not have completely hardened. Generally weigh from 4 to 7½ lbs.

Mature duck or old duck A duck of either sex with toughened flesh and a hardened bill. The meat is used in processed products.

Young goose or gosling A young goose weighing from 12 to 14 lbs. A gosling weighs about 8 lbs.

Mature goose or old goose A spent breeder whose meat is used in processed products.

Gander A male goose.

STUDY QUESTIONS

1. What is the monetary contribution of the poultry industry to U.S. agriculture? How do poultry species compare to other livestock species in monetary importance?
2. What species other than chickens and turkeys have a place in the poultry industry, and what is that place?
3. What is the purpose of the poultry industry in the United States? Describe this in terms of feed and use of resources. What is the role of the hobbyist?
4. Why are chicks used for research?
5. Trace the development of the poultry industry from early colonial times to modern integration.
6. Briefly describe the structure of the modern broiler industry in the United States. Compare it to the turkey- and egg-producing sectors. Where is each major segment located?
7. Describe a typical integrated broiler firm and a layer firm.
8. Describe three major ways that poultry breeding and genetics is different from the breeding and genetics of the other livestock species.
9. What are the major breeding methods used in poultry breeding?
10. Generally, there are two types of chickens. What are they?
11. A system has been established to identify the different breeds and strains of chickens. Briefly describe class, breed, variety, and strain.
12. What is the *American Standard of Perfection*?
13. What is the importance of breeds to modern poultry production? What is the importance of breeds to hobbyists?
14. What are the major mating systems for the production of hatching eggs?
15. Describe how to collect, store, and incubate eggs in a way that maximizes fertility.
16. Why is poultry nutrition more complicated than nutrition for other species? Compare and contrast different types of poultry rations in terms of ingredients and amounts. What is the reason for the differences? What is an omnivore?
17. Why was the National Poultry Improvement Plan developed?
18. Briefly discuss the nutritive value of eggs and the various poultry meats described in the chapter.
19. What is the per capita consumption of broiler meat in the United States? Why does it continue to increase?
20. Briefly discuss trends and factors affecting the poultry industry.

REFERENCES

For the 5th edition, Melanie A. Breshears, DVM, PhD, Diplomate ACVP, assistant professor of veterinary pathobiology, Center for Veterinary Health Sciences, Oklahoma State University, contributed material to this chapter.

Angulo F. J., and D. L. Swerdlow. 1998. *Salmonella enteritidis* infections in the United States. *Journal of the American Veterinary Medical Association* 213:1729–1731.

Ensminger, M. E. 1991. *Animal science.* 9th ed. Danville, IL: Interstate.

Ensminger, M. E. 1992. *Poultry science.* 3rd ed. Danville, IL: Interstate.

FAO. 2011. *FAOSTAT statistics database. Agricultural production and production indices data.* http://apps.fao.org/.

Ferket, P. R., and G. S. Davis. 1998. *Feeding ducks.* Publication PS Facts #2. Raleigh: North Carolina State University Extension. http://www.ces.ncsu.edu/depts/poulsci/.

Hanke, O. A., J. K. Skinner, and J. H. Florea. 1974. *American poultry history, 1823–1973.* Mount Morris, IL: American Poultry Historical Society.

Kellems, R. O., and D. C. Church. 1998. *Livestock feeds and feeding.* Upper Saddle River, NJ: Prentice Hall.

Moreng, R. E., and J. S. Avens. 1985. *Poultry science and production.* Reston, VA: Reston Publishing Company.

Oberholtzer, L., C. Greene, and E. Lopez. 2006. *Organic poultry and eggs capture high price premiums and growing share of specialty markets.* Outlook report from the Economic Research Service. LDP-M-150-1. December 2006.

Schrader, L. F., H. E. Larzelere, G. B. Rogers, and O. D. Forker. 1978. *The egg subsector of U.S. agriculture: A review of organization and performance.*

N.C. Project 117. Monograph #6. West Lafayette, IN: Purdue University.

Skinner, J. 1978. *Chicken breeds and varieties bulletin.* A2880. Madison: University of Wisconsin Extension.

Smith, T. W. 1997. *Hatching quality chicks.* Publication 1182. Extension Service of Mississippi State University, cooperating with U.S. Department of Agriculture. http://www.msstate.edu/dept/poultry/exthatch.htm.

Taylor, R. E., and T. G. Field. 1998. *Scientific farm animal production.* 6th ed. Upper Saddle River, NJ: Prentice Hall.

USDA. 2011. *USDA nutrient database for standard reference.* Release 23. Nutrient Data Laboratory home page: http://www.nal.usda.gov/fnic/foodcomp.

USDA-ERS. 2011. *Food consumption (per capita) data system.* Accessed online May 2011. http://www.ers.usda.gov/data/FoodConsumption/.

USDA-NASS. 2007. *2007 census of agriculture.* Washington, DC: National Agricultural Statistics Service, USDA.

USDA-NASS. 2011a. *Briefing room. Farm income and costs.* Accessed online May 2011. http://www.ers.usda.gov/Briefing/FarmIncome/.

USDA-NASS. 2011b. *Quick stats: Agricultural statistics data base.* Accessed online May 2011. http://www.nass.usda.gov/QuickStats/.

USDA-NASS 2011c. *Charts and maps.* http://www.nass.usda.gov/Charts_and_Maps/Poultry/brlmap.asp.

12

Swine

Key Terms

Backfat	Heterosis
Barrow	Monogastric
Biosecurity	Nursery pig
Boar	Omnivore
Closed herd	Optimal growth
Creep	Palatability
Cross-fostering	Pork
Farrow	Pork Quality Assurance Plus
Feed efficiency	Show pigs
Feeder pig	Sow
Generation interval	STAGES
Gestation	Wean
Gilt	

SCIENTIFIC CLASSIFICATION OF SWINE

Phylum:	Chordata
Subphylum:	Vertebrata
Class:	Mammalia
Order:	Artiodactyla
Suborder:	Suina
Family:	Suidae
Genus:	*Sus*
Species:	*domesticus*

THE PLACE OF THE SWINE INDUSTRY IN U.S. AGRICULTURE

The swine industry is a large sector of U.S. agriculture. Hogs are the fourth most important money generator in food animal agriculture. The gross annual income from the swine industry is approximately $14 billion. Hogs currently generate 5.5% of all U.S. farm cash receipts (Figure 12–1) and over 11% of animal agriculture's share of all U.S. farm cash receipts (Figure 12–2). Four states have in excess of $1 billion yearly in gross income from hogs. An additional 6 states have at least $0.5 billion. A total of 15 states have in excess of $100 million. Hogs rank in the top 5 commodities in 13 states. The United States

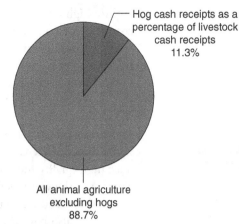

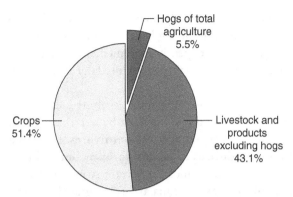

Figure 12–1
Hog farm cash receipts as a percentage of total U.S. farm cash receipts, 2001–2009. Source: Based on USDA-NASS, 2011a.

Figure 12–2
Hog yearly farm cash receipts as a percentage of total animal agriculture's cash receipts, 2001–2009. Source: Based on USDA-NASS, 2011a.

produces 10% of the world's **pig meat (pork)** with 7% of the world's hogs. The swine industry is an aggressive industry. It is very technologically driven and expansion minded.

PURPOSE OF THE SWINE INDUSTRY IN THE UNITED STATES

The purpose of the swine industry in the United States is to use surplus grain production and high-quality by-product feeds to produce meat. The United States is capable of producing millions of tons of grain in excess of the needs of the human population and the export market. Swine are monogastric and, as such, can use only limited amounts of forage. However, they are the most efficient converters of grain to red meat of all the livestock species (Figure 12–3). In times of plentiful grain production, pigs can be used to add value to the grain and create an additional market for it. Like the other grain-using species, swine production helps moderate the fluctuations in grain prices preventing disruptions in agronomic practices and jeopardizing the agricultural economy and the grain supply for humans. Because of their **monogastric** digestive tract, swine

Pig meat The meat from a hog. Synonymous with *pork*.

Pork The meat from a hog. In many parts of the world, the term *pig meat* is preferred.

Monogastric Class of animals that do not have a rumen. Humans are monogastrics. Monogastrics require a better diet than ruminants do.

Figure 12–3
The purpose of the swine industry is to turn surplus grain production and by-product feeds into meat. (Photo courtesy National Pork Board.)

require high-energy feeds to be produced economically. Feed costs are a high fixed cost, and economical production depends on minimizing labor and maximizing efficiency of production by reducing time to market. Expensive confinement facilities and full feeding of high-energy rations maximize weight gain but require large investments in facilities and equipment.

In spite of the fact that they are monogastric, swine are distributed all around the world, including developing countries. When grain cannot be fed, they are fed on wastes and are often allowed to forage for themselves. As **omnivores**, they eat a wide variety of feedstuffs. They do not produce as efficiently this way but still produce high-quality food for their owners. The single most important swine-producing country in the world is China. Many of the pigs in China are in integrated systems, where they produce manure to be used as fertilizer, which is an important product. Swine also have the distinction of being the world's dominant meat-producing species. Pork production on a worldwide basis accounts for approximately 37% of the world's meat production. Swine are used predominantly for meat and, therefore, a large percentage of them are slaughtered annually worldwide. There are approximately 940 million head of hogs in the world; they are the third most numerous of the large livestock species.

Omnivore An animal that eats both plant- and animal-based foods.

HISTORICAL PERSPECTIVE

Pigs were probably domesticated around 8000 B.C., roughly the same time the sheep and goat were domesticated. Columbus first brought the hog to this hemisphere on his second voyage in 1493. In 1539, Hernando DeSoto brought pigs to the North American continent when he landed near what is now Tampa Bay, Florida. During DeSoto's three years of exploration, the original 13 hogs grew to 700. This occurred in spite of the fact that many were eaten, some were lost to predators, some escaped, and some were probably traded to the native people. This gives DeSoto the distinction of being the first swine producer in North America.

By the time swine were imported by settlers to North America, well-established breeds and types had been developed in different places around the world. Breeds from England, Ireland, France, Spain, and Africa all contributed to the unique breeds subsequently developed in North America.

In colonial times, the pig became an important agricultural animal. By 1641, colonists had established a meatpacking plant and were exporting salt pork and lard. (The term *meatpacker* dates to this time and came from the practice of colonists packing pork in salt as a means of preserving it.) Hogs were tended much as they had been in Europe. They mostly ran free and fended for themselves, feeding on roots, tubers, fruits, nuts, mushrooms, snakes, rodents, and so on. As omnivores, they were able to select from a wide range of foods, and they thrived. In the fall of the year, pigs were rounded up and slaughtered. Some were fattened on excess grain, table scraps, or skim milk.

The meat was less important than the body fat (lard) in the early days. Lard had many uses and was a valuable, tradeable product. Breeds of hogs were developed for their ability to lay down excessive body fat. By the mid-1800s, much of the corn grown in the Tennessee, Kentucky, and Ohio areas was being fed to hogs, which were then walked to market as live hogs. Cincinnati, Ohio, became the first pork-packing center and was even known as Porkopolis. The center of activity changed to Chicago by 1860. Hogs were shipped there from throughout the country by railroad. Chicago became known as hog butcher for the world.

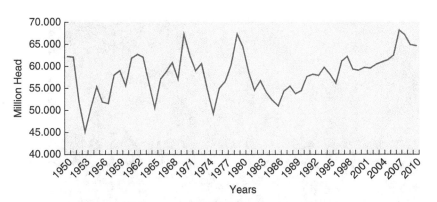

Figure 12–4
Historic swine inventory in the United States. Source: USDA-NASS, 2011b.

The production and marketing of hogs became more decentralized after World War I. Slaughter facilities were built near where the animals were produced, largely in the grain-producing areas. Other products replaced lard, and hogs were bred to be leaner. The restructuring of the agricultural industries that became so evident in the 1950s started affecting the swine industry as well. Improvements in genetics and performance evaluation methods, crossbreeding systems, and nutrition improved efficiency and performance. New disease treatment and prevention strategies and tools facilitated concentration of animals. All of this has led swine operations to fewer but larger units that are partially or totally confined, just as the other animal industries have done.

The swine industry of the 1980s and 1990s was characterized by the incorporation of increasingly sophisticated technologies into production. Producers in states other than traditional hog states became important producers because they aggressively incorporated the available advancements. This led to a further restructuring of the industry, and it brought such states as North Carolina to the second most-important swine state and other states to prominent positions from previous positions of obscurity. Oklahoma, for example, jumped from 23rd to 8th place in 7 years. This restructuring led to a distinct difference among the swine states, with some being dominated by more traditional approaches, and the new swine states being characterized by better and more uniform genetics, better economies of size, and state-of-the-art facilities and management techniques. These new areas are dominated by large operations and a vertically integrated structure.

Figure 12–4 gives a historical look at swine numbers in the United States. Hog numbers have not really changed much in the United States since 1950, if you disregard cyclic ups and downs. However, increased production of red meat per animal has kept the supply of meat available, and per capita consumption has remained relatively stable during that period.

STRUCTURE OF THE SWINE INDUSTRY

There are five primary types of swine operations:

1. **Farrow** to **wean**. Consists of a breeding herd, which produces early-weaned pigs at 10–15 lbs or **feeder pigs** at 35–50 lbs. Pigs are generally early weaned in modern operations and placed in a nursery where they can receive specialized care until ready for **finishing** (Figure 12–5).
2. **Finishing**. Feeder pigs are grown to market weight (Figure 12–6).
3. **Farrow-to-finish operation**. A breeding herd is maintained. Pigs are produced and finished for market on the same farm (Figure 12–7).

Wean The process of removing pigs from the dam to prevent them from nursing.

Farrow In swine, the term used to indicate giving birth.

Feeder pig Generally thought of as a pig weighing between 30 and 90 lbs. There is some regional difference in this range.

Finishing The process of growing a pig to market weight.

Figure 12–5

Feeder pigs such as these are the primary product of the farrow-to-wean segment. They are often marketed to other producers who finish them for market. (Photo courtesy National Pork Board.)

Figure 12–6

The finishing segment grows pigs to market size. (Photo courtesy National Pork Board.)

Figure 12–7

Farrow-to-finish operations maintain a breeding herd and produce pigs that they then raise to market weight. (Photo courtesy National Pork Board.)

Boar An intact male hog kept only for breeding purposes.

Gilt Any female pig that has not yet given birth. Sometimes producers use the term "first-litter gilt" after the first litter is born.

Show pigs Pigs bred for exhibition, usually by 4-H and FFA students.

4. **Purebred or seed stock operations**. These are similar to farrow-to-finish except their salable product is primarily breeding **boars** and **gilts** or **show pigs**, which may be purebred or controlled crossbreeds (Figure 12–8).

5. **Integrated corporate production**. Integrated operations can generally be described as farrow-to-finish and often have their own seed-stock production (or long-term arrangements with seed-stock providers) as well. The various phases

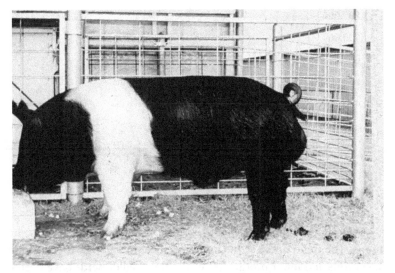

Figure 12–8
Purebred and seedstock operators are specialized farrow-to-finish operations, except that their primary salable products are breeding boars, gilts, and show pigs.

of the operation are usually located on different sites. For instance, several brood **sow** facilities may be found in general proximity to each other but far enough apart that **biosecurity** measures between the facilities are easily handled. Nursery facilities for early-weaned pigs may be found on the same site or one close by. When pigs are ready for finishing, they are taken to another site, which may be a company-owned facility or a contractor (Figure 12–9). The boars that provide the semen to breed all the sows in a cluster of sow facilities are ordinarily housed in a centrally located facility. Semen is collected from them and transported to the sow facilities.

The growth of integrated corporate swine production has caused several changes in the industry. First, the ownership of pigs has shifted to facilities in which more pigs are owned by fewer people. A contracting system has developed similar to that of the poultry industry, and with the general consolidation has come a consolidation of decision making. The most startling feature brought by these changes is the size of the operation and the total number of swine producers. In 1950, there were 2.2 million swine producers. In 1970, there were 871,200 swine operations in the United States, and, by 2000, the number of swine producers was 10% of that in 1970. This trend is not over (Figure 12–10).

Sow Female pig that has given birth.

Biosecurity Procedures designed to minimize disease transmission from outside and inside a production unit.

Figure 12–9
Separate finishing facilities that are company-owned or contractor-owned allow for rapid incorporation of available technology, the application of stringent biosecurity measures, and available land that can benefit from the application of animal wastes. (Photo courtesy of National Pork Board.)

Figure 12–10

Swine operations in the United States. In 1950, there were 2.2 million swine producers. Today, there are only about 3% as many. Source: USDA-NASS, 2011b.

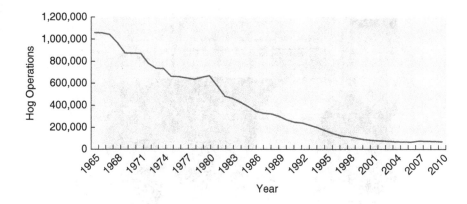

Along with the reduction in operations has come an increase in the size of operations. The trend in the swine industry since the 1970s has been a move toward larger operations and fewer producers. While the smaller herds have been disappearing, the larger herds have been getting even larger (Figure 12–11). Some of this has been facilitated by vertically integrated structuring. Although these changes did not occur uniformly from region to region or from state to state, current industry structure is fairly uniform across the swine-producing regions. The industry is now dominated by large producers.

Changes in the segmentation of the industry has also occurred. Specialization and contracting have become the industry norms and have allowed individual operations to take maximum advantage of technology and increase individual farm productivity. At the same time, producers have reduced feed, labor, and other production costs. As one indication of this change, over 80% of all market hogs in the United States are now produced in specialized hog-finishing operations. The swine industry now looks and acts very much like the consolidated, integrated poultry industry.

GEOGRAPHIC LOCATION OF SWINE IN THE UNITED STATES

Swine are produced in all 50 states (Figure 12–12). The major concentration of hogs in the United States is in the Corn Belt. Iowa has had approximately 25% of the nation's pigs for a number of decades and is increasing its share (28% at the beginning of 2011). Iowa and its border states, plus Indiana, Ohio, Michigan, Oklahoma, and Kansas, contain 73% of the nation's hogs. Hogs are found in these states because they comprise the major area of grain production in the United States or are near grain. Feed prices are generally lower. With feed representing 65% of the total cost

Figure 12–11

U.S. hog operations and the percentage of inventory controlled by each size group. As shown here, as of the end of 2010, the largest 3.1% of the hog operations controlled 62% of the hogs in the United States. A staggering 95% are found in herds with 1,000 or more inventory. Source: USDA-NASS, 2011b.

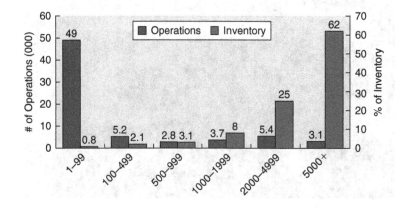

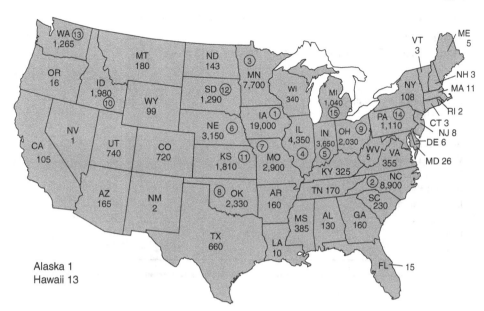

Figure 12–12
Swine inventory (× 1,000) by state in Dec 2010. The circled numbers represent the rank of the most important swine-producing states. Swine are produced in all 50 states. The Corn Belt has the major concentration of hogs. In recent years, the Hog Belt has moved outside the confines of the Corn Belt. North Carolina and states west and south of the Corn Belt have developed major swine industries.
Source: USDA-NASS, 2011b.

of hog production, low-cost feed is a powerful magnet to hog production. Also, most large hog-slaughter plants are located in this region, so the markets are usually better and are more conveniently located.

Even with the powerful lure of less-expensive grain, the traditional Corn Belt states have been losing their share of the total U.S. hog population. Although they are still major players in the swine industry, the Hog Belt has moved outside the confines of the Corn Belt. North Carolina came from relative obscurity as a swine state to become the second-largest swine producing state. Other states like Oklahoma—which was never a major swine-producing state before 1991—and Kansas have developed swine industries of consequence. The development of the swine industry in some states followed the development of the poultry industry. In fact, some large poultry producers have significant involvement in the swine industry. Other factors that have contributed include milder weather, less expensive labor, and a willingness to adopt new technologies. Decreased costs of production and greater efficiency of production have more than offset the difference in grain price. Large swine producers who have moved to these areas have driven much of the increased production in these newer swine states.

The Hog Belt must now be considered to have decentralized from its previous Corn Belt shape and moved south, east, and west. The most important direction for the long term seems to be west. The ultimate location of the swine industry will likely be determined by six major factors:

1. Availability of feed.
2. State regulations, state restrictions on facilities, and waste disposal options.
3. Technological advances of the industry.
4. Availability of an adequate transportation infrastructure.
5. Labor availability.
6. Fossil fuel availability.

GENETICS AND BREEDING PROGRAMS

The fundamentals of genetics and breeding are discussed in Chapters 6 and 7. See those chapters for more detailed information on these topics.

<table>
<tr><td colspan="2">Table 12–1
HERITABILITY ESTIMATES OF SOME TRAITS IN SWINE</td></tr>
</table>

Trait	Heritability (%)
Litter survival to weaning	5
Litter size	10
Number weaned	7
Birth weight	30
Weaning weight	20
Feed efficiency	30
Backfat thickness	50
Loin eye area	45
Tenderness	26
Drip loss	16
Sperm motility	37

The economic traits are influenced by both the environment to which the animal is exposed (feeding, climate, and so on) and the genetics of the animal. Heritability is the portion of the difference that can be passed on to the next generation. The pace of progress in a herd to improve the genetic potential of the offspring depends on how heritable the trait is. Progress in swine genetics is easier to make than genetic progress for some species because the number of offspring from which to select in litter-bearing species is much higher than for species that bear only one offspring in a year. A sow can produce 30 pigs in a year compared to one calf for a cow. In addition, the **generation interval** for swine is fairly short. Pigs from a sow's litter can easily produce offspring within a year of their birth because of their rapid maturing rate and short **gestation** length.

Table 12–1 gives heritability estimates of some economically important traits in swine. It is easy to see that some traits (e.g., **backfat** thickness and **feed efficiency**) are under more genetic control than others (e.g., litter survival and litter size). By using such tools as performance testing, sire summaries for boars available through artificial insemination, the **STAGES** program, and EPDs, the selection and breeding program of a herd can be enhanced.

Swine breeders have made remarkable progress in swine genetic improvement. Most notable is the decrease in fat content of the average pork carcass. Modern consumers demand lean pork, and today's hogs are much leaner than those of the past. Overall body fat has been reduced by more than 50%.

Breeds

For many years, there were two recognizable categories of hogs in the United States. The first was the lard type. These hogs were developed and reared to get extremely fat so they would produce the maximum amount of lard. A fat carcass is also the best to preserve with salt. Salt-cured pork was in high demand in this country in the past. At one time, the Duroc, Chester White, Poland China, Spotted Poland China, and Ohio Improved Chester White were considered the major breeds in this category. The second type of hog was the bacon type. These animals were leaner, longer hogs. Because they were longer-sided animals, they produced more bacon. The major breeds in this category were the Tamworth and the Yorkshire. The Hampshire and the Berkshire were considered to be intermediate between these two types, although most classifications put them into the lard type. Today's hogs are considered to be meat-type hogs. They are something of an intermediate type between the previous

Generation interval In a herd, the average age of the parents when their offspring are born.

Gestation The period when the female is pregnant.

Backfat The fat on a pig's back. It is highly correlated to total body fat and often measured and used as a means of selecting lean brood stock.

Feed efficiency The amount of feed required to produce a unit of gain. A 3:1 ratio means that 3 units of feed were needed to produce 1 unit of gain. The smaller the number the better. Also referred to as *feed conversion ratio*.

STAGES Swine Testing and Genetic Evaluation System. A series of computer programs that analyze performance data of purebred swine and their crossbred offspring.

(a)   (b)   (c)

Figure 12–13

Swine breeders have made tremendous progress turning lard-type (a) and bacon-type hogs (b) into the modern meat-type hog (c).
(Photos [ac] courtesy of National Pork Board.)

types but are more muscular and much leaner. The emphasis on selecting and developing this meat-type animal can be dated to roughly 1950 (Figure 12–13).

Breeds of importance in the United States today include Yorkshire, Duroc, Hampshire, Landrace, Spots, Chester White, Poland China, Pietrain, and Berkshire, or synthetic lines developed from these breeds by breeding companies. Yorkshires, Landrace, and Chester White (all-white breeds) are considered to be mother breeds and are emphasized on the female side, although in recent years they have both improved in carcass merit and growth rate. The Hampshire is most often acknowledged to be the best carcass breed. It tends to be used more on the sire side. The Duroc is a good all-around sire breed with no major weaknesses. Durocs have good disease resistance, rates of gain, feed conversion, meat quality, and carcass characteristics. The swine industry is increasingly coming to depend on synthetic lines of hogs rather than purebreds. This, coupled with the decreased number of small producers who previously purchased purebred breeding stock for their operations, has caused a decline in the numbers of purebred swine being produced and is reducing the influence of several of the previously important breeds.

There is some concern today that the genetic base of swine is lacking the diversity of former years. However, with the continuing trend of large-scale confinement production, there is little demand for many breeds and several are nearly extinct. These breeds often did not have the traits desired in modern pork production and were better adapted for outside or open-range conditions. The American Livestock Breeds Conservancy of Pittsburg, North Carolina, an organization working to preserve endangered breeds of livestock, is a source of interesting information on minor breeds. There is also a growing interest in these heritage breeds by some chefs, food entrepreneurs, and hobbyists.

Swine Breeding Programs

Standards for the Ideal Market Hog   The National Pork Board has set forth standards for the ideal market hog to give producers a uniform goal. The standard for the ideal market hog, named Symbol III, includes a hog marketed at 270 lbs in 156 days for a **barrow** or 164 days for a gilt that produces a 205-lb carcass. Both barrows and gilts are to have a live-weight feed efficiency of 2.4 lbs of feed or less for each pound of gain. Loin eye area at 270 lbs is expected to be at least 6.5 sq. in. for barrows and 7.1 sq. in. for gilts. Barrows are expected to have a fat-free lean index of at least 53 and gilts should be 54.7 or better.

Symbol III is expected to be free of the stress gene (Halothane 1843 mutation) and all other genetic mutations that have detrimental effects on pork quality and be the product of a systematic crossbreeding system emphasizing a maternal dam line and a terminal sire selected for growth, efficiency, and superior muscle quality. The maternal line should be greater than 25 pigs per year, after multiple parities. Symbol

Barrow A castrated male hog.

Pork Quality Assurance Plus A voluntary educational program introduced by the National Pork Producers Council as a tool to enhance the quality of pork sold to the world's consumers.

TQA Trucker Quality Assurance Program is an educational program for all involved in the transportation process of swine.

Heterosis The superiority of the crossbred animal as compared to the parents' breeds. Commonly referred to as *hybrid vigor*.

III should be produced under the **Pork Quality Assurance Plus** and the **Trucker Quality Assurance Program (TQA)**.

There are direct paybacks to producers who produce superior animals. The majority of the market hogs are sold on carcass merit pricing systems. These systems reward producers whose animals are heavily muscled and have low body fat. Further refinements in these systems are expected in the future.

Crossbreeding   To produce the best hogs in the most economical manner, commercial swine-breeding programs rely on crossbreeding. Virtually all market hogs in the United States are crossbred. Crossbred animals exhibit hybrid vigor, or **heterosis**. The advantages of crossbred hogs compared to purebred hogs represent a 20–30% improvement in productivity and efficiency. Swine producers started to practice and widely use crossbreeding programs effectively several decades ago. They were among the first livestock breeders to use systematic multibreed crossing programs.

Crossbreeding programs specify the breeds to be used and in what order. Figures 12–14, 12–15, and 12–16 show examples of some effective crossbreeding schemes for swine. Table 12–2 gives the percentage of heterosis that can be expected from several different crossbreeding schemes. The crossbreeding scheme chosen should be based on the size of the herd, availability of replacements, and several other management-related factors.

Figure 12–14

A three-breed rotational crossbreeding scheme for swine. Replacement gilts are selected from the market crosses and the breed of boar is changed every generation. In the initial cross, heterosis in the offspring is 100%. After the rotation has stabilized, the heterosis in the offspring and the sows is 86% for both. This general scheme can be extended to include additional breeds in the rotation. A six-breed rotation has a stable heterosis equilibrium of 98.4%. Source: Adapted from the *Pork Industry Handbook*.

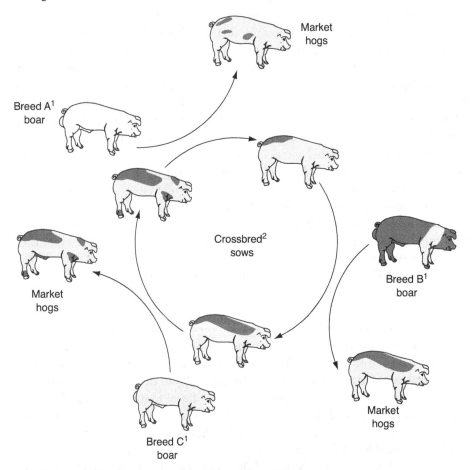

[1]The boars are alternated between breeds with different strengths. Breed A might be a boar from a breed known for maternal traits such as Yorkshire or Landrace; Breed B from a strong carcass and growth trait breed such as the Hampshire or Spotted; and Breed C from one known for being a more balanced breed such as the Duroc.

[2]The sow is always a crossbred once the rotation is stabilized.

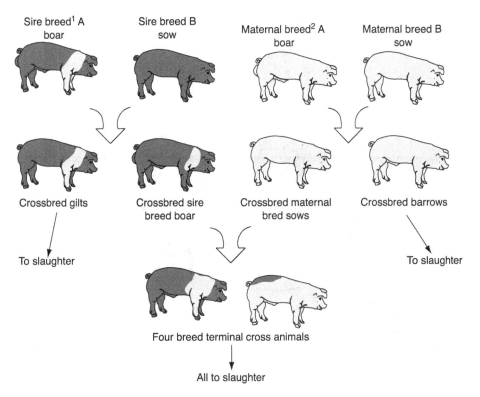

Figure 12–15
A four-breed terminal crossbreeding scheme for swine. Terminal crosses take advantage of breed differences. The sow is a cross of breeds known for their maternal traits. The boar is a cross of breeds known for carcass merit and fast, efficient gain. Breed differences are used to maximum advantage, and maximum heterosis is realized because there are no common breeds in the parents of the meat animals. Source: Adapted from the *Pork Industry Handbook.*

Sire breed[1] A boar   Sire breed B sow   Maternal breed[2] A boar   Maternal breed B sow

Crossbred gilts   Crossbred sire breed boar   Crossbred maternal bred sows   Crossbred barrows

To slaughter   To slaughter

Four breed terminal cross animals

All to slaughter

[1]The boar is from a group of breeds known for carcass merit and fast, efficient gain. The Hampshire, Duroc, Spotted, and Poland breeds are examples.

[2]The sow is a cross of white breeds known for their maternal traits. The Yorkshire, Landrace, and Chester White (all white breeds) are generally acknowledged the best for maternal traits.

Purebred Programs   Purebred operations have as their main function the production of seedstock for other purebred breeders and commercial producers. Purebreds should rarely, if ever, be used in commercial production except as the parents of crossbreds. Less than 1% of all the hogs in the United States are registered

Table 12–2
BREED COMPOSITION AND PERCENT OF MAXIMUM HETEROSIS EXPECTED FROM TWO-BREED AND THREE-BREED ROTATIONAL CROSSING PROGRAMS

| | 2-Breed Crosses | | | | 3-Breed Crosses | | | | |
| | % Blood | | Expected Heterosis | | % Blood | | | Expected Heterosis | |
Generation Number	A	B	Offspring	Dam	A	B	C	Offspring	Dam
1	50	50	100	0	50	50*	0	100	0
2	75*	25	50	100	25	25	50*	100	100
3	38	62*	75	50	63*	12	25	75	100
4	69*	31	62	75	31	56*	12	88	75
5	34	66*	69	62	16	28	56*	88	88
6	67*	33	66	69	58*	14	28	84	88
7	33	67*	67	66	29	57*	14	86	84
8	67*	33	67	67	14	29	57*	86	86

*Breed of sire used to produce offspring.
Source: Buchanan et al., 1999. Used with permission.

Figure 12–16

A rota-terminal crossbreeding system for swine. This specialized crossing system is designed to make use of breed strengths while minimizing weaknesses. This system allows 100% heterosis in the offspring and 86% maternal heterosis. Source: Adapted from the *Pork Industry Handbook.*

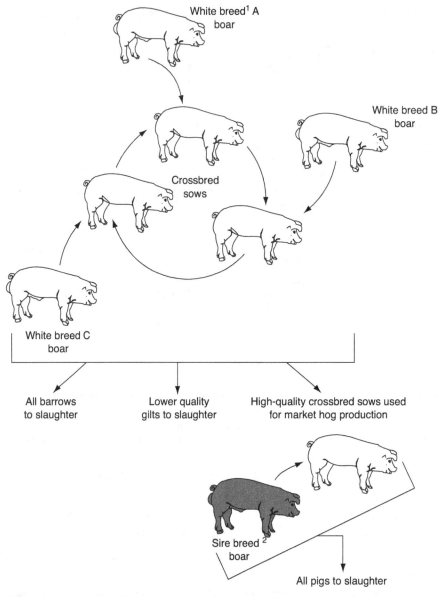

White breed[1] A boar

White breed B boar

Crossbred sows

White breed C boar

All barrows to slaughter

Lower quality gilts to slaughter

High-quality crossbred sows used for market hog production

Sire breed[2] boar

All pigs to slaughter

[1]The Yorkshire, Landrace, and Chester White (all white breeds) are generally acknowledged as the best for maternal traits.

[2]The boar is from a group of breeds known for carcass merit and fast, efficient gain. The Hampshire, Duroc, Spotted, and Poland breeds are examples.

purebreds. However, effective crossbreeding programs require the availability of superior purebred livestock. Breeds are by definition animals that have been selected for a more uniform set of characteristics than their species shows as a whole. Breeds in common use in the U.S. swine industry were discussed previously.

Crossbred Seedstock   The ability to use sophisticated computer models to predict the breeding value of animals has speeded the development of breeding programs that use controlled crossbreeding to select for and develop synthetic lines of breeding animals. These are commonly referred to as *maternal lines* and *sire lines.* Although purebred animals are needed to develop these breeding lines, fewer purebreds are needed than before. This is especially true because the crossbred boars from these programs are taking the place of purebred boars for producing market hogs. Several swine seedstock companies in the United States develop and market crossbred seedstock. The selection of the breeds and all other decisions within the companies relative to the breed composition of these animals is proprietary information that is not generally made available to producers. The lines are generally a mixture of three to four breeds. When a producer purchases seedstock, he or she also purchases the breeding program of the seedstock company.

REPRODUCTIVE MANAGEMENT IN SWINE

Chapter 8 is devoted to reproductive physiology. See this chapter for the fundamentals of reproduction.

Modern swine production systems demand high reproductive rates from swine. Litters need to be large. Sows need to either be lactating or gestating with as little nonproductive time as possible. Use of facilities must be maximized. Expensive confinement facilities cannot be paid for if they are empty. New gilts must be brought into the herd as early as they can be properly developed. Boars must maintain a high level of sperm production and have good libido. On the whole, reproductive management in a swine herd is a time-consuming task that has many facets and absolutely must be done well. Good reproductive efficiency is very dependent on good animal health management and good nutritional management.

Gilts

New gilts must be brought into the breeding herd with regular frequency. They are needed to replace cull sows. They are also expected to have better genetics than their mothers and, therefore, produce more desirable offspring. Gilts should come from family lines of known mothering ability and should display no observable genetic defects. They should be grown to reach 250 lbs in their first 7 months of life. They may be bred at this weight. The exact timing of mating for gilts is dictated by the demands of the farrowing schedule for the whole herd, current costs, salvage values of cull breeding stock, and other management decisions.

Sows

Sows must be managed such that they produce ample milk for the litter and also to be ready to rebreed within 4 to 7 days of weaning the litter. For every 21-day delay in rebreeding, a sow must produce one to two additional pigs per litter just to pay for the feed and labor of the delay. Sows are easy to synchronize in heat. Within 3 to 7 days of weaning a litter, most sows come into heat. With today's commonly used practice of all-in-all-out, in which all litters born within a 7-day period are weaned together, the majority of sows are automatically synchronized.

Estrus Detection

Estrus detection in gilts and sows is critical to the success of a swine operation. Having a boar present can enhance heat detection. Sows and gilts in heat generally have a swollen vulva, respond to pressure on their back by standing solidly (hence the term *standing heat*), stiffen their ears (called popping their ears), and may display other behavioral signs.

Farrowing Management

The presence of an experienced farrowing manager is acknowledged to be worth one additional pig per litter on the average. Intervals longer than 15–20 minutes between pigs may signal a problem that requires intervention. Baby pigs frequently succumb to being tangled in the afterbirth, and they suffer other mishaps like bleeding navels or inability to nurse in a timely manner. All of these problems can be alleviated. Many producers manage farrowings with the use of hormones to induce parturition.

This helps keep litters closer to the same age and makes other management practices, such as equalizing litter sizes by **cross-fostering**, easier to accomplish.

Cross-fostering Moving young from their dam and placing them with another female for rearing.

Boars

Boars should be evaluated for genetic contribution and breeding soundness before they are used in a breeding program. One in 10 untried boars is likely to have a fertility problem. The major factors that should be evaluated in a breeding soundness exam include testicular development, penile lacerations/scarring, physical ability to breed females and/or mount a collection dummy, semen quality, and libido. Serologic testing procedures for disease control are increasingly part of boar evaluation. Most boars are sexually active by 7 months of age. Boars and females can be run together for breeding in pen-mating systems. Another method is hand-mating. In this method, the animals are only put together specifically to mate and are then separated. Large swine facilities use artificial insemination as the predominant form of mating.

Artificial Insemination in Swine

The greatest advantage of artificial insemination (AI) is the opportunity to use genetically superior boars. Currently, fresh boar semen is readily available from many different boar studs in the United States and anyone can purchase semen out of many outstanding boars. Pork producers who collect their own boars can reduce the number of boars needed in their herd and thus reduce the cost of breeding. One collection from the average boar will produce enough sperm cells to breed ten or more females. Producers who have **closed herds** can use AI to reduce the risk of introducing new disease. They may purchase semen or collect their own boars at a different location. AI facilitates the mating of animals of different sizes and allows the detection of an infertile boar immediately.

Closed herd A herd into which no new animals are introduced.

Problems of swine AI include the storing of semen. Generally, the best success with AI is obtained by using fresh semen within 3 days of collection. However, long-term extenders can maintain semen viability for 10 to 14 days. Proper use of semen extenders and storage at correct temperature are necessary for the storage of fresh semen. Commercial frozen semen is available. Unfortunately, the average pregnancy rates are 25% lower and litter size is one to three fewer pigs per litter. Frozen semen is not commonly used in the United States. Fresh semen is used extensively by all segments of the industry including the commercial industry, seedstock industry, and show-pig producers.

Record Keeping

Good records are essential to managing reproductive issues in the swine herd. Because management practices and standards vary with conditions across the country and the specifics of the swine operation, producers are encouraged to contact their local extension service or state extension specialists for help in setting up a recordkeeping program. Several programs are available commercially as well. These range from simple record books to powerful and sophisticated computer programs. As the average size of swine units increases, it is hard to imagine that a hand-kept record book can be adequate. Keeping good records, interpreting the information in the records, and basing management decisions on those records are essential pieces of modern swine management.

In past years when swine were raised mostly in outdoor systems, sows were usually mated to farrow twice a year. The farrowings were timed to weather conditions as much as possible. Modern confinement and partial confinement systems represent such a capital outlay that they must be maximally used if they are to be profitable. Thus, the modern approach to farrowing is to farrow year-round. The gestation period for a sow is 112–115 days. The estrous cycle for a sow is 18–24 days, with 20–21 days the average. The duration of estrus is 2–3 days. The average number of pigs reared per litter on a national basis is approximately 10. Sows are capable of having 20 or more pigs per litter. However, such large litters rarely thrive. This is an area of swine production in which efficiency of production can be improved. The more pigs a sow can rear, the fewer sows will be needed. Obviously, a greater pigs-per-litter average is desired.

NUTRITION IN SWINE

Swine are monogastric. They have a cecum, which develops and digests some fiber if they are fed forages. However, modern production systems do not make use of this capacity. The feeding niche that swine occupy is for concentrated feeds such as grains, soybean meal, and high-quality by-product feeds. Feed costs represent 65% of the cost of swine production. The nutrition and feeding of swine in most of the production stages revolve around optimizing growth because the faster an animal reaches market, the smaller the percentage of total lifetime feed is used for body maintenance. In addition, the faster an animal reaches market, the fewer days it requires housing, labor, and so on. Thus, the fixed costs of production can be reduced on a per animal basis. Chapters 3, 4, and 5 give detailed information relating to digestive anatomy, nutrition, feeds, and feeding. See those chapters for more detailed information than is provided in this section.

Managing the nutrition of swine is very dependent on the intended purpose of the animal. Market animals are fed differently than the breeding herd. Likewise, different ages of growing pigs require different nutrient quantities and ratios. Monogastrics have exacting nutrient needs. Not only must they receive the absolute quantities of digestible nutrients to meet their nutritional needs, but the nutrients must also be in proper ratio to each other to ensure appropriate consumption and maximum utilization of the nutrients. **Palatability** of the feed is also an issue. If the animals do not consume the feed, it does no good to feed it. Following are some general comments relative to providing **complete diets** for swine:

Palatability The acceptability of a feed or ration to livestock.

Complete diet Diet formulated to meet all the nutritional needs of an animal.

- **Energy**. Age, activity level, level of production (for example, the number of pigs a sow is nursing), and environmental temperature all affect energy requirements. The energy density of the feed can affect how much of a ration the pigs will consume.
- **Protein**. Appropriate swine feeding is as much about quantity and quality of amino acids as it is about total protein. The essential amino acid requirements for the appropriate function must be met for cost-effective production. The younger the animal, the more exacting the requirements for protein and for specific amino acids. Young pigs are started on a 20–22% protein diet, and as they grow, the percentage is lowered until it is around 13–15% protein.
- **Essential fatty acids**. Most practical swine diets provide adequate essential fatty acids.
- **Minerals and vitamins**. Careful consideration of total amounts and ratios of minerals and vitamins is essential. Some minerals are toxic if fed in excess. Vitamins are easily damaged and may not be available to the animal.
- **Water**. Good-quality clean water should be provided free choice. It is important to provide adequate watering space for all animals.

Feeding Practices

Swine operations across the country tend to have very similar feeding practices, due to the similarities in adopted technology, methods of production, and desired uniformity in the market animals produced. What is different from region to region is the

Table 12–3
EXAMPLE DIETS FOR FOUR DIFFERENT CLASSES OF HOGS

Ingredient	Gestation	Lactation	Growing
Corn	1,651	1,412	1660
Soybean meal, 44%	270	470	300
Limestone	18	22	16
Dicalcium phosphate	38	38	13
Salt	10	10	7
Vitamin/trace mineral/additive mix	13	13	4
Total, lbs	2,000	2,000	2,000

Source: Harper et al., 2010.

availability of certain feedstuffs, which vary with regional agronomic practice and the types of by-product feeds available. Least-cost ration formulation programs factor in the cost of nutrients from the available feeds and calculate the lowest cost, balanced diet. Table 12–3 shows some examples of diets for various classes of hogs. All of the examples in the table are based on corn and soybean meal to show how different proportions of these same ingredients can produce diets intended for different purposes. However, economics dictate that other feeds are also used if they can cheapen the ration by making it less expensive. In general, growing and finishing pigs are fed for **ad libitum** intake. Other classes of hogs are usually fed a limited amount of feed consistent with the production function.

Ad libitum Having feed available at all times.

Boars and Gestating Females   These animals can easily consume their daily needs in one feeding. The biggest problem is keeping these animals from becoming overly fat. Thus feed quantities frequently must be restricted. With restricted total intake, nutrient balance of the feed is critical. Generally, boars and gestating females are fed measured amounts one or two times a day. The amount of feed given varies with condition, size, and reproductive stage. For group-housed sows, feeding space should be adequate to allow all sows access to feed. Individual feeding stalls can be used to ensure that individual animals receive the appropriate amount.

Farrowing and Nursing Sows   Just before and directly after farrowing, sows are often fed laxative feeds or additives to minimize constipation. Modern sows with large litters have difficulty eating enough to support the litter and keep adequate body condition. The sow must also be managed in such a way that she is nutritionally capable of rebreeding within a few days of weaning the litter. The general feeding strategy is to feed a balanced diet two or more times a day and minimize weight loss during lactation. Many are fed ad libidum.

Creep An area where young nursing animals can have access to starter feeds. Creep feeds are the high-quality feeds made available to the young animals.

Nursing pig A pig still nursing the sow.

Nursery pig An early-weaned pig of light weight that is housed in special environmentally controlled nursery facilities.

Nursing Pigs   It is common to provide **creep** feeds to **nursing pigs**. They ordinarily consume a small quantity. However, it is important to get the pigs started on solid feeds so that the weaning process is less stressful.

Nursery Pigs   The balance of the feeds offered to **nursery pigs** is the most exacting of all the swine rations. Modern swine systems wean pigs as young as 14 days old. Nutritional balance of the feed is critical to the success of these early-wean systems. Even in systems that wean at older ages (this is done with increasing rarity), the diet must meet exacting nutritional needs. The baby pig is not a very forgiving biological entity. Inadequate care and nutrition at this stage have health and performance implications in later growth stages and affect the ability of the animal to be profitable. Adequate feeder space and access to water is also critical in this class of pig.

Growing and Finishing Pigs   The goal in the growing and finishing phases is to take pigs to slaughter weight as quickly as feasible. Most often, finishing pig diets are designed to achieve **optimal growth**. Such diets consider the influence of fixed costs of production, stage of production, weight of the animal, environmental conditions, and genetic potential of the pigs. Barrows and gilts have slightly different nutrient requirements and are often grouped and feed different diets.

> **Optimal growth** When optimizing growth, such factors as cost of the ration, environment, labor, and other nonfeed inputs are considered.

HERD HEALTH MANAGEMENT

Numerous diseases can bring havoc to a swine operation. The greater the number of animals on one site and the closer they are to other animal operations, the greater the chance of having an infectious disease outbreak. Concise descriptions of a few of the most important diseases are presented in the "Challenges to Swine Health" section. Here, we take a brief look at methods of prevention.

A preventive herd health management program should be designed specifically for the conditions and facilities of each herd. The key to swine health is to prevent problems. Not only are swine diseases difficult and expensive to treat, but many diseases so affect the survivors that they never perform well. It is essential to include a veterinarian in the planning process to provide the expertise for prevention, control, diagnosis, and treatment of diseases. Other areas to be included in the plan include biosecurity, management practices, standards of production efficiency, updates on new information, record keeping, and data analysis. Many producers and veterinarians use the National Pork Board's Pork Quality Assurance Plus® program as a guide in developing a comprehensive herd health plan.

Biosecurity

Biosecurity refers to procedures designed to (1) minimize the risk of disease transmission from sources outside the production unit, and (2) reduce the transmission of diseases among groups of pigs on the same farm. Some important biosecurity measures include the following.

For new animals to be added to the herd:

- **Assess**. The health status of any animals to be added to the herd should be assessed in advance. This is best accomplished by a "let my veterinarian talk to your veterinarian" approach. Health status can thus be assessed and potential problems avoided or at least anticipated.
- **Isolate**. New animals should be isolated from the herd until their health status can be evaluated on site. People who come in contact with the isolated animals should shower and change clothes and boots before returning to the main herd.
- **Stabilize**. New animals should be stabilized by allowing isolation to last long enough for any incubating disease to manifest itself. Any detected diseases and parasites should be diagnosed and treated. The animals should be intentionally exposed to pathogens present in the recipient herd to allow them to develop immunity.

For day-to-day management of the herd:

- **People**. Minimum precautions of changing boots and coveralls when moving between houses or rooms should be observed. Anyone going off premises should shower and change into clean clothes and boots before returning to the facility. It is best to avoid contact with other hogs. When contact is necessary, a shower and change of clothes is a requisite precaution before returning. Visitors should be strictly controlled and provided clothing and footwear when allowed on site (Figure 12–17).

Figure 12–17
Proper biosecurity on swine farms demands that visitors be screened. Many farms post signs such as the one at the entrance to a hog farm in North Carolina. (Photographer Ken Hammond. Courtesy of USDA.)

- **Pigs**. Pig groups should be segregated by age. This helps decrease disease transmission and facilitates cleaning and disinfecting facilities.
- **Vehicles**. Any vehicle is a potential source of pathogens. General transportation vehicles should be parked a safe distance from the facility. Feed trucks should either be washed before entering the premises or unloaded a safe distance away and the feed augered or hauled by a farm vehicle to the barns. Trucks entering the farm to load and transport pigs and trucks returning to the farm after transport should be washed thoroughly. Rendering trucks should never be allowed on premises.
- **Vermin**. Flies, mosquitoes, rodents, skunks, starlings, pigeons, sparrows, stray dogs and cats, wild animals, and feral pigs can pass diseases to swine and should be controlled.

CHALLENGES TO SWINE HEALTH

Despite conscientious management practices and diligent efforts at preventing health problems, diseases will still occur. Some of the most common diseases that affect the health and production of nursery pigs, as well as growing and finishing pigs, are described below. This is an overview of only a few important diseases; many of the diseases that affect swine are beyond the scope of this book.

Diarrhea (scours)

Diarrheal diseases or scours are common in nursing piglets as well as in older growing or finishing pigs. Generally, the causes of diarrhea vary between pigs of different ages. Whatever the cause, severe diarrhea can lead to life-threatening dehydration, especially in young pigs, or may result in decreased gains and performance in less severely affected and older animals. Infectious agents are the most common causes of serious diarrhea in pigs, and include viruses, bacteria, and protozoa, as well as internal parasites (Figure 12–18). Many of these microorganisms are shed in the feces of sick animals and transmitted to the uninfected. Treatment for diarrhea will vary depending on the specific cause, but may involve antibiotic therapy and supportive care, such as providing a warm and dry environment with availability of adequate water or electrolyte solutions to combat dehydration. Prevention is the best means of decreasing problems caused by diarrhea in pigs and may be achieved through vaccination of pregnant sows, good sanitation practices, and maintaining a closed herd with all-in/all-out production system.

Respiratory disease

In pigs, respiratory disease may affect the upper respiratory tract (i.e., the nose) or may involve the lungs and cause pneumonia. Respiratory tract infections may be due

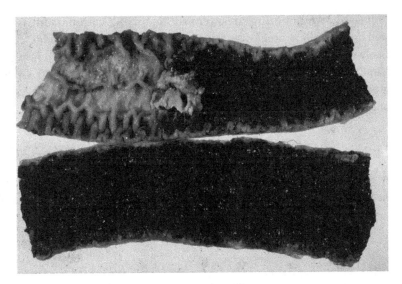

Figure 12–18
This is an opened segment of intestine from a feeder pig that had diarrhea due to a bacterial infection. This disease, called proliferative enteritis, causes thickening and possible bleeding of the intestinal lining. Note the abnormally darkened intestinal lining that is partially peeled away in the upper segment of bowel. (Photo by Dr. Rodger Panciera. Courtesy Oklahoma Center for Veterinary Health Services.)

to either viruses or bacteria, or they may be due to simultaneous infection with multiple microorganisms. Some respiratory infections in pigs lead to serious but short-lived disease, whereas others cause mild or **subclinical** disease that may persist for long periods. Both categories of respiratory disease can cause significant economic loss by either causing death or leading to **chronic** disease. Because many respiratory infections are readily transmitted from pig to pig and are therefore difficult to clear from the herd once they are present, maintaining a closed, disease-free herd is the best approach to controlling respiratory disease. In other circumstances, in which herds have **endemic** infections, disease is minimized by decreasing stress and maintaining good ventilation and temperature control.

Subclinical Without readily observable clinical signs or outward indications of disease.

Chronic Continuing over a long period or having a gradual effect.

Endemic Commonly occurring or widespread within a herd or other group.

Gastric ulcers

Gastric ulcers (Figure 12–19) are often a significant health problem in intensively managed swine herds, especially among growing and finishing pigs. In some operations, a substantial percentage of grower-finisher pigs may die due to severe bleeding from gastric ulcers, and over 50% of pigs may have non-fatal ulcers at the time of slaughter. Even in pigs that don't die from bleeding ulcers, growth rate and overall health of affected animals is likely to be decreased. Risk of gastric ulcer formation is

Gastric ulcers Area in which the inner lining of the stomach is lost and deeper layers are exposed to potential damage from stomach acid.

Figure 12–19
This is the inner lining of a pig's stomach. Note the gastric ulcer, which is the roughly square-shaped, sunken area at the center of the photo. The stomach lining is gone from this area and deeper layers of the stomach wall are exposed. Bleeding is minimal in this example. (Photo by Dr. Rodger Panciera. Courtesy Oklahoma Center for Veterinary Health Services.)

decreased by minimizing stress (crowding, mixing with unfamiliar animals, etc.) as well as controlling other diseases, especially respiratory infections. Also, pelleted and finely ground feeds are known to contribute to ulcer formation in pigs. On the other hand, these types of feed are an advantage to producers, as they significantly improve growth rate and feed efficiency. Therefore, the risk of ulcers versus the growth benefit of such feedstuffs must be considered for each herd.

NUTRITIONAL BENEFITS OF PORK TO HUMANS

A 100g serving of cooked, lean pork provides 180 calories and the following proportion of the recommended daily dietary allowance for a 19- to 30-year-old man:

Protein	46%
Phosphorus	31%
Iron	9%
Zinc	20%
Riboflavin	17%
Thiamin	47%
B_{12}	22%
Niacin	49%

Nutrient-dense food A food that has a variety of nutrients in significant amounts.

Like other meat products, pork is a **nutrient-dense food**, which means it has lots of nutrition per calorie. Pork is also much lower in fat than it was just a decade ago. Pork is a healthful food that can be part of the diet of virtually all people (Figure 12–20).

TRENDS AND FACTORS INFLUENCING THE SWINE INDUSTRY

Pork Consumption

For the past three decades per capita pork consumption has remained essentially flat while poultry continued to enjoy healthy increases in consumption and beef declined and then stabilized (Figure 12–21). Total pork consumed in the U.S. should increase modestly because of population increases. However, some of the growing minority groups, especially Hispanics, tend to consume less pork than the overall average.

Figure 12–20
Coriander-pepper pork chops. Modern pork is low in fat and nutrient dense. Pork is a healthful food that can be part of the diet of virtually all people. (Photo courtesy National Pork Board.)

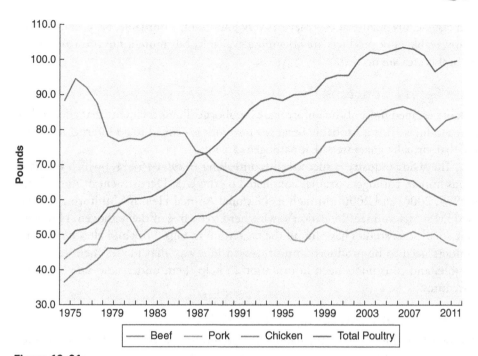

Figure 12–21
Per capita consumption of red meats and poultry. Source: USDA-ERS, 2011b.

Unless they change their eating habits, this could dampen the growth in the pork sector. Older people eat less pork than younger ones, and there is a graying population trend in the United States that could also affect overall pork consumption. Increased consumption of pork could be brought about through the production of a higher-quality, lower-cost product and additional convenient value-added products. Products that could significantly affect pork consumption include **functional foods** (omega-3 and selenium-enriched pork), natural pork, organic pork, vegetarian-fed pork, pork reared without the use of gestation and farrowing crates, and growth-enhancer-free pork. Also, look for new pork cuts.

Functional foods Foods enriched with nutrients that may not be inherent to the food.

Nutrition and Health Consciousness

Nutrition and health consciousness will continue to play a role in food choices. The pork industry has made tremendous strides in producing a lean product and one that better fits into consumer preferences. The educational efforts of the "Pork—The Other White Meat" campaign by the National Pork Board apparently did a credible job of taking this message to consumers and led to the introduction of the new *Pork*® *Be inspired*ˢᵐ campaign, relegating the "other white meat" campaign to heritage brand status. A continuation of this effort and other informational campaigns should continue to improve the image of pork as a healthy food.

Convenient Foods

The expanded integration of the pork industry is bringing about a shift in focus. Instead of considering itself to be in the pig-producing business, it is increasingly considering itself to be in the food business. With this change in focus (one the poultry industry adopted long ago) has come an expanded volume of good, convenience-oriented pork foods. Recognition that today's consumer has very different needs than those of the past is a key to maintaining or increasing consumption levels of any product. Surveys tell us that the average cook wishes to spend a total of 20 to 30 minutes in the kitchen preparing dinner. Children cook a big percentage of in-home meals. Younger people readily admit they do not really know how to cook. More and more, eating habits emphasize the need for less preparation time, ease of consumption, and

good taste. Convenience at every level is very important. Affordable, tasty, convenient, microwavable pork products are now more available, but more innovation and progress in this area are needed.

Food Safety Concerns

Pork has escaped most of the unfortunate foodborne illness incidents that affect other meat products. This is probably because most pork is cooked to an internal temperature that virtually guarantees that pathogens are killed.

The swine industry is successfully controlling *E. coli* 0157:H7, which is a dangerous human pathogen. Studies conducted by the U.S. Department of Agriculture in 1995, 2000, and 2006, through its National Animal Health Monitoring System (NAHMS), determined the nation's swine herd to be free of the pathogen. However, some small-scale studies have found the bacterium in pigs. Pork and all other animal products need to be produced and processed in a way that makes them as safe as possible, and consumers need information to help them understand safe handling procedures.

Last Stages of Restructuring-Consolidation

U.S. swine production is in the hands of large producers with over 95% of the pigs in operations of 1,000 or more animals. These 1,000-plus animal operations represented just 11% of the total swine operations. Small operations will continue to go out of business, and the larger operations will continue to consolidate into even larger operations.

Technological Innovation and Standardization

The swine industry has embraced technology and reinvented the way pigs are raised in the United States. With technological innovation, the swine industry continues to produce more uniform animals around which value-added products can be more easily designed and marketing strategies developed. Technology that has driven the emergence of large producers and technology will drive the production changes that are to come.

Waste Disposal

Along with the increasing prevalence of larger swine facilities, manure disposal become a major issue. During the late 1990s, several well-publicized spills from swine lagoons occurred. Iowa and North Carolina were hard hit by adverse publicity, and other states had their share of problems. In addition to the physical waste, the public made it clear that odor from swine operations is pollution and that they wanted it controlled, as well. State legislatures responded with moratoriums on building swine facilities, new and tougher rules for lagoon construction and safety, and, in some states, very explicit laws about where facilities could be located in relation to public roads, existing human housing, and so on.

Tighter controls, new technology, and common sense have all contributed to improved waste management. The use of biofilters to control odor from swine houses is becoming more common. Nitrogen and phosphorus contribute to odor and other waste management issues in waste. Dietary manipulation has proven an effective way to reduce nitrogen and phosphorus levels in wastes. Diet alteration has also contributed to lower fecal mineral concentrations of other minerals, which helps keep them from building up in land where wastes are spread. Lagoons are being managed differently, covered, aerated, and used in conjunction with methane digesters. Many other measures are being developed and tested. It is too early to declare this problem fixed. However, great progress has been made, and the state of manure/odor management is

Figure 12–22

The swine industry has many tools available to control wastes and odor. (a) Experimental unit with biofilters, the means to separate solid from liquid waste and reuse water to flush holding pits under the houses, a methane digester, two covered lagoons, and an irrigation system that distributes excess liquid waste onto adjacent hay land. It sits adjacent to a housing development and receives no complaints from neighbors. (b) Filtering system to clean wastes from a hog operation. A series of hillside terraces form constructed wetlands where bacteria purify wastewater. (Photo by Tim McCabe courtesy USDA-Natural Resources Conservation Service.)

much improved (Figure 12–22). The U.S. EPA will continue to have a say in the way swine waste is managed in the future, and there will be new challenges.

Biotechnology

Numerous tools will ultimately come to assist the swine producer as a result of biotechnology. Biotechnological tools already developed or in various developmental stages for swine include:

- Innovative and faster techniques for the diagnosis of swine infectious diseases, gene-deleted or genetically engineered vaccines, more sophisticated diagnostic tests that differentiate vaccinated animals from infected animals, tests for the identification of infectious agents, and differentiation of related infectious agents, DNA fingerprinting of infectious agents, detection of carrier animals that are often difficult to diagnose by conventional techniques.
- Methods for the control of reproductive functions, such as induced estrus, induced ovulation, synchronization of prepubertal and mature gilts, superovulation, artificial insemination, embryo transfer, and sexed semen.
- Changes in body composition such as pork with significant amounts of omega-3 fatty acids—the kind believed to stave off heart disease.

Marker-assisted selection has made significant contributions to swine genetics and selection by helping decrease the incidence of specific genetic flaws, for example, stress gene and Napole gene, and by improving performance traits, for example, growth rate, feed efficiency, carcass leanness, and litter size. Most of the economically valuable traits are under the influence of multiple genes, perhaps hundreds. To make significantly faster progress with these traits, genomics and marker-assisted selection will be used to discover genes that affect a large proportion of the variation for individual quantitative traits and then select the next generation accordingly. Breeding companies have been and will continue using this tool in the development of their breeding stock. Commercial laboratories already make available tests for various trait-linked markers, which any producer can use. More tests that are less expensive are inevitable.

Foreign Competition/Trade

Enhanced trade agreements and a general opening of world markets have created, and will continue to create, import–export opportunities for the United States and other countries. Several European countries are pork-exporting nations. Some of the South American countries are potential pork-producing and pork-exporting nations. Canada is making great progress in swine production, in both quality and quantity. Competition from foreign imports to the United States, and competition against the United States for other markets, is inevitable. However, U.S. pork exports are significant. In 1995, the United States became a net exporter of pork. The value of U.S. pork exports rose to $4.8 billion in 2010. This export volume has allowed the industry to produce above domestic demand. Exports amount to approximately 20% of total production. The export market for pork shows promise for the long term. Burgeoning human populations, along with developing economies in some of those populations, are creating very favorable prospects for many agricultural exports from the United States. Although normal economic cycles and sporadic consumer concerns will surely affect year-to-year purchases, the overall trend is expected to be very positive.

Animal Welfare/Animal Rights

The confinement systems of the swine industry have long been criticized by animal rights groups. Gestation and farrowing crates have been considered especially irksome. The European Union enacted a gestation crate ban to be complete in 2013, and other countries have announced similar actions. Several state referenda and legislative actions banning sow crates brought the issue to new attention in the United States, with several states enacting bans. A cascade of announcements by major pork purchasers (Burger King, McDonald's, Chipotle Mexican Grill, Panera Bread, and Oregon-based New Seasons Market) altering their buying preferences based on whether the supplier used gestation crates was followed by a similar set of announcements by major pork producers (Smithfield Foods, Cargill Pork, Maple Leaf Foods in Canada) that they were phasing out gestation crates or "transitioning to group housing" for their sows. The issue is a controversial one with proponents on both sides.

In recognition of the continuing need to improve animal welfare in pig production, and with an understanding that consumers increasingly want assurances about the way that animals are raised and cared for, the National Pork Promotion and Research Board officially launched the Pork Quality Assurance Plus program in 2007. It combines food safety, animal health, and welfare elements into one program

Work Force

Developing and retaining a workforce has become a major problem for the swine industry. The labor force, both skilled and unskilled, is predicted to tighten dramatically. This problem will be further complicated by such issues as group housing of sows, which requires more labor and management skills than gestation crate management, and other such developments.

INDUSTRY ORGANIZATIONS

American Livestock Breeds Conservancy

http://www.albc-usa.org/

National Pork Board

http://www.pork.org/default.aspx

Composed of members who are nominated by producers and appointed by the Secretary of Agriculture. They are responsible for administering the funds from the pork checkoff. The checkoff was created by the Pork Promotion and Research Act of 1985. This act provided that all producers contribute a portion of their sales (0.4) to be used for pork promotion, research, and consumer education.

National Pork Producers Council

http://www.nppc.org/

"The National Pork Producers Council conducts public-policy outreach on behalf of its 43 affiliated state associations enhancing opportunities for the success of U.S. pork producers and other industry stakeholders by establishing the U.S. pork industry as a consistent and responsible supplier of high-quality pork to the domestic and world markets."

U.S. Meat Export Federation

http://usmef.org/

A nonprofit integrated trade organization representing a wide variety of groups including livestock producers, meatpackers, processors, farm organizations, grain promotional groups, agribusiness companies, and others. The organization works to develop foreign markets for U.S.-produced beef, pork, lamb, and veal.

SUMMARY AND CONCLUSION

The U.S. gross annual income from pork is approximately $14 billion. Pigs currently generate 5.5% of all U.S. farm cash receipts. The swine industry is not only a major industry, but it is also an aggressive, technologically driven, expansion-minded industry. The purpose of the swine industry in the United States is to produce meat from millions of tons of excess grain and available by-products. Swine are monogastric and use only limited amounts of forage. However, they are the most efficient livestock converters of grain to red meat. They help moderate the fluctuations in grain prices, which could otherwise disrupt the economy and the supply of grain for humans.

Feed costs are a high fixed cost, so economical production depends on minimizing labor and maximizing efficiency by reducing time to market. This requires a large investment in facilities, equipment, and technology. This has caused an increasingly integrated and consolidated swine industry with larger operations. Distinct regional shifts have occurred in the swine industry. A group of megaproducers have driven expansion east, south, and west. The Hog Belt has let out a few notches, and producers are consolidating into larger operations. Swine breeders have made remarkable progress in genetic improvement, especially in reducing the fat content of the average pork carcass.

Modern consumers demand lean pork, and today's hogs are much leaner than those of the past. Modern swine production systems demand high reproductive rates from swine. Expensive confinement facilities must be kept full. There is tremendous overlap among good reproductive management, good animal health management, and good nutritional management.

Feeding practices in swine operations across the country have become more uniform. Most hog rations are formulated with the use of least-cost ration formulation programs. In general, growing and finishing pigs are fed for ad libitum intake and other classes of limited intake consistent with level of production. Herd health programs should be designed for each herd. Prevention is much more important than treatment. Swine diseases are difficult and expensive to treat and affect the survivors to a degree that prevents them from ever performing well. Many producers and veterinarians use the Pork Quality Assurance Plus Program as a guide in developing a comprehensive herd health plan.

Like other meat products, pork is a nutrient-dense food, which means it has lots of nutrition per calorie. Increased consumption of pork could be brought about through the production of a higher quality, lower cost product, more convenient foods, and emphasis on pork's excellent record in food safety.

FACTS ABOUT SWINE

Birth weight:	2–3 lbs
Weaning weight:	10–12 lbs at 2–4 weeks; 30–40 lbs at 6 weeks
Mature weight:	Male 500–800 lbs; female 400–700 lbs; miniatures 140–170 lbs
Slaughter weight:	230–270 lbs
Weaning age:	2–6 weeks
Breeding age:	6–8 months
Normal season of birth:	Traditional, spring and fall; modern, year-round
Gestation:	112–115 days
Estrous cycle:	19–21 days
Duration of estrus (heat):	2–3 days
Boar/sows services:	Pasture 1/15; hand-mating 1/20 (limit to 1–2 per day); AI 6–10 sows per service
Litter size:	7–15, although larger litters are common
Names of various sex classes:	Sow, gilt, boar, barrow
Digestive system:	Nonruminant, monogastric

STUDY QUESTIONS

1. What is the economic value of the swine industry to U.S. agriculture? Describe the magnitude of this industry in other ways.

2. What is the purpose of the swine industry in the United States? Describe it in terms of feed and use of resources.

3. What is the importance of the pig to worldwide meat production?

4. When were the first hogs brought into the Western Hemisphere? Who else brought them? What was the most important use of the pig until well into the 20th century? How do current U.S. swine numbers compare to those of the past?

5. What are the major types of swine production in the United States today? Describe each. Compare the number of swine producers today to the past. What are the factors that will ultimately determine the location of the U.S. swine industry?

6. Why are swine located where they are in the United States? Describe what is happening to the swine industry in terms of its geographical location.

7. What are some of the tools available to help swine producers make sound decisions about the genetics they use? What are the roles of the different breeds

in the swine industry? How are synthetic lines being used in the breeding of swine? Briefly discuss the value of crossbreeding in swine production.

8. Describe the ideal market hog according to the National Pork Board.

9. Briefly describe swine management for maximal reproductive efficiency. What is the role of artificial insemination in the swine industry?

10. Briefly discuss nutrition in hogs for each class of animal. What are the similarities and what are the differences?

11. Why is having and following a herd health plan so important in raising hogs?

12. Describe methods of addressing the concept of biosecurity in a swine unit. Be specific. Can you think of any additional ones that might be used?

13. What does a serving of cooked pork provide nutritionally? What does "nutrient dense" mean? Are other animal-based foods nutrient dense?

14. How much pork does the U.S. population consume on a per capita basis? Is that amount changing?

15. What changes have been made in pork to make it a more health-conscious food? How do you think nutrition and health concerns will affect the future of the swine industry?

16. Will swine operations continue to grow bigger? Briefly discuss how and why vertical integration is involved in swine industry consolidation.

17. How do confinement operations and the adoption of technology go together? Speculate about the role that technology will play for the swine industry in the future.

18. Why is the issue of waste disposal so important to the swine industry? Will laws and regulations for swine waste disposal get tougher? Does the issue of odor differ from the issue of solid waste? If so, how?

19. What role will exports likely play in the growth of the future swine industry?

REFERENCES

For the 5th edition, Melanie A. Breshears, DVM, PhD, Diplomate ACVP, assistant professor, veterinary pathobiology, Center for Veterinary Health Sciences, Oklahoma State University, contributed material to this chapter.

Arnot, C. and C. Gauldin. 2007. Sow stall debate is at a "tipping point." *Feedstuffs* 79 (15).

Buchanan, D. S., W. G. Luce and A. C. Clutter. 1999. Swine crossbreeding systems. Oklahoma State University Fact Sheet, ANSI-3603.

Cleveland, E. R., W. T. Ahlshwede, C. J. Christians, R. K. Johnson, and A. P. Schinkel. 1999. *Genetic principles and their applications.* PIH-106. Pork Industry Handbook.

Ensminger, M. E. 1991. *Animal science.* 9th ed. Danville, IL: Interstate.

FAO. 2011. *FAOSTAT statistics database. Agricultural production and production indices data.* http://apps.fao.org/.

Harper, A. F., R. D. Coffey, G. R. Hollis, D. C. Mahan, and J. S. Radcliffe. 2010. *Swine Diets.* Accessed online may 2011 at http://www.extension.org/pages/27436/swine-diets.

Jones, R. D. 1989. History of the pig: Swine over 40 million years old. *Livestock Newsletter.* Athens: University of Georgia.

NPPC. 2011. *Pork facts.* Des Moines, IA: National Pork Producers Council.

USDA. 2011. *USDA nutrient database for standard reference.* Release 23. Nutrient Data Laboratory Home Page, http://www.nal.usda.gov/fnic/foodcomp.

USDA-NASS. 2011a. *Briefing room. Farm income and costs.* Accessed online May 2011. http://www.ers.usda.gov/Briefing/FarmIncome/.

USDA-NASS. 2011b. *Quick Stats: Agricultural Statistics Database.* http://www.nass.usda.gov/QuickStats/.

13

Sheep and Goats

Key Terms

Anestrus	Kidding
Angora	Lamb
Breed complementarity	Lambing
Browse	Mohair
Conception	Palpation
Doe	Range sheep production
Doeling	Roughage
Estrous cycle	Seasonal market
Estrus	Sheep
Ewe	Specialty market
Farm flock production	Survival of the fittest
Flock	Trimester
Forage	Wool
Heterosis	

SCIENTIFIC CLASSIFICATION OF SHEEP AND GOATS

Phylum:	Chordata
Subphylum:	Vertebrata
Class:	Mammalia
Order:	Artiodactyla
Suborder:	Ruminata
Family:	Bovidae
Genus:	*Ovis* (sheep); *Capra* (goat)
Species:	*aries* (sheep); *hires* (goat)

THE PLACE OF THE SHEEP AND GOAT INDUSTRIES IN U.S. AGRICULTURE

The sheep industry has declined in the United States and is now approximately two tenths of 1% of the total U.S. farm revenue from livestock and products (Figure 13–1). The gross annual income from

sheep, lambs, and **wool** in the United States is approximately $460 million. It comprises only four tenths of 1% of animal agriculture's share of cash receipts (Figure 13–2). The U.S. population consumes very small amounts of lamb meat, less than 1 lb per capita on a boneless weight basis. The sheep industry was once a mighty industry in the United States, but those days are long gone and are not likely to return. If the United States stopped raising sheep altogether, there would be ample imports to supply the needs of the whole country.

Clearly, the current status of this industry now places it in the ranks of a specialty or niche industry when compared to other livestock species. However, production of sheep has been historically profitable, and it is an important industry to the more than 81,000 individual farms and ranches in the United States that raise sheep. It seems that the long, steady decline in the United States sheep industry is tending to level out, and there has even been some modest growth in recent years. Sheep are also an important 4-H and FFA club species. Many young people who may not have the size, skill, space, or money to raise a steer or horse can raise a lamb and have a meaningful project. It is also a species that produces a specialty meat product in demand in the hotel and restaurant trade and, in certain parts of the country, in grocery stores as well. The dairy sheep industry shows some potential to become an industry segment of significant value to some states.

The goat industry has always been a small specialty or niche industry in the United States. The goat industry is made up of three main types of enterprises. These are dairy goats, fiber-producing goats, and goats produced for meat. The dairy goat industry is a small, but stable part of goat production. The **Angora** goat industry has been on a precipitous decline since the phasing out of the wool and **mohair** incentive program in the mid-1990s. The third type of goat enterprise is the production of meat goats. The meat goat industry has realized a very rapid increase in animal numbers and operations raising meat goats. From 2002 to 2007, the production of meat goats increased 58% across the United States, which made it the fastest growing livestock enterprise in the United States for that period. Two main factors contributed to the growth of the meat goat industry; 1) importation of new breeds of goats that were larger, faster growing, and had superior carcass conformation than the traditional breeds used and 2) the increase in the United States population of people from different cultures, countries, and religious backgrounds that historically consumed goat meat. The growth of the meat goat industry has seemed to level off to a more stable growth rate.

Wool The fiber that grows instead of hair on the bodies of sheep.

Sheep An animal of the genus *Ovis* that is over 1 year of age.

Lamb A sheep under 1 year of age. Also, the meat from a sheep under 1 year of age.

Angora A specialized fiber-producing breed of goat.

Mohair The fiber produced by the Angora goat.

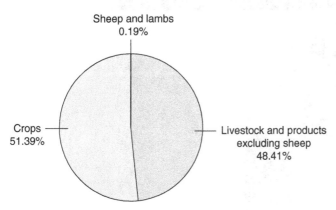

Figure 13–1
Sheep, lambs, and wool combined farm cash receipts as a percentage of total U.S. farm cash receipts, 2000–2009.
(Source: Based on USDA statistics.)

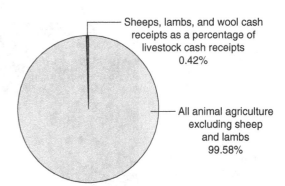

Figure 13–2
Sheep, lamb, and wool farm cash receipts as a percentage of animal agriculture's cash receipts, 2000–2009. (Source: Based on USDA statistics.)

PURPOSE OF THE SHEEP AND GOAT INDUSTRIES IN THE UNITED STATES

Forage Fiber-containing feeds like grass or hay. Can be grazed or harvested for feeding. Contain at least 18% fiber but have high digestible energy (>70%).

Roughage A bulky feedstuff with low weight per unit volume. Contains at least 18% fiber but can range up to 50%. Less digestible than forages.

Flock A group or band of sheep.

The purpose of sheep and goats in the United States is much the same as the purpose of other ruminant species: to take advantage of **forage** and **roughage** to produce products that humans can use (Figure 13–3). The products include milk, meat, and fiber, with meat the most economically important. Historically, sheep have been used as part of a mixed farm in the eastern states and in large **flocks** that graze rangelands in the western part of the country. Range production, in turn, differs depending on whether the range is dry or wet. In most situations in which sheep are kept as part of a diversified farm, meat production is more profitable than wool production. Therefore, when forage conditions are good enough to permit weaning a high percentage of lambs ready for slaughter, meat production is the primary goal. Wool production is secondary and is more of a by-product. Wool production is likely to be more profitable than meat production if forage conditions are poor. In this case, wool production is emphasized and meat production is the secondary product. This is the situation in the dry range areas, but not in the wet range areas. In wet range conditions, the nutritional level is high enough that both meat and wool can be produced satisfactorily. The value of wool has declined to the point that raising sheep for wool in the United States is rarely profitable (Figure 13–4). Thus, most systems focus on meat production.

Figure 13–3

Sheep are excellent converters of forage into food and fiber. Range sheep production operations have large numbers of breeding ewes and specific breed types, and they use large land areas. (Photo courtesy American Sheep Industry Association.)

Figure 13–4

Wool is a naturally grown, renewable fiber with unique physical properties and was once vital to the comfort and economy of the country. Competition from synthetics and availability of wool on the world market have reduced the importance of its production. (Photo courtesy of the American Sheep Industry Association.)

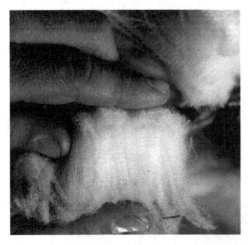

Sheep and goats have always been able to help us better use our forage resources when used in conjunction with cattle. When sheep and/or goats use the land along with cattle, they make better use of the resources because they graze slightly different forage. Sheep are better able to select their diet than cattle and can thus pick a better diet. Goats like to eat **browse** and select it first if it is available. In this way, goats and cattle complement each other. It is generally accepted that one **ewe** or **doe** can be added per each existing cow unit and no additional forage will be needed. In wooded or scrub conditions, goats can be the preferred species because they like the browse. Both goats and sheep can actually improve pastures and other grazing resources be-cause they eat many species, including weeds, that cattle leave behind. For this rea-son, sheep farms frequently have cattle on the same operation. However, the use of mixed species to make better use of our grazing land has not been practiced as widely as it might be in this country. This is so in spite of the fact that research has demon-strated the economic and biological value of grazing mixed species. Goats have been used even less widely as part of mixed grazing systems. Much of this is because sheep require more care and are subject to greater predation losses than cattle. Because of their liking for browse, **mobs** of goats are often used as brush clearers in lands that need to be reclaimed. They are also often used in brush control under power lines and other similar areas in some states.

Although the United States is not a major sheep- and goat-producing country, much of the rest of the world has sizable sheep and goat interests. Sheep and goats are used extensively around the world for their grass conversion ability by a wide variety of people. With 1.1 billion head of sheep and 880 million head of goats distributed globally, they are the second and fourth most numerous agricultural animals, respec-tively, excluding the poultry species. Because of their smaller size, five sheep or seven goats can be kept on the same amount of feed as one cow. Also, because of their smaller size, a goat or sheep carcass can be consumed more rapidly than the carcass of cattle and is thus less likely to spoil. This is important for people who do not have cold storage available for meat. Goats and sheep are thus a better choice for people in less-developed economies. On a worldwide basis, goats and sheep are increasing modestly. They are also widely distributed. It is believed that every country in the world has some sheep and some goats.

HISTORICAL PERSPECTIVE

Sheep and goats were probably both domesticated by 8000 B.C. The sheep was probably domesticated first. It is generally accepted that sheep, goats, and pigs were all domesticated around the same time, with the pig the last of the three. This makes sheep and goats the first of the food-producing animals to be domesticated. Both sheep and goats went with humans as we populated the globe.

Christopher Columbus has the distinction of being the first sheep and goat producer in the Western Hemisphere, just as he was for cattle. He brought sheep and goats to the West Indies on his second voyage in 1493. Cortez brought sheep and goats, as well as cattle, to Mexico with him in 1519. Sheep were brought to the East Coast in 1609 by the English who settled in New England. Early on, the value of sheep as a fiber producer was recognized. Importations improved the value of the wool until the sheep industry eventually supported a thriving wool industry. As the settlement of the continent proceeded, the grasslands became increasingly used as sheep-producing areas. Eventually, the sheep industry became located predomi-nantly in the West.

Figure 13–5 gives a historical look at sheep numbers in the United States. The numbers of sheep have undergone wide swings to reach the industry's **specialty market**

Browse The tender twigs and leaves from brush and trees.

Ewe A female sheep.

Doe A female goat.

Mob A group or herd of goats.

Specialty market A term that suggests a product generally aimed at a spe-cific segment of the overall market.

Figure 13–5

Sheep and lamb inventory.
(Source: USDA-NASS, 2011a.)

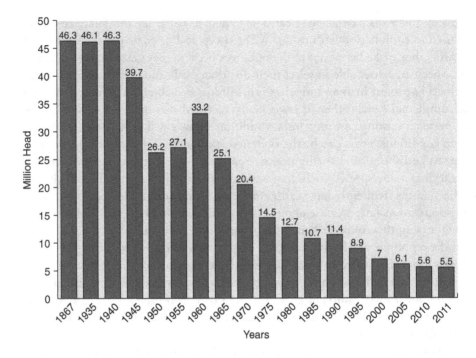

status. During the early colonial period, they were especially important for their wool production. This was really the case until the early 1900s. The production of wool was of primary importance and the production of slaughter animals was incidental. Starting in the late 1800s this began to change and the production of lambs for slaughter became increasingly important. This is also when U.S. sheep production shifted to the western states.

The total count of sheep and lambs on January 1, 1867, just after the Civil War, was 46.3 million head. From 1867 until now, sheep numbers have passed through many cyclical phases. The all-time high was in 1942, when sheep numbers totaled 56.2 million head. The numbers declined after World War II to less than 30 million head in 1950 and dropped to less than 15 million by the early 1970s. Since the early 1970s, the numbers have cycled to successively lower levels. The declining importance of sheep and lambs has been attributed to a number of causes, including:

1. Less demand for wool. As more synthetics and cheaper substitute materials were introduced, wool wasn't as competitive.
2. The low consumer demand for lamb in consumer diets and the relatively high price of lamb relative to other meats.
3. Increased difficulty in obtaining and keeping reliable herders to manage and care for range flocks.
4. Increased competition for public-owned rangeland and increasing government regulation.
5. An increasing problem of predators in many range and farm flock-producing states.
6. Decreased government support, especially the demise of the wool support program.
7. Farmer diversification into other enterprises.
8. Seasonal nature of lamb production and consumption.
9. Inadequate profit to keep producers producing.

Although large decreases in numbers have left the sheep industry a much smaller part of U.S agriculture, there does seem to be a new optimism about the sheep industry. The declines in total numbers have become less drastic. The inventory value for

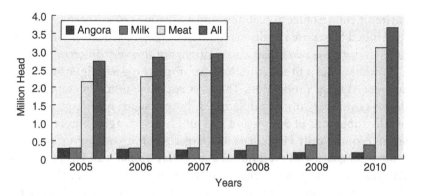

Figure 13–6
U.S. goat inventory by class.
(Source: USDA-NASS, 2011b.)

sheep increased during the 2000s. Toward the end of the decade, sheep operations actually showed a modest increase. There are still problems to overcome, however. Per capita demand for lamb has declined to the point that it is no longer in the diet of most people in the United States. The outlook for attracting new consumers is poor. Current consumers are also unlikely to increase their consumption levels significantly unless the cost of lamb declines substantially. That is unlikely to happen. It seems likely that the sheep industry will remain a small industry, but a stable and profitable one.

Since North American colonial times, goats have been used in very small numbers as milk and meat animals. Later, Angora goats became useful as fiber producers for a time in the Southwest, especially in Texas. However, goat numbers and goat meat consumption in the United States has historically been so low that it has not even been reported regularly by the federal government. Prior to 2005, no annual statistics were reported for goats except for Angora goats, although data were included in the Census of Agriculture. Increasing interest in goats and demand for goat meat led USDA-NASS to publish its first annual goat survey in 2005. Goat numbers in the United States increased through 2008 with almost all of the growth related to increased meat-type goat production and have stabilized (Figure 13–6). Much of the increased demand for goat meat is attributed to growing immigrant and ethnic populations. Additionally, many states offered incentives to farmers who participated in the tobacco buyout program if they would get into other areas of agriculture. The Southeast is where the majority of the tobacco was grown and has also seen the largest increases in goat numbers. Goat production appeals to people who have limited access to land and want an animal enterprise. Goat production is also appealing to women and children and requires little start-up costs in terms of equipment and buildings. A substantial youth exhibition industry has also developed around the goat, with some states having more students enrolled in 4-H and FFA goat projects than sheep projects.

STRUCTURE OF THE SHEEP AND GOAT INDUSTRIES

Sheep

Sheep and goats can be raised under many different production systems, and there are many different segments and support industries for the production of small ruminants. Because sheep and goats are ruminants, the nutritional requirements can be met by a number of different production methods.

The U.S. industry is made up of producers, lamb feeders, lamb processors, wool buyers/warehouses, shearers, and other support industries. The specific type of producer or production system is determined by geographic location, production environment, resource availability, and marketing goals. Sheep production systems in the United States are usually categorized as range production or farm flock production. Under these two broad classifications are also very different production systems.

Range sheep production has two distinct types, migratory range production and fenced range production. These systems have much in common, however, they do have some very distinct differences. Both systems have large numbers of sheep—usually thousands of ewes—and they use large acreages (Figure 13–3). Often, they are an economically viable part of a larger ranching operation, possibly with cattle, sometimes goats, and even hunting and recreational leases as part of the operation. Range operations produce the majority of lamb and wool in the United States It is also the range operations that help maintain the important infrastructure present to support the sheep industry. Operations with 500 or more breeding ewes account for about 1% of U.S. producers but have 44% of the total number of ewes. Most of these are in range production systems.

Fenced range production is primarily located in Texas and other southwestern states. Texas leads the country in total sheep numbers and operations with sheep. The fenced areas are often a section (640 acres) or more in size. Sheep are left unattended to graze native forage and browse. Specific breeds of sheep have traditionally been used in fenced range operations. The Rambouillet (Figure 13–7) is a hardy sheep that does well in the hot dry climate present in these geographic areas and has historically been the most commonly used breed. The fine wool breeds Merino and Debouillet are also used. In recent years, there has also been some use of hair sheep and hair sheep crosses because their hardiness suits fenced range production. Lamb production is the most important product, usually feeder lambs, but wool production is relatively important due to the dry climate, which limits grazing.

Migratory range operations are located in the intermountain states and use very large land areas that are often a combination of privately owned land and land leased from the Bureau of Land Management (BLM). Grazing permits issued by the BLM allow for grazing specific parcels of largely unimproved, mountainous areas. Ranching operations pay a yearly fee for use of BLM lands. Migratory range operations typically keep ewes at lower elevations in the winter. The lambs are born in these lower ranges or in lambing sheds. Summer grazing of ewes and lambs occurs on the higher elevation BLM grazing land (Figure 13–8). Ewes and lambs are grouped into large flocks, often termed *bands*. Each band is tended by a herder. Herders are often from South America and have U.S. work visas. Similar to fenced range areas, specific breeds or breed types of sheep are used in a migratory range operation. Breeds such

Figure 13–7

Rambouillet-type ewes are the most commonly used ewes in range sheep production. They are hardy, long lived, flock well, and are good lamb and wool producers. (Photo courtesy of the American Sheep Industry Association.)

Figure 13–8
A band of ewes with lambs grazing Bureau of Land Management land on high elevation mountain mead- ows. (Photo courtesy of the American Sheep Industry Association.)

as Rambouillet, Targhee, Columbia, Polypay, and Merino crosses are the most common. Sheep in this type of production system need to be hardy, have well-developed flocking instincts, and produce high quality lamb and wool.

Farm flock production is the second major classification of sheep production. Farm flock production is defined by the size of the operation and can be found in any geographic location. However, farm flock production has historically occurred in the Midwestern and eastern areas of the U.S. farm flock operations are usually less than 500 head of breeding ewes and average 30 to 40 head. Farm flocks with fewer than 100 breeding ewes make up 94% of U.S. sheep operations and have about 36% of the national ewe inventory. Farm flock operations are very diverse and often have differing production goals. Although the overall goal of a farm flock—especially a large farm flock—is to realize a positive economic return, many do not have a sizable economic return as the primary goal. Although it may be desirable to make a profit, other objectives may be equally or more important.

Commercial farm flock operations produce primarily lambs for either the traditional meat markets in the United States or the emerging ethnic-market trade. These operations tend to be larger than the average farm flock, yet not large enough to serve as the sole income for a family. They are either part of larger agricultural enterprise or supplement off-farm income. Compared to range operations, they are smaller, more diverse, and have higher production costs. However, they are generally more productive on a per-ewe basis. Because the production environment is not as demanding, and input costs for feedstuffs is generally higher, more variations in breeds are used. Often, producers desire 150 to 200% lamb weaning rates to enhance economic returns. To achieve this production rate, crossbreeding using prolific breeds is often practiced.

Purebred sheep production primarily occurs in farm flock settings (Figure 13–9). These tend to be smaller operations that specialize in producing purebred breeding stock for commercial producers or other purebred breeders. These operations are often hobby operations that serve as family recreation. Breeders market and exhibit sheep at livestock shows or sales. The value of some of these individual animals can often be quite high.

Club lamb production is another activity that derives primarily from farm flocks. The lambs are marketed to 4-H and FFA youth and their families as project animals. The youngsters may purchase lambs at lighter weights, raise and feed them to market weight, and then exhibit them at county, regional, or state shows. Sheep make very desirable club projects because the costs can be affordable, and they tend to be safe projects due to the size and nature of the animals. And yet, many lessons on life and animal agriculture can be learned through a lamb project.

Figure 13–9

Hampshire ewes are part of a purebred farm flock sheep operation. (Photo courtesy of the American Sheep Industry Association).

The production of high quality, specialty wool is a small but thriving part of farm flock sheep production. Producers will often market these high-quality wools directly to hand spinners and weavers at fiber festivals or fleece fairs. These producers and consumers of the fibers often tend to be educated professional people with disposable income. Fiber events often draw large crowds and help educate the public about sheep, livestock, and agricultural production.

Dairy sheep production is a small but growing aspect of farm flock production. In many countries, particularly those surrounding the Mediterranean, sheep dairying has a rich history and is a viable, modern agricultural enterprise (Figure 13–10). Until the mid-1980s, sheep dairying did not exist in North America. With the opening of some sheep milk-processing plants, this has changed. Interest is growing. Dairy sheep is not yet an industry segment because it is not large enough. It is considered to be in the developmental stage. Wisconsin has been the state with the most producers, although several milking flocks exist across the country. The primary market for sheep milk is for the production of very-high-quality cheese. Specific breeds that have been selected for milk production are used in sheep dairies.

Lamb feedlots are an important part of the U.S. industry. Under the traditional method of lamb production, feeder lambs (weighing between 60 and 110 pounds) are placed in a feedlot and fed high-energy diets until they reach a suitable weight and

Figure 13–10

Sheep dairying is an important aspect of sheep production in many countries. It is a growing part of the U.S. sheep industry. (Photo courtesy P. A. Oltenacu and R. G. Mateescu.)

carcass finish. The average live weight of lambs harvested in the United States is 130 to 140 pounds for the traditional market. Some feedlots are extremely large, feeding tens of thousands of lambs each year, while some are termed farmer feedlots. These generally feed a truckload (400 to 500 lambs) or two over the winter. Many of the large lamb producers do not have the facilities or feedstuffs to finish lambs, so they either sell feeder lambs to the feedlots or retain ownership of the lambs through the feedlot phase. Retained ownership means that the original grower pays the feedlot enterprise a fee for growing and finishing the lambs to market size and sells them only when they are ready for slaughter.

Lamb processing facilities are not very different from beef or pork processing facilities although there are far fewer of them. In the United States, there are 5 or 6 processing facilities that harvest and process the vast majority of lambs. These are federally inspected facilities that ship lamb products all over the country. The sheep and goat industries are somewhat different than the other meat animal species in that a significant number of animals are harvested at smaller, state inspected facilities, or even on farm (depending on the laws and regulations of specific states). These lambs and goat kids are often sold into the ethnic market, which generally desires a smaller, leaner animal than the traditional lamb meat markets. Essentially all the goats in the United States are harvested and processed in what would be traditionally considered a small facility, whether it is state inspected or federally inspected.

Support industries for the sheep and goat industry are crucial to the health and economic well-being of these industries. Just as with other livestock industries, the economic impact extends beyond the farm or ranch gate. Shearers (Figure 13–11), feed companies, veterinarians, pharmaceutical companies, sale barns and auction outlets, wool buyers and warehouses, and trucking companies are just some examples of an industry interdependent on other infrastructure.

Goats

Goat industry structure is very similar in many respects to the sheep industry. However, there are some very different and important characteristics in meat goat production as compared to sheep. There is no migratory range form of goat production, for example, as there is with sheep. The larger meat goat operations are primarily

Figure 13–11
Shearing sheep is a skilled and labor-intensive method of harvesting wool crops.
(Photo courtesy of the American Sheep Industry Association.)

located in Texas under systems of production similar to fenced range production of sheep. Texas leads the nation in total numbers of goats and in numbers of meat goats. Smaller herds, or operations similar to sheep farm flocks, are also an important part of the goat industry. These are located in different geographical areas of the United States than traditional sheep farm flocks. Smaller meat goat operations are more numerous in the south, southern border states and are increasing in some of the Midwestern states that are more eastern (closer to ethnic population centers). The meat goat industry also caters almost exclusively to an ethnic based market. There are no large processing facilities that harvest and process thousands of goat kids per day, as there are for lambs. The majority of harvesting occurs in smaller processing facilities or on farm. Goat kids are not grown to heavy weights like lambs. The clientele consuming goat meat desires a lean product, which precludes heavy finished weights. Very often, kids are grown for a short time after weaning to a live weight of 40 to 60 pounds and then harvested. Therefore, the need for feedlots is not as important in the goat industry as it is in the sheep industry.

GEOGRAPHIC LOCATION OF SHEEP AND GOATS IN THE UNITED STATES

Sheep

Table 13–1 shows the top ten states in terms of sheep numbers and operations with sheep. Texas leads the nation in sheep numbers and operations with sheep. The greatest sheep numbers in Texas tend to come from the large fenced range ranches, while the numbers of producers in Texas come from farm flock operations. This trend is the same nationwide. Texas and the western states have the majority of all breeding sheep, predominantly because of the arid rangeland found there. Much of the terrain, climate, and forage types favor harvesting forages with ruminant animals, such as cattle and sheep. Sheep are often found on operations that have cattle holdings as well. A mixture of sheep and cattle generally make better use of available forage because they select different diets and the native range species therefore do better. Rented Bureau of Land Management and Forest Service lands

Table 13–1

DISTRIBUTION OF SHEEP, GOATS, AND OPERATIONS WITH SHEEP AND GOATS BY TOP TEN STATES

Total Sheep & Lambs[1]		Operations with Sheep[2]		Meat goats[1]		Operations with meat, dairy, or fiber goats[2]	
Texas	830,000	Texas	8,750	Texas	990,000	Texas	26,366
California	610,000	Arizonaz	4,978	Tennessee	125,000	Tennessee	6,828
Wyoming	375,000	California	4,063	California	93,000	Oklahoma	5,716
Colorado	370,000	Iowa	3,522	N. Carolina	90,000	N. Carolina	5,589
S. Dakota	325,000	Pennsylvania	3,672	Oklahoma	90,000	Kentucky	5,298
Utah	290,000	Ohio	3,409	Missouri	84,500	California	4,985
Montana	245,000	Oregon	3,209	Kentucky	79,000	Ohio	4,910
Oregon	225,000	NewMexico	2,896	Georgia	77,000	Pennsylvania	4,844
Idaho	220,000	Wisconsin	2,816	Alabama	60,000	Missouri	4,476
Iowa	210,000	Minnesota	2,522	Virginia	52,000	Georgia	4,283

[1]Source: USDA-NASS, Sheep and Goats, 2011
[2]Source: USDA-NASS, 2007 Census of Agriculture

have traditionally supplied the grazing for 30–40% of the sheep in the West. With the increase in user fees for these lands, the increase in government regulations, and the increase in predation and difficulty in obtaining herders, these operations struggle to continue raising sheep. This is contributing to the decline in western sheep numbers.

Even though the greatest numbers of sheep are found in Texas and the West, the largest numbers of producers are scattered across the country. Iowa is a classic farm flock state. The state is tenth in the nation in sheep numbers and is fourth in operations with sheep. Pennsylvania, Ohio, Minnesota, and many other states are also farm flock states. The climate, soil types, and terrain of many of the traditional farm flock states are conducive to a broad range of agricultural activities. This creates competition in the use of raw resources in agricultural production. Land is used to grow grain crops and hay, and swine, poultry, and dairy cattle production also compete with sheep production. In these states, sheep production is often a part of an overall agricultural enterprise, is supplemented by off farm income, or is a hobby. The farm flock states contribute about one-third of the sheep and wool produced in the United States, but the influence of these producers is probably best felt through political activity across the country, even though the industry they advocate for is not economically crucial to their area and state.

The Great Plains and California are the areas of greatest concentration of lamb feeding operations. Lamb feeding operations are normally located with reasonable proximity to processing plants and supplies of grains and forages used in the finishing of lambs for harvest. Colorado is the primary lamb feedlot state. Other important lamb-feeding states are Texas, and Wyoming. Many lambs are also finished for market on winter alfalfa pastures in the Imperial Valley of California.

Goats

Goats are distributed across the United States (Figure 13–12). The most numerous type of goat enterprise is meat goat production. This has dramatically changed the makeup of the goat industry in the United States the last decade or so. Table 13–1 lists the top ten states in regard to meat goat production and operations with all (meat, dairy, fiber) types of goats. Texas leads the nation in production of all goats and has the most farms and ranches that raise goats. Texas has over three-fourths of the Angora goats in the United States, with most located in the Edwards Plateau region.

It is probably no coincidence that the top-10 dairy goat states are also important dairy cow states. Most goat dairies are smallholdings that are part of a hobby or part-time operation, and are comprised of 5 to 20 animals. The family probably uses most of the product, with some excess sold or given to neighbors and friends.

The meat-producing sector of the goat industry is the most dominant aspect of goat production in the United States. Many of the larger ranches that raise meat goats do so much in the same way as fenced range sheep operations. Because goats are browsers, they fit into operations that also have cattle or sheep. Texas also has many smaller operations with goats that are very similar to farm flock sheep production. Other states have seen an increase in the production of meat goats and have developed significant meat goat industries (Table 13–1). Sheep and goats share many similarities, but the geographic distribution of the industries is one of the greatest differences. Meat goats are not raised in migratory range type of operations as are sheep, so the western range and intermountain regions are not the primary regions of meat goat production. Southern and border states like Tennessee, North Carolina, Kentucky, Oklahoma, and Missouri are important in meat goat production. States that have access to large population centers and that have an ethnic population base also tend to have thriving meat goat industries.

Figure 13–12

U.S. goat inventory (× 1,000 head) by type and state. (Source: USDA-NASS, 2011c.)

SELECTION AND BREEDING PROGRAMS

Sheep

The fundamentals of genetics and breeding are discussed in Chapters 6 and 7. See those chapters for more detailed information on these topics.

It is the job of the person in charge of the selection program (the breeder) for a flock of sheep to combine the best set of genetics available for the environment in which the animal will be producing. When the breeder makes decisions determining which individuals will become the parents of the next generation, he or she is practicing the science and art of *selection*. The challenge of selection is to improve the genetic potential of the next generation. Of course, selection will take place according to the principles of **survival of the fittest** if nature is allowed to run its course. However, natural selection rarely leads to improvement in the economically important traits in any species. Improving the ability of a species to produce a needed product in an economically beneficial way takes a more studied approach. In sheep production, breeding programs revolve around the goals of the individual producer. These can be as varied as producing high-quality wool for the hand spinning and weaving segment, producing high-quality lambs for the 4-H and FFA club market, or producing lambs for the slaughter market. In part, much diversity exists in sheep breeds because this adaptable animal has been selected for different uses in different environments.

The producers of seedstock animals generally practice purebreeding in their flocks and produce registered animals. The various breed associations that offer member

Survival of the fittest
Natural selection. A process whereby those best equipped for the conditions in which they are found survive and pass their genetic material on to the next generation.

services to help their breeders in recordkeeping and breeding decisions facilitate this. Some commercial lamb and wool producers may practice purebreeding techniques even if their animals are not registered. Examples in which this is justified include those whose production environment is uniquely suited to the specific set of characteristics possessed by a certain breed or those that produce for a specialty market.

For most commercial sheep producers, crossbreeding is the method of choice for a breeding program. The reason is simply that crossbred sheep perform better than purebred sheep for meat production. Crossbreeding programs for sheep are fairly easy to design, and a good variety of productive, adaptable breeds of sheep from which to select is available. Crossbreeding is practiced when the benefits of **heterosis** are desired in the offspring. Crossbreeding in sheep produces beneficial effects in many economically important traits including, but not limited to, birth weight, weaning weight, daily gain, yearling weight, body weight, prolificacy, survival rate, fertility, pounds of lamb weaned per ewe exposed, and fleece weight. Most crossbreeding is done within the confines of a system designed to maximize diverse and complementary traits in the individual parent breeds. These systems rely not only on heterosis for their benefits, but also on breed selection to take advantage of **breed complementarity.** This simply means that we select breeds based on what they have to offer and place them in the appropriate place in the crossbreeding system. For example, breeds whose strengths are in maternal traits are used on the dam side and carcass-trait breeds are used on the sire side. Most sheep produced in the United States are a product of a crossbreeding system. This is because these systems produce the best slaughter lambs, and producing slaughter lambs is the primary purpose of the majority of ewes in the United States. Crossbreeding can be effectively accomplished using any of the systems shown in Figures 13–13 and 13–14.

The National Sheep Improvement Program (NSIP) was established in 1986 to assist sheep breeders in making genetic decisions. It has undergone many changes since its inception and currently the NSIP contracts with Meat & Livestock Australia to run the performance data from U.S. producers through the LambPlan genetic evaluation program. It is a computerized genetic evaluation that can be used to estimate the breeding value of every sheep in a flock for most commercially important traits. NSIP calculates genetic values for the traits from producer-provided information.

Heterosis Hybrid vigor. The performance improvement of a crossbred animal above the average of the parents' breeds.

Breed complementarity When the characteristics of different breeds complement each other in crossbreeding systems.

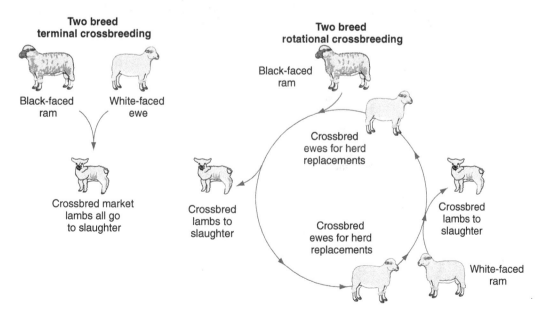

Figure 13–13
Crossbreeding systems in sheep using two breeds.

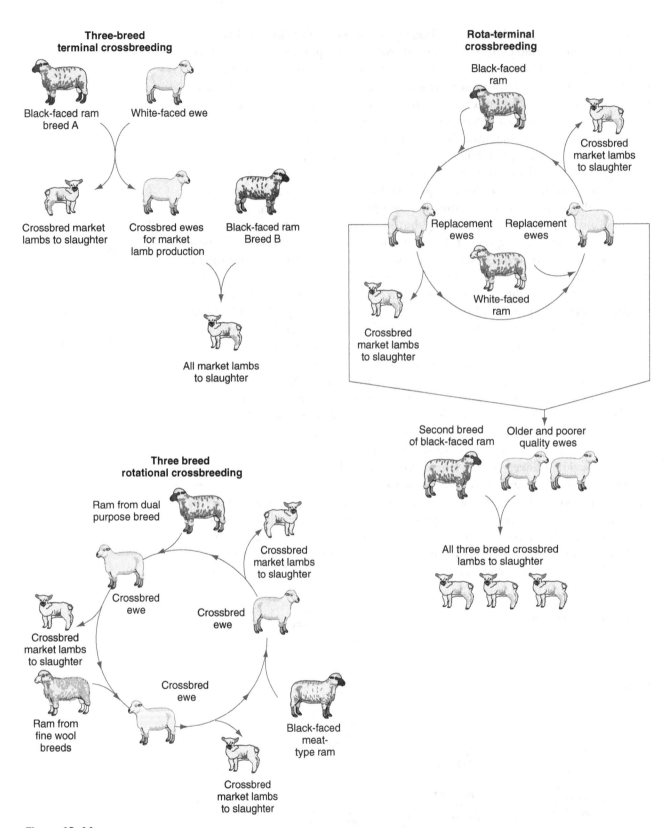

Figure 13–14

Crossbreeding systems in sheep using three breeds.

Figure 13–15
Goats prefer to browse on woody and weedy plant species rather than graze, and they have been used in vegetation control programs. This makes goats a good choice for marginal areas containing brush species and for controlling or eliminating invasive plant species. However, this use has not led to intense selection for production traits.
(Photographer Scott Bauer. Courtesy of USDA.)

Traits for which estimates of genetic value can be calculated include maternal traits for each ewe, that is, **lambing,** growth traits both pre- and post-weaning, wool traits, carcass traits, and parasite resistance for some breeds. A variety of reports derived from the data are available to the producer to help make breeding decisions. The website detailing the NSIP program is located at http://nsip.org/.

Lambing Parturition in sheep.

Goats

The state of knowledge about genetics and breeding for goats of all types is in a very rudimentary state compared to the state of the knowledge for any other traditional livestock species (Figure 13–15). Goats have historically been used as scavenger-like animals; often they have been managed almost as if they were feral. There has been very little selection pressure on goats for economically important production traits, as there has for other livestock species. However, there are some genetic evaluations for dairy goats. The program for dairy goats can be found at http://www.aipl.arsusda.gov/ or on the website of the American Dairy Goat Association at http://www.adga.org/. For meat goats, in 2003, the American Boar Goat Association initiated the Boer Goat Improvement Network, or "B-GIN" (pronounced "begin"), a genetic improvement program developed with assistance from the Texas Agricultural Experiment Station. The International Kiko Goat Association initiated a similar program in 2005. These programs are currently in a state of change with producer participation at low levels. The Australian LambPlan and KidPlan genetic evaluation programs generate EBV data for sheep and goats and NSIP contracts with them to provide genetic evaluation services for U.S. producers.

When choosing and breeding goats, the best line of approach is to combine a general understanding of the principles of their genetic improvement with any available research information on how animals perform in specific environments. That information should be applied to the selection of whatever trait is important in the goats in question, whether it is milk, meat, or fiber. If the meat goat industry is to emerge and thrive, a concerted effort aimed at the genetics of the goat is essential.

BREEDS

Sheep

Historically, sheep have been bred for different uses and purposes. Sheep breeds or types are often a function of the environment where they originated, which dictated, to a large extent, the feed and other resources available. In dry areas around the

world, with more limited feed resources, wool production was emphasized. In areas of abundant rainfall, meat production became more important. Thus, a variety of characteristics are found in different breeds. Some have been bred for quality wool production (Box 13–1). In some areas, meat production has been more emphasized and breeds have been developed that emphasize growth and carcass characteristics. Modern dual-purpose breeds have been developed to produce both quality meat and quality wool. In mature adults, size varies among breeds, ranging from 100 to 400 pounds. Some ewes routinely have single offspring, others routinely twin, and still others are capable of litters of three to six offspring. Breeds of sheep can be classified in many ways. Examples include wool type, face color, productive function, or commercial use. They can also be described or categorized by a breed in their background (e.g., Merino-derived) or geographic background (e.g., British or European breeds, synthetic breeds, and hair sheep breeds).

It is estimated that approximately 200 breeds of sheep exist in the world today. Because of their widespread use and distribution, sheep breeds have been developed

---

BOX 13–1
WOOL GRADES

Wool is graded by three systems based on the fineness of the fiber. The American, or blood, system was developed in the United States using the fleece of the Merino as the standard. Merino wool was considered the standard and is referred to as fine wool. The standard was actually based on the quality of fleece generally produced by sheep with different percentages of Merino breeding. The Bradford system is a system developed in England. It is based on the length of yarn that can be spun from 1 pound of clean wool. Very fine wool yields 120 hanks (560 yards) of wool. Its Bradford grade is 120's. A Bradford grade this high is very rare. The third system is based on the measurement of the diameters of the fibers. It is measured in microns. One micron is 1/25,400 of an inch.

COMPARISON OF WOOL GRADING SYSTEMS

Blood or American System	Bradford or English System	Micron Count System
Fine	Finer than 80's	Under 17.70
Fine	80's	17.70–19.14
Fine	70's	19.15–20.59
Fine	64's	20.60–22.04
1/2 Blood	62's	22.05–23.49
1/2 Blood	60's	23.50–24.94
3/8 Blood	58's	24.95–26.39
3/8 Blood	56's	26.40–27.84
1/4 Blood	54's	27.85–29.29
1/4 Blood	50's	29.30–30.99
Low 1/4 blood	48's	31.00–32.69
Low 1/4 blood	46's	32.70–34.39
Common	44's	34.40–36.19
Braid	40's	36.20–38.09
Braid	36's	38.10–40.20
Braid	Coarser than 36's	Over 40.20

with quite a range of genetic variation. Certainly not all breeds have found use in the U.S. sheep industry. For example, the Merino is one of the most numerous breeds in the world, but is little used in the United States. The Rambouillet, a Merino-derived breed, is used in its place. The Seedstock Committee of the American Sheep Industry Association (ASI) lists 47 breeds of sheep in the United States. However, only about a dozen are used in any significant number. Table 13–2 lists these breeds and characterizes them according to traits of interest in sheep production. In general, the breeds of sheep in the United States are classified by their major commercial use. The categories are all-purpose (dual-purpose or general) breeds, sire (ram) breeds, dam (ewe) breeds, hair breeds, and milk breeds. Brief descriptions follow.

All-Purpose or Dual-Purpose Breeds These breeds are those that have utility as both meat and wool producers and are adapted to diverse environments. Classic examples of dual-purpose breeds include the Dorset and Columbia. Breeds in this category can be used as either ewe breeds or ram breeds in crossbreeding schemes for different production situations. For example, the Columbia is a popular ewe breed in the West, but it is a ram breed in the Midwest. These breeds are often chosen for small flocks in which crossbreeding is difficult to maintain. They can be used effectively in three-way crossbreeding systems.

All-purpose or general-purpose breeds tend to be average or slightly above average for most productive traits. They usually are not extreme in any trait or traits

---

Table 13–2

BREEDS OF SHEEP WITH MOST ECONOMIC IMPORTANCE TO U.S. SHEEP INDUSTRY

Breed	Classification	Primary Industry Use	Comments
Rambouillet	Ewe breed	Primarily range operations, some farm flock	White-faced, most numerous breed in U.S., fine wool producers hardy, long breeding season, moderate to low prolificacy
Targhee	Ewe Breed	Range operations in Northern tier states, some farm flock	White-faced, hardy, medium wool diameter, moderate prolificacy
Polypay	Ewe breed	Northern range, popular farm flock breed	White-faced, synthetic breed of 25% each of Rambouillet, Finn, Dorset, Targhee. Works well in a number of environments
Finnish Landrace	Specialized Ewe breed	Farm Flock	Pure Finns have over a 300% lambing rate. Used in cross breeding programs in farm flocks to increase fertility and prolificacy.
Romanov	Specialized Ewe breed	Farm Flock	Russian origin with high prolificacy and fertility, similar to Finns
Dorset	Dual Purpose	Farm Flock	White-faced, known as fall lambing breed, good mothers, milkers, and carcass conformation.
Columbia	Dual Purpose	Range, Farm Flock	Large mature size, white-faced, medium wool, high growth for white face breed.
Suffolk	Specialized ram breed	Range, Farm Flock	Blackface, large size, fast growth, lean carcasses complement most ewe breeds.
Hampshire	Specialized ram breed	Range, Farm Flock	Blackface, similar traits as Suffolk
Texel	Ram breed	Range, Farm Flock	White-faced ram breed, often used to improve carcass conformation for lighter weight lamb production.
Katahdin	Hair breed	Farm Flock	Hardy, parasite resistant, long breeding season, used in hot and humid areas, easy care breed.
St. Croix	Hair breed	Farm Flock	Most parasite resistant improved breed, traits similar to Katahdin
Dorper	Hair breed	Farm Flock	Imported from South Africa, larger, with better carcass conformation than most hair breeds

that would classify them as specialized breeds. Examples of these breeds include Border Cheviot, Clun Forest, Coopworth, Dorset, Montadale, North Country Cheviot, Polypay, and Texel. Some people include the Columbia, Targhee, Romney, and Corriedale breeds in this group.

Dam or Ewe Breeds These breeds include the Rambouillet, Merino, Targhee, Polypay, Debouillet, and Columbia. These are white-faced breeds of fine-wool type or crosses of fine-wool types (Figure 13–16). The Finnsheep and Romanov are two additional dam breeds that are highly prolific, and are used mostly in the larger farm flocks in crossbreeding programs. The Corriedale, Border Leicester, Coopworth, and Romney are considered ewe breeds by some and general-purpose breeds by others. The Rambouillet cross is the most important of these breeds and the most numerous in the United States. The majority of the sheep in the United States are producing females in range sheep operations, and the majority of the ewes are Rambouillet or Rambouillet crosses. Ewes that carry a predominance of breeding from this group are mated to rams from the sire breed group to produce lambs for meat. These breeds contribute traits for good mothering ability, hardiness, good fleece characteristics, and good volume of wool. They also need adequate meat-producing characteristics.

Sire or Ram Breeds These breeds are selected for the growth and meat qualities of their offspring because they are used as terminal sires in crossbreeding programs. They are further grouped by the target weight of lambs at slaughter. Breeds favored for heavyweight lamb production are the Suffolk, Hampshire, and Texel. Some range producers favor a Suffolk × Hampshire crossbred ram. These breeds are the most commonly used sire breeds in the United States, with the Suffolk having the distinction of being the single most common sire breed; the Hampshire is next. The Shropshire and Oxford are also used to a lesser extent, and the Cheviot and Southdown produce lightweight lambs. Crossbreeding is used extensively in the U.S. sheep flock, and this is the major use of the ram breeds.

Hair Sheep Breeds Not all sheep have wool. In hot, often underdeveloped parts of the world, wool is not especially useful or needed and has not been selected for in the animals that developed there. To the untrained eye, hair sheep often look more like goats than sheep. Considerable interest developed in these sheep in the United States because they can have superior fertility, livability, and parasite resistance, plus the

Figure 13–16
Most maternal type ewe breeds are whiteface, medium size, and have good reproductive traits.
(Photo Courtesy of the American Sheep Industry Association).

added bonus of having an extended breeding season when compared to wool sheep. The greatest interest in hair breeds has been for hot climates.

Expansion of the use of hair breeds has increased all over the United States in recent years because they require less labor and fewer inputs than wool sheep. They do not need to be shorn or have their tails docked, they lamb with minimal assistance, and they can be finished on pasture. Hair sheep breeds generally grow slower, convert feed less efficiently, and have inferior carcasses as compared to wool sheep. However, the increase in ethnic demand for lighter weight lambs has largely mitigated these weaknesses. The most common breeds used are the Katahdin, Dorper, and St. Croix.

Dairy Breeds It is only recently that an interest in dairy sheep has developed in the United States. Dairy breeds include East Friesian, Lacaune, Sarda, Manchega, Chios, Awassi, and Assaf. The extent to which any of these become common in the United States will depend on the success of those trying to develop this new industry segment.

Goats Goats are generally grouped as milk breeds, meat breeds, dual-purpose breeds, or fiber breeds, reflecting the uses for which they have been bred. There is great diversity in the breeds. The few that are in use in the United States have come from several parts of the world. A visit to the Oklahoma State University Breeds of Livestock website (http://www.ansi.okstate.edu/breeds) provides information about different breeds. Goat breeds vary tremendously from dwarf goats with a 20-lb mature female body weight, to large meat breeds with **bucks** weighing in at 340 lbs. The males in some breeds can be 50 in. at the withers; the dwarfs may be less than 20 in. Normal birth weights range from 3 to 9 lbs. Multiple births are so normal that flocks may have more than a 200% kid crop.

Buck An intact male goat.

Dairy Breeds Goats of Swiss origin are the world's leaders in milk production. The most important are Saanen, Toggenburg, and Alpine. The LaMancha is a dairy breed developed in the United States. The most popular U.S. breed is the Anglo-Nubian, a breed developed in England. The color insert of this text provides pictures of some of the more commonly used dairy goat breeds in the United States.

Meat Breeds The meat breeds include the South African Boer (Figure 13–17), Kiko, Savanna, Myotonic, and the U.S. Spanish goats. Other breeds include Indian Beetal, Black Bengal, and the Latin American Criollo. The South African goats are best known for meat-producing ability. However, many meat-type goats are quite

Figure 13–17
The Boer goat is a meat-type goat developed in South Africa using performance testing. It has become increasingly popular in the United States.

variable in appearance and can be best described as nondescript. It is only since the 1990s that there has been enough demand for goat meat to cause breed development work and/or extensive importation and upgrading of meat-type goats and their breeds.

Dual Purpose Indian- and Nubian-derived goat breeds are dual-purpose meat and milk producers. The Anglo-Nubian, or Nubian as it is often called in the United States, is generally considered to be a dual-purpose breed. In addition, Pygmy goats from Western Africa are of increasing interest as laboratory and pet animals.

Fiber Producers The Turkish Angora, Asian Cashmere, and Russian Don goats are kept for fiber production. The long upper coat (mohair) is the valuable product in the Angora, whereas fine underwool is the product from the Cashmere.

Pygmy In their native Africa, these are multipurpose goats known for their superior disease resistance, especially to *Trypanosoma*, which limits the use of other livestock. They have been used in the United States as a laboratory species. However, their diminutive size and all-around cuteness have earned them a spot as a livestock pet breed in the United States.

REPRODUCTIVE MANAGEMENT

Sheep

Chapter 8 is devoted to reproductive physiology. Refer there for the fundamentals of male and female reproductive anatomy, physiology, and function.

Sheep are seasonally polyestrous and thus have multiple heat cycles within a season or time of the year. Sheep are short day breeders. Through late winter, spring and early summer sheep are in an **anestrus** period where they do not cycle or come into estrus. As days start to become shorter in mid to late summer and nights become cooler, this triggers a hormonal response in the ewe to start the process of an estrous cycle. The **estrous cycle** for a ewe averages 16 to 17 days and the duration of **estrus** is 24 to 36 hours. Gestation length is from 144 to 152 days. Rams are also affected by day length, although not to the extent ewes are. They produce the greatest volume of high-quality semen during the same period that ewes of their breed are in the breeding season.

There are many factors that affect the seasonality of breeding in ewes. Some breeds of sheep are known to be less seasonal in their breeding habits. Some sheep cycle in the spring, when days are becoming longer and can produce fall lambs. When this occurs naturally without hormone manipulation, it is largely due to genetic ability to breed out of season.

The latitude sheep are produced at also can affect the seasonality of breeding. Regions of the country that are closer to the equator have less annual variation in the daylight to dark ratio. Often, sheep from areas with less pronounced variations in day length will have a longer breeding season or less pronounced anestrus period.

Sheep are capable of routinely producing more than one offspring per pregnancy. This gives them an advantage in efficiency of reproduction over cattle, the major species with which they compete for resources. However, it also creates a different set of physiological circumstances for the ewe, which must be managed well if the sheep flock is to be profitable. Good management of the reproductive process is critical because reproductive efficiency, or the overall percentage of lamb crop raised and marketed per ewe, is the most important variable affecting profitability of a sheep flock. Optimal reproductive efficiency may not be the same as maximal reproductive efficiency. Optimal efficiency is that which is maximal for the set of production

Anestrus Any period of time when a nonpregnant adult female is not having regular heat cycles. In sheep it is most frequently caused by sensitivity to the length of the photoperiod.

Estrous cycle The time from one estrus to the next. Occurs at a regular, periodic rate.

Estrus Heat. The period when the female is receptive to mating.

constraints in an individual operation. The national lambing rate per ewe routinely ranges from 105 to 110%, but there is a very wide range largely depending on the production environment. A farm flock producer, with higher cost of production, may desire to achieve a lambing rate of 180 to 200%, whereas a fenced range producer in Texas, with more limited feed resources, may be happy with a 90 to 100% lambing rate. A hobbyist who has little market for lambs and is rather interested in colored fleece production would consider an optimal reproductive efficiency to be one that produced just enough replacements for the flock. Rarely is greater than 200% lamb crop desirable because of ewes only having two teats.

Reproductive efficiency must be optimized within the context of the operation and its goal. For the majority of the sheep in production in the United States, the production goal is to maximize output from the most limiting resource, usually feed or land. In the majority of these situations, increasing reproductive rate is the best way to accomplish this because the maintenance costs of the ewe are spread over more and/or larger lambs. Several reproductive strategies can improve reproductive efficiency. The most obvious, perhaps, is to produce more lambs per lambing by increasing the number of multiple births and decreasing the number of ewes that do not lamb.

A substantial portion of good reproductive management can be attributed to good animal health management and good nutritional management. Replacements must be economically reared and managed with optimal reproductive efficiency in mind. The nutritional plane of both the ewe and the ram affects reproductive rate. Managing the ewe flock to minimize the negative effects of high temperature and humidity during breeding and shortly after is critical in some regions. Disease prevention programs are different from flock to flock. However, all sheep producers should be aware that sheep are especially sensitive to the effects of internal parasites. A regular program of parasite control will pay for itself. Any commonly occurring disease can reduce reproductive efficiency by reducing the general thriftiness of the flock and should be controlled. Diseases that affect reproductive efficiency directly include enzootic abortion of ewes, toxoplasmosis, *Brucella ovis* abortion, *Vibrio* campylobacteriosis (vibriosis), salmonellosis, leptospirosis, vaginal prolapse, hypocalcemia, and pregnancy toxemia. Control of these and other diseases can be easily accomplished by developing and following a complete health program for the flock.

Most of the nation's ewes are mated by natural service in pasture or range conditions. However, artificial insemination techniques are available and are being used, especially by progressive purebred breeders.

To maximize the value of high-quality rams and give each ewe the best chance at early **conception**, each ram used in a breeding program should have a breeding soundness exam before being placed with the ewes. The major factors that should be evaluated in a breeding soundness exam by **palpation** and observation include testicular, epididymis, and penis development and soundness. Feet, legs, eyes, and jaws should be examined. The ram should also be screened for common diseases. Observations should be made on physical ability to breed females and libido. Semen evaluations are useful and can screen rams that have potential problems with semen quality and viability. Rams are capable of breeding more females in a breeding season than other livestock species. Their semen has higher concentration of sperm than males of other food animal species.

Other management techniques include the use of ram breeding harnesses to monitor breeding activity. The use of real-time ultrasound is a technology that has been embraced by many in the sheep industry. Ewes can be scanned to determine if they are bred, how far along they are in the pregnancy cycle, and how many lambs

Conception When the sperm fertilizes the ovum.

Palpation Physically touching and examining with one's hand.

they are gestating. They can then be fed and managed more effectively based on number of fetuses they are carrying.

Ewe lambs will reach puberty from 5 to 8 months of age, depending on breed type and nutrition program. Many producers breed ewe lambs to lamb at 12 to 14 months of age to increase productivity of the operation and to increase the productive life of the individual ewes. Ewe lambs should be at least 65% of their mature size at the time of mating in order to achieve a high level of fertility.

Goats

Like sheep, many breeds of goats are seasonally polyestrous. Goats are short day breeders. Also like sheep, reproductive performance largely determines profitability. The number of kids born and weaned is crucial to economic success of a meat goat operation. Dairy goats have to go through parturition to lactate. The doe is different from the ewe during pregnancy, in that the primary source of progesterone in the doe to keep the pregnancy viable originates from the corpus luteum, and not the placenta, as it does in sheep. Therefore, the doe is more susceptible to embryonic death loss, stress induced abortions, and other reproductive failures as compared to the ewe.

Many of the same reproductive management techniques used in sheep are used in goats to enhance reproductive performance. Good nutrition, a sound health program, and selection programs that have an emphasis on twinning ability and fertility are important things producers can manage. Bucks can be subjected to a breeding-soundness exam to try to identify potential reproductive problems. Mature bucks are capable of breeding 30 to 50 does in a two-estrous-cycle breeding season. Yearling bucks are capable of breeding 15 to 20 does if they are well grown out and healthy. Bucks have scent glands located around the base of the horn. They help stimulate estrus and improve conception. These glands are the source of the goat odor, which can be very unpleasant to the human nose! The smell can also be taken up by the milk and can give it a terrible off-flavor. For this reason, bucks are generally kept separate from the milking does if the milk is to be used for human consumption.

Goats come into puberty at about 4 to 7 months of age, depending on feeding program and genetics. Doelings can be bred to kid at 12 to 14 months of age, but they will need to have attained 65% of the mature weight to be successful. The normal estrous cycle of a doe is 21 days, and estrus lasts 1 to 2 days. Length of gestation is about 150 days. In most of the continental United States, the normal time of breeding for goats is August through February. Some breed twice per year; this is more prevalent the farther south the animal is found.

NUTRITION

Sheep

Feed is the single most expensive part of sheep production. Thus, a cost-effective program of feeding and nutrition is essential. Sheep have the ability to use forages and roughages because they are ruminants. In fact, only limited amounts of grain are used in sheep production. Some exceptions occur in creep feeding and feedlots; for show, club, and purebred animals; and sometimes for ewes just before breeding and then again just before lambing. Thus, most feeding strategies for sheep revolve around how to get the most from forage. Chapters 3, 4, and 5 give detailed information relating to nutrition, feeds, and feeding. See those chapters for more detailed information than is provided in this section.

The cost of feeding the ewe is 50 to 70% of the entire production cost of a lamb-producing operation. The nutrients need to be met in a way that minimizes feed costs and optimizes production to optimize returns. It is easy to over feed ewes for part of the year and to underfeed them for the other part. The ewe must be fed with the goals of the specific program in mind and with appropriate consideration for the specific environment in which she is producing. For instance, nutritional requirements are different for a purebred ewe producing rams for breeding stock than they would be for a range ewe producing lambs for the feedlot. Yet there are certainly similarities between the two. The first of three crucial times in a ewe's productive cycle are approximately 2 weeks before breeding when she should be **flushed** for breeding. The second is the last **trimester** of gestation when it may be difficult for her to eat enough low-quality feeds to appropriately nourish the fetus. This is especially true for ewes having more than a **singleton**. A third crucial time of feeding the ewe is the first 6 weeks of lactation. Commonly used feeds for ewe flocks include grasses, legumes, by-products, and crop residues. These may be grazed by the animal or harvested, stored, and hand fed. Sheep are very adaptable. They can effectively use rangelands, pastures, and forage crops to meet their nutrient needs.

Sometimes it is advantageous to get lambs to market as soon as possible, either to capture a **seasonal market** or simply to take advantage of available labor that will have other, more pressing uses later on. In these situations, lambs may be creep-fed a high-energy ration from a very young age. Creep feeding is also commonly done with winter lambing flocks when pasture is not available. Examples of lamb creep rations are given in Table 13–3.

Feedlots are specialized finishing operations. High-quality feeds are needed to bring lambs to a suitable slaughter end point as cost-effectively as possible. Different rations and feeding regimes can be used to effectively finish lambs. Table 13–4 shows examples of specialized feedlot diets for lambs. Lambs may also be finished on high-quality pastures with only the addition of appropriate mineral supplementation and perhaps a small amount of grain. This type of pasture finishing is commonly done in California.

Goats

One of the values of goat meat production is that they can be produced without intensive feeding strategies or systems. Although some goats are no doubt given supplemental feed as a means of making them market ready, there is no market for fattened goat. The ethnic market for goats is largely for a 40 to 70 lb animal. Thus, grain is not used as much in finishing kids. In addition, goats grow more slowly and

Flushing The practice of increasing feed to a female just before and during the breeding season.

Trimester A third of a pregnancy. The last trimester in a ewe is approximately the last 50 days.

Singleton An offspring born singly.

Seasonal market A time of the year when there is increased demand for a product.

Table 13–3
CREEP FEEDING RATIONS FOR LAMBS

Feedstuff	20% Protein Total Grain Ration to Be Fed with High-Quality Hay	20% Protein Total Grain Ration to Be Fed Without Hay	16% Protein Grain Ration to Be Fed with High-Quality Hay
Corn, no. 2, yellow, rolled[1]	53.7%	—	59.0%
Oats, whole or crimped	13.4%	63.6%	14.8%
Soybean meal, 44%	30.4%	27.6%	19.7%
Molasses	—	6.36%	3.93%
Limestone	1.07%	1.06%	1.18%
Salt	1.07%	1.06%	1.18%
Vitamin pre-mix and feed additives	0.36%	0.32%	0.21%

[1]Wheat can be substituted for corn on an equal basis up to 50% of the ration. Any more can cause digestive problems.

Table 13–4
FEEDLOT DIETS FOR FINISHING LAMBS

Ingredient	Diet 1	Diet 2
	Percentage of Diet	
Corn, no. 2, yellow, unprocessed	37.32	—
Corn, no. 2, yellow, cracked	37.33	—
Corn, no. 2, yellow, whole ears, ground		76.85
Cottonseed hulls	10.00	—
Soybean meal (48% CP)	12.80	15.60
Liquid molasses	—	5.00
Limestone	1.00	1.00
Trace mineral salt	1.00	1.00
Vitamin premix and feed additives	.55	.55

Table 13–5
SAMPLE LACTATION RATIONS FOR MILK GOATS[1]

Ingredients	16% Protein Ration	20% Protein Ration
	Percentage of Ration	
Corn, no. 2, yellow, steam rolled	40.0	32.8
Oats, whole or crimped	15.0	10.0
Soybean meal	17.8	30.0
Beet pulp	10.0	10.0
Dried brewers grain	7.5	10.0
Molasses	7.5	30.0
Trace mineral salt	1.0	1.0
Dicalcium phosphate	0.5	1.0
Monosodium phosphate	0.5	—
Magnesium oxide	0.2	0.2

[1]These feeds to be fed in addition to forage and/or browse.

with less efficient feed conversions than sheep, making it less economical to feed high quantities of expensive feedstuffs to goats. In periods of drought and perhaps in winter, supplemental feedstuffs are used, but they tend to be roughages and forages. Like sheep, producers of breeding stock, show animals, and club projects often feed more grain than commercial producers. Similar feeding strategies are employed for Angoras. Neither the profit margins nor the production level support the use of expensive feed.

Dairy goats require higher-quality feed in general, especially during lactation. Good-quality forage supplemented with commercially available dairy goat feeds is probably the best approach for the vast majority of goat owners. Examples of supplement feeds for dairy goats to be fed in addition to good-quality forages are shown in Table 13–5.

CHALLENGES TO SHEEP AND GOAT HEALTH

Although the most common diseases that affect sheep and goats may vary with management methods and production type (meat, milk or fiber), some diseases have the potential to affect many types of small ruminant operations. A few of the most important diseases are described next. Other factors may have a significant effect on sheep or goat herd health, but are beyond the scope of this book.

Gastrointestinal parasitism

In pastured and free-ranging sheep and goats, **nematode parasites** involving the digestive tract can have significant health implications. Moderate to heavy parasite burdens can cause poor growth, weight loss, diarrhea, **anemia** and **bottle jaw**. Young animals are affected most frequently, although older adults may also develop signs of disease. Problems with gastrointestinal parasites are worse when pastures are over stocked, therefore, adequate pasture space and a well-planned parasite control regimen are important steps in decreasing production losses due to heavy worm burdens.

Contagious ecthyma

Also known as orf or sore mouth, contagious ecthyma is a skin disease that is common among young sheep and goats and can be easily passed from affected to unaffected animals. Most youngsters with the disease have scabby or crusty sores on their lips and mouths (Figure 13–18). Sometimes ewes or does will have similar sores on their udders, which result from viral infection passed from nursing lambs or kids to their dams. In most cases, the disease will resolve on its own in a few weeks. During that time, kids or lambs with large numbers of sores on their lips or mouths may not eat normally and lose condition or require extra attention to feeding. The virus is very resistant in the environment, so once a herd or flock is infected, it is likely that young animals will be exposed and develop disease. To prevent severe disease in infected animal groups, pregnant dams and youngsters may be vaccinated. For uninfected herds, quarantine or maintaining a closed-herd status is the best prevention. The virus that causes orf may be transmitted to people through contact with infected animals and causes similar skin sores. For this reason, caretakers handling diseased animals should wear rubber gloves and thoroughly wash exposed skin soon after animal contact.

Caseous lymphadenitis

Caseous lymphadenitis, also called contagious abscesses, is a bacterial infection that commonly affects sheep and goats. In infected herds, many animals may be affected and will develop **abscesses** that are visible under the skin or in internal organs (Figure 13–19). When abscesses open and drain, large numbers of bacteria are shed into the environment and may potentially infect more animals. The disease is usually the result of bacterial infection of minor skin wounds that may occur during shearing or other handling. Treatment is often difficult, so the best means of control is isolation of diseased animals, which prevent environmental contamination and animal-to-animal

Nematode parasites Roundworms that are categorized in the phylum Nematoda.

Anemia Disease state in which the number of red blood cells in an animal's blood are abnormally decreased.

Bottle jaw Condition in which fluid accumulates and causes a swelling under the jaw, especially in cattle, sheep, or goats. It is often due to protein loss caused by severe parasitism.

Abscess Collection of pus in a cavity as the result of infection with microorganisms or as a response to embedded foreign material, such as a splinter.

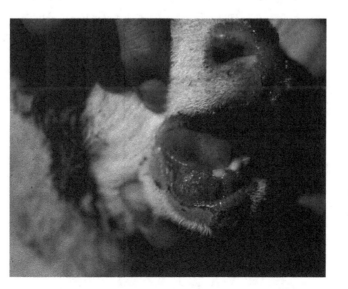

Figure 13–18
The raised and raw areas on the gums and the scabby areas on the nose of this sheep are typical of contagious ecthyma or sore mouth. Animals with a severe form of this disease may have difficulty eating because of the painful sores. (Photo by Roger J. Panciera. Courtesy Oklahoma Center for Veterinary Health Services.)

Figure 13–19

Abscess within the liver of a sheep with caseous lymphadenitis. Note the layered, tan material that makes up the abscess. The onion-ring appearance of abscesses is typical of this bacterial infection in sheep. (Photo by Roger J. Panciera. Courtesy Oklahoma Center for Veterinary Health Services.)

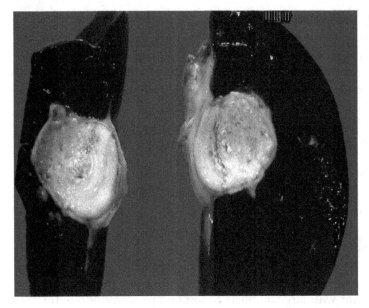

spread. Other helpful steps include disinfecting shearing equipment and decreasing the risk of skin wounds by removing sharp objects from feeders and pens. Vaccination may reduce the severity of disease but is not capable of preventing infections altogether or curing animals that already have disease.

Pregnancy toxemia

Twin lamb disease, or pregnancy toxemia, is seen in ewes and does during the last few weeks of pregnancy and is most common in animals pregnant with twins or triplets. Ewes or does that are either abnormally thin or abnormally fat are more likely to develop **metabolic** problems leading to pregnancy toxemia. Affected dams may lose their appetites; become depressed and uncoordinated; wander about aimlessly; and may become blind, go into a coma and die if they do not receive appropriate veterinary care early in disease. Because severely affected animals often do not recover, even with medical therapy, proper nutritional support and management of pregnant animals during the last few weeks of pregnancy is the best approach to disease prevention.

Metabolic Relating to the biochemical processes that occur within a living organism, especially involving the breakdown of food and its transformation into energy.

NUTRITIONAL BENEFITS OF LAMB AND GOAT MEAT TO HUMANS

The proportion of the recommended daily dietary allowance for a 19- to 30-year-old man that a 3-oz serving of cooked, lean lamb (175 calories), and a serving of goat meat (122 calories) provides is as follows:

	Lamb (%)	Goat Meat (%)
Protein	43	41
Phosphorus	25	24
Iron	22	40
Zinc	41	41
Riboflavin	18	40
Thiamin	7	6
B$_{12}$	93	42
Niacin	34	21

Lamb and goat are nutrient-dense foods, just like other animal products. However, it is doubtful that nutritional benefit has anything to do with the level of consumption of lamb in this country. People who eat lamb eat it as a specialty product, and we tend not to care about nutritional value in such situations. Nevertheless, it is nice to know that lamb is good food. It is hard to assess whether those who routinely eat goat meat take its nutrient content into consideration when doing so. Given that most consume it as a part of their traditional diet, nutrient content is probably not a consideration. However, goat meat has the advantage of generally being a lean product.

NUTRITIONAL BENEFITS OF GOAT MILK TO HUMANS

A 1-cup serving of whole goat milk is 168 calories and provides the following proportion of the recommended daily dietary allowance for a 19- to 30-year-old man:

Protein	16%
Phosphorus	39%
Calcium	41%
Zinc	7%
Riboflavin	26%
Thiamin	10%
B_{12}	7%

Goat's milk is very similar to cow's milk and is also a nutrient-dense food.

TRENDS AND FACTORS INFLUENCING THE SHEEP AND GOAT INDUSTRIES

Consumption

The sheep industry has seen a long, steady decline in sheep numbers, operations with sheep, and economic value of the industry since the end of World War II. The goat industry has always been a small industry. There are many reasons why these are small, niche industries, but low per capita consumption of meat products is the primary one. Increasing demand for lamb and goat meat would help solve many of the production challenges facing these small-ruminant industries. Lamb, in particular, needs to adapt to the modern lifestyle needs for meat products. It needs to be leaner, more convenient to cook, and more consistent in quality. The high amounts of fat in lamb products makes it less desirable as an eating choice for some consumers and makes it more expensive to produce. The sheep industry has made some strides in providing a more convenient, shelf ready, and cooking friendly product, but they are considerably behind other meat industries and foreign contributors of lamb. If the industry truly wants to grow, it will address product composition and resulting demand for lamb. The goat meat industry has always been an ethnic based industry and this clientele demands a lean product.

Dairy products, especially cheeses, from goats and sheep are high quality specialty items with a high value. Wool and mohair have competition in the fiber market from synthetic materials, but wool remains the gold standard when comparing fibers. Wool becomes more competitive as a fiber source when oil prices increase, and both wool and mohair are natural, renewable products.

The sheep and goat industries have long needed to expand the base of consumers that include sheep and goat meat in their diet. This has been helped in recent years with the large influx of immigrants and ethnic peoples into the United States. The largest such groups are Hispanic, Asian, Caribbean, and various Muslim groups.

Figure 13–20

Number of goats slaughtered. (Source: USDA-NASS, 2011d.)

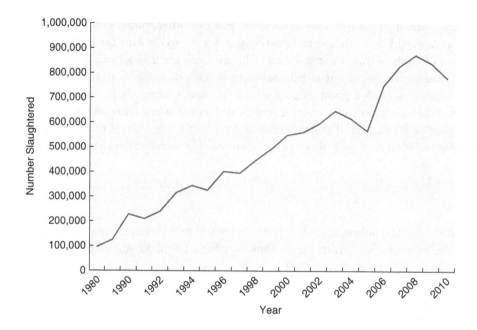

These populations are settling predominantly in California, Texas and other south-western states, New York City, Atlanta, Detroit, and Miami. Many of these groups are accustomed to eating lamb and goat. As a result, the ethnic market for sheep and goat meat has expanded rapidly, increasing overall demand for lamb and goat meat. The ethnic market now accounts for one third of the demand for lamb in the United States. If these population trends continue, the potential demand for lamb and goat meat could increase substantially. Many animals that go to this market are slaughtered at small state-inspected facilities, local facilities, or even on farms. It is hard to accurately document the actual slaughter rate for goats and sheep because of this hidden market. Thus, the numbers in Figure 13–20 underestimate to some unknown extent the actual slaughter rate. The sheep and goat industries also need to further capitalize on the increasing public interest in the United States in ethnic foods, goat products, lean meats, farm-fresh product, and natural and organic products.

Industry Size and Structure

The number of sheep in the United States has been declining. Figure 13–21 shows both the numbers of operations and total inventory for recent years. The downward trend in each is evident. However, a recent slight upturn in both the number of producers and total sheep is cause for cautious optimism in this industry. No one knows how many sheep are necessary to sustain this industry.

Figure 13–21

Sheep operations and total sheep. (Source: USDA-NASS, 2011a.)

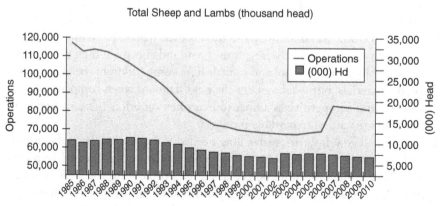

Some shift in the geography of production will probably occur. The western range bands of sheep are probably destined to be reduced in numbers even further. Some of those animals could move into smaller farm flocks in the more eastern states. The increased use of hair sheep breeds may allow an expansion into the nontraditional sheep areas of the southern United States.

Environmental Concerns

On the whole, the small-ruminant industry has an advantage in waste concerns as compared to other livestock species because most are not typically kept in large confinement facilities. The large range operations of the western states, however, have concerns with environmental issues and restrictions by the federal government when grazing public lands. Environmental concerns will be an increasing consideration to all concentrated animal feeding units like lamb feedlots. Finding low-cost, effective means of disposing of animal waste will help offset the costs of complying with new rules.

Technology

Science and technology are underused in the sheep and goat industries. Some of the tools of biotechnology could be especially useful. Accelerated, or out-of-season, lambing and **kidding** could help the sheep and goat industries be more productive and thus more competitive. Ewes and does that produce once per year are being maintained for a significant portion of the year while they are doing nothing. Under good management, offspring could be produced twice a year, if not for the physiological limitation that the period of anestrus imposes. Successful strategies have been developed, but more research and work are needed.

Kidding Parturition in goats.

Technology to determine carcass composition is underused. Pricing models based on lean value rather than dressing percentage would encourage production of leaner, less costly product that has higher consumer appeal.

Predators are a potential problem for both goats and sheep virtually anywhere they are found in the country. Surveys indicate that combined losses to producers of the two species are between $15 and $20 million annually, amounting to nearly 40% of all annual losses. Another $10 million is spent on predator control measures. Predators include coyotes, dogs, mountain lions, bears, foxes, eagles, bobcats, and other animals, with coyotes the most common. Many of the approaches to dealing with predators such as poisons and traps are increasingly unacceptable to certain elements of society. Other approaches such as guard animals have helped but have not been totally effective (Figure 13–22). Any goat or sheep operation needs an effective predator plan in place. The costs and worry of predator control is a deterrent to producers.

Figure 13–22
Guard dogs are used as one method to control predation of sheep and goats. These specialized breeds bond with and protect animals. The Great Pyrenees dog guards a farm flock of ewes.
(Photo courtesy of the American Sheep Industry Association).

INDUSTRY ORGANIZATIONS

American Boer Goat Association

www.abga.org

American Dairy Goat Association

http://www.adga.org/

American Goat Federation

http://www.americangoatfederation.org/

American Kiko Goat Association

http://www.kikogoats.com/

American Sheep Industry Association, Inc. (ASI)

http://www.sheepusa.org/

ASI distributes the *Sheep Production Handbook*, which is an excellent resource.

National Lamb Feeders Association (NLFA)

http://www.nlfa-sheep.org/

National Sheep Improvement Program (NSIP)

http://www.nsip.org

North American Dairy Sheep Association

www.dsana.org

United States Meat Export Federation

http://www.usmef.org/

SUMMARY AND CONCLUSION

The sheep industry at one time was a major industry but has since declined to become a specialty industry in the United States. Sheep remain an important industry on an international scale. Sheep are able to make use of forages and roughages that are inaccessible to harvest mechanically, but they must compete with other ruminant species for those same resources. Sheep have an advantage reproductively in terms of potential number of offspring weaned, but the length of the anestrus period is a disadvantage. Sheep can work well in multispecies grazing systems with other ruminants, and they are increasingly used as a means of vegetation management. The United States is no longer a major lamb producer or consumer, but signs point to stabilization and even some increase in the industry.

There is a distinct regionality to the sheep industry. Most of the sheep are found in the western states in large flocks. Most of the producers are found in the Midwest, southwest, and northeast and generally have small flocks. The net result is that many producers are scattered across the country but not so many sheep. The sheep industry is struggling to retain enough numbers to even be considered a viable agricultural enterprise in the United States. Recent increases in sheep numbers and inventory value may signal better prospects for the sheep industry. The ethnic market has really helped the sheep industry find new consumers of its products.

The goat industry has always been a specialty industry in the United States. Although there have certainly been numerous individuals who have kept goats, those who have done so as a bona fide commercial enterprise have been few and are restricted geographically. Texas has been the largest goat-producing state and will probably continue to be so. However, the production of goat meat on a larger scale should not be ruled out as an expanding industry because the number of consumers is increasing due to the current demographics of the immigrant population. Producers are entering this industry, especially the meat industry, and it is a growing industry.

Facts about Sheep

Birth weight:	5–15 lbs (varies with breed and number born)
Mature weight:	Varies with breed, sex, and condition; Female 100–200 lbs; Male 150–300 lbs
Slaughter weight:	120–140 lbs for traditional market, 50–80 lbs for ethnic market
Normal season of birth:	Spring, fall—some breeds
Gestation:	144–152 days
Estrous cycle:	16–17 days
Duration of estrus:	24–36 hours
Ram/ewes:	Range 1/75 mature ram, 1/25 ram lamb
Normal lamb crop:	100–160% (range usually lower than farm flock)
Age weaned:	3–6 months
Weight at weaning:	50–80 lbs
Names of various sex classes:	Ewe, ram, wether
Fleece weight:	6–14 lbs

Facts about Goats

Breeds:	Dairy: Alpine (French, Swiss, Rock), American La Mancha, Nubian, Saanen, Toggenburg Fiber: Angora Meat: Spanish-type, Boar, Kiko, Savanna, Myotonic
Birth weight:	6–8 lbs
Mature weight:	Varies with breed, sex, and condition; doe 110–135 lbs; buck 120–150 lbs
Weaning age:	12–13 weeks for meat goats
Recommended breeding age:	8–9 months or weighing at least 65% of mature weight
Normal season of birth:	Tend to be seasonal breeders (bred late August–March)
Gestation:	145–155 days
Estrous cycle:	19–21 days
Duration of estrus:	1–2 days
Buck/doe:	Buck 6–8 months = 6–8 does, 18–20 months = 25–30 does; mature 50–60 does per season.
Normal kid crops:	High conception rate. Does over 18 months of age normally average 1.5 kids per birth; frequently have three and sometimes four kids.
Average milk production per doe:	Good producing doe averages 1,800 lbs in 10-month lactation. This is equal to 3 quarts per day. Can get 3,000 lbs/year.
Names of various sex classes:	Kid, doe, buck

STUDY QUESTIONS

1. Describe the relative size of sheep and goat industry segments compared to other animal industries.

2. What is the purpose of the sheep and goat industries of the United States? What are the resources they use and what are the products they return?

3. What is the value of mixed-species grazing? Why does it work?

4. How do the sheep and goat industries in the United States compare to other countries?

5. Give a brief historical account of the sheep and the goat in U.S. agriculture.

6. What is a specialty market and how does it pertain to the sheep and goat industries?

7. What are the reasons for the long decline in sheep numbers and thus the sheep industry in the United States?

8. The sheep and goat industries have similar structures in many ways and different structures in other ways. Compare and contrast them to each other and to the beef industry.

9. Why is there currently interest in dairy sheep in the United States?

10. Compare and contrast the relative information available about selection and breeding programs for sheep and for goats.

11. What is breed complementarity? How does it work in crossbreeding?

12. Describe crossbreeding systems for sheep.

13. How is the quality of wool measured?

14. Give a brief accounting of the breed classification for both sheep and goats. What are the similarities? The differences? How do these compare to the breed classification of other species?

15. Give a brief overview of reproduction in the sheep and goat.

16. What role does day length play in sheep reproduction? Goat reproduction?

17. Why are ewes flushed?

18. What are the similarities and differences in sheep and goat feeds and feeding?

19. Look at the rations described in the chapter for the various classes of animals. What differences and what similarities do you see?

20. Describe some of the common health challenges to goats and sheep.

21. What does a 3-oz serving of cooked lamb provide nutritionally to a human?

22. What does a 3-oz serving of cooked goat meat provide nutritionally to a human?

23. What does a 3-oz cup of goat milk provide nutritionally to a human?

24. Describe the trends influencing the sheep and goat industries.

25. What is your opinion about the future of meat goats in the United States? Dairy goats? Dairy sheep? Meat sheep?

REFERENCES

For the 5th edition, Melanie A. Breshears, DVM, PhD, Diplomate ACVP, assistant professor, veterinary pathobiology, Center for Veterinary Health Sciences, Oklahoma State University, contributed material. Dr. Michael Neary, extension sheep specialist, Purdue University, assumed co-authorship of the chapter.

Ensminger, M. E. 1991. *Animal science.* 9th ed. Danville, IL: Interstate.

FAO. 2011. *FAOSTAT statistics database. Agricultural production and production indices data.* http://apps.fao.org/.

Gibson, T. A. 2007. *Demand for goat meat: Implications for the future of the industry.* Langston University Field Day Proceedings. Accessed online October 2007. http://www2.luresext.edu/goats/library/field/goat_meat_demand99.htm.

Jones, K. G. 2004. *Trends in the U.S. sheep industry.* USDA-ERS, Agricultural Information Bulletin Number 787. Electronic report accessed online. http://jan.mannlib.cornell.edu/reports/general/aib/aib787.pdf.

Pinkerton, B., ed. 2007. *Meat goat production and marketing handbook.* Raleigh, North Carolina and Mid-Carolina Council of Governors: Rural Economic Development Center. Accessed online October 2007. http://www.clemson.edu/agronomy/goats/handbook/cover.html.

Ross, C. V. 1989. *Sheep production and management.* Upper Saddle River, NJ: Prentice Hall.

Sheep production handbook. 2002. Englewood, CO: Sheep Industry Development Program.

Solaiman, S. G. 2005. *Meat goat industry outlook for small farms in Alabama and surrounding states.* George

Washington Carver Agricultural Experiment Station, Tuskegee, AL: Tuskegee University.

Spencer, R. 2008. *Overview of the United States meat goat industry*. Huntsville, AL: Alabama A&M University. Accessed online June, 2011. http://www.aces.edu/pubs/docs/U/UNP-0104/

USDA. 2011. *USDA nutrient database for standard reference*. Release 23. Nutrient Data Laboratory home page: http://www.nal.usda.gov/fnic/foodcomp.

USDA-APHIS. 2004. *The goat industry: Structure, concentration, demand and growth*. Electronic report from APHIS. Accessed online June 2011 at http://www.aphis.usda.gov/animal_health/emergingissues/downloads/goatreport090805.pdf

USDA-ERS. 2011. *Farm income data*. Accessed online May, 2011. http://www.ers.usda.gov/Data/farmincome/finfidmu.htm.

USDA-NASS. 2011a. *Agricultural statistics data base*. Accessed online June 2011. http://www.nass.usda.gov/Data_and_Statistics/index.asp.

USDA-NASS. 2011b. *Sheep and goats*. Accessed online June 2011. http://usda.mannlib.cornell.edu/MannUsda/viewDocumentInfo.do?documentID=1145.

USDA-NASS. 2007. *Overview of the U.S. sheep and goat industry*. Accessed online October 2007 At http://usda.mannlib.cornell.edu/usda/nass/ShpGtInd//2000s/2007/ShpGtInd-09-28-2007.pdf.

USDA-NASS. 2011c. *Livestock slaughter*. Accessed online June 2011. http://usda.mannlib.cornell.edu/MannUsda/viewDocumentInfo.do?documentID=1097.

14

Horses

Learning Objectives

After you have studied this chapter, you should be able to:

- Put the horse industry in economic context.
- Compare historical and current uses of the horse and understand the very unique features that make the horse industry different from all the rest of the commercial livestock industries.
- Give a historical perspective on horses in North America and the United States.
- Describe the change in the purpose of the horse in the developed world over the course of the 20th century.
- Describe the structure and geographic location of the horse industry as far as available information will allow.
- Explain the basics of horse genetics, especially color genetics.
- Classify the types of horses.
- Discuss the important tasks to be accomplished if a mare is to reproduce.
- Cite the basics of how to feed a horse.
- Identify and discuss areas of concern for the horse industry.
- Discuss some of the opportunities for growth in the horse industry.

Key Terms

Alleles
Anestrus
Artificial vagina
Body condition
Colic
Colt
Conformation events
Continuous eater strategy
Cutting
Diluter gene
Dorsal
Dressage
Equine
Estrous cycle
Filly
Foal
Foaling; to foal
Gait
Gelding
Hand
Horsepower
Horse slaughter
Hunter under saddle
Impacted intestine
Incompletely dominant
Laminitis
Mare

Modifier gene
Mustang
National Animal Identification System
Pellets
Points
Prepotent
Ration
Recreational horses
Reining
Saddle seat pleasure
Sclera
Seasonally polyestrous
Stadium jumping
Stallion
Stock horse
Stud
Stud book
Stud fee
Teasing
Three-day eventing
Trail
Ultrasonography
Unsoundness
Western pleasure
Western riding
Working cow horse

SCIENTIFIC CLASSIFICATION OF HORSES

Phylum:	Chordata
Subphylum:	Vertebrata
Class:	Mammalia
Order:	Perissodactyla
Family:	Equidae
Genus:	*Equus*
Species:	*caballus* (horse); *asinus* (ass)

THE PLACE OF HORSES IN THE UNITED STATES

It is impossible to present facts and figures for the horse that are comparable to those of the other livestock species. The federal government does not collect and summarize information on the horse as it does for other species. After the horse was replaced by the petroleum-fueled engine on the nation's farms, and before it emerged as an important leisure and recreation species, the government decided it was no longer a good use of taxpayers' money to collect and publish extensive information about horses and stopped doing so in 1960, when it estimated there were 3 million horses in the United States. However, information is collected periodically by private agencies and organizations and for the Census of Agriculture. The most authoritative information currently available on the **equine** industry is found in studies commissioned by the American Horse Council, the latest released in 2005. The 2005 study, *The Economic Impact of the U.S. Horse Industry on the United States* (EIHI), found 9.2 million horses in the United States that produced $29 billion in direct economic impacts to the U.S. economy. More than 1.96 million people were horse owners, with an additional 2 million involved as supportive family members and volunteers. The study did not include people under the age of 18 in these numbers or each would have been much higher. At the time of that study, the industry directly provided 1.4 million **full-time equivalent** (FTE) jobs yearly and paid $1.9 billion in taxes. Racing and showing each contributed 27% of the employment generated, with recreation contributing approximately 31%. The remaining activities accounted for 15% of the employment generated. A good deal has happened in the horse industry since 2005, due to the economic downturn in the United States and the world. There is little doubt that these numbers overestimate the current horse industry. Based on limited statistics collected by the USDA, horse sales account for approximately 0.45% of total U.S. farm cash receipts (Figure 14–1) and approximately 0.9% of animal agriculture's share of all U.S. farm cash receipts (Figure 14–2).

Equine Pertaining to horses.

Full-time equivalent In referring to employment, a 40-hour equivalent position.

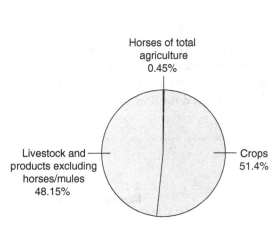

Figure 14–1
Horse/mule yearly farm cash receipts as a percentage of U.S. farm cash receipts, 2000–2009. Source: Based on USDA statistics.

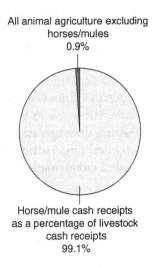

Figure 14–2
Horse/mule yearly farm cash receipts as a percentage of total animal agriculture's cash receipts, 2000–2009.
Source: Based on USDA statistics.

Figure 14–3

Although considered a livestock species, the horse industry is a unique hybrid. Certain of its interests are firmly rooted in agriculture; however, entertainment, sports, and recreation segments are also important parts of the horse industry.

Hunter under saddle An English division class in which movement and mannerisms are judged with the intent of a pleasurable ride, which is to depict a horse on the hunt chasing the hounds.

Saddle seat pleasure An English event in which the horse's movement and mannerisms are judged.

Dressage A competition in which horses are required to perform highly advanced maneuvers in a specified pattern. This competition may be held alone or may be part of a three-day event.

Stadium jumping A competition in which horses jump a course of fences (jumps) in a specified order.

Three-day eventing An event of the Olympic Games since 1912. It is comprised of three parts—stadium jumping, dressage, and cross-country.

Reining A competition in which a horse and rider perform a specified pattern of advanced maneuvers. These include long sliding stops; spins (up to four 360° turnarounds at high speeds); rollbacks (180° turns after a sliding stop); and circles of different sizes.

Cutting A competition in which a horse cuts one cow from the herd and holds the cow away from the herd. The horse must work the cow without assistance from the rider for 2½ minutes.

PURPOSE OF THE HORSE INDUSTRY IN THE UNITED STATES

The horse industry is unlike the industries that surround other livestock species. It is a hybrid industry with interests and segments in agriculture, and in the sports, recreation, and entertainment industries. The feed for all horses, as well as most of the horses themselves, come from the agricultural sector, but most people who own horses are not in agriculture. Also, a wide variety of people who never owned a horse have interests in the horse industry. This makes the people of the horse industry very diverse (Figure 14–3). They range from those who spend their leisure time with horses to those who own horses as a business. The major purposes for keeping horses can be broken down into four categories: racing, showing, recreation, and other activities, which includes rodeo, polo, ranch use, police work, and breeding. Table 14–1 summarizes the number of horses involved in each activity as of 2005.

People tend to be in the horse industry for one or more of three general reasons: competition, leisure, and youth education. All can be considered as tools that improve the quality of human life. Many people are willing to spend large amounts of time and money for the satisfaction of winning a competition such as showing and racing. The horse industry produces one of the few leisure activities that allows for rapid recognition of excellence for relative newcomers in the industry. Many of those people recognized as leaders in various competitions today were not even involved 5 years ago. The variety of competition events include English events such as **hunter under saddle**, **saddle seat pleasure**, **dressage**, **stadium jumping**, and **three-day eventing**; and Western events such as **reining**, **cutting**, **working cow horse**, **western pleasure**, **trail**, **western riding**, and **conformation** judging, which are broken down into age and sex divisions.

Table 14–1
NUMBER OF HORSES BY ACTIVITY

Activity	Number of Horses
Racing	844,531
Showing	2,718,954
Recreation	3,906,923
Other	1,752,439
Total	9,222,847

Source: The American Horse Council Foundation, 2005.

Figure 14-4

The single largest reason for interest in the horse industry is recreation. (Photo courtesy Emily Cooper.)

Working cow horse A western event broken into two scored performances with those scores combined for a grand score to determine the winner. The two categories include dry work, which is the reining portion, and cow work, in which the horse shows its ability to control the cow.

Western pleasure A western event in which the manners and movement of the horse are judged. A good western pleasure horse is quiet, responsive, and gives a very smooth ride.

Trail A western event in which the horse is scored on its ability to pick cleanly through a set course that mimics outdoor trail riding.

Western riding A western event in which the horse is scored on lead changes through one of three potential patterns as well as its manners.

Conformation events A competition in which the horse's conformation is judged.

New activities like team sorting, team penning, mounted shooting, and more are gaining in numbers and becoming solid events. There are also shows for draft horses and miniature horses. The reason most people have interest in the horse industry is recreation. People like horses and enjoy owning and caring for them. Also, many parents consider owning and caring for horses, and competitions that involve horses, to be wholesome and educational experiences and activities for their children (Figure 14–4).

The horse industry is unique, as compared to the cattle, swine, sheep, and aquaculture industries, in that the horse is not primarily kept to provide food or fiber, or to convert otherwise unusable material to something useful. On the contrary, horses compete with food-producing livestock for high-quality feedstuffs and return little food to humans at all. Their contributions to humans are not as practical as that, but are just as important. Horses contribute quality to our lives. Horses bring a satisfaction that defies description to those who are involved with them. Most livestock feed our bodies; the horse feeds our being (Figure 14–5).

Figure 14-5

"There's nothing so good for the inside of a man as the outside of a horse."* That could well be the motto of therapeutic riding. Here young Matthew Sitton takes part in one of his regular outings aboard Bucky.

(Courtesy Shelly R. Sitton. Used with permission.) *The quote is attributed to Henry John Temple, Viscount Palmerston (1784–1865). Teddy Roosevelt, Sir Winston Churchill, Will Rogers, Ronald Reagan, and a host of others have used it in different forms.

Another unique feature of the horse industry when compared to other livestock industries is that many horse owners have a decidedly nonpragmatic attitude toward horses. Many have bonded with their animals. In this regard, horses have much more in common with pets and companion animals than with livestock. Thus, a different set of human values enters the horse industry than is associated with the livestock species. The ramifications of this are enormous. Certainly, this view of the horse has not always held sway. The horse has been a very practical animal to own in the past serving humans as a beast of burden, a means of transportation, and a tool of war (Figure 14–6). The horse is still doing those things somewhere around the world. However, during the 20th century, recreation, sport, and companion became the most important uses of the horse, especially in the United States and other developed countries. No longer is the horse needed to provide **horsepower**—machines do that. The horse has been given a higher purpose. This purpose sets the horse apart from the other livestock species (Figure 14–7).

Horsepower Term that originated as a measure of the pulling power exerted by a horse. Technically equal to the rate of moving 33,000 lbs a distance of 1 foot in 1 minute.

Figure 14–6
The rise and fall of many of the world's great civilizations have been inexorably linked to the horse. The Lippizzaner was developed by the Hapsburg monarchy for military and riding-school use in the 16th century. (Photo courtesy of Mike Brake/Shutterstock)

Figure 14–7
In the developed countries, and to a degree in the entire world, the horse underwent a transformation in use during the 20th century. Its utilitarian roles were largely replaced by its role as a sport and recreational animal. Pictured here is Oklahoma State University's Spirit Rider and Spirit Horse, Bullet. (Photo courtesy George Bulard, Genesee Photo Systems.)

HISTORICAL PERSPECTIVE

Although the horse was among the last of the livestock species to be domesticated, this hasn't deterred it from having a fascinating history. The domestic horse's fate has been inexorably linked to the rise and fall of many of the world's great civilizations. The ancestors of the horse developed about 1 million years ago in North America and spread throughout South America and the Old World via land bridges. They then became extinct in North America but luckily flourished in other parts of the world. The exact date and place of domestication is as difficult to pinpoint for the horse as it is for all the other species. Evidence suggests that it probably occurred at more than one place at approximately the same time. China and Mesopotamia are among the earliest places of domestication, probably somewhere close to 3000 B.C.

Columbus is credited with introducing horses to the Western Hemisphere in 1493 by bringing them to the West Indies along with several other species of livestock. The first horses to be reintroduced to North America were those of the Spanish conquistadors, beginning with those of Cortez in 1519 when he invaded Mexico, and then to what is now the United States by de Soto in 1539. Myth has it that the **mustang** herds of the American West were descendants of strays from these expeditions. They might have contributed, but if so, only in a minor way. The Spanish missionaries, who established missions in the late 1500s and early 1600s, brought horses and other livestock in significant numbers. At these missions, Native Americans learned the ways and value of the horse. From these early exposures to the horse until roughly 1750, Native Americans all across the Western Plains acquired and spread the horse, which led to the development of the great horse culture of the Native American. From 1750 to 1850, the "wild" horse adapted and flourished along with the Longhorn cattle, setting the stage for the most colorful and romanticized period of the history of the United States, "The Wild, Wild West," which lasted roughly from the end of the Civil War to the turn of the century. Franciscan missionaries brought horses to the Southeast at the same time the missions were established in the West. These became the base for what would become known as the Chickasaw horse. Over the course of colonization, various breeds and types of horses were brought to the continent by the settlers. From the 1890s to the late 1920s, the horse was used in this country mostly for draft. From 1920 to 1960, horse numbers declined steadily in the United States. In 1920, there were 25 million horses in the United States. By 1960, there were only 3 million. Thanks to the 40-hour workweek and a booming U.S. economy, the horse began a comeback as a recreational animal and numbers increased to a probable 10 million head in the early 1980s. Then, because of the economic turmoil of the 1980s and changes in the tax code, which removed some of the tax incentives of horse ownership, horse numbers declined to 6.9 million head in 1996. Horse numbers increased to 9.2 million by 2005. There has been a great deal of disruption in the horse industry since 2005, and reliable statistics are difficult to obtain. There are undoubtedly fewer horses now than in 2005. It is hard to estimate the total number of horses; however, new registrations with the major purebred associations declined by 45% from 2005 to 2010. This is an indication of a decline within the whole population.

Mustang The term used to describe the feral horse of the American West.

STRUCTURE AND GEOGRAPHIC LOCATION OF THE HORSE INDUSTRY

Horses are found in all 50 states (Figure 14–8). There is both a rural and an urban segment to the industry. Breeding, rearing, and training are generally rural activities. Racetracks, shows, and so on, are generally urban. Table 14–2 shows that a substantial number of horses are owned by people in all income brackets.

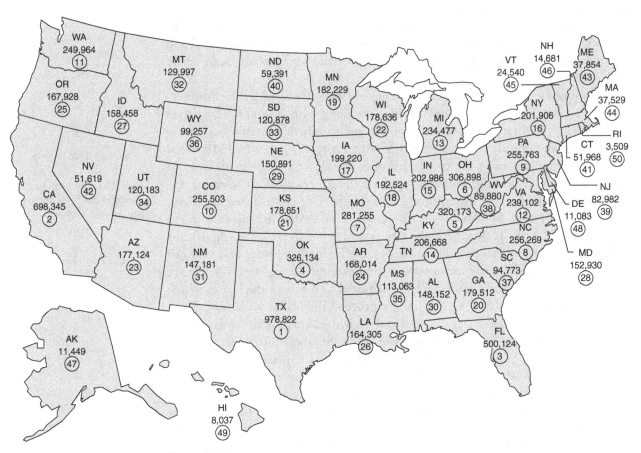

Figure 14–8

Horses by state. (Source: American Horse Council Foundation, 2005.)

Table 14–2
HORSE OWNERSHIP BY HOUSEHOLD INCOME

Household Income	Horses Owned	Percentage
$0–$24,999	209,879	11%
$25,000–$49,999	453,511	23%
$50,000–$74,999	435,930	22%
$75,000–$99,999	306,797	16%
$100,000–$124,999	199,646	10%
$125,000–$149,999	94,672	5%
$150,000+	179,268	9%
Not Reported	76,124	4%
TOTAL	**1,955,827**	**100%**

Source: American Horse Council Foundation, 2005.

Several classification schemes can be used to describe the horse industry. The EIHI divides them into the categories shown in Table 14–3.

In general, the **recreational horses** follow the population and the racehorses follow the racetracks, which also follow the population. Racing produces big revenues from relatively few animals (Figure 14–9). Heavily populated states like California, Florida, and Texas have more horses because their human population is so large. Some states that have strong show horse industries, like Oklahoma, as well as substantial use of horses for other reasons, gain significant economic impact on their state's economy and provide employment (Figure 14–10). Regional and economic factors also affect horse distribution.

Recreational horses
Horses of the light breeds kept for riding, driving, or nonprofessional racing and show.

Table 14–3
HORSE INDUSTRY PARTICIPANTS BY FORM OF PARTICIPATION[1]

Type of Participation	Number of Participants	Percentage of Total Participation
Horse Owners	1,955,827	41.97%
Primary Activity, Breeding	237,868	5.10%
Primary Activity, Competing	481,238	10.33%
Primary Activity, Other	1,117,330	23.98%
Primary Activity, Service Provider	119,392	2.56%
Employees	701,946	15.06%
of Owners	598,398	12.84%
of Racetracks	70,382	1.51%
of Shows	33,166	0.71%
Family Members and Volunteers	2,001,946	42.96%
TOTAL	4,659,719	100.00%

[1]Excludes horse owners under the age of 18.
Source: American Horse Council Foundation, 2005.

Figure 14–9
Event facilities such as racetracks comprise a large segment of the horse industry. Racing produces big revenues from relatively few animals.

Figure 14–10

An important segment of the horse industry is the employees. Shown here are ranch workers training young horses at Oklahoma's Lazy E Ranch. Other segments of the industry also generate significant employment.

HORSE GENETICS

Basic information on genetics and breeding is found in Chapters 6 and 7. Refer to those chapters to gain a basic understanding of genetics.

Scientific approaches to the study of horse genetics are not nearly as extensive as those for other livestock species because less research work has been done on horses. There are several reasons for this. First, horses are more important to recreation than to food and fiber production, and research on them is thus viewed as being less important. Second, many of the traits considered important in horses are difficult to measure and, therefore, are difficult to evaluate in a research study. Other hindrances to horse research include the high cost of animals and the horse's long generation interval. Recently, however, more attention has been placed on horse genetics, and this lack of information is changing. Many breed associations are now sponsoring this work.

There are a number of heritability estimates for some quantitative traits in horses. A list is shown in Table 14–4.

Table 14–4
HERITABILITY ESTIMATES FOR CERTAIN TRAITS IN HORSES

	Average Heritability Estimate
Height at withers	45–50
Body weight	25–30
Body length	35–40
Heart girth circumference	20–25
Cannon bone circumference	20–25
Pulling power	20–30
Running speed	35–40
Walking speed	40–45
Trotting speed	35–45
Movement	40–50
Temperament	25–30
Cow sense	Moderate to high
Type and conformation	Moderate
Reproductive traits	Low
Intelligence	Moderate to high

Source: Johnson, 1993. Used with permission.

One area that has received a good deal of attention is coat color. Some colors are considered more desirable than others, to such an extent that several breed associations have been formed on the basis of color. Horses of certain colors can command higher prices than equal quality animals of less desirable color. This has created a demand for knowledge about color genetics. It is also possible to discover much of the genetics of color by simply observing the results of many matings. Purebred registries have helped in this study by keeping records on color along with parentage. Analysis of these records has produced good information about the genetics of color. The tools used in genetic engineering are also helping. Many DNA tests are now available to determine a horse's genetic code. Table 14–5 shows the various **alleles** and actions of horse color genetics. Table 14–6 gives the genetic formulas for each of several common color types.

Alleles The alternative forms of any given gene.

Table 14–5
ALLELES AND ACTIONS OF HORSE COAT COLOR GENES

Color	Gene	Alleles	Observed Effect of Alleles in Homozygous and Heterozygous Conditions
White	White (W)	W, w	*WW:* Lethal *Ww:* Born white. Horse typically lacks pigment in skin and hair. Eyes are dark. *ww:* Horse is fully pigmented.
Gray	Gray (G)	G, g	*GG:* Horse shows progressive silvering with age to white or flea-bitten, but is born in any nongray color. Pigment is always present in skin and eyes at all stages of silvering. *Gg:* Same as *GG.* *gg:* Horse does not show progressive silvering with age.
Chestnut	Extension (E)	E, e	*EE:* Horse has ability to form black pigment in skin and hair. Black pigment in hair may be either in a points pattern or distributed overall. *Ee:* Same as *EE.* *ee:* Horse has black pigment in skin, but hair pigment appears red/yellow.
Bay/black	Agouti (A)	A, a	*AA:* If horse has black hair (*E*), then that black hair is in points pattern. *A* has no effect on red (*ee*) pigment. *Aa:* Same as *AA.* *aa:* If horse has black hair (*E*), then that black hair is uniformly distributed over body and points. *A* has no effect on red (*ee*) pigment.
Palomino / bucskin/ cremello/ perlino	Cream (C)	C, C^{cr}	*CC:* Horse is fully pigmented. *CC^{cr}:* Red pigment is diluted to yellow; black pigment is unaffected. *C^{cr}C^{cr}:* Both red and black pigments are diluted to ivory. Skin and eye color are also diluted.
Dun	Dun(D)	D, d	*DD:* Horse shows a diluted body color to pinkish red, yellow-red, yellow, or mouse gray and has dark points including dorsal stripe, shoulder stripe, and leg barring. *Dd:* Same as *DD.* *dd:* Horse has undiluted coat color.
Tobiano	Tobiano (TO)	TO, to	*TOTO:* Horse is characterized by white spotting pattern known as tobiano. Legs are usually white. White crosses the dorsal line. *TOto:* Same as *TOTO.* *toto:* No tobiano pattern present.
Overo	Overo (O)	O, o	*OO:* Homozygous lethal (white). *Oo:* White spotting characterized by horizontal pattern (usually) dark legs, white not crossing dorsal line. *oo:* No white spotting.

(continued)

Table 14–5
ALLELES AND ACTIONS OF HORSE COAT COLOR GENES (continued)

Color	Gene	Alleles	Observed Effect of Alleles in Homozygous and Heterozygous Conditions
Leopard spotting	Leopard spotting (*LP*)	*LP* *lp*	*LPLP:* Variable pattern of roaning and spotting with mottled skin, eyes showing white sclera. Also known as appaloosa or tiger spotting. Homozygotes have more white than heterozygotes. *LPlp:* Same as *LPLP* but less white. *lplp:* No white spotting.
Champagne	Champagne (*CH*)	*CH* *ch*	*CHCH:* Red pigment diluted to yellow, black pigment to brown or olive. Both have a metallic sheen. *CHch:* Same as *CHCH*. *chch:* No color dilution.
Silver	Silver (*Z*)	*Z* *z*	*ZZ:* Black pigment diluted to chocolate; minimal effect on red pigment. *Zz:* Same as *ZZ*. *zz:* No color dilution.
Roan	Roan (*RN*)	*RN* *rn*	*RNRN:* Hair is mixture of white and any other color. Points usually dark. *RNrn:* Same as *RNRN*. *rnrn:* Full color.

Source: Bowling, 1999. Used with permission. Modified according to Bowling & Ruvinski, 2000.

Table 14–6
GENETIC FORMULAS AND COLOR DEFINITIONS

Genetic Formula	Color
W	White
G	Gray
E, A, CC, dd, gg, ww, toto	Bay
E, aa, CC, dd, gg, ww, toto	Black (includes brown)
ee, aa, CC, dd, gg, ww, toto	Red (chestnut, sorrel, and so on)
E, A, CC^{cr}, dd, gg, ww, toto	Buckskin
ee, CC^{cr}, dd, gg, ww, toto	Palomino
C^{cr}C^{cr}	Cremello
E, A, CC, D, gg, ww, toto	Buckskin dun
E, aa, CC, D, gg, ww, toto	Mouse dun
ee, CC, D, gg, ww, toto	Red dun
E, A, CC, dd, gg, ww, TO	Bay tobiano
ee, CC, D, gg, ww, TO	Red dun tobiano

Source: Bowling, 1999. Used with permission.

Basic Coat Colors

Points The legs, mane, and tail of a horse.

Gene A segment of a chromosome.

Modifier gene Gene that influences the expression of another gene or genes.

Bay horses have the combination of a red-brown body with black legs, mane, and tail (the **points** of a horse). Black horses are black all over—black body as well as black points. Chestnut horses have red bodies, manes, tails, and legs with no black anywhere. Each of these basic colors has several shades ranging from dark to light. The mechanism for just which shade of bay, black, or chestnut will be exhibited has not been worked out. Adding to the confusion is the fact that the names of the three basic colors differ among the breeds and the regions of the country. All other colors are produced by the action of other **genes** called **modifier genes**. For instance, gray horses are not born gray. Rather they are born one of the colors just mentioned, and they change to gray in response to a modifier gene. They still carry the genes for color they were born with. Sorrel, chestnut, and liver chestnut are just shades of basic red. Brown horses may be blacks that have faded in the sun; palominos are basic chestnut but get changed by a separate **diluter gene**, and so on. Understanding that this is complicated is the first step in understanding the genetics of color in horses.

Diluter gene A type of modifier gene that changes a base color to a lighter color.

Gene G Gene *G* causes horses to be gray. Gray horses are usually born with color and gray as they age. A horse with a *G* allele may become solid gray or gray with red or black flecks. During the process, they may be dappled for a time, even for years (Figure 14–11). A *G* horse keeps its skin pigmentation, which is how it is differentiated from a *W* horse (discussed later).

Gene E Gene *E*, the Extension gene, controls black hair. Pure recessives (*ee*) are some shade of red (dark chestnut to light sorrel) with no black anywhere. Mating red to red always produces red because these horses do not carry the black gene. *E* animals will either have black hair that is restricted to the points or black hair that covers the whole body. Whether that black is restricted to the points or covers the whole body is determined by the action of gene *A* (discussed later). Gene *E* just controls black hair. Both a bay and a black have the same genotype for this gene (*E*) and both have black hair over at least part of their body. Black is dominant to red. This is confusing to some because bay horses have a body color that most of us call red or brown. Just remember that this gene controls the presence or absence of black hair on either the whole body or the points. Bay horses have black points.

Gene A Gene *A*, the Agouti gene, is the determining gene that controls the distribution pattern of black hair. This determines if an *E* horse is a bay or a black. If the dominant allele *A* is present, and is combined with *E*, then only the points of the horse will be black and the body will be some shade of red-brown (i.e., a bay). A bay horse must carry genes *A* and *E*. If a horse carries *aa*, then black hair is not restricted to the points and will cover the whole body (except for stockings and blazes and other patterns to be discussed later). Thus solid black is recessive to bay. If a horse is genetically red (*ee*), then the *A* gene has no effect on the horse. The animal will carry the genetics and pass them to its offspring but will not express them because *A* only affects distribution of black hair, and the animal does not have any black hair.

Gene W Gene *W* makes a horse unable to form pigment in skin and hair. If a horse carries this gene, it will have color according to one set of alleles but will be unable to manufacture the pigments necessary to display the color because of a different set of alleles. A horse carrying the dominant allele *W* will have pink skin, white hair, and

Figure 14–11
Gene G is the gene responsible for gray. Gray horses start out as colored, and the expression of gene G causes them gradually to lose their original color and become gray. During the process, they often become dappled like the horse in this picture. Most will eventually become gray over most or all of the body. These horses are different from W horses in that they keep their body pigment.

brown or blue eyes. These horses are often called *albino*. White horses always carry the *Ww* genotype. The *WW* genotype is lethal and kills the embryo early in pregnancy.

Diluting Genes   Having established the genetic makeup of white, gray, bay, black, and chestnut horses, it is now time to see how the action of diluter genes changes the colors.

Gene C   Gene *C* is the cream gene. This gene causes pigment dilution and is an **incompletely dominant** gene. If a horse carries the genotype *CC,* then nothing happens to its color. However, chestnut horses that are heterozygous (*CC^{cr}*) have their red pigment diluted to yellow and become palomino. Palominos have white manes and tails. Black is generally unaffected by the heterozygous state and stays black, although some horses have a slightly modified color referred to as smoky black. The bay (*E, A*) color is diluted to buckskin, which is yellow with black points. The body color changes but the black points stay the same. A horse of any color that carries the homozygous-recessive condition (*C^{cr}C^{cr}*) has its color diluted to very pale cream with pink skin and blue eyes. These horses are called *cremello* if the base color is red, *perlino* if the base color is bay, and *smoky cream* if the base color is black. Cremello can sometimes be difficult to distinguish from white. Some breed associations use the designation *albino* for all.

Gene D   Gene *D* is also a dilution gene that produces dun coloring. It is different from *C* in that it dilutes the body color only; the points are not diluted. In addition, this gene produces a uniquely recognizable pattern of dark points consisting of a **dorsal** stripe, a shoulder stripe, and leg barring often referred to as *zebra stripes*. Black dilutes to mouse-gray with black points referred to as *mouse dun* or *grulla*. Bay is diluted to yellow or tan with the zebra stripes, and it is called *zebra dun* or *buckskin dun*. Chestnut is diluted to yellowish red with darker red points and zebra stripes and referred to as *red dun* or *claybank dun*. One additional difference is that homozygous *DD* does not produce the extreme dilution to cream seen in *C^{cr}*. Homozygous *dd* has no effect on color.

Gene CH   Gene *CH*, the Champagne gene, has only recently been described. This gene produces a color dilution plus mottled gray skin, a metallic sheen to the hair, and eyes blue at birth that change to hazel as the horse ages. Horses can appear to be palomino, buckskin, or cremello and have been called these colors prior to the discovery of the Champagne gene. Champagne in combination with black produces what is called classis champagne, an olive-hued metallic color. Many breed registries have not yet made provisions to include colors caused by the Champagne gene in their selection of colors for their breeds.

Gene Z   Gene *Z* (proposed) is the Silver gene. Actually described over 100 years ago, it has been difficult to understand and often ignored. In a black horse (*aaE-*), the presence of *Z* causes the color to be diluted to a black-chocolate or chocolate and the mane and tail become silver gray or flaxen. A bay horse with the *Z* gene can appear to be a chestnut. Chestnut horses appear to be changed only in that they get a silver (flaxen) mane and tail and can sometimes look like a palomino. In interaction with Gray, Silver can cause a "white-born" gray. This gene does not appear to be found in all breeds, or at least is found in much greater frequency in some compared to others, and many breeds do not recognize the color variation with an official designation as a color for their breed.

Roan   Gene *RN* controls roan, when white hair is mixed with colored hair over the animal's body. The points generally retain the color with no white. Mixtures of white and any shade of red hair give a red roan. With a black horse, roan produces what is called a *blue roan*. Roan is a simple dominant-recessive gene, with the roan expression dominant. The homozygous-dominant condition *RNRN* has been proposed to be lethal. Animals of this genotype are thought by some to die in early development and

---

Incompletely dominant Neither allele is dominant to the other. Both influence the trait.

Dorsal Refers to the back on an animal.

are never born. This would mean that all roan horses are heterozygous, *RNrn*. This is one of the unknowns of color breeding.

Leopard   The gene *LP* controls whether or not a horse has the complex of spotting and diffuse roan patterns referred to as leopard, appaloosa, and tiger spotting. It is believed the gene controlling all these patterns is a single incomplete dominant gene. The genetics of Leopard coloring leaves many unanswered questions. The patterns included in Leopard coloring include leopard, blanket, snowflake, varnish roan, and others. These different patterns are caused by various modifier genes in combination with *LP*, including some probably not yet identified. Leopard markings can occur on any color. Striped hooves, mottled skin (most evident around the muzzle and eyes), and prominent white **sclera** can also identify Leopards.

Sclera The tough white outer coat of the eyeball.

Spotting   Paint and pinto are horse color patterns characterized by some body color interspersed with white. Think of this pattern as being white spots superimposed over the basic colors. If the horse is black and white, it is called a *piebald*. A horse that is any color other than black with white is called *skewbald*. Paints and pintos are produced in two different color patterns called *tobiano* and *overo*. These patterns are inherited separately and both can occur on the same horse. A horse with both patterns is called *tovero*. Other patterns include *sabino* and *splashed white*.

Tobianos   Tobianos generally have white on the legs below the hocks and white across the back. The skin under the white is pink. The head of a tobiano is usually solid except for facial markings. The pattern of white on the animal's body is arranged vertically. A single gene, *TO,* controls this color. It is a simple dominant-recessive trait. Thus pure dominants, *TOTO,* always produce a tobiano (Figure 14–12).

Figure 14–12
Spotting in horses can be controlled by several genes. This baby is considered a tobiano. A simple dominant gene, TO, is believed to control this pattern.

Overos   The overo pattern seldom produces white across the back. Overo heads have more white as a general rule, displayed as bald faces or what is called a *bonnet* or medicine hat pattern. All four legs are usually colored, although the pattern sometimes produces as few as one colored leg. Overo can be difficult to determine because other genes that control white markings may be present in an overo or any other type of horse. These genes can cause a white leg. When two overo horses are bred together, the product can be a white **foal** that dies shortly after birth because it cannot absorb food from the digestive tract. The precise genetics of overo markings are unknown. Until recently, it was assumed overo coloring was recessive because it sometimes occurs in the offspring of two solid horses. However, work by the late Dr. Ann Bowling of the Equine Research Laboratory, School of Veterinary Medicine, University of California, Davis, suggests it is actually a dominant trait that mutates more frequently than most genes. This would explain how two solid horses could produce an overo paint. Complicating the picture is the fact that the color pattern called overo is variable enough to be produced by additional genes. Sabino and splashed white are other variations that may be controlled differently, because an analysis of the breeding records of overo horses has yet to establish the pattern of a simple dominant-recessive trait. This is one area where there is not yet a definitive answer to the genetic puzzle.

Flaxen Mane and Tail

Gene *F* produces a normal red mane and tail on chestnut (*ee*) horses. The *f* causes a flaxen mane and tail on chestnut or sorrel horses.

Additional Common Markings

When white markings such as stars, stripes, and snips on the face and white stockings are added to horses, the effects can be very appealing to the eye. However, the explanations of how these markings come about are incomplete at this time. It is suspected that at least 10, and probably more, different genes control white markings (Figure 14–13).

Genetic Diseases in Horses

Various genetic diseases and abnormalities occur in horses. Some occur with relative infrequency and others with much higher frequency. Table 14–7 gives some examples of common genetic diseases in horses. The key to controlling these conditions is

Foal A newborn horse of either sex. The term is sometimes used up to the time of weaning, after which *colt* and *filly* are more likely to be used.

Figure 14–13
Perhaps as many as 10 different genes control the presence or absence of stars, stripes, snips, and other white markings. This is one of many pieces of the horse genetic puzzle left to be completed.

Table 14–7
EXAMPLES OF GENETIC DISEASES CAUSED BY A SINGLE OR A FEW GENES

Genetic Disease	Clinical Description
CID	Failure of immune system to form; animals die of infections
HyPP	Defect in movement of sodium and potassium in and out of muscle; animals intermittently have attacks of muscle weakness, tremors, collapse
Myotonic dystrophy	Spasms occur in various muscles
Hemophilia A	Failure to produce blood clotting factor; bleeding into joints; development of hematomas
Hereditary multiple exostosis	Bony lumps develop on various bones throughout the body
Parrot mouth	Lower jaw is shorter than upper jaw; incisor teeth improperly aligned
Lethal white foal syndrome	Failure to form certain types of nerves in the intestinal tract; foals die of colic within several days of birth
Laryngeal hemiplegia	Paralysis of the muscles that move cartilages in the larynx; results in noise production in the throat with exercise and exercise intolerance
Cerebellar ataxia	Degeneration of specific cells in the part of the brain called the cerebellum, resulting in incoordination
Hydrocephalus	Accumulation of fluid within compartments of the brain, resulting in crushing of normal brain tissue
Umbilical hernias	Opening in the body wall of the navel does not close normally, resulting in the presence of a sack into which intestines may fall
Inguinal hernias	Opening through which the testicles descend into the scrotum is too large and intestines can escape into the scrotum, sometimes causing colic
Hereditary equine regional dermal asthenia (HERDA)	Dysfunctional collagen bundles within the dermis, resulting in loss of strength and durability of the skin
Epitheliogenesis imperfecta	Skin fails to form over parts of the body or in the mouth
Cataracts	Cloudiness of the lens in the eye, resulting in blindness

Source: McClure, 1993. Used with permission (modified).

being aware of the ones that affect the breed or breeds you are interested in breeding, and making knowledgeable breeding decisions. Until the last few years, it was often difficult to know the genotype of a horse with certainty where many of these diseases were concerned. However, great strides have been and are continually being made in the genetic mapping of the horse. Already, fairly inexpensive tests have been developed to detect several of these disorders. In the not-too-distant future, a horse breeder will be able to know the exact genetic makeup of breeding stock and can make decisions accordingly.

BREEDS OF HORSES

Horses are generally classified as light horses, draft horses, or ponies. Most horses are in the light horse class. Each of these divisions may be broken down by height, build, weight, use, or other variables. Most authorities classify horses as being over 14.2 **hands** at the withers, and ponies as being under 14.2 hands. Some breed associations take exception to this philosophy, and so do some individuals. The problem arises from the fact that some small horses of established light breeds can be shorter than 14.2 hands. Calling their horse a pony generally upsets breeders and owners of

Hand One hand equals 4 inches. Horses are measured for height at the withers in hands.

those animals. So how does one distinguish between ponies and horses? The breed associations make this decision. One way of knowing the association's decision is that a horse's height is referred to in hands, whereas a pony's height is expressed in inches.

The various horse uses dictated that several types of light horses and ponies were developed from the classes to perform specialized functions. Some were developed primarily for riding, some for work, some for racing, some for driving, and others to be capable of many tasks. Different horses have natural tendencies toward the use of certain **gaits**. Riding horses are generally three-gaited horses. The walk, trot, and canter are the three basic gaits of horses. Five-gaited horses add a slow-gait and rack to the basic three.

The horse industry revolves around breeds and breed associations. Several representative breeds are pictured in the color insert of this text. For a complete look at horse breeds from around the world, visit the Breeds of Livestock page at http://www.ansi.okstate.edu/breeds/. All of the breeds now popular in the United States are light horse and used primarily for riding. Most of these breeds were developed here, usually to meet a specific need in a specific region. There are more than 150 breed organizations in the United States.

Gait Forward movement of a horse. The three natural gaits for most horses are the walk, trot, and canter or gallop. Some breeds have additional or different gaits such as the pace, foxtrot, running walk, rack, and others, and they are considered five-gaited.

Draft Horses

During the peak years of horse numbers in the United States (1910–1920), 75–85% of the total horses in the United States were the heavy draft horses that originated in Europe. The two most popular breeds of draft horses were the Percheron and Belgian, with the Clydesdale and Shire a distant third and fourth. There were some Suffolks, but very few. The Clydesdale was never very popular in this country. This is ironic in light of the TV ads of a well-known beer company, plus the personal appearances of its team of Clydesdales—this is the only draft breed that millions of people have ever seen.

Imported Light Breeds

Only two breeds of light horses imported to the United States have maintained significant importance in today's horse industry. They are the Arabian and the Thoroughbred.

The Arabian is known for its intelligence, durability, and stamina. Its origin is unknown, but it is very likely that Arab peoples had been breeding and improving this breed since the beginning of the Christian era, and probably long before. Whatever the exact date of origin, there is no question it is the oldest breed of horse, perhaps the oldest of any class of agricultural animal. The Arabian has contributed genes to the foundation of most of the breeds of light horses in the world.

The Thoroughbred was developed in England in the late 17th and early 18th centuries using Arabian breeding. It came to the United States in 1730. It has had the greatest direct influence of any breed on the development of the American breeds of light horses. No breed can best the Thoroughbred at distances of three-fourths to 2 miles. Although the Thoroughbred is most known as a racehorse, it is valuable for many other uses as well, including hunting, jumping, and polo.

Breeds of Horses Developed in the United States

Modern American breeds of light horses in use in the United States were developed from two different groups of Native American light horses plus horses imported later (Figure 14–14). One group developed on the Eastern Seaboard. The foundation horses were breeds and strains of light horses brought by the early settlers from Europe. The Thoroughbred was used quite heavily in developing these horses in Europe. The other groups of Native American light horses were those that descended from the Spanish horses that became the mustang and the horse of the Native American.

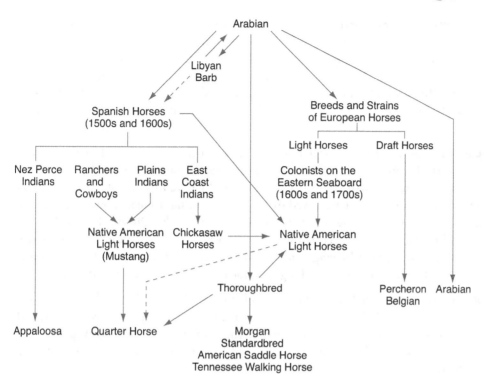

Figure 14–14
Outline of the development of breeds and strains of horses that have been or are of major importance in the United States. (Source: Turman, 1986.)

Morgan The Morgan breed was developed in the Northeast as a versatile animal for light draft and driving as well as for riding. This breed is unusual not only among horses, but among all classes of livestock because it traces to a single foundation animal, the **stallion** Justin Morgan, who was foaled about 1789. Most breed historians believe his sire was a Thoroughbred and his dam carried considerable Thoroughbred breeding. Justin Morgan was an outstanding horse and a **prepotent** sire. His descendants became very popular for both riding and driving. Today, the breed is used primarily for riding, driving, and showing and is most popular in the New England states.

Standardbred This breed was developed initially to meet the need for a carriage horse and also to be used in harness racing. Its foundation included trotters and pacers among the Native American horses, Canadian Trotters, and the infusion of Thoroughbred and Morgan breeding. It is now bred almost exclusively for harness racing. The name Standardbred comes from its ability to trot or pace a mile in under standard time. Standard time was 2:30 for trotters and 2:25 for pacers. Today the standard is 2:20 for 2-year-olds and 2:15 for mature animals. There is no difference for trotters and pacers—most are pacers anyway.

American Saddlebred Horse This breed was developed in the South, especially in Kentucky, with emphasis more on riding comfort than on speed. The foundation included Native American horses, the Thoroughbred, and Standardbred, plus a limited infusion of Arabian and Morgan. The American Saddle Horse can be either three- or five-gaited, and some may be used as fine harness horses. The breed is used primarily as a pleasure and show horse. Many consider it the premier show horse because of its great beauty and very attractive way of moving.

Stallion A mature male horse that is not castrated. Castrated male horses are *geldings.*

Prepotent An animal that transmits its characteristics to its offspring in a consistent fashion.

Tennessee Walking Horse   This breed originated in Tennessee, for much the same purpose as the American Saddle Horse. Its foundation included American Saddle Horse, Thoroughbred, Standardbred, and Morgan as well as Native American Horses. Tennessee Walking Horses are three-gaited. The *gaits* are the walk, running walk, and canter. The running walk is peculiar to this breed. When performing the running walk, the horse overstrides by placing a back hoof significantly ahead of the print of the forehoof. This breed is known for its comfortable gaits and pleasureful ride.

Quarter Horse   The Quarter Horse is the most numerous breed in the United States. The Quarter Horse is still an important work animal that is used on American ranches as a **stock horse**. No other breed can really have this said about it. Its use as a work animal is far overshadowed by its use as a racing, rodeo, show, and pleasure horse. The Quarter Horse originated in Virginia with the Quarter Pather, but the bulk of its improvement occurred in the Southwest. The foundation included Native American horses, the Mustang, and the Thoroughbred. The Quarter Horse is unexcelled for two purposes: as a working cow horse and for speed at short distances.

Appaloosa   The Nez Perce tribe of the Northwest developed these horses. It takes its name from the Palouse River area where the tribe lived. Appaloosas were selected for their very distinctive color pattern. Because of an open **stud book** policy, the modern Appaloosa has varying amounts of Quarter Horse, Thoroughbred, and Arabian heritage.

Breed Popularity

Table 14–8 lists horse breed registration numbers. The Quarter Horse registers by far the largest number of new horses each year (Figure 14–15). In many years, as many or more Quarter Horses were registered as all the others combined. However, several breeds had been growing, prior to the economic downturn of the late 2000s. The annual registrations for most breeds have declined dramatically since 2007.

REPRODUCTIVE MANAGEMENT

As few as 50–60% of the **mares** bred **to foal** the following year actually have a foal. This has earned the horse the reputation of being a fairly infertile animal. It is probably true that horses have more problems with reproduction than other species that have been specifically selected for their reproductive efficiencies. Even though

---

Stock horse Any horse of the light breeds trained and used for working livestock, mainly cattle.

Stud book The set of records a breed association keeps on the animals registered with it.

Mare A mature female horse.

Foaling; to foal Parturition in the horse.

Table 14–8
HORSE BREED REGISTRATION FIGURES

	1960	1975	1980	1985	1990	1995	2000	2005	2010
Appaloosa	4,052	20,175	25,384	16,189	10,669	10,903	10,906	7,055	3,486
Arabian	1,610	15,000	19,725	30,004	17,676	12,398	9,660	6,359	4,912
Morgan	1,069	3,400	4,537	4,538	3,618	3,053	3,624	3,156	1,804
Paint	NA	5,287	9,654	12,692	16,153	34,846	62,511	42,557	17,836
Quarter Horse	35,507	97,179	137,090	157,360	110,597	107,332	127,763	144,955	83,736
Saddlebred	2,329	4,064	3,879	4,353	3,569	3,239	2,908	2,868	1,849
Standardbred	6,413	12,830	15,219	18,384	16,576	10,918	13,846	10,457	10,600
Tennessee Walking Horse	2,623	6,591	6,847	7,633	7,609	10,020	15,000	13,366	4,939
Thoroughbred	12,901	29,225	39,367	50,382	44,143	34,958	36,700	34,070	30,000

Source: breed associations.

Figure 14–15
The Quarter Horse is the most popular breed in the United States.

reproductive rates are generally lowly heritable, substantial improvement has been made with many of the other species because it is a trait that is selected for. In horses, it is not usually one of the traits that is even considered. However, the horse is generally more fertile than it is given credit for. The way that many people breed their horses is destined to a high percentage of failure from the onset. The typical way many approach the task is as follows:

1. Spend months of decision making over just which of the available stallions to use.
2. Scrimp and save to afford the stud fee.
3. Take the mare for an early spring ride and notice her showing signs of heat.
4. Rush back home and call the stallion owner and arrange to bring her right over.
5. Breed the mare, load her up, and bring her home to avoid paying board.
6. Turn her out to pasture and wait 11 months for the blessed event.
7. Be disappointed when no foal appears.

To be fair, people who make their living breeding horses could not survive in the business with such poor management. However, this scenario is all too common and has contributed to the horse's reputation as being infertile. In truth, a high percentage of mares can settle and bring a new foal into the world. An understanding of how to make this happen is all that is needed. The horse is much less frequently the problem than the people managing the breeding.

The mare has a **seasonally polyestrous** estrous cycle and generally conceives only during certain times of the year. Mares respond to the hour of daylight by initiating the estrous season during lengthening days. The common way to think of this is that mares are "long-day breeders." In North America, **anestrus** is usually from mid-November until mid-February. For some mares and even whole breeds, the fertile period tends to start later in the spring. During the rest of the year, the mare generally has an **estrous cycle**, can mate, and can conceive offspring (Figure 14–16). For mares that are to be bred, it is critical to manage breeding so the mare is mated when an egg is present to be fertilized. Because a mare may very well be receptive to the stallion at times other than when she is ovulating, this can be a bit tricky. For most owners of just a mare or two, the best course of action is to choose a stallion that is managed by a knowledgeable **stud** manager, and to trust he or she will get the mare safely in foal. For those who will be standing stallions to the public or breeding larger numbers of mares, the only course of action is to familiarize themselves thoroughly with the hormonal and environmental control mechanisms of reproduction in both the mare

Seasonally polyestrous When an animal has repeated estrous cycles but only in response to some environmental factor associated with the seasons, frequently the photoperiod.

Anestrus Period of time when a female is not having estrous cycles.

Estrous cycle The period of time from one estrus to the next.

Stud A unit of male animals kept for breeding. Also a term for a stallion.

Figure 14–16

Mare seasonality. (Source: Slusher et al., 1998, p. 3974.1. Used with permission.)

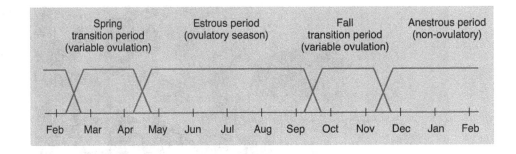

Teasing Placing a stallion and a mare in proximity to each other and observing the mare's actions. Mares that are coming into heat display specific behaviors.

Ultrasonography Using ultrasound waves to visualize the deep tissues of the body.

and the stallion. This knowledge, put to use with good insemination techniques and management for both mare and stallion, is the only course of action. Breeding managers must effectively learn to manipulate the estrous cycle, detect estrus, mate at the proper time, and confirm pregnancy.

Heat detection is usually accomplished through the use of **teasing** with a stallion and palpation. Combining **ultrasonography** with rectal palpation helps determine the time of ovulation. Generally, mares are teased with a stallion to determine if they are showing signs of estrus (Figure 14–17). The ones that are showing signs of estrus are palpated. Signs of estrus in mares include winking of the vulva, urination, squatting, and seeking the stallion. Ultrasound can help determine many of the physical changes that accompany ovulation, and can thus help time the mating (Figure 14–18). Conception rates are best when insemination occurs within the 36 hours directly preceding ovulation. Ovulation most frequently occurs 24 to 48 hours before the end of estrus (Figure 14–19).

Pregnancy is detected in various ways. A good indicator of pregnancy is to wait and see if the mare returns to heat. Generally, a nonpregnant mare should once again come into estrus 18 to 20 days from the time she last ovulated. Rectal palpation can detect a pregnancy in as few as 18 days following insemination. Ultrasonography can be used to detect pregnancy in as few as 10 days. Either of these methods in the hands of a skilled person can take the guesswork out of pregnancy diagnosis.

The estrous cycle can be manipulated in several ways in horses, to varying degrees of success. Because a mare's estrous cycles begin in response to length of day, artificial lights can be used to "extend" the day from 1 to 16 hours. To be successful, this technique must be started 60 to 90 days before the first ovulation is desired.

Figure 14–17

Observing a mare's behavior when in the proximity of a stallion is one useful tool in heat detection. In the pictured arrangement, a stallion is confined to the pipe enclosure and several mares are allowed into the surrounding corral. Trained personnel observe from a distance and keep a daily record of the mares' actions. Analyzing this record of observations helps determine when to start taking ultrasound readings on each mare to detect ovulation.

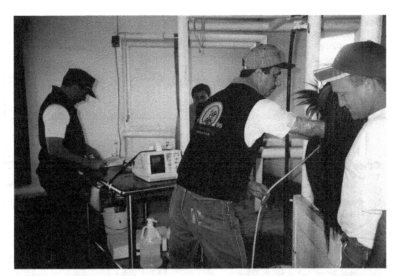

Figure 14–18
Timing of breeding is critical to ensure conception. Combining ultrasonography with rectal palpation helps determine the time of ovulation.

Figure 14–19
Use of a palpation stock such as this one helps ensure the safety of the horse and the people involved in breeding horses.

This must be carefully done. The days must be extended by the same amount each day. Light intensity must be a minimum of 2 foot-candles. Hormonal treatments are also available to alter the length of estrus, change its duration, and even stimulate ovulation.

Good record keeping is an important part of breeding management. Figure 14–20 shows an example of a comprehensive teasing, breeding, and palpation record for a mare.

The stallion should not be overlooked in this process. Breeding soundness examinations and semen evaluation should be carried out on the stallion before the breeding season begins and periodically during the breeding season. Stallions used to breed mares naturally should be checked for transmissible diseases. Stallions used in artificial insemination programs have their semen evaluated much more frequently as part of the processes of extending and dividing the semen for multiple inseminations.

Various methods are used to inseminate mares. At some breeding farms, mares are simply turned into the pasture with a stallion (pasture breeding) and allowed to stay there for a period of time long enough to ensure mating. Such mating systems can result in good conception rates, but risks of injury are higher. This is especially true if outside mares are constantly added and taken from the pasture. This system

Tease Code
1 – resistance
2 – indifferent
3 – interested
4 – winks vulva, urinates
5 – profuse urination and vulvular activity

Other Codes
T – treated
C – culture
S – speculum
P – palpate
B – bred
Pr – pregnant
F – foaled
A – arrived
D – departed
U – ultrasound

TS – tease score
FS – follicle size
CX – cervix
FC – follicle consistency

Mare _____ Color _____ Age _____ Farm number _____
In 20 _____ Book to _____ Mare owner _____
Results of last year's breeding _____

	1	2	3	4	5	6	7	8	9	10	11	12	13	14	15	16	17	18	19	20	21	22	23	24	25	26	27	28	29	30	31
Dec.																															
Jan.																															
Feb.																															
Mar.																															
Apr.																															
May																															
June																															
July																															

Palpation

Date _____ Remarks _____	Date _____ Remarks _____	Date _____ Remarks _____
TS: 1 2 3 4 5 FS: _____ mm CX: 1 2 3 FC: T S O Uterine tone _____	TS: 1 2 3 4 5 FS: _____ mm CX: 1 2 3 FC: T S O Uterine tone _____	TS: 1 2 3 4 5 FS: _____ mm CX: 1 2 3 FC: T S O Uterine tone _____
Date _____ Remarks _____ TS: 1 2 3 4 5 FS: _____ mm CX: 1 2 3 FC: T S O Uterine tone _____	**Date _____ Remarks _____** TS: 1 2 3 4 5 FS: _____ mm CX: 1 2 3 FC: T S O Uterine tone _____	**Date _____ Remarks _____** TS: 1 2 3 4 5 FS: _____ mm CX: 1 2 3 FC: T S O Uterine tone _____

Teasing Code
1 – Mare is visibly resistant to stallion
2 – Mare is indifferent to stallion
3 – Mare is slightly interested in stallion; may urinate, may wink vulva
4 – Mare is greatly interested in stallion; occasional urination, profuse vulva activity
5 – Mare is greatly interested in stallion; frequent urination, squatting, leans into stallion

Follicle Size
Commonly sized as <20, 30, 40, 50 millimeters or greater in diameter

Follicular Consistency
T – Turgid
S – Soft or breedable
O – Ovulated

Cervix Size
1 – ≤10 millimeters
2 – >10 but <30 millimeters
3 – ≥30 millimeters

Uterine Tone
Poor, fair, good, excellent, or pregnant

Figure 14–20
Teasing and palpation record for mares. (Source: Slusher et al., 1998. Used with permission.)

is best if all the mares to be bred are put together and allowed to stabilize into a band before the stallion is introduced. No new mares should be added after this time. Hand mating is more common. In this system, the receptive mares are mated under close supervision. Mares are often placed in breeding hobbles to prevent them from kicking. Their tails are wrapped to help avoid injuries to the stallion, and the stallion is kept on halter and directed by a skilled person. Injuries can be minimized in this way. However, diseases can be transmitted during the act of mating and then passed on to other horses. An increasingly common method in use on progressive breeding farms is to collect the semen of the stallion with the use of an **artificial vagina** (Figure 14–21) and breed the receptive mares artificially. Although some breeds

Artificial vagina Device used to collect semen from a male.

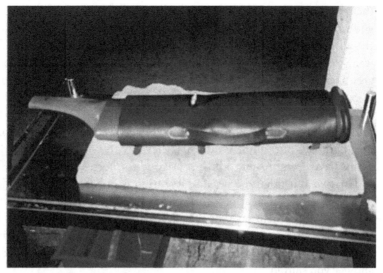

(a)

(b)

Figure 14–21
An artificial vagina (a) is combined with such tools as a mounting dummy (b) to collect semen from stallions to be used in artificial insemination of mares.

do not register the foals born to such matings, most do. This method has several advantages including disease prevention, virtual elimination of injuries, and an increase in the number of mares that can be bred to a given stallion each day.

The needs of the stallion manager to be able to collect, evaluate, extend, and ship semen have increased because several breed associations now allow the use of cooled shipped semen in breeding programs. This allows breeders to use genetics from across the country that they might not otherwise be able to access. Previously, most breed associations required the mare to be on the premises with the stallion when inseminated even if artificial insemination was used. The ability to use sires previously unavailable to many breeders is an exciting opportunity for horse breeders. Embryo transfer is also accepted by some breed associations.

NUTRITION AND FEEDING OF HORSES

Poor feeding choices by horse owners are a major source of economic losses in the horse industry. They can also be a major source of emotional trauma for owners when the results of their feeding actions are illness, permanent disability, or even death for

Ration The feed allotment for an animal for a 24-hour period. Use of the term *ration* should be in conjunction with specific quantities of feeds being consumed.

their animal. Obviously, people who have a recreation/companion horse, who pay good money for it, and who are perhaps emotionally attached to it, want to feed the animal well. People in the horse business have an equal, if different, reason to want to feed well: Properly fed horses make more money. It is unfortunate that both groups frequently fail to seek the advice of those who are trained to help them, such as extension agents and state specialists, and rather rely on advertising or the word of the person who has a horse in the next stall for their nutritional advice. As a result, horse owners spend millions of dollars every year on needless boxes and tubes of magic dust to put in horse **rations**. They pay too much for oats when several other grains have been proven to be just as good for horses. The horse suffers and is not as productive as it might be because its ration is unbalanced and/or deficient. A better and more economical approach is to learn the proper way to feed the horse. Doing so will no doubt help save for that new saddle. A word of caution: Learning what is in this chapter is not enough to make you a competent equine nutritionist. This is an introductory text. The material presented here is just designed to heighten awareness and get you started.

Nutrition and nutritional management of the horse revolve around the fact that the horse is a monogastric with a functional cecum. This allows it to use a significant amount of forage in its ration and do very well on it. As a nonruminant herbivore, the horse has characteristics of the simple monogastric and also some similarities to the ruminant in its ability to use feeds. The horse evolved using its speed as its major survival mechanism. Thus, it developed the **continuous eater strategy** of eating frequently in small amounts and moving from place to place between grazing. Domestic horses on pasture still exhibit these same eating behaviors. Stabled or otherwise confined horses are generally handled in a way that makes them meal eaters instead of continual eaters. This creates problems because the stomach of the horse is small in comparison to the rest of the digestive tract, and poorly muscled. It is not designed to handle large amounts of feed at one time. Yet many horses are fed only once a day. This creates problems for many horses each year in the form of **colic, impacted intestine**, and other digestive problems. Chapters 3, 4, and 5 deal with the particulars of basic nutrition, digestive tract anatomy, and feeds. Refer to those chapters for information not covered here.

Continuous eater strategy Feeding strategy employed by many prey species as a mechanism of survival. They eat many small meals through the day and keep on the move throughout their range.

Colic A broad term that means digestive disturbance.

Impacted intestine Term used to describe constipation in the horse and some other species.

Diet All the feeds consumed by animals, including water.

Different **diets** should be fed to horses in different classes. A mare nursing a foal has different nutrient requirements than when she is standing idle. The yearling has different requirements than the actively breeding stallion. *The Nutrient Requirements of Horses,* published by National Academy Press, should be used to determine the appropriate nutrients required for each particular horse or class of horses to be fed. Table 14–9 shows some examples of feed formulations for various classes of horses. These are example feeds and should not be used without considering the specific nutrient needs of the individual horse. By using the information specific to the horse(s) being fed, the horse will be healthier and the owner will be wealthier. Each of these feeds is formulated to be fed with forage to complete the ration for the animal.

It is important to determine a horse's body weight if it is to be fed accurately. Weighing the horse on a scale is ideal (Figure 14–22). If that is not feasible, then heart girth tapes can be purchased from most feed stores or ordered from equine and/or farm supply catalogs. These tapes give a good estimate of weight for most horses. A formula can also be used to estimate the horse's weight (Figure 14–23). A popular one is:

$$\text{Weight in pounds} = \frac{\text{Heart girth in inches}^2 \times \text{Body length in inches}}{330}$$

Table 14–9

EXAMPLE FEED FORMULATIONS FOR HORSES[1]

Ingredient	All-Purpose Formulation[2]	Maintenance Formulation[3]
	% of Total Formulation	
Corn, no. 2, yellow	32.00	62.86
Oats	63.00	—
Soybean meal (44%)	—	14.30
Molasses	2.00	—
Dehydrated alfalfa meal	—	20.71
Dicalcium phosphate	1.00	0.71
Limestone	1.00	0.71
Salt, trace mineral	1.00	0.71
Nutrient Analysis		
Protein (%)	12.00	17.00
DE (Mcal/lb)	1.3	1.5
Calcium (%)	0.7	0.8
Phosphorus (%)	0.5	0.4

[1]All formulations designed to be fed with bermuda grass hay to balance the daily ration.
[2]Designed to be fed as a textured ration.
[3]Designed to be fed as a pelleted ration.
Source: Cooper, 2004. Used with permission.

Figure 14–22
It is important to determine a horse's weight if it is to be fed accurately. Use of a scale is the best way to get an accurate weight, but heart girth tapes are fairly accurate.

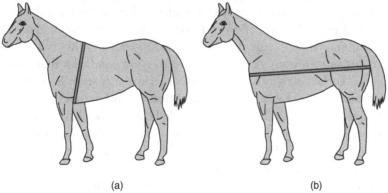

(a) (b)

Figure 14–23
A formula can be used to estimate a horse's weight. Here is popular one:

$$\text{Weight in pounds} = \frac{\text{Heart girth in inches}^2 \times \text{Body length in inches}}{330}$$

(a) *Measure a horse's heart girth from the base of the withers down to a couple of inches behind the horse's front legs, under the belly, and up the opposite side to where you started.*
(b) *Measure a horse's length from the point of the shoulder to the point of the hip.*

Figure 14–24

A horse should receive a minimum of 0.75–1% of its body weight daily in the form of roughage as pasture, hay, or cubed hays.

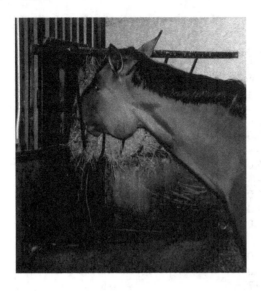

Long hay Hay that has not been chopped or ground; the individual forage.

Cubed hay Hay is forced through dies to produce an approximate 3-cm product of varying lengths.

The horse's digestive tract is such that it needs to have forage in its diet in long form. Generally, a horse should receive a minimum of 0.75–1% of its body weight daily in the form of roughage. Although **long hay** is probably the least expensive and most available to horse owners, research has shown that **cubed hays** can be fed without development of behavioral or digestive problems. Horses allowed to graze acceptable pastures consume enough forage to satisfy their requirement. However, stabled or otherwise confined horses may not receive enough forage (Figure 14–24). Many owners intentionally reduce the amount of forage to levels below 0.75–1% of body weight to keep their horses from having a large cecum, which is referred to as a "hay belly." The look of the horse is thus placed above its health. Failure to allow the horse adequate forage can lead to a wide variety of vices such as chewing wood, eating feces, eating bedding, cribbing, or chewing the manes and tails of their stable or pen mates. It can also lead to colic and other digestive upsets. Horses need forage! The grain portion of a ration for horses should be formulated to balance the forage the horse is being given. However, a cautionary note: Horses need hay of good quality. Feeding hay that is too mature to be easily digested, with weeds, insects, or foreign material, can also lead to digestive problems. It should also be free of mold and dust.

There is still something of an art to feeding horses. Even if you become skilled at using the nutrient requirement tables and at ration formulation, there is a good deal of individual variation in horses. Anyone with much experience with horses has observed that some horses are easy keepers, and others are hard keepers. This means some horses are easier to keep in good condition than others are. Metabolisms, normal activity levels, and other factors vary from horse to horse. Thus, feeding a horse to a particular **body condition** is another tool that horse nutritionists use (Figure 14–25). In general, horses should be fed so they have a moderate to fleshy body condition—neither too thin nor too fat. One of the inherent problems with this is that many horse owners like to see a horse in body condition that is fatter than is really healthy for the animal. By taking the time to learn how to body condition horses properly, the horse owner can save money and keep the horse healthier and performing better.

Body condition The amount of fat on an animal's body.

Pellets Feeds that are generally ground and then compacted by forcing them through die openings.

The concentrate portion of rations for horses can be mixed, ground, and then pelleted. **Pellets** have the advantage of ensuring that the horse receives all the proper nutrients in proper amounts because it cannot select its diet. Further advantages include a reduction in dust, being able to use less palatable feedstuffs, and ease of feeding. For operations with larger numbers of horses, the advantages will be greater than for those with just a horse or two (Figure 14–26). It is still recommended that horses receive 0.75–1% of their body weight as forage when pelleted rations are fed.

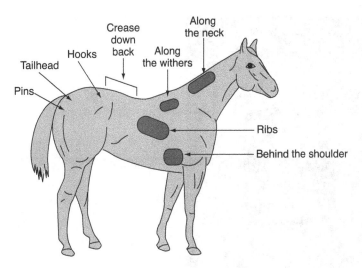

Body Condition Scoring System

<u>Score</u>
1   Poor. Animal extremely emaciated. Spinous processes (portion of the vertebra of the backbone which project upward), ribs, tailhead, and bony protrusions of the pelvic girdle (hooks and pins) projecting prominently. Bone structure of withers, shoulders, and neck are easily noticeable. No fatty tissues can be felt.

2   Very Thin. Animal emaciated. Slight fat covering over base of spinous processes, transverse processes (portion of vertebrae which project outward) of lumbar (loin area) vertebrae feel rounded. Spinous processes, ribs, shoulders, and neck structures are faintly discernible.

3   Thin. Fat built up about halfway on spinous processes, transverse processes cannot be felt. Slight fat cover over ribs. Spinous processes and ribs are easily discernible. Tailhead prominent, but individual vertebrae cannot be visually identified. Hook bones (protrusion of pelvic girdle appearing in upper, forward part of the hip) appear rounded, but are easily discernible. Pin bones (bony projections of pelvic girdle located toward rear, mid-section of the hip) not distinguishable. Withers, shoulders, and neck accentuated.

4   Moderately Thin. Negative crease along back (spinous processes of vertebrae protrude slightly above surrounding tissue). Faint outline of ribs discernible. Tailhead prominence depends on conformation, fat can be felt around it. Hook bones are not discernible. Withers, shoulders, and neck are not obviously thin.

5   Moderate. Back level. Ribs cannot be visually distinguished, but can be easily felt. Fat around tailhead beginning to feel spongy. Withers appear rounded over spinous processes. Shoulders and neck blend smoothly into body.

6   Moderate to Fleshy. May have slight crease down back. Fat over ribs feels spongy. Fat around tailhead feels soft. Fat beginning to be deposited along the sides of the withers, behind the shoulders and along sides of neck.

7   Fleshy. May have crease down back. Individual ribs can be felt, but noticeable filling between ribs with fat. Fat around tailhead is soft. Fat deposited along withers, behind shoulders and along neck.

8   Fat. Crease down back. Difficult to feel ribs. Fat around tailhead very soft. Area along withers filled with fat. Area behind shoulder filled in flush. Noticeable thickening of neck. Fat deposited along inner buttocks.

9   Extremely Fat. Obvious crease down back. Patchy fat appearing over ribs. Bulging fat around tailhead, along withers, behind shoulders and along neck. Fat along inner buttocks may rub together. Flank is filled in flush with the rest of the body.

Figure 14–25

Location of fat deposits used in body condition scoring system. Source: Freeman, 1997. Used with permission.

One of the big problems in horse nutrition is overfeeding. One of the causes of overfeeding is the major misperception that a coffee can holds the same amount of oats or corn as it does coffee. Not so! It holds 1.3 times as much oats and 1.8 times as much corn. Feeds have different densities, and processing further affects density.

Figure 14–26
The concentrate portion of a horse's diet can be pelleted.

Laminitis An inflammation of the laminae of the hoof. It is commonly caused by overeating of grain but may also be related to eating lush pastures, road concussion, retained afterbirth in the mare, and other causes.

Horse feed—both hay and grain—should be weighed. Scales are cheap compared to the expense, trauma, and potential lifetime effects of colic or **laminitis**. This does not mean that every morsel given to the horse must be weighed. Scoops and cans can still be used. What it does mean is that the amount of the particular feed being used should be weighed periodically so the feeder can calibrate his or her eye and container accordingly (Figure 14–27).

Because the horse developed as a continuous eater, it is best served by feeding practices that increase the number of times it eats in a day. However, most horses are meal-fed. Because of management, labor, housing, and production needs, that practice will probably continue. If a horse is receiving grain in excess of 0.5% of its body weight, it is recommended that the grain be split into a minimum of two feedings per day. This reduces the amount of digestive upset the horse is likely to have. Once grain

Figure 14–27
A horse's feed should be weighed, or at least the containers being used to measure feed should be filled and weighed regularly so that the person doing the feeding can "calibrate" his or her eye to the container. This will help prevent the most common problem in horse nutrition: OVERFEEDING!

exceeds 1.0% of body weight, the grain should be fed in at least three equal portions. The feedings should be as evenly spaced apart as feasible. It is also important to feed very close to the same time each day, even on weekends. Any time a ration is changed, especially if the grain portion is increased, it should be done at an increasing rate of no more than a half lb per day until the new feeding level is reached. Even moving horses to a different pasture or turning them into pasture after a period of stall confinement should be done gradually by limiting the access to the pasture for several days before they are allowed to stay in it full time.

Many times a horse suffers digestive upset for reasons not directly related to the feed. Two prevalent reasons are parasites and water. Clean, palatable water should be available to horses at all times. Waterers and buckets or troughs should be cleaned regularly. The only time that unlimited water is not a good idea is when a horse is hot from exercise. Unlimited water at this time can be dangerous. The horse should be cooled and allowed small quantities of water until normal body temperature is reached. Then the water supply should be made available again. Horses should be treated for internal parasites regularly. Several of the parasites to which horses are susceptible can cause digestive tract disorders and interfere with feed utilization by the animal.

For many horse owners, the safest way to feed is to purchase the grain portion of a horse's diet from a reputable company and feed according to the manufacturer's instructions. Forage should be provided at the recommended levels just discussed. The amount of grain can then be adjusted based on body condition of the horse. Horse owners should avoid the temptation to buy all of those cartons and bottles of magic dust and tonic on the shelves at the feed store. By feeding on time, and by keeping the horse exercised and dewormed, the benefits and joys of horse ownership can be enjoyed—at greatly reduced prices.

CHALLENGES TO HORSE HEALTH

Because of the unique nature of the horse industry as a hybrid of areas based in agriculture, sports, recreation, and entertainment, health management of horses may vary widely with their specific purpose. It ranges from herd health care that is more in line with that of agricultural livestock to individual medical management that is much more similar to the treatment of pet or companion animal species. Often, horses have great economic as well as emotional value. For this reason, horse owners are often willing to pursue extensive and expensive medical and surgical procedures to treat a variety of health problems in horses. However, as with other species, an ounce of prevention is worth a pound of cure when it comes to horse health management. Several infectious diseases are effectively controlled by well-designed vaccination and deworming programs. A few of the more common health problems that occur in horses are described next. Other infectious, genetic, and use-related diseases or ailments occur in horses but are beyond the scope of this book.

Colic

Colic is a broad term that is used to refer to a painful digestive disturbance that may involve one or more regions of the intestinal tract. The abdominal pain of colic may have many different causes, including intestinal impactions (in which the intestine becomes obstructed by tightly packed, coarse, or overly dry feed material) or intestinal displacements (in which part of the small or large intestine shifts to an abnormal location and becomes entrapped or even twisted). Consequences of such intestinal problems may include a tear, rupture, or even death of a part of the intestine, which is often life-threatening. The signs of colic can range from restlessness, a quickened

heart rate, and pawing at the ground to violent rolling and thrashing in the most severe and painful cases. Oftentimes, the precise intestinal abnormality leading to colic pain is difficult to determine, and may require surgical exploration and treatment in cases that don't respond to pain medications, sedatives, and other medical therapies. Colic risk increases for horses that are confined and fed meals once or twice daily rather than grazing continually and consuming small amounts of food throughout the day, as pastured horses typically do.

Laminitis

Coffin bone The bottom-most bone of a horse's leg that is encased within the hoof.

Laminitis, also referred to as founder, is inflammation or other damage to the sensitive laminae of the hoof. The laminae (lamina = singular form) are infoldings of tissue that make up the layer of the horse's hoof between the **coffin bone** at the very center and the external horny wall. Inflammation or swelling of this layer causes the hooves to become hot and painful, leading to lameness and abnormal posturing in which the horse crouches, stands with feet gathered together or continually shifts weight from one painful foot to another. After the initial painful stages of laminitis, horses may suffer from irregularly shaped hooves and abnormally thickened soles, which often causes continued gait abnormalities. Such hoof problems may be managed by corrective trimming and shoeing in some instances; however, in severe cases, horses may no longer be considered sound for performance or pleasure riding. Laminitis is typically due to some sort of metabolic disturbance. Specific causes include excess consumption of grain or lush pastures, colic or other intestinal disease, excess exercise on hard surfaces, or infection secondary to retained afterbirth or the like.

Heaves

Heaves, also known as recurrent airway obstruction, is an allergic disease of horses that may cause coughing, nasal discharge, and difficulty in breathing that is severe enough to limit athletic performance. This disease typically affects older horses (average age of nine years) and may be at least partially inherited. Heaves cannot be readily cured, but steps may be taken to lessen the symptoms. It is typically worsened by exposure to dust and mold in the environment, thus one of the primary treatments is limiting exposure to these problematic pollutants. This can be achieved by decreasing or eliminating hay from the diet and environment, as even hay that doesn't appear moldy may cause symptoms in sensitive horses. Pasturing affected horses on fresh grass is best, but feeding alternative roughage sources, such as hay cubes, may be used for horses that require stabling. Some medical treatments are also beneficial in helping affected horses recover more quickly from episodes of breathing difficulty (similar to asthma attacks in people). Poor feeding choices by horse owners are a major source of economic losses in the horse industry.

TRENDS AND FACTORS INFLUENCING THE HORSE INDUSTRY

Education and Research

The typical owner of a recreational horse and the typical horse of a recreation-minded person are the most vulnerable beings in the horse industry. This is because of the general lack of knowledge of the typical owner. The uneducated horse owner is a menace to himself or herself, to horses everywhere, and to the entire horse industry. Their feed costs too much, their vet bills are too high, too many horses and people are injured, and, subsequently, overall satisfaction is lower than it should be. These owners often quit the horse in disgust and convince other would-be owners not to bother. Because they are also the most frequently occurring horses and people in this business, they are also the ones most in need of services. Yet they have proven to be very difficult to reach with good information. The valiant efforts of professionals in the business and in education don't seem to make a dent in the problem. Educating the new owner should be a top priority for everyone in the horse industry. Education is important because the new horse owner has much to learn to be a successful horse owner. Old horse owners are often woefully ignorant of any of the scientific information about horses. New owners tend to get most of their information from old owners. This creates a vicious cycle of ignorance, which needs to be broken for the good of all! One welcome trend is that many of the new horse owners now entering the industry seem hungry for information and readily seek educational opportunities. An unfortunate aspect is that not all the information they are receiving is credible.

There is a great need for more research and support for research on the horse (Figure 14–28). Currently, only a comparative pittance of the time and money spent on other species is directed to equine research. Scores of problems need answers that research could provide. Too many horses must be retired because of **unsoundness.** The root of this problem is frequently genetic and/or management related. Diseases and parasites cost the industry millions per year. A huge percentage of this loss is unnecessary and could be prevented. The nutritional needs of horses are poorly understood compared to those of the food-producing species. All of these problems need to be much better addressed with research and information dissemination. It is hard to argue for integrating science and technology into the horse business when some of the science and technology is so poorly supported by research.

Unsoundness Any injury or defect that interferes with the ability of the animal to be used for its given purpose.

Two areas of research are receiving increased attention. Although not all the bugs have been worked out, artificial insemination techniques for the horse have been developed and are currently meeting with increased usage. As more and more breed

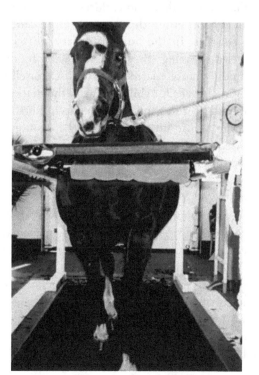

Figure 14–28
Solid research work, like the exercise physiology research being conducted with this mare, is sorely lacking. The industry needs more research to help it prosper.
(Photo courtesy of Dr. Steven R. Cooper, Oklahoma State University.)

associations allow the use of frozen semen, these techniques will get better. Also, the first draft of the horse genome map was completed in 2006. Once the genome is mapped, great advances can be made in horse genetics and health.

Competition

The recreational horse owner faces many choices for his or her leisure dollar and time. The horse industry must find ways to continue to attract the leisure dollar or risk shrinking in size. Horse breed associations have expanded shows to include more divisions in which to compete. This is a positive development.

Examples of new ways that are being explored include a trend toward objectively timed or scored events. Such timed or scored events that seem to be growing in popularity include barrel racing, team roping, team penning, reining, dressage, and ranch horse competitions. In a move to attract the **baby boomers**, divisions for 50-and-over participants are already commonplace and growing in equine sports and other activities.

Baby boomer Demographic term for the U.S. population born between 1946 and 1964. The U.S. Census estimates there are nearly 83 million boomers.

New Owners

There is a growing trend among adults to compensate for the perceived missed opportunities of childhood. Many people, baby boomers in particular, were unable to have that much-dreamed-of horse or pony when they were children. Times are more affluent now and so are the baby boomers. They can now afford a horse or three if it suits them. On January 1, 2008, Kathleen Casey-Kirschling, recognized as the first baby boomer, also became the first one to start collecting Social Security. Born one second after midnight on January 1, 1946, the retired teacher leads the way for 83 million fellow boomers.

Others of us wish to recreate the part of our childhood that included horses for our children or grandchildren. Those young people are largely part of the "echo boom" or "Generation Y," names used to refer to the group of Americans born between 1977 and 1994. This echo boom generation is the second largest generation of Americans, second only to the baby boom generation. (In case you are counting on your fingers just now, I'll save you the trouble. Many of the echo boomers are the grandchildren and children of the baby boomers.) The baby boom generation is an affluent group that controls unprecedented and enormous collective economic resources. In the horse industry, this is being translated into baby boomer–fueled spending. They are either entering the horse industry as direct participants or funding horse-related opportunities for children or grandchildren. The demand for riding lessons for children is up, the market for kids' horses and well-trained horses for adults is up, and membership in horse-related youth groups as well as those for adults is also up (Figure 14–29). Also, adult first-time horse owners were recognized as a significant market segment in the 1990s. These trends show every sign of continuing.

Safety Concerns

A concern for safety is working its way through the horse industry and is evident at competitive events and other horse-related activities. This is probably being fueled by concerns for personal safety by first-time horse owners of more advanced age and by the increased care and concern for safety that is a more general part of modern society. Here again the baby boom generation is contributing significantly. Remember, many of these people are introducing themselves and their grandchildren to the horse world. In addition, there is a heightened awareness of liability issues on the part of event facility management. Expect more and more safety gear and safety measures to be a part of the horse world.

West Nile Virus

In 1999, the West Nile Virus was discovered for the first time in the Western Hemisphere. This disease is a threat to the human population, horses, dogs, and several species of birds, most notably the crow and its cousins. A vaccine and combination of vaccines exist and should be added to the complement of regularly administered vaccinations for horses.

Social Issues

Animal Rights/Animal Welfare   Animal rights/animal welfare concerns will continue to be a part of this industry. Because so much of the horse industry is sport and exhibition oriented, the industry is under more scrutiny than other animal industries and thus more vulnerable. It is also an easy target for activist groups because of the horse's place in the minds and/or hearts of people. The industry must learn to face legitimate concerns while fending off the unreasonable activist groups. Many breed organizations have adopted codes of conduct and addressed humane care issues. These efforts are to be applauded. However, nothing less than full care and attention to this issue is acceptable.

Horse Slaughter   As of 2007, horse slaughter in the United States has effectively ceased. This was an emotional debate that will continue to rage. What remains to be seen is the long-term effects this change will have on the horse industry. A decline in horse values has been observed since 2007, but the U.S. recession in the late 2000s likely contributed also. Horses continued to be sent to slaughter in Mexico and Canada after 2007.

Technological Innovation

The horse industry is a poorly mechanized industry, partly because of the wishes of horse owners. Caring for the animal is important to horse owners. However, improvements such as simple, affordable automatic feeders could add to the horse's health and help the horse owner as well. It is hard to see how it would decrease the joy of horse ownership to have the horse fed at intervals, even in the owner's absence. Other labor-saving devices could help attract new owners.

INDUSTRY ORGANIZATIONS

American Connemara Pony Society
http://www.acps.org

American Donkey and Mule Society
http://www.lovelongears.com

American Hackney Horse Society
http://www.hackneysociety.com

American Horse Council
http://www.horsecouncil.org

American Indian Horse Registry, Inc.
http://www.indianhorse.com

American Miniature Horse Association, Inc.
http://www.amha.org

American Morgan Horse Association
http://www.morganhorse.com/

American Mule Association
http://www.americanmuleassociation.com

American Paint Horse Association
http://www.apha.com/

American Quarter Horse Association
http://www.aqha.com/

American Quarter Pony Association
http://www.aqpa.com

American Saddlebred Horse Association, Inc.
http://www.asha.net

American Shetland Pony Club
http://www.shetlandminiature.com/

Registers: American Miniature Horse, Classic Shetland Pony, Modern Shetland Pony, Foundation Shetland Pony, National Show Pony, and American Show Pony.

American Warmblood Registry
http://www.americanwarmblood.com/

Appaloosa Horse Club Inc.
http://www.appaloosa.com/

Arabian Horse Association
http://www.arabianhorses.org

Belgian Draft Horse Corporation of America

http://www.belgiancorp.com/

Cleveland Bay Horse Society of North America

http://www.clevelandbay.org

Clydesdale Breeders of the United States

http://clydesusa.com

The Jockey Club

http://www.jockeyclub.com

National Show Horse Registry

http://www.nshregistry.org

Palomino Horse Breeders Association of America

http://www.palominohba.com/

Paso Fino Horse Association, Inc.

http://www.pfha.org

Percheron Horse Association of America

http://percheronhorse.org/

Pinto Horse Association of America, Inc.

http://www.pinto.org/

Pony of the Americas Club

http://www.poac.org

Tennessee Walking Horse Breeders' and Exhibitors' Association

http://www.twhbea.com

U.S. Trotting Association (Standardbred)

http://www.ustrotting.com/

SUMMARY AND CONCLUSION

In the United States, the horse began the 20th century as a partner with humans in the pursuit of food production and in everyday life. The majestic horse pulled plows, wagons, and threshing machines during the week, and it took the family to town on Saturday afternoon and to church on Sunday morning. Horses were an integral component of survival. All of this gave way to the petroleum-powered engine and the general onslaught of technology. The industrialization of the country took the population to the cities and left the farmer on a tractor with little need for the beasts that had so recently been his or her partners. By 1960, the horse was deemed to be so unimportant that the federal government quit counting them. With the growing prosperity of the nation, however, the horse made an interesting conversion around mid-century to become an animal of recreation rather than utility. A new hybrid industry developed around the horse, with interests and segments in agriculture, sports, recreation, and entertainment. People whose grandparents plowed with horses took to the horse as a tool to improve the quality of their urban, industrialized, high-tech life. The high-touch needs of the horse generated an industry very different from the other animal industries. It is an industry in which the values of people figure very prominently in the politics and actions of its participants.

FACTS ABOUT HORSES

Terms Used in Describing Horses

Head markings:	Star, stripe, snip, blaze, bald face, spot, race
Body markings:	Appaloosa, bay, black, brown, buckskin, chestnut, dun, gray, palomino, pinto, paint, roan
Leg markings:	Boot, sock, 1/2 stocking, stocking

Mature Weight and Height

Ponies:	500–900 lbs; 11–14.2 hands
Saddle and light harness horses:	800–1,400 lbs; 14.2–16 hands
Draft horses:	1,700–2,200 lbs; 15–17 hands

The weight will be dependent on breed, sex, nutritional state, and so on. The height of a horse is determined by standing it squarely on a level area and measuring the vertical distance from the highest point of the withers to the ground. The unit of measurement used in expressing height is the hand; each hand is 4 inches.

Breeding age (female): Horses reach puberty at 12–15 months, but should not be bred until after 2 years of age and up to about 15–20 years of age.

Stallion/mare ratio (# of hand-mating/year): 2-yr-old stallion/10–15; 3-yr.-old stallion/20–40; 4-yr.-old stallion/30–60; mature/80-100; over 18 yrs. old/20–40

Gestation: 336 days (a little over 11 months); varies from 310–370 days depending on age, size, and physical condition

Estrous cycle: 18–20 days

Duration of estrus: 5–7 days, breed on the 3rd day of estrus and on alternate days thereafter as long as the mare remains in heat

Age weaned: 4–6 months

Names of various sex classes: *Foal*, **filly**, **colt**, mare, stallion, **gelding**

Filly A young female horse.

Colt A young male horse.

Gelding A castrated male horse.

It is impossible to present facts and figures for the horse that are comparable to those of the other livestock species because the federal government does not collect and summarize the same information on the horse as it does on other species. The industry is very closely tied to its breed associations and activities, recreation activities, and racing of several types.

STUDY QUESTIONS

1. Why is it difficult to present the same kinds of statistics about the horse industry as there are for the other animal industries?

2. Describe the magnitude of the horse industry.

3. Explain why the horse industry is referred to as a "hybrid" industry.

4. Describe the structure of the horse industry. Compare and contrast it with the other animal industries discussed thus far in this text.

5. What makes the horse industry unique from the other animal industries?

6. Why is it so hard to say with certainty how many horses are in the United States?

7. Give a quick thumbnail sketch of the history of the horse in North America.

8. What are the major participant groups within the horse industry?

9. Discuss the various contributions the horse industry makes to the U.S. economy.

10. List some of the quantitative traits for horses and make a statement about how successful you would expect selection programs for those traits to be.

11. Horse genetics is complicated by the fact that so many different genes control it. Select a horse color and write a genetic formula for it.

12. Create a table like this for the breeds of horses listed in the text.

Breed	Where Developed	Major Use(s)	Other Breeds Important to Development
Complete the table for each breed.			

13. You have decided to breed your super-duper mare "Whiz-Kid." Outline how you will go about this from a reproductive management perspective.

14. What are the five most important things about feeding horses that you feel all horse owners should know? You must settle on only the five most important!

15. How can one estimate a horse's weight?

16. What are some common challenges to horse health?

17. You are responsible for directing the Horse Owner Education Program for the XYZ Horse Breed Association. Explain what your educational program would be for each of the trends discussed in the chapter that are affecting or likely to affect the horse industry.

REFERENCES

For the 5th edition, Melanie A. Breshears, DVM, PhD, Diplomate ACVP, assistant professor, veterinary pathobiology, Center for Veterinary Health Sciences, Oklahoma State University, contributed material to this chapter.

American Horse Council Foundation. 2005. *The economic impact of the U.S. horse industry on the United States.* Washington, DC: American Horse Council Foundation.

Barclay, H. B. 1980. *The role of the horse in man's culture.* London & New York: J. A. Allen.

Bowling, A. T. Aug. 1997. Coat color genetics. *The Quarter Horse Journal* 49(11).

Bowling, A. T. 1999. *Horse genetics.* Available from http://www.vgl.ucdavis.edu/~1vmillion/coats2.html.

Bowling, A. T., and A. Ruvinsky (eds.). 2000. *The genetics of the horse.* New York: CABI.

Cooper, S. R. 2004. Oklahoma State University, Stillwater. Personal communication.

Evans, J. W. 2006. *A guide to selection, care, and enjoyment of horses.* 3rd ed. New York: W. H. Freeman.

Freeman, D. W. 1997. *Body condition of horses.* Extension Bulletin No. F-3920. Stillwater: Cooperative Extension Service, Oklahoma State University.

Freeman, D. W. 1998a. *Ration formulation for horses.* Extension Bulletin No. 3997. Stillwater: Cooperative Extension Service, Oklahoma State University.

Freeman, D. W. 2011. Cooperative Extension Service, Oklahoma State University, Stillwater. Personal communication.

Geddes, C. 1978. *The horse—The complete book of horses and horsemanship.* London: Octopus Books.

Griffin, J. M. and T. Gore. 1998. *Horse owner's veterinary handbook.* New York: Howell Book House.

Harland, J. R. 1976. The plants and animals that nourish man. *Scientific American* 3, 235.

Johnson, E. L. 1993. Basic equine genetics. In *Horse industry handbook.* Lexington, KY: American Youth Horse Council.

Jordan, R. M. 1998. *Horse nutrition and feeding.* Publication Number: FA-0480-GO. St. Paul: University of Minnesota Extension Service, University of Minnesota.

Kjersten, D., and J. M. Griffin. 1999. *Veterinary guide to horse breeding.* New York: Howell Book House.

Landers, T. A. 2002. *The career guide to the horse industry.* Albany, NY: Delmar Thomson Learning.

Loch, W. 1998. Agricultural publication G2780. Columbia, MO: Department of Animal Sciences, University of Missouri. http://muextension.missouri.edu/xplor/agguides/ansci/g02780.htm.

Loch, W., J. F. Lasley, and M. Bradley. 1993. *Genetics of coat color of horses.* Agricultural Publication G2791. Columbia: Department of Animal Sciences, University of Missouri.

McClure, J. J. 1993. Genetic abnormalities in horses. In *Horse industry handbook.* Lexington, KY: American Youth Horse Council.

Parker, R. 2007. *Equine science.* Albany, NY: Delmar.

Pilliner, S., and Z. Davies. 2004. *Equine science.* Ames: Iowa State Press.

Siegal, M., ed. 1996. *UC Davis book of horses: A complete medical reference guide for horses and foals.* New York: HarperCollins.

Slusher, S. H., C. Taylor-MacAllister, and D. W. Freeman. 1998. *Reproductive management of the mare.*

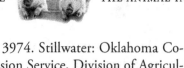
Fact Sheet No. 3974. Stillwater: Oklahoma Co-operative Extension Service, Division of Agricultural Sciences and Natural Resources, Oklahoma State University.

Spoonberg, D. P., and A. T. Bowling. 1996. Champagne, a dominant color dilution of horses. *Genetics, Selection, and Evolution* 28: 457–462.

Thorson, J. S. 2001. 21st century horse trends. *Western Horseman,* January 2001, p. 50.

Turman, E. J. 1986. *Agricultural animals of the world.* Stillwater: Oklahoma State University.

Vogel, C. J. 1996. *An illustrated guide to veterinary care of the horse.* Ames: Iowa State University Press.

15

Aquaculture

THE PLACE OF AQUACULTURE IN U.S. AGRICULTURE

Aquaculture is the farming of aquatic organisms, including fish, ornamental fish, baitfish, mollusks, crustaceans, reptiles, and aquatic plants. This may be done in freshwater, brackish water, or saltwater. Fish and other aquatic species have long provided a significant amount of food to the world's population. Much of this food is in the form of wild catch. However, because of the decline in wild catch, interest in the cultivation and harvest of aquatic species has accelerated. Aquaculture also has recreational and aesthetic dimensions. Production of stock game fish and ornamental fish and plants fall into these categories.

Aquaculture is a rapidly growing segment of agriculture, although U.S. production of aquaculture products is still small by comparison with mainstream agriculture (Figures 15–1 and Figure 15–2). It is predicted that this growth will continue and the industry will become a more important segment of agriculture. Fish and other aquatic species provide a substantial portion of the world's food (Figure 15–3). However, the harvest of seafood from the oceans and other waters appears to have hit a plateau. To meet the demand for products, the world is increasingly turning to aquaculture (Figure 15–4).

Aquaculture is practiced in a way that is quite analogous to other types of agriculture. The systems may be quite intensive, with high stocking densities or low-density systems integrated with other farm production as part of a diversified farm. The variety of enthusiasts ranges from those whose livelihood is taken from aquaculture to backyard hobbyists. Aquaculture is quite different from fishing for wild species, which

Learning Objectives

After you have studied this chapter, you should be able to:

- Define *aquaculture*.
- Describe the purpose of aquaculture and its worldwide importance.
- Describe the place of aquaculture in agriculture and explain its role in feeding the world.
- Describe the growth rate of aquaculture as an industry segment.
- Name the species that make up the bulk of U.S. aquaculture.
- Discuss the various types of aquaculture systems.
- Identify the general life cycles of aquatic species.
- Compare the challenges of the geneticist who works with aquatic species with those faced by geneticists who work with the species previously studied.
- Explain the nutritional benefits of aquatic products to humans.
- Discuss trends affecting aquaculture.

Aquaculture The farming of aquatic organisms including fish, mollusks, crustaceans, and plants in fresh water, brackish water, or salt water.

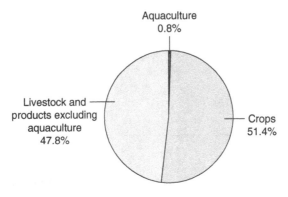

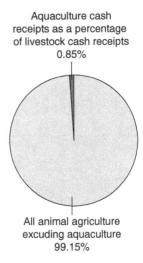

Aquaculture
0.8%

Livestock and
products excluding
aquaculture
47.8%

Crops
51.4%

Figure 15–1
Aquaculture farm cash receipts as a percentage of total U.S. farm cash receipts, 2001–2009. (Source: USDA-NASS, 2011a and Fisheries of the United States, 2011.)

Aquaculture cash
receipts as a percentage
of livestock cash receipts
0.85%

All animal agriculture
excuding aquaculture
99.15%

Figure 15–2
Aquaculture yearly farm cash receipts as a percentage of total animal agriculture's cash receipts, 2001–2009. (Source: USDA-NASS, 2011a and Fisheries of the United States, 2011.)

Figure 15–3
Fish and other aquatic species provide a significant amount of food for the world's population. Much is in the form of wild catch, such as provided by these fishermen photographed off the coast of Eritrea. (FAO Photo/19458/Roberto Faidutti. Used with permission by the Food and Agriculture Organization of the United Nations.)

Figure 15–4
Aquaculture, which has been practiced in some parts of the world for centuries, is growing throughout the developing and developed world.
(FAO Photo/20905/K. Pratt. Used with permission by the Food and Agriculture Organization of the United Nations.)

is called **capture fisheries**. The term **blended fisheries** is used to describe the practice of using aquaculture techniques to enhance or supplement capture fisheries. Compared to activities surrounding land animals, think of fishing and hunting as analogous activities, aquaculture and farming as analogous, and blended fisheries as an enhanced form of wildlife management.

THE PURPOSE OF THE AQUACULTURE INDUSTRY

Aquaculture provides a means of expanding agriculture. Expansion may be through diversification by the addition of part-time employment opportunities and supplemental income to existing agricultural enterprises. It may also provide large-scale, full-time opportunities. Either way, the purpose of the aquaculture industry is to diversify the farming sector by providing a product that is in demand by several different sectors of the consuming public. Aquaculture species can be used to exploit land-surface area in a very efficient way because the space requirements of fish in relation to surface area are fairly small. Areas that are marginal or unusable for other forms of agriculture, due to heavy clay soils or other factors, may be well suited for aquaculture. In addition, fish are very efficient converters of feed to flesh and, as such, help provide high-quality food for the human population by using feedstuffs rather than foodstuffs, and doing so in a manner that is equal to or even more efficient than that done by poultry. Some aquatic species are also quite capable of using wastes and waste by-products, thereby converting something with little or no use to a highly palatable and valuable food source.

Recent per capita consumption of seafood from all sources in the United States has been around 16 lbs (Table 15–1). Aquaculture's share of that consumption is growing. Table 15–2 shows the U.S. per capita consumption for the 10 most popular species.

WORLDWIDE IMPORTANCE OF AQUACULTURE

The world's population consumes approximately 37 lbs of live weight equivalent of seafood per capita each year. That quantity has remained constant to increasing even though total human population continues to increase. Clearly, aquatic species are an important part of the world's diet. Worldwide, aquaculture production of fish, crustaceans, mollusks, and so on, is approximately 55 million metric tons (MT). It accounts for nearly half of the seafood used for direct human consumption. Aquatic plants provide an additional 17 million MT of food.

Capture fisheries The harvesting of wild aquatic animal species.

Blended fisheries A combination of aquaculture and capture fisheries. Aquaculture techniques are used to enhance or supplement capture fisheries.

Table 15–1

U.S. ANNUAL PER CAPITA CONSUMPTION OF COMMERCIAL FISH AND SHELLFISH, SELECTED YEARS

Year	Per Capita Consumption (Pounds)			
	Fresh and Frozen	Canned	Cured	Total
1910	4.5	2.8	3.9	11.2
1930	5.8	3.4	1.0	10.2
1950	6.3	4.9	0.6	11.8
1970	6.9	4.5	0.4	11.8
1990	9.6	5.1	0.3	15.0
2000	10.2	4.7	0.3	15.2
2005	11.6	4.3	0.3	16.2
2009	11.8	3.7	0.3	15.8

Source: National Marine Fisheries Service, Fisheries Statistics and Economics Division, 2009.

Table 15–2
APPROXIMATE U.S. PER CAPITA CONSUMPTION OF FISH AND SEAFOOD

Species	Pounds Per Capita	Rank
Shrimp	4.10	1
Tuna	2.50	2
Salmon	2.04	3
Pollock	1.45	4
Tilapia	1.21	5
Catfish	0.85	6
Crab	0.59	7
Cod	0.42	8
Clams	0.41	9
Pangasius	0.36	10

Source: National Fisheries Institute, 2009.

One of the reasons for aquaculture's rapid climb as an agricultural industry is the increase in world population. However, of equal importance is the fact that the amount of wild fish harvested from the world's waters has been static to lower since 1990 at 90–93 million MT. This has been attributed to various reasons, including overfishing, environmental degradation, and social and economic influences. The social and economic influences include competition and conflicts for the fishery resource with recreation and commercial uses, conservation issues, and animal rights advocacy. If seafood supplies are to be maintained for the human population, then an alternative source is needed. On a worldwide basis, aquaculture production has been increasing at a rate of 8.3% since 1970, with a concurrent increase in the per capita supply of farm-raised fish from 0.7 kg to 7.8 kg. The world leader in aquaculture production as of 2008 was China with 32,736 thousand MT produced. India was second with 3,479 thousand MT, followed by Vietnam, Indonesia, and Thailand. The United States was thirteenth, with 500 thousand MT. These data do not include aquatic plants.

Worldwide, aquaculture is dominated by various species of carp (including bighead, silver, grass, rohu, mrigal, cutla, and common), salmon (Figure 15–5), shrimp, tilapia, and mollusks. Tonnage produced by aquaculture exceeds

Figure 15–5

Salmon are produced in sea cages, like these off the coast of Norway. (Source: Lee Torrens/Shutterstock)

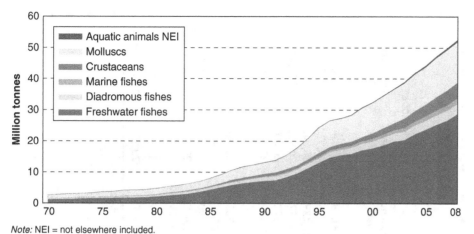

Figure 15–6
Trends in world aquaculture production by species group. Source: FAO 2010. p. 24.

Note: NEI = not elsewhere included.

wild catch on most of these species. Consumption of the Chinese carps (bighead, silver, grass, etc.) is primarily associated with ethnic Chinese and other Asian cultures. The Chinese carps have diverse food habits and so are ideal species for polyculture. Common carp, although disliked by most Americans, is a popular food and sport fish in Europe. Figure 15–6 shows the increasing production of different aquaculture food categories, excluding aquatic plants.

HISTORICAL PERSPECTIVE

Aquaculture has been practiced in varying forms for centuries dating to the time of the Phoenicians. The Chinese also have a rich aquaculture heritage, with the first recorded references prior to 1100 B.C. Aquaculture began in the United States in the mid-1800s with the development of government-run fish hatcheries that produced fish for **stocking** ponds and lakes for recreation and resource management purposes. Similar to the ways that other agricultural industries have developed, the nation's colleges and universities initiated basic and applied research and education programs on aquaculture management, genetics, nutrition, reproduction, diseases, herbicide testing, and other areas. The commercial industry started shortly after World War II with the production of **baitfish**. Golden shiners, the fathead minnow, and goldfish were easy to raise and were all popular species as bait. During the 1950s and 1960s, species such as buffalo fish, common and Chinese carps, and several species of catfish such as the channel, blue, and white, were experimented with and culture practices were established. In addition, production of some sport fish species as **fingerlings** for pond stocking became widespread. These species include black bass, crappie, and bluegill. However, it was only in the last two decades of the 20th century that aquaculture became an important food supplier and an important economic sector in the United States.

Stocking The practice of placing fish from a hatchery or other source into a pond or lake to either establish a new species or augment an already existing species.

Baitfish Fish selected and produced to be used as bait to catch much larger fish.

Fingerlings The stage is a fish's life between 1 inch and the length at 1 year of age.

STRUCTURE AND GEOGRAPHIC LOCATION OF THE AQUACULTURE INDUSTRY

Aquaculture production zoomed from $347 million in 1985 to approximately $1.1 billion in 2005, but now food fish producers are faced with increasing competition from foreign producers (Table 15–3). United States aquaculture production is diverse but is dominated by channel catfish. United States catfish production levels are down in response to competition from imported aquaculture products. Strong

Table 15–3

ESTIMATED U.S. AQUACULTURE PRODUCTION

Species	1990 Thousand Pounds	1990 Thousand Dollars	1995 Thousand Pounds	1995 Thousand Dollars	2000 Thousand Pounds	2000 Thousand Dollars	2005 Thousand Pounds	2005 Thousand Dollars	2008 Thousand Pounds	2008 Thousand Dollars
Finfish										
Baitfish	21,610	53,978	21,759	72,522	13,954	45,790	—	38,018	—	38,018
Catfish	360,435	273,210	446,886	351,222	593,603	445,919	605,530	428,476	514,920	390,052
Salmon	9,069	26,341	31,315	75,991	49,372	99,208	20,726	37,439	36,848	45,128
Striped bass	1,590	3,490	8,315	21,156	11,237	29,513	12,010	30,277	11,980	30,430
Tilapia	0	0	15,075	22,613	20,000	30,000	17,203	29,620	20,000	34,383
Trout	56,816	64,640	55,934	61,447	59,164	63,690	60,636	65,469	35,744	49,774
Shellfish										
Clams	3,680	13,486	4,325	19,709	9,929	32,595	12,564	72,783	11,420	88,088
Crawfish	71,000	34,000	58,146	34,714	17,025	27,626	77,539	42,557	117,473	127,351
Mussels	607	1,173	410	1,221	424	525	962	4,990	853	4,474
Oysters	22,192	77,949	23,221	70,628	16,822	42,419	13,711	92,602	20,340	79,666
Shrimp	1,984	7,937	2,205	8,818	4,782	14,559	8,999	20,859	4,259	8,520
Miscellaneous	23,548	98,908	23,359	75,243	26,207	140,989	—	254,738	—	298,775
Totals	572,531	655,112	690,950	815,284	822,519	972,833	829,880	1,117,828	773,837	1,194,659

Note: Table may not add due to rounding. Clams, oysters, and mussels are reported as meat weights (excludes shell); other identified species such as shrimp and finfishes are reported as whole (live) weights. Some clam and oyster aquaculture production are reported with U.S. commercial landings. Weights and values represent the final sales of products to processors and dealers. Miscellaneous includes ornamental/tropical fish, alligators, algae, aquatic plants, eels, scallops, crabs, and others. The high value and low production of Miscellaneous occurs because production value, but not weight, are reported for many species, such as ornamental fishes.

Source: Fisheries of the United States, 2007; Fisheries of the United States, 2009.

acceptance of U.S. aquaculture products remains as a base upon which growth may resume if imported products become costly, less available, or there are worries about contamination and other food safety factors. Aquaculture offers an opportunity to select producers who have the right combination of resources, management ability, and marketing skills. Factors to ponder when considering getting started as an aquaculture producer are discussed by Beem (1998).

United States aquaculture includes the culture of catfish, trout, salmon, shrimp, mussels, clams, oysters, tilapia, hybrid striped bass, crayfish, ornamental fish, other species, and plants. The total industry is dispersed throughout the United States, although there is a definite regionality to the individual types of production. Operations range in size from the large and well established, employing hundreds of people, to hobby ventures.

Aquaculture is an agricultural activity whose importance is expected to increase in the United States. Factors influencing this growth include (1) an increasing demand for fish and seafood that exceeds supply; (2) the fact that the wild fish harvest has reached its limit and will probably decline; and (3) concerns over the foreign trade deficit in fishery products. Aquaculture can remedy these problems. Water availability is a major constraint. Climate generally determines which species can be cultured. United States aquaculturists cultivate approximately 30 species of fish and shellfish and a substantial number of aquatic plants for which substantial income is generated (Figure 15–7).

Catfish

Channel catfish culture began with a pioneering phase in the 1960s and '70s characterized by high production costs and low yields. A shakeout phase occurred in the 1970s when many farmers were forced out by their lack of management expertise and the absence of developed markets. A period of rapid expansion followed as lowered production costs and expanding market conditions occurred. At present, production

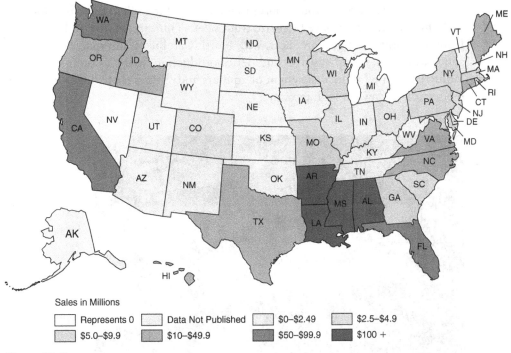

Figure 15–7

U.S. aquaculture sales by state. (Source: USDA-NASS, 2005.)

Figure 15–8

Total U.S. catfish processed annually. (Source: USDA-NASS, 2011b)

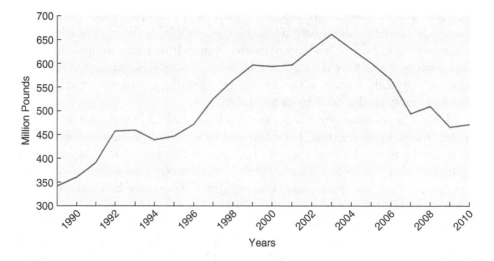

acreage is contracting in response to competition from imported products. Table 15–3 confirms that the channel catfish segment is the leading form of U.S. aquaculture and accounts for approximately 30% of the income generated. Farmer sales of catfish to processors reached 520 million lbs in 1997, exceeding a half billion lbs for the first time (Figure 15–8). Catfish production is currently the largest aquaculture sector in the United States. It is an industry of the Southeast. The most important producing states are Mississippi, Alabama, and Arkansas, with Mississippi producing over half the total. The United States is the world's leading catfish producer, although production has declined in recent years.

Trout

Trout culture has the distinction of being the oldest form of U.S. aquaculture, dating to the 1800s (Figure 15–9). Trout farming began in the United States in a measurable way in the 1930s to provide fish for stocking and replenishing streams and lakes. USDA statistics for trout report production of 49.8 million pounds of food fish in 2008. Twenty states have food-size trout sales significant enough to be reported. Idaho is clearly the largest producer, with North Carolina, California, Pennsylvania, and Washington occupying a second tier of production. Idaho's dominance in this industry is related to its vast system of aquifers and springs that allow for intensive production in flow-through raceways.

Figure 15–9

Trout culture is the oldest form of U.S. aquaculture. (Source: Evok20/Shutterstock):

Tilapia

Domestic production of tilapia in the United States (Table 15–3) continues in spite of stiff direct competition from foreign producers. Tilapia imports from China and other countries have skyrocketed from 35 million lbs in 1990 to 475 million lbs in 2010. This mild, white-fleshed fish is attractively priced, offering an excellent way to add a seafood item to menus. Tilapia production is limited by climate to warm-water areas. They require water that stays above 10°C (50°F) to live.

Crawfish

Crawfish production is essentially restricted to Louisiana. There are over 140,000 acres of crawfish ponds in Louisiana. Production for recent years is shown in Table 15–3 and highly variable. Wild catch can add a third to a half again to the production. Crawfish are an integral part of Louisiana culture and cuisine and increasingly popular elsewhere (Figure 15–10). Harvest involves labor-intensive trapping and specialized equipment to access highly weedy ponds.

Salmon

Salmon farming is predominantly practiced in Washington and Maine in ocean pens. Additional salmon are cultivated in hatcheries in various locations on the East and West coasts for release back to the wild. United States salmon production can be seen in Table 15–3.

Mollusks

Oysters, clams, and mussels are produced on the mid-Atlantic Coast, in the Gulf of Mexico, and in Washington State. Florida has recently expanded its clam production. Farmed mollusks account for about 40% of the world mollusk supply. They are also a significant percentage of total world aquaculture production. Concerns about alternative uses for shoreline, high labor demands, and pollution seem to be affecting the overall growth of this sector.

Figure 15–10
Crawfish are the leading aquaculture crop in Louisiana.
(Source: kentoh/Shutterstock.)

Ornamental Fish

Not all of U.S. aquaculture is focused on food species. There is an active ornamental fish industry. The import/export market is always very dependent on the strength of the dollar against other currencies. Ornamental fish account for approximately 5% of U.S. aquaculture and amount to more than $50 million annually.

TYPES OF AQUACULTURE SYSTEMS

Because environments, socioeconomic conditions, and species vary tremendously around the world, it is logical to expect a variety of aquaculture systems and practices. Aquaculture is also a dynamic industry with new segments being developed and tried in all parts of the world (Figure 15–11). Most aquaculture production systems fit into one of the following categories.

Levee ponds are standing water impoundments built by excavating the pond area to a shallow depth and using the soil obtained to build a perimeter of levees or dikes (Figure 15–12). The advantages of levee ponds include the ability to harvest by seine without draining and the availability of oxygen all the way to the bottom of the pond. Disadvantages include relatively high construction costs and the need for a site with a slope of less than 5%, soil clay content of at least 20%, and wells or other reliable water sources.

Watershed ponds are standing water impoundments built by damming ravines or small valleys. In most regions, from 5 to 30 acres of watershed are needed to supply the water for 1 surface acre of pond. Advantages of watershed ponds include lower construction costs than levee ponds and the ability to make use of steeper sites. Disadvantages include the inability to refill ponds at will and lack of oxygen at greater depths, which can lead to fish kills if a turnover occurs.

Cages are floating enclosures in which fish are grown and fed a complete feed. The main advantage of cages is that fish are cultured in existing water bodies that would otherwise be impractical to harvest. Main disadvantages are quick spread of disease and greater vulnerability to theft, disturbance, and moderately low oxygen levels. Cage culture is practiced in lakes, rivers and coastal areas.

Figure 15–11

The number of alligators raised in the United States is quite small but may increase in the future. (Source: Andy Holligan/Dorling Kindersley/ DK Images)

Figure 15–12
Levee ponds in Jiangsu Province, China. Mulberry plants are grown on the pond levees to supply silkworm production. (FAO Photo/20044/H. Zhang. Used with permission by the Food and Agriculture Organization of the United Nations.)

Raceways and flow through tanks are long channels or tanks through which fresh water flows continuously and is then discarded (Figure 15–13). Main advantages of raceways and flow through tanks are ease of handling and harvesting fish and control of waste buildup by flushing. The main disadvantage is the shortage of sites having abundant water of the right temperature that is artesian water or water available without excessive pumping costs. Heating or cooling water for raceways is prohibitively expensive.

Recirculating systems are tank systems in which water is filtered and reused. Filtration is conducted by large beds of bacteria, known as biofilters. Main advantages of recirculating systems are that ideal growing temperatures can be maintained year-round and they can be located anywhere. Main disadvantages are lack of reliability, high production costs, and need for constant attention. Biofilter bacteria can be killed by chemicals that are used for disease treatments. They also can die unexpectedly without any apparent reason. More research and development work appears necessary before recirculating systems will be economical for most applications.

Figure 15–13
Trout raceway culture system in Serbia and Montenegro.
(FAO Photo/23488/L. Miuccio. Used with permission by the Food and Agriculture Organization of the United Nations.)

Other systems include:

- Mussel rafts with mollusks on wooden stakes, hanging ropes, off-rafts, or floats in the intertidal zone.
- Seaweed strung on lines off the bottom of shallow coastal areas.
- Integrated systems of aquaculture, which may include rice and fish, livestock, vegetables and fish, or various combinations of these.

These systems are variably designed to take advantage of aquaculture's strengths in terms of productivity compared to terrestrial agriculture. Aquaculture is considered to have the following advantages in productivity compared to land systems: (1) First, a water environment provides a three-dimensional growing space rather than the two-dimensional agriculture field. This allows these systems to exploit the various niche environments available in the three-dimensional space. Different species can take advantage of different foods and different water spaces. (2) Further, aquatic species are **cold blooded** and therefore convert more food to growth than do other agricultural animals because they expend fewer nutrients to maintain body temperature. They also use both naturally occurring food sources and those provided by humans, which improves their gain-to-feed-provided ratio. (3) In addition, aquatic species have a higher flesh-to-bone ratio than do land species, because they live in a low gravity environment.

Cold blooded Animals that cannot control their own body temperature.

WATER QUALITY

An essential difference between aquaculture and other systems of animal agriculture is the vulnerability of aquatic organisms to stress and death due to unfavorable water quality conditions. Before an aquaculture facility location is selected, it is vital to test the quality of water available on site. Requirements will vary by species, but typically include the proper range of temperature, total alkalinity, total hardness, pH, and salinity, as well as the absence of persistent pesticides and other toxic substances. In most cases, improper water quality characteristics cannot be economically remediated and so such sites should be rejected.

The great majority of aquaculture species are cold-blooded animals, so proper temperature is critical to growth and survival. In most production systems, it is uneconomical to heat or cool water. Therefore, it is essential to match the species to climate and other site factors affecting the available temperature of water.

Of equal importance are water quality monitoring and corrective actions once fish are present. An aquaculturist must have a good understanding of water quality chemistry, be able to accurately use meters and chemical test kits, and take the proper actions to quickly correct problems.

Dissolved oxygen is so scarce in water that it is measured in parts per million. To appreciate this scarcity, consider a 1 gal container sitting in a typical municipal water tower tank, which has a volume of 1 million gallons. This is 1 part per million (ppm). Typically, oxygen levels vary between 3 and 12 ppm in ponds. Oxygen makes up approximately 20% of air or 200,000 ppm, so shortages are essentially never a factor in land based animal agriculture. Oxygen levels in standing water systems undergo a typical daily cycle with the lowest levels occurring at night. This means work throughout the nighttime hours to monitor and take actions ensuring good oxygen levels. Even under good management, massive low oxygen fish kills are possible. In standing water ponds, the photosynthetic activity of microscopic algae, known as phytoplankton is an integral factor in dissolved oxygen dynamics, as well as many other water quality parameters.

Ammonia is a waste product released by aquatic animals as a part of the digestion of protein. It cannot be mechanically filtered out of water since it is released from fish gills as a dissolved gas. It exists in two forms: NH_3 and NH_4. The unionized form, NH_3, can reach stressful or toxic levels in aquaculture systems receiving large feed inputs typical of commercial production systems. Corrective measures vary with production system but, like dissolved oxygen, there is no automatic system or additive which ensures that harmful levels will be avoided. Proper monitoring, interpretation, and corrective actions by a knowledgeable manager are essential. Ammonia is degraded by bacterial action first to nitrates (NO_2) and then to nitrites (NO_3). Some aquaculture species accumulate nitrites and so are sensitive to them, while other species are not.

AQUACULTURE LIFE CYCLES

All stages of an aquatic organism's life cycle must be amenable to culture under controlled conditions, or reliable production will not be possible. The breeding and management of the aquatic species is, of course, quite varied. However, the life cycle is broken into similar stages for each species and the production units are generally segmented based on the stages of the life cycle of the animals. The hatchery is responsible for maintaining the **broodstock**, **spawning** them, hatching the fertilized eggs to produce **larvae**, and nurturing the larvae to the appropriate stage to move to the nursery. In the nursery, the young **fry** (fish), **postlarvae** (shrimp, prawns), or **spat** (shellfish) are raised to the **juvenile** stage. Juveniles attain a size at which they can be used to stock a production or grow-out unit. The production unit is segmented into units named according to the stages in the life cycle of the animals. For some species, there are separate holding areas for broodstock. For some species, the broodstock is selected from the grow-out and moved to the hatchery.

GENETICS

The application of genetic principles to aquaculture is no different than their application to any other species. The state of the science is that the techniques are perhaps not as widely known and practiced by aquaculturists as they are by land-based agriculturists. However, that is bound to change as aquaculture develops as an industry. Already, the types of practices used are becoming increasingly common and new practices are being introduced. Much is left to learn on this topic, and significant breakthroughs are expected.

Hybridization between different species in the same genus has yielded several hybrids with improved growth rates, better feed conversions, greater survival rates, greater disease resistance, and improved adult weights. The technique of **polyploidy** has been used to sterilize some species so they can be introduced into nonnative waters without running the risk they will reproduce. Transgenic animals have been developed and most probably will become a standard part of aquaculture as geneticists seek to change individual species in their resistance to diseases and parasites, growth rates and patterns, and ability to survive and produce in different environments. Research in transgenic fish has advanced more rapidly than has research for traditional farm animals. However, regulations from the FDA and/or USDA/APHIS could restrain the use of this and other biotechnologies that would assist the development of this industry.

One of the greatest challenges in the genetics of aquaculture species is the fact that several thousand species are available for the long term to potentially become a part of aquaculture systems. This contrasts with only a few dozen land animals that have been domesticated. The jobs of the "aqua-geneticist" are seemingly without end.

Broodstock The mature animals kept for reproductive purposes.

Spawn To produce eggs, sperm, or young.

Larva (plural, larvae) The first stage after hatching. An independent, mobile, developmental stage of development between hatching and juvenile.

Fry Fish in the postlarval stage.

Postlarvae Beyond the larval stage but not yet a juvenile.

Spat For shellfish such as oysters, the stage when they settle down and become attached to some hard object.

Juvenile Aquatic species between the postlarval stage and sexual maturity.

Polyploidy Condition in which the number of chromosomes of an individual is more than two paired (homologous) sets of chromosomes. The animals are sterile and generally have increased growth rates.

NUTRITION OF AQUATIC SPECIES

The challenge of nutrition in aquaculture is the same as the challenge to other farming industries: Create balanced rations that will promote good production at reasonable costs. However, the nutrition of these species is complicated by the fact that many of them are carnivores. The U.S. catfish industry has successfully developed a cereal-based floating food that the naturally carnivorous catfish thrive on. For the other industries to develop and prosper, the development of equally successful feeding strategies and feeds seems essential. Luckily, generally good diets have been formulated for the major species. Most are available commercially, although a custom mix is probably more economical for large operations. Table 15–4 shows examples of diets that have been developed and successfully fed to some species.

Many of the challenges of feeding the aquatic species are not related to the specific nutrient requirements, although those are certainly important. However, formulating feeds and correctly feeding the aquatic species includes giving consideration to:

- Physical stability sufficient to allow the pellet to be consumed before it disintegrates in water.
- Nutrient stability to minimize loss through diffusion into water.
- Pellet or particle size appropriate to the species and life stage.
- Feeding technique that avoids waste because wasted feed degrades water quality.
- Ingredients which are both palatable and digestible. An animal's natural dietary habitats can provide insights
- The frequency of feeding and manner in which feed is presented may need to mimic the animal's natural feeding habits.

BENEFITS OF CONSUMING FARM-RAISED FISH

Two major benefits recommend aquacultured species. First, farm-raised species avoid or minimize concerns about contaminants, such as mercury, which are of increasing concern in wild caught fish. Secondly, fish and seafood offer superior nutritional

Table 15–4
EXAMPLE DIET FORMULATIONS FOR SELECTED SPECIES OF FISH

Ingredient	Channel Catfish Grow-Out	Channel Catfish Fingerling	Salmon	Trout
	Percentage of Ingredient in Formulation			
Fish meal	4.0	12.0	52.0	30.0
Soybean meal	37.0	54.5	—	13.0
Corn gluten meal				17.0
Cottonseed meal	15.0	—	—	—
Poultry meal	—	—	1.5	—
Blood meal	—	—	10.0	—
Dried whey	—	—	5.0	10.0
Milk solubles	—	—	3.0	—
Corn, no. 2, yellow	33.3	30.8	—	—
Wheat middlings	4.0	—	12.2	16.4
Fat	1.5	1.5	9.0	11.6
Wheat germ meal	—	—	5.0	—
Dicalcium phosphate	1.0	1.0	—	—
Bone meal	4.0	—	—	—
Trace mineral and vitamin premix	0.2	0.2	2.3	2

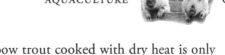

benefits. A 3-oz serving of farm-reared rainbow trout cooked with dry heat is only 143 calories and provides the following proportion of the recommended daily dietary allowance for a 19- to 30-year-old man:

Protein	36%
Phosphorus	33%
Zinc	4%
Vitamin A	9%
Thiamin	10%
B_{12}	145%
Niacin	35%
Riboflavin	7%

Seafoods are nutritious foods that contain a variety of vitamins, minerals, and high-quality protein. The calories per serving are usually lower than those in most meats. There is increasing evidence that omega-3 fatty acids, which are found in substantial quantities in some fish, have nutritional benefits. The nutrient values for trout and catfish show each to be a nutrient-dense food

TRENDS AFFECTING AQUACULTURE

The indicators suggest a solid future for aquaculture in the United States. The techniques and the infrastructure are partially in place and the demand for the product, demonstrated successes, and people interested in developing this industry are all positive. However, there are challenges. This section discusses factors and trends affecting, or likely to affect, aquaculture and its development.

Species

The currently cultured species will continue to be used, and their use will even be expanded. However, other species will also become part of U.S. aquaculture. This expansion will be driven by the need to diversify, coupled with the different environments available in this country and the demand for different products. These factors will almost certainly encourage the development of appropriate culture techniques for additional species not currently grown. Species that consume vegetable matter will be of special interest. Many of the high-value fish now cultured are carnivorous and use fishmeal and trash fish as their food source. This feed source is probably not reliable for the long term. Species like carp and tilapia eat lower on the food chain.

Technology

Technology will come to play a larger role in the aquaculture industry. Areas in which the adoption of available technologies and the development of new technologies are of potential benefit include monitoring and altering water quality; improved, more efficient harvesting techniques; inventory techniques; automated feeders; feed additives; and disease-prevention measures.

Constraints to Expansion

Expansion of the aquaculture industry will be a challenge in the United States. Aquaculture production sites need land and water, both of which are in decreasing supply.

Marine expansion is possible, but marine sites are being jealously guarded by environmental groups who fear unwanted ecological changes such as increased disease or genetic alterations in the indigenous species, pollution, and an altered aesthetic of the oceans. There is also competition for marine sites with recreational and industrial interests, as well as concerns over interference with navigation of the waters. Marine expansion is often opposed by the commercial fishing industry because of perceived competition. The actual numbers of marine sites with the requirements for good aquaculture are limited as well. Marine sites are also at risk from storms.

Expansion in the freshwater sector also faces challenges. Agriculture, industry, or municipalities are already using most of the freshwater resources in the United States. An exciting possibility for expansion of the aquaculture industry in the face of water shortages is a joint usage of water with row crop agriculture. Dubbed Joint Aquaculture/Agriculture Water Sharing (JAWS), the concept revolves around placing aquaculture facilities near the sources of agriculture irrigation water. The aquaculture enterprises use the water and then send it on to the row-crop partner to be used as irrigation water. This saves the aquaculture partner the need to treat the water before release to the environment. Instead, the water is provided to the agriculture partner containing some nutrients, which are needed by the crops, thus saving on fertilizer costs. The partners share the cost of the water. Estimates suggest that adoption of this practice using just 4% of the available Western irrigation water would allow aquaculture to double in size. Similar joint use production has long been practiced in Israel, where freshwater is scarce.

Labor costs offer another impediment to domestic aquaculture expansion. Relatively speaking, labor costs are high in the United States and many aquaculture production methods are labor intensive. Firms wanting to expand find cheaper labor an incentive to include other countries in their expansion plans. In addition to cheaper labor, the aquaculture industries of other countries can often offer more abundant resources, fewer environmental constraints, and few or no government regulations.

Feed costs are also relatively high for many of the currently cultured species and could get expensive enough to limit production in the future. As mentioned earlier, many of those species in current use are carnivores and their feed contains significant amounts of animal protein. With rising concerns over the practice of feeding animal-based feeds to food species, this practice is losing its consumer acceptance. In addition, other uses compete with aquaculture for availability of these feeds.

Disease Control

The aquaculture industry faces disease problems and the challenge of developing new therapeutants when the market for new drugs is small in comparison to mainstream animal species. Aquatic species are susceptible to a variety of diseases that cause mass mortalities. Already, the world shrimp industry has had to deal with a variety of viral diseases that have affected the harvest in an important way. The major one is the Taura syndrome, a virus that deforms and kills pond-reared shrimp. Shrimp viral diseases have caused problems in California and caused some shrimp farms to close. Epizootic ulcerative syndrome (EUS) has caused massive losses in many countries in Asia. Norway now has a parasite in its salmon population that threatens its wild populations. The parasite was introduced by salmon brought from the Baltic. Many of the diseases that affect the aquaculture species currently have no cure. This problem is actually worse in aquaculture than in other livestock species. In poultry, the average mortality for broilers in the grow-out phase is only about 3%. With fish species, the loss is much higher. Any decrease in the mortality rate will also improve the economic efficiency of the farming operation.

Environmental Concerns

With the introduction of the new species will come the need to deal with the inevitable escapes of exotic species from aquaculture into indigenous waters. These are of concern because they have the potential to alter the new host environment, disrupt the indigenous animal and plant communities, contribute to genetic degradation of local fish, introduce parasites and diseases, and have socioeconomic effects.

Wastes are generated from all forms of aquaculture. Obviously, the more intensive the system, the greater the waste problem. These wastes include uneaten feed, excreta, chemicals, therapeutic agents, and dead fish. Issues of feed quality, methods of feeding, and general husbandry practices need to reflect concerns about waste management. Creative methods of cleansing and reusing the water from aquaculture need to be developed, the information disseminated, and the techniques incorporated. With greater concerns about the polluting effects of wastes on the environment, this industry certainly faces regulations at both the state and federal levels. In 2004, the EPA put in place new rules establishing wastewater controls for concentrated aquatic animal production facilities (see http://www.eps.gov/guide/aquaculture/fs-final.htm).

In every region of the world, the amount of clean water available per capita is declining. In North America, the amount of clean water has declined by 50% since 1950. Clean water is needed for aquaculture, and aquaculture pollutes the water it uses. Regulation of pollution and water availability issues will increase socioeconomic costs for this industry, just as in any other animal industry, and will affect its viability.

Predator Loss

Fish and other aquaculture species are concentrated and so are attractive to predatory species including mammals, turtles, and various fish-eating birds. The economic loss amounts to tens of millions of dollars annually. In addition to direct consumption, predators also cause reduced production when the aquatic animals seek shelter and stop feeding and by causing stress, which makes cultured species more susceptible to disease. Solutions are difficult because of the adaptability of predator behavior and the protected status of many wildlife species. For instance, many bird species are protected by law in the United States.

CULTURE OF AQUATIC SPECIES

Because so many aquatic species are a part of aquaculture, it is not practical to handle the specifics of each in this chapter. However, information on a variety of topics ranging from culture to marketing to law is available. The County Cooperative Extension Service Office can usually help. They are commonly listed under "county government" in the phone directory. In addition, the U.S. Department of Agriculture has regional aquaculture centers. Their addresses are listed at the end of this chapter. As a means of exposing you to the type of information available, three representative publications have been selected. Edited versions appear in the following section. Literally thousands of other publications are available to the producer. Anyone considering an aquatic venture is encouraged to contact his or her extension service and the appropriate regional aquaculture center.

The Mississippi State University Extension Service provided the articles *Farm-Raised Catfish* and *Freshwater Prawns Pond Production and Grow-Out*. The fact sheet entitled *Reproduction of Angelfish* was provided courtesy of the Illinois–Indiana Sea Grant Program.

FARM-RAISED CHANNEL CATFISH (*ICTALURUS PUNCTATUS*)*

Production Process

The production process begins with mating of quality broodstock, which have been carefully selected a year in advance and fed a high quality diet. The brooders are stocked in spawning ponds with containers for egg laying. After fertilizing the eggs, the male guards them and must be chased out of the spawning container before the egg mass (Figure 15–14) can be transported to the hatchery and held in controlled hatching troughs where they are closely monitored. The eggs hatch in 7 days at a controlled temperature of 78°F. When the eggs first hatch, the young fish are called *sac fry* because their yolk sacs are attached to their abdomens. The sac fry live off food stored in the yolk sacs. As the yolk sacs are depleted, the fish begin to swim and take a starter diet. They are then stocked into nursery ponds, which have been managed to discourage predatory insects. When the fingerlings are about 4 to 6 in. long, they are transferred to grow-out ponds at various rates per surface acre of water.

Feeding

Catfish are fed a high-protein, floating feed ration that is produced by several catfish feed mills located in the producing regions. Use of floating pellets allows observation of feeding response and minimizes wasted feed. This protein diet consists of soybean meal, corn, wheat, and fishmeal. Annual feed requirements are estimated to be about 5 tons of feed per surface acre of water. Catfish convert feed at an average yield of about 1 lb of fish for every 2.0 lbs of feed. Compared to other feed-converting animals, catfish produce one of the highest yields per pound of feed.

Water Quality

The oxygen content of the water must be checked on a regular basis because lack of oxygen can kill fish in a matter of minutes. When the oxygen content begins to reach a dangerously low level, such as on hot summer days, producers use paddle wheels or

Figure 15–14

A channel catfish egg mass ready to be transferred to an indoor hatching trough.

(Source: Auburn University's Department of Fisheries & Allied Aquacultures.)

*By Dr. Martin W. Brunson, Extension Leader, Wildlife and Fisheries, and Dr. Robert Martin, Extension Economist, Department of Agricultural Economics. Information Sheet 1526, Extension Service of Mississippi State University. Ronald A. Brown, Director.

Figure 15–15
Aeration equipment is used to avoid mortalities of channel catfish during periods of low dissolved oxygen levels. It is also used during harvest operations, such as this one, to lessen stress on the fish as they are crowded by seining and then transferred by lift basket to the hauling truck. (Photo courtesy USDA.)

other devices to aerate catfish ponds (Figure 15–15). This technique introduces air into the water and replaces the oxygen that has been depleted. Other water chemistry parameters that affect fish health and production include ammonia and nitrite levels, alkalinity, and chloride levels.

Disease Management

Intensive culture of channel catfish requires close attention to the stress situations that can predispose fish to disease. Several diseases affect channel catfish in production ponds. Some of the major diseases include ESC, channel catfish virus, winterkill, proliferative gill disease, columnaris, fungus, and assorted parasites.

Harvest and Marketing

By the time farm-raised catfish are 18 months old, they are usually ready for harvest. Averaging 1–1.5 lbs live weight, they are removed from the ponds by seines and placed in aerated tank trucks for live shipment to the processing plant. Some of the fish instead go to pay-fishing ponds or fish markets, but the majority are processed. Catfish are kept alive right up to the time they are processed. Within just a matter of minutes they are processed and then placed on ice or frozen to temperatures of 40° below zero, using a quick-freeze method that allows the taste and quality to remain in the fish longer. Farm-raised catfish are taste-tested at the farm before the fish are harvested and again at the processing plant before the fish are unloaded. These quality control procedures ensure that the consumer receives a product of superior flavor.

Farm-raised catfish are marketed through three major channels: retail grocery store outlets, food service distributors, and catfish specialty restaurants. Each channel accounts for about one-third of total catfish sales. A self-funded promotion and marketing program called the Catfish Institute constantly works on behalf of farm-raised catfish and has greatly increased the stature and prominence of this food product.

Quality Assurance

Farm-raised catfish are not exposed to external environmental factors, so producers can more easily control the quality of their product. Even in cultured products, however, potential contamination by pesticides, drugs, or other environmental factors is becoming a major consumer concern. Catfish producers responded to increased consumer awareness and sensitivity with a Catfish Quality Assurance Program (CQA). This is an opportunity to demonstrate that catfish production practices are safe, carefully monitored, and that the safety and quality of farm-raised catfish can be assured.

Catfish producers recognize that a producer–client relationship built on mutual trust and confidence is paramount to the survival of the industry.

Catfish producers are aware, however, that quality assurance goes far beyond the pond bank. Quality assurance begins, and hinges upon, activities at the production level. The quality of the product as it leaves the farm greatly influences the quality of the product reaching the consumer. Safety and quality cannot be added or increased at the processing or retail level; it must be guaranteed by the producers.

FRESHWATER PRAWN POND PRODUCTION AND GROW-OUT (MACROBRACHIUM ROSENBERGII)*

The final phase of freshwater prawn (shrimp) production is grow-out of juveniles to adults for market as a food product (Figure 15–16). Unless you have a hatchery/nursery, you must purchase juveniles for the pond grow-out phase. Commercial hatcheries in Texas, California, and Mexico produce postlarvae and juveniles.

Site Selection and Pond Design

Ponds used for raising freshwater prawns should have many of the same basic features of ponds used for the culture of channel catfish. An ample supply of freshwater is important, and the soil must have excellent water-retention qualities. Well water of acceptable quality is the preferred water source for raising freshwater prawns. Run-off from rivers, streams, and reservoirs can be used, but quality and quantity can be highly variable and subject to uncontrollable change. The quality of the water source should be tested before any site is selected. Locate ponds in areas that are not

Figure 15–16
A large male freshwater prawn. (Source: think4photop/Shutterstock)

*By Dr. Louis R. D'Abramo, Professor; Dr. Martin W. Brunson, Extension Leader/Fisheries Specialist; and Dr. William H. Daniels, former Research Assistant, all with the Department of Wildlife and Fisheries. Publication 2003. Extension Service of Mississippi State University. Ronald A. Brown, Director. Mississippi State University Extension Service. Mississippi State University, http://ext.msstate.edu/pubs/pub2003.htm.

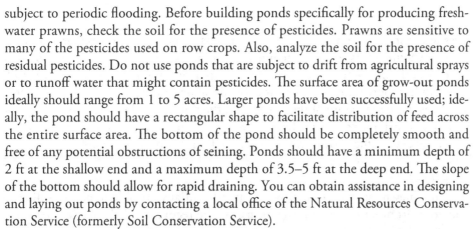

subject to periodic flooding. Before building ponds specifically for producing fresh-water prawns, check the soil for the presence of pesticides. Prawns are sensitive to many of the pesticides used on row crops. Also, analyze the soil for the presence of residual pesticides. Do not use ponds that are subject to drift from agricultural sprays or to runoff water that might contain pesticides. The surface area of grow-out ponds ideally should range from 1 to 5 acres. Larger ponds have been successfully used; ideally, the pond should have a rectangular shape to facilitate distribution of feed across the entire surface area. The bottom of the pond should be completely smooth and free of any potential obstructions of seining. Ponds should have a minimum depth of 2 ft at the shallow end and a maximum depth of 3.5–5 ft at the deep end. The slope of the bottom should allow for rapid draining. You can obtain assistance in designing and laying out ponds by contacting a local office of the Natural Resources Conservation Service (formerly Soil Conservation Service).

Collect a soil sample from the pond bottom to determine whether lime is needed. Take soil samples from about six different places in each area of the pond, and mix them together to make a composite sample that is then air-dried. Put the sample in a soil sample box, available from your county extension agent, and send it to the Extension Soil Testing Laboratory, Box 9610, Mississippi State, MS 39762, and request a lime requirement test for a pond. There is a charge of $3 per sample for this service. If the pH of the soil is less than 6.5, you must add agricultural limestone to increase the pH to a minimum of 6.5, and preferably 6.8.

After filling the pond, fertilize it to provide an abundance of natural food organisms for the prawns and to shade out unwanted aquatic weeds. A liquid fertilizer, either a 10-34-0 or 13-38-0, gives the best results. Apply one-half to 1 gal of 10-34-0 or 13-38-0 liquid fertilizer per surface acre to the pond at least 1 to 2 weeks before stocking juvenile prawns. If a phytoplankton bloom has not developed within a week, make a second application of the liquid fertilizer. Do not apply directly into the water because it is denser than water and will sink to the bottom; liquid fertilizer should be diluted with water 10:1 before application. It can be sprayed from the bank or applied from a boat outfitted for chemical application. Wait until any clay turbidity has settled before applying fertilizer.

At least 1 or 2 days before stocking the juvenile prawns, check the pond for aquatic insect adults and larvae that might eat the juvenile prawns. You can control the insects by using a 2:1 mixture of motor oil and diesel fuel at the rate of 1 to 2 gals per surface acre on a calm day. The oil film on the water kills the air-breathing insects and is more effective when applied on calm days.

If a water source other than well water is used, it is critically important to prevent fish, particularly members of the sunfish family (e.g., bass, bluegills, and green sunfish), from getting into the pond when it is filled. The effects of predation on freshwater prawns by these kinds of fish can be devastating. If there are fish in the pond, remove them before stocking prawns, using 1 quart of 5% liquid emulsifiable rotenone per acre-foot of water (restricted pesticide–applicator license required).

Stocking of Juveniles

Water in which postlarvae and juveniles are transported should be gradually replaced by the water in which they will be stocked. This acclimation procedure should not be attempted until the temperature difference between the transport and culture water is less than 6–10°F.

Juveniles, preferably derived from size-graded populations ranging in weight from 0.1 to 0.3 g, should be stocked at densities from 12,000 to 16,000 per acre. Lower stocking densities will yield larger prawns but lower total harvested poundage.

TEMPERATURE

Freshwater shrimp cannot survive in most ponds in the United States year-round due to temperature limitations. The temperature of the pond water at stocking should be at least 68°F (20°C) to avoid stress. Juvenile prawns appear to be more susceptible than adults to low water temperatures. The duration of the grow-out period depends on the water temperature of the ponds, and the time generally is 120 to 150 days in central Mississippi. Prawns could be grown year-round if you can find a water source that provides a sufficiently warm temperature for growth.

Feeding

Juvenile prawns stocked into grow-out ponds initially are able to obtain sufficient nutrition from natural pond organisms. At the recommended stocking densities, begin feeding when the average weight of the prawn is 5.0 g or greater. Commercially available sinking channel catfish feed (28–32% crude protein) is an effective feed at the recommended stocking densities. The feeding rate is based on the mean weight of the population. A feeding schedule has been developed by researchers at the Mississippi Agriculture and Forestry Experiment Station and is based on three factors:

1. A feed conversion ratio of 2.5:1.
2. One percent mortality in the population per week.
3. Mean individual weight determined from samples obtained every 3 weeks.

At the end of the grow-out season, survival may range from 60–85%, if you have practiced good water quality maintenance. Yields typically range from 600–1,200 lbs per acre. Weights of prawns range from 10 to 13 per lb.

Water Quality Management

Water quality is just as important in raising freshwater prawns as it is in raising catfish or any other species of aquatic animal. Dissolved oxygen (DO) is particularly important, and a good oxygen-monitoring program is necessary to achieve maximum yields. You should routinely check and monitor levels of dissolved oxygen in the bottom 1 ft of water, which the prawns occupy. Electronic oxygen meters are best for this purpose but are rather expensive and require careful maintenance to ensure good operating condition. The need for an electronic oxygen meter increases as the quantity of ponds to be managed increases. With only one or two small ponds, a chemical oxygen test kit is sufficient. Chemical oxygen test kits that perform 100 tests are commercially available from several manufacturers.

Use a sampler for collecting samples from an appropriate water depth for dissolved oxygen analysis. These sampling devices are commercially available or can be fashioned. It is important that the dissolved oxygen concentration in the bottom 1 ft of water does not fall below 3 parts per million (ppm). Dissolved oxygen concentrations of 3 ppm are stressful, and lower oxygen concentrations can be lethal. Chronically low levels of dissolved oxygen result in less-than-anticipated yields at the end of the growing season. Emergency aeration can be achieved by an aerator. The design and size of the aerator depend on the size and shape of the culture pond.

Specific information on water quality requirements of freshwater prawns is limited. Although freshwater prawns have been successfully raised in soft water (5 to 7 ppm total hardness) in South Carolina, a softening of the shell was noticed. Hard water, 300-plus ppm, has been implicated in reduced growth and lime encrustations on freshwater prawns. Therefore, use of water with a hardness of 300-plus ppm is not recommended.

Nitrogen Compounds

Nitrites at concentrations of 1.8 ppm have caused problems in hatcheries, but there is no definitive information as to the toxicity of nitrite to prawns in pond situations. High nitrate concentrations in ponds would not be expected given the anticipated biomass of prawns at harvest. High levels of un-ionized ammonia, above 0.1 ppm, in fish ponds can be detrimental. Concentrations of un-ionized ammonia as low as 0.26 ppm at a pH of 6.83 have been reported to kill 50% of the prawns in a population in 144 hours. Therefore, you must make every effort to prevent concentrations of 0.1 or higher ppm un-ionized ammonia.

pH

A high pH can cause mortality through direct pH toxicity, and indirectly because a higher percentage of the total ammonia in the water exists in the toxic, un-ionized form. Although freshwater prawns have been raised in ponds with a pH range of 6.0 to 10.5 with no apparent adverse effects, it is best to avoid a pH below 6.5 or above 9.5, if possible. High pH values usually occur in waters with total alkalinity of 50 or less ppm and when a dense algae bloom is present. Before stocking, liming ponds that are built in acidic soils can help minimize severe pH fluctuations.

Another way to avoid any anticipated problems of high pH is to reduce the quantity of algae in the pond by periodically flushing (removing) the top 12 in. of surface water. Alternatively, organic matter, such as corn grain or rice bran, can be distributed over the surface area of the pond. This procedure must be accompanied by careful monitoring of oxygen levels, which may dramatically decrease due to decay processes.

In some cases, dense phytoplankton growth may occur in production ponds. To control algae, do a bioassay before using any herbicide in a freshwater prawn pond. To do a bioassay, remove a few prawns, put them in several plastic buckets containing some of the pond water, and treat them to see if the concentration of herbicide you plan to use is safe. Be sure there is adequate aeration, and observe the response of the prawns for at least 24 hours afterward.

Diseases

So far, diseases do not appear to be a significant problem in the production of freshwater prawns, but as densities are increased to improve production, disease problems are bound to become more prevalent. One disease you may encounter is blackspot, or shell disease, which is caused by bacteria that break down the outer skeleton. Usually it follows physical damage and can be avoided by careful handling. At other times, algae or insect eggs may be present on the shell. This condition is not a disease, but rather an indication of slow growth, and is eliminated when the prawn molts.

Harvesting

At the end of the grow-out season, prawns may be seine or drain harvested. For seining, depth (or water volume) should be decreased by half before seining. Alternatively, ponds could be drained into an interior, large, rectangular borrow pit (ditch) where prawns are concentrated before seining. You can effectively drain harvest only if ponds have a smooth bottom and a slope that will ensure rapid and complete draining. During the complete drain-down harvest procedure, prawns generally are collected on the outside of the pond levee as they travel through the drain pipe into a collecting device. To avoid stress and possible mortality, provide sufficient aeration to the water in the collection device.

Selective harvest of large prawns during a period of 4 to 6 weeks before final harvest is recommended to increase total production in the pond. Selective

harvesting usually is performed with a 1- to 2-in. bar-mesh seine, allowing those that pass through the seine to remain in the pond and to continue to grow, while the larger prawns are removed. Selective harvest may also be accomplished with properly designed traps. Prawns can be trapped using an array of traditionally designed crawfish traps.

Polyculture and Intercropping

Culture of freshwater prawns in combination with fingerling catfish has been successfully demonstrated under small-scale, experimental conditions, and appears possible under commercial conditions. Selective harvest can help to extend the duration of the availability of the fresh or live prawn product to the market. However, there is a lack of research to show whether selective harvesting or a complete bulk harvest is the most economical approach.

Before introduction of catfish fry, stock juvenile prawns at a rate of 3,000 to 5,000 per acre. Stock catfish fry at a density to ensure that they will pass through a 1-in. mesh seine used to harvest the prawns at the end of the growing season. Although polyculture of prawns and a mixed population of channel catfish has been successfully demonstrated, logistical problems arising from efficient separation of the two crops is inherent in this management practice. Moreover, when harvest of prawns is imminent due to cold water temperatures, catfish may not be a harvestable crop due to an "off flavor" characteristic. Polyculture of channel catfish and freshwater prawns may be best achieved through the cage culture of the fish.

Recently, a scheme for the intercropping of freshwater prawns and red swamp crawfish was developed and evaluated. Intercropping is the culture of two species that are stocked at different times of the year with little, if any, overlap of their growth and harvest seasons. Intercropping provides for a number of benefits that include:

1. Minimizing competition for resources.
2. Avoiding potential problems of species separation during or after harvest.
3. Spreading fixed costs of a production unit (pond) throughout the calendar year.

Adult mature crawfish are stocked at a rate of 3,600 per acre in late June or early July. Juvenile prawns are stocked at a density of 16,000 per acre in late May and harvested from August through early October. In late February, seine harvest of the crawfish begins and continues through late June before stocking of new adult crawfish. Prawns are small enough to pass through the mesh of the seine used to harvest crawfish during the May–June overlap period.

Processing and Marketing

Production levels and harvesting practices should match marketing strategies. Without this approach, financial loss owing to lack of adequate storage (holding) facilities or price change is inevitable. Marketing studies strongly suggest that a "heads off" product should be avoided and that a specific market niche for whole freshwater prawns needs to be identified and carefully developed.

To establish year-round distribution of this seasonal product, freezing, preferably individually quick frozen (IQF), would be an attractive form of processing. Block frozen is an alternative method of processing for long-term distribution. Recent research at the Mississippi Agriculture and Forestry Experiment Station suggests that adult freshwater prawns can be successfully live hauled for at least 24 hours, at a density of 0.5 lb per gallon, with little mortality and no observed effect on exterior quality of the product. Transport under these conditions requires good aeration. Distribution of prawns on "shelves" stacked vertically within the water column assists in avoiding mortality due to crowding and localized poor water quality. Use of holding water with a comparatively cool temperature (68–72°F) minimizes the incidence of water quality problems and injury by reducing the activity level of the prawns.

REPRODUCTION OF ANGELFISH (PTEROPHYLLUM SCALARE)*

Since their introduction around 1911, angelfish have held a unique position in the fish-keeping world; angelfish have been called the kings of the aquarium. They are extremely beautiful animals with highly varied finnage and color schemes (Figure 15–17). Angelfish are members of the Cichlidae family, as are tilapia species grown for food. The genus *Pterophyllum* comprises three species. The spectacular *Pterophyllum altum* (Pellegrin 1903), which can measure 13 in. from the tip of the dorsal to the tip of the caudal fin, is native to the upper Orinoco River basin in South America.

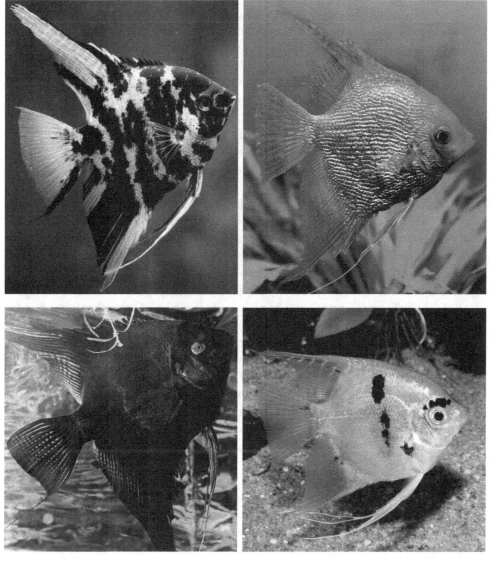

Figure 15–17
Angelfish are a popular ornamental fish produced for the pet fish market. (Source: (a) Corneliu LEU/ Shutterstock; (b) cynoclub/Shutterstock; (c) RedTC/Shutterstock; (d) iliuta goean/Shutterstock)

---

*By LaDon Swann, Aquaculture Extension Specialist, Illinois-Indiana Sea Grant Program, Purdue University, West Lafayette, IN.

The two remaining species, *P. scalare* (Lichtenstein 1823) and *P. dumerilii* (Castelnau 1855), are found throughout the Amazon basin and in the coastal rivers of the Guineas. Both *P. altum* and *P. dumerilii* are aquarist rarities. Even though *P. altum* is as attractive as *P. scalare,* both are seldom exported. The stringent water-quality requirements may partially expand the limited availability of these two species compared with the widely available congener *P. scalare.*

Pterophyllum scalare is without question the most popular and generally more available member of the entire family Cichlidae. Both the silver- and black-banded and a myriad of artificially selected color and finnage varieties are commercially produced. These Cichlids make a magnificent solo display, but there is no practical reason for excluding other fish from their aquarium. No aggressive tank mates or habitual fin-nippers belong in the company of any *Pterophyllum* species. Gouramis of the genera *Colisa* and *Trichogaster* are particularly well suited for this role. The only Cichlids that can be safely housed with angelfish are festivums, discus, keyhole acaras, and most of the South American and West African dwarf species.

Unfortunately, many specimens are purchased by neophyte aquarists whose ignorance of proper aquarium care dooms the overwhelming majority to a short and not-so-particularly pleasant life. The usual mistake entails introducing juvenile angelfish to a newly set-up aquarium. All of the laterally compressed Cichlids are extremely sensitive to nitrite and ammonia. They cannot cope with the fluctuations of these substances, which inevitably occur during the first few weeks of an aquarium's life.

The biological requirements and spawning techniques for *Pterophyllum scalare* are presented in this report.

Water Quality

As in any form of aquatic animal husbandry, excellent water quality should be maintained. Maintaining good water quality is as important to the ornamental fish producer using a spare room in the household as it is for the 1,000-acre catfish farm. In certain instances, it may be more difficult to provide ideal water quality requirements for a non-native fish species than for a species that evolved to fit the characteristics of its ecosystem. The water in which angelfish are naturally found is soft and slightly acidic. Angelfish will survive and grow in wide varieties of water hardness, but for good reproduction, the producer should attempt to provide the spawners with their preferred water. Water for broodstock reproduction should be 100 mg/l hardness and 6.8 to 7.2 pH. Controlling water temperature is essential to angelfish reproduction. Maintain angelfish at 24–26°C, and at 26–28°C for spawning. Day length for angelfish should be 8–12 hours. Nitrate levels should be maintained below 100 mg/l. Partial water changes are done weekly or biweekly by siphoning approximately 30% of the water from the bottom of the aquarium. If under gravel filters are used, the water is siphoned from under the gravel plate.

Nutrition

Angelfish are omnivores. Flaked foods are readily taken by angelfish of all sizes. Far more important to the well-being of angelfish is the proportion of roughage to protein in the diet. In nature, the food of most species comprises 50–85% roughage by weight, yet few food manufacturers take this into account in their formulations. Most angelfish can be kept in good condition on an exclusive diet of prepared foods and may even spawn freely on such a regime. However, all do better when regularly offered live and fresh food. This is particularly true when conditioning fish for breeding. It is not the superior nutritional value of such foods, as much as their superior palatability, that makes them so valuable.

Newly hatched brine shrimp (*Artemia salina*) nauplii are essential first food for newly hatched angelfish and are good for conditioning brooding angelfish. Brine shrimp and *Daphnia* exoskeletons rupture during freezing and the nutritional value after thawing decreases. Chrinonomid larvae, glassworms, and krill withstand freezing well and are preferred. Ground beef heart is also used as a staple angelfish food, but it degrades water quality more rapidly than other types of feed.

Some commercial operations use supplements of fresh vegetable food to maintain the full intensity of coloration as well as general well-being. This requirement is easily met, for a wide range of such foods is readily available. Romaine or other leaf lettuce varieties and spinach are particular favorites. Thinly sliced young zucchini or other marrow squashes are a superb food. These foods should be blanched by brief contact with boiling water, then cooled, before being offered to the fish. Live foods include shrimp, *Tubifex* worms, and mosquito larva. A variety of dried foods is also used. The higher the protein content, the better. The broodstock are fed to satiation twice per day.

As soon as the fry are free-swimming, they are fed exclusively newly hatched brine shrimp, three to four times a day. Within 15 minutes after each feeding, the bottom of each aquarium is siphoned clean and fresh water is added. This is done because live shrimp give off a tremendous amount of ammonia. The fry tank has a clean glass bottom and no gravel of any kind. A sponge filter raised approximately 6 mm off the bottom is used. The elevated filter prevents fry from being trapped underneath the filter.

Spawning

The reproductive biology of Cichlids is extremely diverse and falls into two distinct categories—mouth brooders or substrate spawners. The mouth brooders incubate the fertilized eggs in the buccal cavity of the female. In a few species, the male will incubate the fertilized eggs. *Oreochromis niloticus* is an example of a maternal mouth brooder. Eggs of substrate spawners are incubated in a nest. The nest may either be formed on the river or lake bottom or, in the case of angelfish, the eggs are adhesive and are laid on plants or rocks. In nature, *Pterophyllum* sp. are monogamous, biparental, custodial substrate spawners. *Pterophyllum scalare* spawns freely under aquarium conditions. The altum angelfish has infrequently, but successfully, bred under aquarium conditions. No spawning by *P. dumerilii* has been reported in captivity.

The prospective angelfish breeder's chief problem is identifying males and females. Angelfish are not easily sexed. Large males typically have a more rounded cranial profile than do females. Apart from this less-than-convincing effort to produce a nuchal hump, they are somewhat larger than their consorts, and their ventral profile from the origin of the ventrals rearward slopes sharply downward. In contrast, the female's vertical profile is almost flat. These distinctions are virtually useless when dealing with young adults.

The extreme lateral compression of their bodies obscures the genital papillae sufficiently to render this otherwise infallible indicator of sex quite valueless. An accurate sign of imminent spawning is the appearance of the pair's genital papillae. The genital papilla of the female usually appears first and is more noticeable because it is larger and more blunt, while that of the male is more slender and pointed. These small protuberances that appear at the vent are used respectively for depositing the eggs and fertilizing them.

Broodstock Selection The easiest means of securing a pair is to raise a group of fry together and allow them to pair naturally. Professional breeders do not have time to wait for the fish to pair off on their own. They select approximately 20 to 30 fish as

breeders and place them in a large aquarium, preferably 208 liters (55 gals) or larger. The water temperature should be approximately 27°C. Feed the fish as much live food as possible. Several slates measuring 30 cm × 10 cm are inclined along the walls of the aquarium. The fish pair off and attempt to breed at around 10 months, give or take a couple of weeks.

Courtship will begin if the fish are of mature age. Angelfish become very territorial during this process. Courtship works both ways, with the male selecting his mate or the female selecting hers. In either case, the pair selects a territory and protects it against all intruders. Once obvious courtship has started, the pair should be transferred to a separate tank depending on the spawning method chosen. The transfer will allow the pair to be alone and prevent aggressive behavior from tank mates.

Parental Spawning   Parental spawning occurs when the eggs are laid and the parents provide parental care to the eggs and newly hatched fry until they are large enough to fend for themselves. This is an excellent method for the hobbyist who wants to observe the behavior of the parents. If one intends to allow the pair to rear their progeny undisturbed, a tank of at least 120-liter capacity is necessary to afford the fry sufficient living space. In nature, angelfish select a stout plant leaf as a spawning site. The aquarium strain of *P. scalare* will lay their eggs on any vertical surface that can be nipped clean. Usually 2 to 3 days before spawning, the pair selects and begins cleaning the spawning site, using their mouths to bite and scrub the surface of the leaf, slate, or whatever has been chosen.

After a few false passes at the site, the female passes over the site and deposits eggs, which adhere to the surface. The male makes alternate passes and releases spermatozoa, fertilizing the eggs. Continual movement of the angels over the eggs after the spawning serves the purpose of creating circulation through fanning movement of the pectoral fins.

Fish eggs usually are small (between 1.5 and 3 mm on the average) and round. Spawns numbering 500 eggs are not unusual. Egg size depends on the availability and quality of food fed to the spawners. Eggs are translucent when first laid. Infertile eggs turn white and are removed by the parents.

Eggs hatch in 36 to 48 hours. The pair chews the zygotes out of their eggshells 36 hours post-spawning. The larvae are initially shifted from one vertical resting place to another, but as they grow more active, their parents often move them to shallow pits in the substratum. The fry first attempt swimming 4 to 5 days later, but they usually require an additional day-and-a-half to 2 days to become fully proficient. At this stage they are called swim-up fry.

Young pairs often eat their first few spawns, but given time, most settle satisfactorily into parenthood. Parental care can persist up to 8 weeks in captivity, but it is prudent to remove the fry from the breeding tank no later than the fourth week postspawning. By this time, most pairs show signs of wishing to respawn.

Egg Removal Method   The majority of domestic angelfish are raised without parental care. The differences between parental spawning and the egg removal method occur after the eggs are fertilized. Once brood fish start to exhibit courtship behavior (either the male or the female begins cleaning slate), they are transferred to an 80-liter spawning tank. The spawning tank is aerated and has two sponge filters. This interruption will affect the pair for 2 or 3 days, after which they will resume the process for breeding. After fertilization, the slate with attached eggs is placed in a 12–20 liter

aquarium containing enough methylene blue to give a dark-blue color. An air stone should be placed underneath the slate to provide circulation. After hatching, one-half of the aquarium water should be replaced each day, so that by the time the fry are free-swimming, the water is only slightly blue. Dead eggs should be removed each day to prevent the spread of fungus to live eggs.

When the fry are free swimming, they should be transferred to an aerated 60 liter long aquarium at 300 fry per aquarium. The aquarium should have a water depth of approximately 10 cm and should be filtered with a sponge filter. The shallow water depth facilitates the feeding of the fry. When the fry are approximately 15 mm in diameter, they should be transferred to a 120- to 200-liter aquarium with aeration and filtration. Fry should grow to a marketable size in 6 to 8 weeks.

Angelfish fry are not difficult to raise, provided every effort is made to keep metabolite concentrations as low as possible. If their finnage is to develop to its fullest degree, they must not be crowded during their first months of life. This is particularly true of the so-called veil strain. With heavy feeding and frequent partial water changes, the young grow quickly. Under exceptional circumstances, females begin spawning by the eighth month postspawning. In most instances, sexual maturity is attained 10 months to a year postspawning.

Diseases   Many disease outbreaks can be attributed to excessive parasitism complicated by secondary bacterial infections. When angelfish are purchased, they should be examined for external and internal parasites. Newly acquired fish should be strictly quarantined for at least 1 month before they are placed with established populations. This practice will substantially reduce the risk of introducing new pathogens to hatcheries or home aquariums.

Two of the most commonly encountered pathogens in angelfish are *Hexamita* and *Capillaria*. The prevalence of the enteric parasites can be reduced by periodically treating fish with metrinidazole and an anthelmintic. This is particularly important in commercial hatcheries. Treatment for other infectious agents, particularly bacterial diseases, should only be administered following identification of agents causing disease outbreaks. Sensitivity testing of bacteria is strongly encouraged to ensure proper use of antibiotics during disease outbreaks. Assistance is available from your aquaculture extension specialist and animal disease diagnostic laboratory. Currently, the diagnosis of viral disease is hampered by the lack of a cell culture system to isolate and thereby characterize viruses of angelfish. However, the structures can be observed in tissue and feces by electron microscopy, thereby permitting presumptive viral diagnosis.

Conclusions   Producing angelfish is a relatively simple procedure if a few guidelines are followed:

1. Maintain good water quality. Angelfish prefer soft and slightly acidic water, a spawning temperature of 26–28°C, and 8–12 hours of daylength.
2. Provide high-quality feed to broodstock and newly hatched fry. The feed should consist of flakes and live foods.
3. Do not overstock tanks. Use only one brooding pair per spawning tank and do not stock more than 200 swim-up fry per 80-liter tank.

Spawning angelfish is a lot of fun for novice fish keepers and can be profitable for the more serious aquaculturists. Angelfish hatcheries can provide supplemental income to niche marketers or provide a primary income source for large-scale hatcheries that sell angelfish to wholesalers.

SOURCES OF INFORMATION

Center for Tropical & Subtropical Aquaculture
http://www.ctsa.org/

North-Central Regional Aquaculture Center
http://www.ncrac.org/

Northeastern Regional Aquaculture Center
http://www.nrac.umd.edu/

Southern Regional Aquaculture Center
http://www.msstate.edu/dept/srac/

Western Regional Aquaculture Center
http://www.fish.washington.edu/wrac/

STUDY QUESTIONS

1. Define *aquaculture*. What species are involved? What kinds of water? What are capture fisheries? Blended fisheries?

2. Describe the different types of aquaculturists.

3. What is the purpose of the aquaculture industry in the United States? Worldwide?

4. What is the per capita consumption of seafood in the United States?

5. How did aquaculture develop in the United States? What is the potential for future growth?

6. Describe the magnitude of each of the following species in relationship to the overall aquaculture industry: catfish, trout, tilapia, crawfish, salmon, mollusks, and ornamental fish.

7. What are the general types of aquaculture systems?

8. What are aquaculture's advantages over land-based systems?

9. What are the stages in the life cycle of most aquatic organisms? How are these segmented into production units?

10. Describe the state of the study of genetics of aquatic species compared to that of land-based livestock. How about nutrition?

11. What is the challenge of aquaculture where nutrition is concerned?

12. Describe the trends affecting aquaculture's growth as an industry.

REFERENCES

For the 5th edition, Dr. Marley Beem, Oklahoma State University, assumed co-authorship of this chapter.

Avault, J. W. 1996. *Fundamentals of aquaculture.* Baton Rouge, LA: AVA.

Baird, D. J., M.C.M. Beveridge, L. A. Kelly, and J. F. Muir. 1996. *Aquaculture and water resource management.* Cambridge, MA: Blackwell Scientific.

Bardach, J. E. 1997. *Sustainable aquaculture.* New York: Wiley.

Beem, M.D. 1998. *Aquaculture: Realities and potentials when getting started.* Southern Regional Aquaculture Center Publication number 441.

Beveridge, M. C. M. 1996. *Cage aquaculture.* Cambridge, MA: Fishing News Books, Blackwell Science.

Boyd, C. E. 1990, *Water quality in ponds for aquaculture.* Alabama Agricultural Experiment Station,

Carlberg, J. M., and J. C. Van Olst. 2001. U.S. aquaculture: Current status and future directions. *Aquaculture Magazine* 27 (4):36–43.

Collins, C. 1998. *Warm water finfish aquaculture in the United States: Past, present and future.* Davis: University of California.

Costa-Pierce, B. A. 1998. *The role of aquaculture in farming systems.* Department of Environmental

Analysis and Design, School of Social Ecology, University of California, Irvine, CA. Published by the Food and Agriculture Organization of the United Nations, Rome, Italy. http://darwin.bio. uci.edu/~sustain/FAO-may98version1.html.

Dupree, H. K. and J. V. Huner. 1984. *Third report to the fish farmers.* U.S. Department of the Interior, Fish and Wildlife Service.

FAO. 2010. *The state of world fisheries and aquaculture 2010.* Accessed online May 2011. http://www. fao.org/docrep/013/i1820e/i1820e00.htm.

FAO. 2010. *World review of fisheries and aquaculture.* Accessed online April 2011. http://www.fao.org/ docrep/013/i1820e/i1820e01.pdf

Fisheries of the United States, 2009. Accessed online April 2011. http://www.st.nmfs.noaa.gov/st1/ publications.html

National Fisheries Institute. 2009. *Top 10 U.S. consumption of seafood by species.* Accessed online April 2011. http://www.aboutseafood.com/about/ about-seafood/top-10-consumed-seafoods.

National Marine Fisheries Service, Fisheries Statistics and Economics Division. 2009. Silver Springs, MD: NOAA. Accessed online April 2011. http://www. st.nmfs.noaa.gov/st1/fus/fus09/08_perita2009.pdf.

New, M. B. 1997. Aquaculture and the capture fisheries—Balance of the scales. *World Aquaculture* (June 1997): 11–30.

Parker, R. 2002. *Aquaculture science.* 2nd ed. Albany, NY: Delmar.

Stickney, R. R. 1994. *Principles of aquaculture.* New York: Wiley.

USDA-ERS. 2011. Aquaculture outlook. Accessed online May 2011 at http://usda.mannlib.cornell. edu/MannUsda/viewDocumentInfo.do? documentID=1375

USDA-NASS. 2005. *Census of aquaculture.* Accessed online May 2011. http://www.agcensus.usda.gov/ Publications/2002/Aquaculture/index.

USDA-NASS. 2011a. *Farm income data.* Accessed online November 2007. http://www.ers.usda.gov/ Data/farmincome/finfidmu.htm.

USDA-NASS. 2011b. *Catfish production, January 2011.* Accessed online May 2011. http://usda.mannlib. cornell.edu/MannUsda/viewDocumentInfo. do?documentID=1016.

USDA-NASS. 2011c. *Catfish processing, April 2011.* Accessed online May 2011. http://usda.mannlib. cornell.edu/MannUsda/viewDocumentInfo. do?documentID=1015USDA-NASS. 2011d. *Trout production.* Accessed online May 2011. http://usda.mannlib.cornell.edu/MannUsda/ viewDocumentInfo.do?documentID=1172.

USDA-NASS. 2011d. *Aquaculture data sets,* Accessed Online May 2011. http://www.ers.usda.gov/ Data/Aquaculture/

16

Pet and Companion Animals

Learning Objectives

After you have studied this chapter, you should be able to:

- Describe the place of the pet species in the lives of the people of the United States.
- Discuss the types of pets that find service in the United States.
- Give a historical perspective to the keeping of pets.
- Discuss the geographic differences in pet ownership in the United States.
- Compare the roles of breeds and breeding programs in pet and livestock species.
- Describe the rudiments of reproductive management in the dog and cat.
- Explain the nutritional information found on a container or bag of pet food.
- Describe some common health challenges to pets.
- Cite the trends shaping the ownership of pets in the United States.

Key Terms

AAFCO Dog or Cat Nutrient Profiles

AAFCO Feeding Trial

Association of American Feed Control Officials (AAFCO)

Bitch

Companion animal

Human-developed cat breed

Natural breeds

Net quantity statement

Pet

Polymorphism

Queen

Spontaneous mutation

THE PLACE OF PET AND COMPANION SPECIES IN THE UNITED STATES

Timely statistics on pet species are difficult to obtain. The American Veterinary Medical Association (AVMA) conducts surveys periodically. The common pet species in the United States are shown in Table 16–1, along with their estimated populations in selected years, according to the AVMA's survey results. A number of additional species, including llamas, several amphibian species, crabs, crickets, tarantulas, chinchillas, hedgehogs, and others, are also kept as pets (Figure 16–1). Horses are included in the survey but are omitted here because they were covered in an earlier chapter. Many households have more than one type of pet. For instance, approximately 15% of the households in the United States have at least one cat and one dog. The AVMA study indicates that approximately 57.4% of U.S. households own at least one pet. Approximately 37.2% of U.S. households have a dog. Approximately 32.4% of U.S. households have at least one cat.

There are generalities that can be drawn about pet ownership. For example, families with children are the most likely of all demographic groups to have a pet; people older than age 65 who live alone are the least likely to have a pet. In general, the greater the household income, the more likely a pet will be found in the home. Homeowners are more likely to have a pet than those who rent their homes. Also, the larger the number of people in a household, the more likely it is to have a pet.

The pet industry generates approximately $50 billion (2011) from pet food, supplies, veterinary care, live animal purchases,

Table 16–1
COMMON PET SPECIES[1] AND THEIR POPULATIONS IN THE UNITED STATES

Type of Pet	Pet Populations (millions) Year			
	1991	1996	2001	2007
Dogs	52.5	52.9	61.6	72.1
Cats	57.0	59.1	68.9	81.7
Birds	16.22	17.02	10.1	11.2
Other birds (pigeons and poultry)	—	—	2.894	4.97
Fish	23.997	55.554	49.25	75.8
Ferrets	0.275	0.791	0.99	1.06
Rabbits	4.574	4.940	4.81	6.2
Hamsters	1.316	1.876	0.881	1.2
Guinea pigs	0.838	1.091	0.629	1.0
Gerbils	0.619	0.764	0.319	0.4
Other rodents	0.875	1.053	0.786	0.9
Turtles	0.708	0.950	1.07	1.99
Snakes	0.735	0.900	0.661	0.59
Lizards	0.314	0.705	0.545	1.08
Other reptiles	0.281	0.924	0.598	0.199
Livestock	3.371	6.083	2.936	10.99
All other pets	0.638	1.225	2.013	3.66
Total	164.261	205.876	208.982	275.039

[1]Excluding horses.
Source: AVMA, 1997, 2002, 2007.

Figure 16–1
Sugar gliders are part of a group of exotic/specialty pets kept in a growing number of households.
(Photo courtesy of Jamie Smith.)

grooming, boarding and pet sitting. The annual rate of growth for the industry is approximately 5.0% annually.

It is obvious that pets have less to do with agriculture than they do with the larger picture of life in the United States. However, there are links to agriculture. The pet food market is linked to agriculture because agriculture provides most of the raw ingredients for pet food manufacture. The pet food industry is estimated at approximately $19 billion (2011) annually and is growing. Cat food sales are increasing

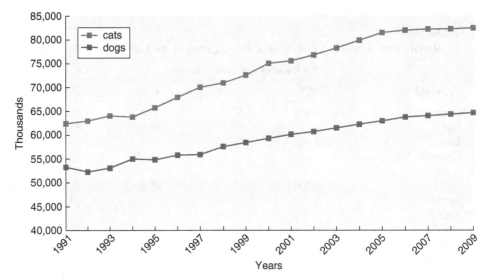

Figure 16–2
Dog and cat population growth in the United States.

more rapidly than dog food sales, which is reflective of the fact that cats are increasing in numbers more rapidly than dogs (Figure 16–2).

Because of the increasingly varied uses of and needs for pet species, careers and opportunities in the pet industry have increased. Recognition of these opportunities and the fact that pets and companion animals are becoming a more important part of modern life have driven colleges and universities to change course offerings. Some have included material about pets in existing courses. In addition, many are adding courses on pet management, nutrition, and genetics. This is tacit recognition that animal science is no longer just about livestock species. Pets are an integral part of the daily lives of humans. With less than 2% of the American population involved in agriculture but a majority having an association with pets and companion animals, logic has prevailed.

PURPOSE OF THE PET AND COMPANION ANIMALS INDUSTRY

The purpose of the pet and companion animal industry is to support the animals in service and companionship to people. Pets provide many practical services to society. Guard dogs, police dogs, narcotics-sniffing dogs, search-and-rescue dogs, hunting dogs, herding dogs, service dogs, and therapy dogs are just a few of the important ways that dogs are in service to humans. Cats catch vermin just as they have from the dawn of their domestication. In addition to these uses, we have recently begun to understand and appreciate many other ways in which companion animals contribute to our lives. Once a source of derision, the human–companion animal bond is now recognized as a contributing factor in the physical, mental, emotional, and social health of the owner. Dogs and cats provide the greatest service in this regard, but birds and small pets also do admirable service. However, the most common purpose for pet ownership is companionship (Figure 16–3). The value of pet species as companions sets the species apart from those domestic animals that primarily provide practical or economic benefit. The purpose of the industry can be more clearly seen by defining the pets themselves.

Figure 16–3
The most common purpose of pet ownership is companionship.

Pets and Companion Animals Defined

In the classic definition, **pets** are differentiated from livestock in that they are kept for pleasure rather than for utility. The more modern term, **companion animal**, describes an animal whose owner has an intense emotional tie to the animal. People often have relationships with animals that mirror relationships with humans, and describing these mirror relationships is how the term companion animal should be used.

Not all of the individuals of the companion/pet species qualify as either pets or companion animals. For instance, there are many barn cats across the country whose job in life is just to keep the rats and mice at bay. They are not kept for pleasure purposes, nor do they have a human companion. Neither term necessarily implies that the animals in question are domestic species (Figure 16–4). Although most pet/companion animals are undoubtedly of a domestic species, the keeping of tamed

Pet An animal kept for pleasure rather than utility.

Companion animal An animal to whom an owner has an intense emotional tie.

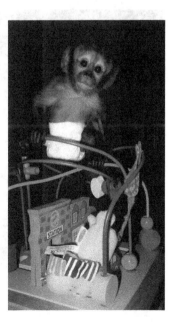

Figure 16–4
The keeping of tamed members of wild species as pets predates domestication and is still common. (Photo courtesy Buffy McKee.)

specimens of wild animals as pets predates domestication and is still a common practice around the world. As a means of clarifying the ambiguity of terminology, pets have been classified into six categories: ornamental pets, status symbols, playthings, hobby animals, helpers, and companions. These categories are not a complete solution to the nomenclature issue, but they go a long way in helping clarify the roles of pet/companions in modern society. Each category is discussed in the following sections.

Ornamental Pets   Ornamental pets serve the same purpose that houseplants serve—they decorate and enhance the atmosphere. Ornamental pets are usually brightly colored birds or fish or some type of animal that adds aesthetic appeal to an environment. It is common to find an aquarium filled with brightly colored or otherwise interesting aquatic species in restaurants, professional offices, or homes (Figure 16–5). Decorators have been known to bring fabric swatches to pet stores to pick a bird that matches carpet and draperies. Outdoor environments are often graced by flashy species such as peacocks, pheasants, Sumatra chickens, swans, geese, and ducks. Rarely are these ornamental pets handled, named, or treated in any special way. They are not considered companion animals.

Status Symbols   Strong evidence indicates that at least part of the domestication of the wolf was linked to the status its presence in camp gave the human occupants. A wolf as totem *and* companion would have conveyed a powerful message to rival clans or tribes. Sometimes we succumb to this same symbolism in modern life. This explains the motives of some people who keep poisonous snakes, piranhas, vicious dogs, big cats, bears, or wolves as pets. The animals are usually admired and well cared for as long as they satisfy the owner's expectations. In a more benign example, the symbolism of animals as totems for ancient people is not so different from that conveyed in modern society by what we generally refer to as "mascots." Status can also be conveyed by a pet kept for another primary reason. Purebred animals generally convey more status than mixed breed animals. Sometimes unusual, rare, and expensive animals are status symbols.

Playthings   Pets as playthings may range from living toys given to children to animals used in sports such as hunting or riding. Some of the people involved in sports

Figure 16–5

Fish are a common ornamental pet in homes, businesses, and professional offices. (Source: paul prescott/ Shutterstock)

Figure 16–6
This Golden Retriever, who fits into the "plaything" category of pets, is a field trial dog, a working sporting dog, and a valued member of the family of one of the author's colleagues.

that involve animals are only interested in the animal during the competitive season and lose interest and enthusiasm rather quickly at the close of the season. Certainly this is not always the case. The fact that a dog will retrieve downed game hardly prevents it from being a treasured pet and valued companion as well, such as the Golden Retriever shown in Figure 16–6.

Hobby Animals The hobby animal category is intended specifically to identify those animals displayed by their owners in organized exhibitions. Frequently, the owners breed and exhibit their own animals. The owners frequently belong to clubs and societies devoted to their animal's species. These clubs organize shows and events, which can be quite competitive (Figure 16–7). Many species are included in this category. Although dog and cat events are most common, there are clubs that sponsor events and shows for birds, rodents, and fish.

Work, Helper, or Service Animals Frequently, pet species perform vital services. Many of these are traditional services. For example, dogs have been trained to herd and track for millennia. Dogs still pull sleds and carts in some parts of the world

Figure 16–7
Hobby pets are those displayed by their owners in conformation and performance events, such as this Parson Russell Terrier competing in an agility trial.

BOX 16–1
SLED DOG RACING

Sled dog racing is a sport that, much like horse racing, arose from the informal competition of dogs involved in work. Dogs have been a preferred means of hauling supplies in cold climates for centuries, and organized sled dog racing originated from hunters and trappers using their working dog teams for amusement as well as a vital part of their livelihood. In many cases, this arrangement persists in modern times, with a number of high-profile competitive mushers racing dogs that, between races, are used to work trap lines and haul supplies to and from remote areas.

There are numerous forms of sled dog racing, ranging from skijoring (using 1 to 3 dogs to pull a musher on skis) to sprint racing (from 6 to 18 dogs in a team, running 10- to 25-mile sprints, often on consecutive days for cumulative times), but the type of sled dog racing most widely recognized by the general public is the endurance and ultra-endurance racing typified by the annual Iditarod sled dog race. In these events, teams of 12 to 16 dogs race for hundreds of miles. Race officials establish checkpoints along the race course for judges and veterinarians to monitor the health, safety, and progress of all participants, and for mushers to cache supplies to avoid having to carry hundreds of pounds of food and gear throughout the race. The Iditarod, held every year on the first Saturday in March, attracts nearly 100 teams with a first-place purse of over $100,000 in cash and prizes. The race, which commemorates a historic lifesaving relay by dogsled of diphtheria antiserum to Nome in 1925, runs 1,100 miles from Anchorage to Nome. The winning team typically finishes in 9 to 10 days, with the last finisher arriving 5 to 6 days later. In an average race, a third of the teams fail to reach Nome and instead are flown out of a checkpoint after withdrawing from the race.

The relationship between a musher and his or her dogs is complex because of the nature of the sport. The dogs are highly trained athletes, and the musher's role is often very similar to the coach of any human sports team: part disciplinarian, part motivator, part decision maker and strategist.

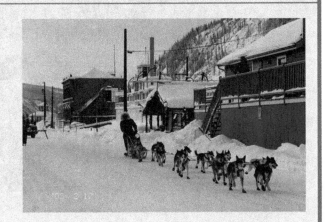

However, the bond between a musher and the dogs necessarily goes much deeper, for there must be mutual trust and devotion to have a successful team. Because of the vast distances covered during races, the teams must travel through raw wilderness in which there is a very real danger of injury and even death. A musher must earn and maintain the respect and trust of the dogs to complete a race safely, and many mushers have failed to complete a race when the dogs, having lost confidence and trust in their musher, elect to go on strike and refuse to leave a checkpoint. In some cases, mushers have suffered from frostbite and exposure when the dogs, well equipped to survive the extreme conditions of the wilderness, elect to go on strike between checkpoints, stranding the musher until such time that the dogs elect to continue on. Mushers place an extraordinarily high value on treating the dogs well, for it is no exaggeration that their lives may depend on their bond with their dogs.

Contributed by Michael S. Davis, DVM, PhD, Dipl ACVIM
Department of Physiological Sciences
Center for Veterinary Health Services,
Oklahoma State University

Photo contributed by Dr. Kathy Williamson. Used with permission.

(Box 16–1). In our modern society, they are trained as police dogs, search-and-rescue dogs, water rescue dogs, and drug dogs (Figure 16–8). Personal service dogs are an exciting and increasingly important part of modern society. In addition to seeing-eye dogs, there are service dogs that are trained to assist people with physical disabilities. Monkeys are also proving useful as service animals.

Companion Animals   Regardless of where in the previously mentioned categories an individual animal may fall, it is clear that some animals are also included in the ranks of companion animals. The Parson Russell Terriers that own the author's family, for example, keep armadillos out of the yard, moles out of the flowerbeds, rabbits out of the vegetable garden, possums and coons out of the hen house, and raise a ruckus when a strange car enters the drive. They also fetch sticks, play tag, and elicit their

Figure 16–8
Dogs are used to detect contraband of several kinds. Shown here is a member of the USDA/APHIS Beagle Brigade. Among other things, these dogs inspect luggage from international flights for food items that could bring disease into the United States. (Photo courtesy of USDA/APHIS.)

share of "oohs and ahs" from admiring visitors. They are status-service-plaything pets at a minimum. However, their greatest value is that defined by their relationships with the adults who have shared their lives with the dogs since childhood. They clearly view the Russells as companions, and thus they are (Figure 16–9). The Council for Science and Society states, "An animal employed for decoration, status-signaling, recreation, or hobby is being used primarily as an object—the animal equivalent of a work of art, a Rolls-Royce, a surfboard, or a collector's item. The companion animal, however, is typically perceived and treated as a subject—as a personality in its own right, irrespective of other considerations. With companion animals it is the relationship itself which is important to the owner." A companion pet may be treated as a member of the family, receiving presents at holidays, having its own chair, and so on.

Dogs, cats, small mammals, and birds are the most common species that become companion animals. Several reasons have been suggested for this. Perhaps most

Figure 16–9
This dog served her family in a variety of roles. The service that transcended all practical and monetary considerations was as friend and companion to Joshua.

Figure 16–10

Dogs, cats, small mammals, and birds are the species that most commonly transcend mere pethood to become companion pets. (Photo courtesy of Linda Guenther. Used with permission.)

important is that each of these species is either easily restrained or does not require restraint. In addition, they can be easily house trained or don't require house training at all. They are large enough to be treated as an individual and still small enough to be nonthreatening (Figure 16–10).

Value of Pets

Parents often use pets as a tool in child rearing. Pets provide a mechanism for teaching children about basic biology as well as the larger lessons about life and death. Children learn responsibility by caring for the animal (Figure 16–11). In addition, the affection of a pet helps children cope with the stresses of modern life. Pets also provide children with willing play-acting partners. There is surely a special place in the hereafter for the dog or cat that allows itself to be dressed in doll clothes and

Figure 16–11

Parents often provide pets to help teach their children responsibility. It was Aubry's job to feed Timone.

pushed around in a baby stroller, or dressed in an army helmet and dragged across the yard in a tank (little red wagon). In such games, children develop their imaginations, emotional responses, and conflict resolution skills.

Medical studies have verified physical, emotional, and social benefits of pet ownership. The animals provide companionship. However, multiple studies have demonstrated that pets provide a means for people to meet and interact with other people, helping to alleviate loneliness. Pets help people to be more active because they need daily care. If the pet is a dog, this care often includes walks for the dog, which exercise the owner as well. Pet owners (both children and adults) have lower blood pressure than people who don't have pets. Studies on the aged have confirmed that pet owners have increased longevity and live more satisfying lives compared to their peers without pets. Elderly pet owners visit the doctor less often and use fewer medications. Pets give some elderly individuals the opportunity to nurture, to touch and be touched, and to feel a sense of safety and security. Interestingly, even birds are successful in making people feel safer. There is increasing interest in the ways that animals can be used to improve the physical and emotional health of the elderly. Studies suggest that animal visitation and full-time residence of pets with their owners in nursing homes and retirement communities should be more the norm than the exception.

The use of service animals is one of the most exciting of the developing interests in pet species, predominantly dogs. Nearly 20% of the population of the United States has some type of disability, with approximately 12% considered to have a serious disability. Over half of these people are disabled because of serious visual impairment or blindness, loss or lack of physical mobility, or hearing impairment or complete deafness. Service animals can help people with these handicaps. Dogs have been trained as seeing-eye dogs in the United States in a serious, formal way since the 1929 founding of The Seeing Eye® Inc., of Morristown, New Jersey. Dogs for the Deaf of Central Point, Oregon, is a hearing-dog training and placement service that began in 1978. This group takes unwanted dogs from animal shelters and trains them to alert their partners to such sounds as telephones, doorbells, smoke alarms, and other important sounds. Canine Companions for Independence, with national headquarters in Santa Rosa, California, and regional offices across the United States, is perhaps the best known of several groups that train service, hearing, and social dogs. The dogs help individuals in wheelchairs by carrying packages, pulling wheelchairs, turning electric switches on and off, opening doors, and performing other chores to allow independent living for their human companions (Figure 16–12).

Figure 16–12
Nikita with her Skilled Companion Morell. "Thanks to an extraordinary dog, Nikita's just an ordinary kid."
(Photo Courtesy Canine Companions for Independence®.)

Animals are being increasingly used in mental and emotional therapy. Emotionally disturbed children and adults are often more willing to talk in the presence of an animal, often directing responses to questions by the therapist to the animal. This phenomenon is being expanded to help abused children, children with autism, persons with mental illness, dysfunctional families, and adult victims of violence. Rehabilitation centers use pets to help patients improve their strength, coordination, and mobility. Therapeutic riding programs have been started all across the country. With a growing body of research findings to support their value, these programs have developed into a legitimate health profession with special training and formal certification procedures.

In prisons, innovative programs have been started that help rehabilitate inmates, as well as providing benefits to broader society. Two programs associated with prisons have been established with the encouragement of Sister Pauline Quinn. The Wisconsin Correctional Liberty Dog Program is located at the Sanger B Powers Correctional Facility in Oneida, Wisconsin. One goal of the Liberty Dog Program is to meet the needs of people who have physical challenges by providing them with a service dog to help them live more independent lives. The other goal is to allow the prisoners the opportunity to serve their community. The Prison Pet Partnership Program, at the Washington State Corrections Center for Women, helps inmates learn how to train, groom, and board dogs. Animals are placed with individuals and families dealing with disabilities. Inmates at 20 different Ohio prisons work with Pilot Dogs Inc., a Columbus-based organization that provides guide dogs for the blind. The inmates raise and socialize the dogs prior to their training as seeing-eye dogs. These and similar programs around the country benefit both the inmate and ultimate recipient of the animal.

HISTORICAL PERSPECTIVE

Humanity's association with animals, and our uses for them, has long been dominated by their contributions to our needs for food and power, and by their association with religion. However, pet keeping is probably the use that led to the first domestications. Archaeological evidence from Paleolithic times suggests that people kept several different mammals as tame animals for short periods. An obvious explanation is that they were brought home as playthings for children (and probably adults, too). Tame wolves may have been kept as cave-mates as far back as 500,000 years ago. No doubt the young of other species of carnivores were also brought home and tamed. However, it was the gray wolf, *Canis lupis,* that gave rise to the first domestic animal, the dog (Figure 16–13). The readily accepted reason for this is that humans and wolves share many of the same social characteristics. Human social structures at the time were similar to those of pack animals. Wolves easily assimilated into the human

Figure 16–13
Canis lupis *has been established as the progenitor of the domestic dog. As unlikely as it seems, the Chihuahua and the gray wolf have the same blood coursing through their veins.* (Photo Courtesy USDA.)

pack. Wolves and humans were competitors in the hunt for the same grazing species as a food source. Tame wolves may have been used by humans to help in the hunt. They would have, no doubt, retained their defensive nature and protected the camp. At a minimum, they could have warned of intruders. Some suggest that the motive for the earliest associations may have been the wolves' and that it was no more noble than to scavenge scraps from human encampments. Proximity led to tameness and then to domestication.

Regardless of who had what motive in the beginning of the association, at some point the nature of the relationship developed beyond any utilitarian motive. Evidence from a late Paleolithic burial cave dated to 10,000 B.C. suggests that the nature of the relationship between humans and the dog had evolved to include a bond. The human and the dog found in the tomb were arranged with the human's hand on the shoulder of the dog. The potential implications of the gesture (bonding, affection, devotion, and so on) are clear to anyone who has ever had a pet of any sort. Other archeological evidence suggests 12,000 B.C. as a date for the domestication of the dog. Recent DNA sequencing technology has suggested that the dog may well have been domesticated as long as 135,000 years ago. However, those methods are not accepted by all experts at this time and the research lacks corroboration. It is also likely that there were actually multiple domestications in the road from *Canis lupis* to *Canis familiaris*.

Because modern dogs and wolves are different in so many traits, it is obvious that the tamed wolves were subjected to controlled breeding and subsequent domestication. Many of the physical traits that differentiate dogs from wolves were already in evidence by the time of the New Kingdom in Egypt. These traits included prick and pendant ears, solid and spotted coats, and curly and straight tails. Differentiation as to use was already apparent as well. Obviously the process has continued, as evidenced by the many breeds of dogs available today.

Domestic dogs were brought to the Western Hemisphere with the ancestors of the Native Americans who were living here when Europeans "discovered" the New World. Substantial archaeological evidence for domestic dogs in the Western Hemisphere dates as far back as 8000 B.C. Europeans brought very different dogs with them when they came to explore and settle the land.

It has long been believed that cats were not domesticated until after settled agriculture developed. The grain produced and stored by farmers provided a clear purpose for having them around human settlement—to help control vermin. Grain storage associated with settled agriculture attracts mice and rats. Wild cats were no doubt attracted to the vermin that any food store is likely to attract (Figure 16–14). The

Figure 16–14
Felis lybica, ancestor of the domestic cat. (Source: EcoPrint/ Shutterstock.)

Egyptians had long been credited with domestication of the cat. Evidence indicates that the Egyptians had domestic cats as long as 6,000 years ago and it is known that cats were confined in temples and used for religious purposes 5,000 years ago. Priests adopted cats as objects for deification. The cult of the cat-headed goddess Bast lasted 2,000 years. New DNA sequencing evidence suggests that the cat was domesticated in approximately 7000 B.C. in the Near East from the Near Eastern Wildcat (*Felis silvestris lybica*) as agricultural villages developed in the Fertile Crescent (Driscoll et al., 2007). Archeological evidence from a gravesite in Cyprus along with the DNA findings now suggests the cat was domesticated by at least 7500 B.C. and possibly earlier. Some even suggest that cat domestication could have been as early as 10,000 B.C.

No doubt the unique cat ability of purring played a role in their domestication. It is not hard to imagine an Egyptian temple worker or priest bringing a kitten home for the amusement of his or her children. One can imagine such a scene, with the father telling the child to shut his or her eyes and placing the purring kitten up to the child's ear. The look of fascination and wonder that spread across the child's face was the clincher that kept the animal in the home longer than first planned. By 3,000 years ago, and probably earlier, cats had entered commerce. Ships and sailors crossing the seas and caravans crossing the desert spread cats throughout the known world.

After reaching Europe, cats were at first quite popular as rodent killers. Unfortunately, they became associated with Satan worship and its practitioners—witches and warlocks—during the Middle Ages. This led to the killing of large numbers of cats by religious zealots. With fewer cats, black rats proliferated and took with them the oriental rat flea that spread the Black Death across Europe. A third of the human population died. The Sabbath day for the Norse goddess Freya (cat goddess) became known as Friday. When the Christians barred her worship, Friday became known as the black Sabbath.

European ships brought cats to the Americas as pets and for their rodent-killing skills. Ships of the time were notorious for their rat and mouse populations. The pilgrims are known to have had at least one cat on board when they landed on Plymouth Rock. The cat fancy dates to 1871 with the first cat show held in England. This was followed by the first organized cat show in the United States in 1895. Today, the cat enthusiasts of the world are a strong and devoted group.

Whether viewed as rodent-slayer, goddess, harbinger of evil, or companion, the cat elicits unusually strong emotions from humans. Many contend that there are only two kinds of people in the world—cat-lovers and cat-haters. That may be an exaggeration (although only a mild one), but everybody knows which kind of person a cat seems to single out first for its affections.

The other species (except the horse and llama, which are companion species to many but have their own chapters in this book) have been relatively recent domestications. Many were domesticated for their value as laboratory species and have found homes in the hearts of companion/pet owners either for their novelty or because they offer price or space advantages. Hedgehogs, both the European and African varieties, were apparently only imported into the United States for zoos beginning in the 1980s and made the transition into pet status shortly thereafter. Hamsters were not even taken into captivity until 1930. They started appearing as pets sometime during the 1940s. Rats have been bred in captivity only for approximately 100 years, and they have been considered pets for a couple of decades at most. Guinea pigs have been kept as a food species in South America for centuries. However, the keeping of the familiar domestic variety as a pet is a decades-old phenomenon in this country. Parakeets, which are more appropriately called *budgerigars,* have been kept in captivity only since 1840 and are still quite capable of reverting to wild type if released into an environment warm enough to suit their needs. Many other birds kept as pets are probably not even classifiable domestic species because they are so difficult to breed in captivity.

GEOGRAPHIC LOCATION

The AVMA surveys provide demographic information about pet ownership. Figure 16–15 shows the percentage of households that have pet animals within each region of the United States. All regions in the country have rates of ownership exceeding 50%.

Figure 16–16 shows the rate of dog ownership in the United States. Dogs are the most popular pet in terms of rate of ownership. When the AVMA survey was done in 1996, dogs were found in 31.6% of all households. The 2001 survey found the percentage had increased to 36.1%, very similar to the rate of ownership in 1991.

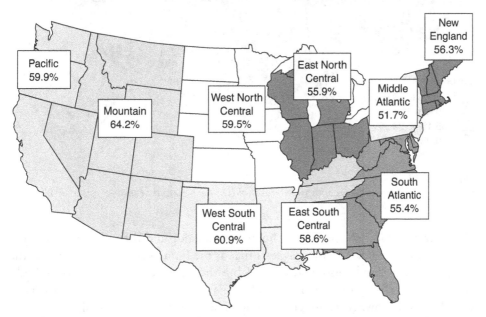

Figure 16–15

U.S. pet ownership—the percentage of households within each region that owned companion animals, 2007. (Source: American Veterinary Medical Association.)

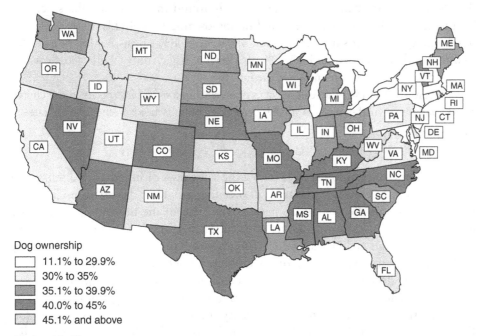

Figure 16–16

U.S. dog ownership—the percentage of households in each state that owned dogs in 2007.

(Source: American Veterinary Medical Association.)

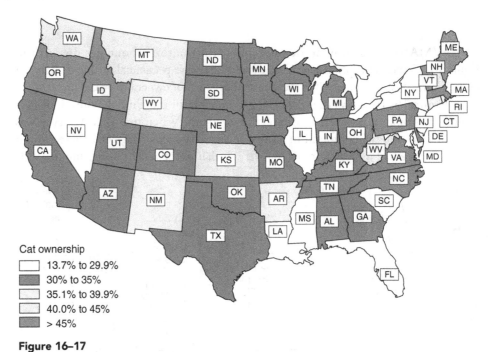

Cat ownership
- 13.7% to 29.9%
- 30% to 35%
- 35.1% to 39.9%
- 40.0% to 45%
- > 45%

Figure 16–17

U.S. cat ownership—the percentage of households in each state that owned cats in 2007.
(Source: American Veterinary Medical Association.)

However, in 2006, 37.2% of households owned a dog and the number of dogs per household had increased. This suggests that as the human population increases the dog population should also increase, which is the trend currently observed in both. About 60% of all dog-owning households own just one dog, and 42% also own a cat. Over half of dog owners consider their dog to be a member of the family.

Figure 16–17 shows the distribution of households that own cats. The total number of cats is greater than the number of dogs, but cats are found in fewer households, 31.6% in 2001, a number that increased from 27.3% in 1996. By 2006, 32.4% of U.S. households had a cat. Cats are found in greater numbers per cat-owning household than dogs are found in dog-owning households. Only 37.8% of dog-owning households have more than one dog; 51.8% of cat-owning households have more than one cat, and 47.2 % also own a dog. Almost half of cat owners consider their cat to be a member of the family.

Figure 16–18 shows the regional rates of ownership for the bird species in the United States. Birds are owned in a much smaller percentage of households in the United States.

GENETICS AND BREEDING PROGRAMS

Genetics of the companion species follow the same laws of inheritance discussed in Chapters 6 and 7. However, the types of breeding programs discussed in Chapter 7 are nonexistent for the pet species because the goals of the breeding programs are entirely different. The pet species are selected for breeding based almost exclusively on phenotypes and pedigree selection. This approach to breeding has allowed many undesirable genetic diseases to become widespread problems in certain breeds of dogs and, to a lesser degree, in cats and other species as well. At best, the majority of breeders have only rudimentary skills in the scientific aspect of breeding. For those who do have expertise in genetics, it tends to be fairly specific for certain traits, often color. Certainly, a few knowledgeable breeders can be found for all of the species. Sadly, they are the exception rather than the rule. However, those who are knowledgeable tend to be highly competent. The cat fancy has a group of breeders who are excellent geneticists and have been very active in improving existing breeds and developing

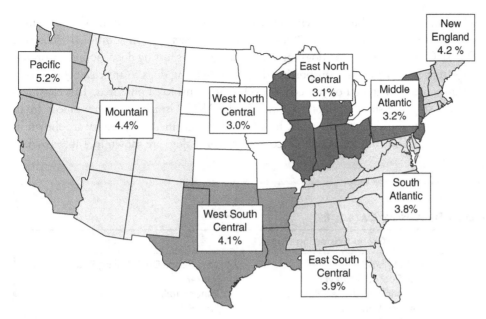

Figure 16–18

U.S. bird ownership—the percentage of households in each region that owned birds in 2007.

(Source: American Veterinary Medical Association.)

new ones. The increasing numbers of cat breeds are a testament to their work and dedication. Perhaps with the rapidly advancing state of DNA technology, the level of knowledge about overall genetics will increase for all pet species.

Advanced tools for improved selection and breeding of dogs will soon be available. The dog has a very large spectrum of **polymorphism** within the 400 or so breeds. This has made the dog a very attractive model for gene identification of phenotypic, behavioral, and pathological traits. The first draft of the dog genome sequence was made available in July 2004, and a complete sequence was published in 2005. The genome of the cat was published in 2007. Inexpensive technology is already available to positively identify parentage, but parental identification is just a small part of what is possible. In the very near future, it will be possible to compare genetic similarity between the individuals of a proposed mating. Ultimately, all breeding dogs and cats can be screened for all genetic diseases. In dogs, the genes for herding instinct, protective instinct, scenting ability, running speed, and so on, will be identified and knowledgeable matings will be made. Even though the technology has not yet reached this stage, it is coming. SNP array genetic evaluation is available for cats for some genetic diseases, color genetics, hair length, blood type, and sex markers. Similar tests are available for dogs, and more are available each year.

Polymorphism The existence of two or more discontinuous, segregating phenotypes in a population.

BREEDS OF DOGS

It did not take humans long to begin shaping the genetics of the wolves that were to become domestic dogs. It is likely that some of the wolf disposition characteristics were altered fairly quickly. The progression of the other genetic changes is no more than a matter of speculation. It is known that by Roman times, wolf characteristics and behaviors had been refined into various categories of dogs, including herding, war, sight and scent hunters, terriers, and companions. Because dogs were domesticated earlier than any other species, it is logical that they were developed into numerous types and breeds. There are estimated to be between 400 and 450 dog breeds in the world today. The primary dog registry in the United States is the American Kennel Club (AKC). The AKC was established in 1884 as a nonprofit organization devoted to the advancement of purebred dogs. The AKC currently registers more than 170 recognized breeds, with

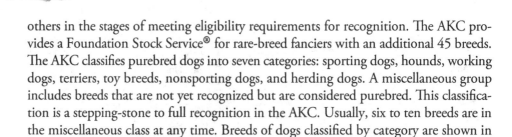

others in the stages of meeting eligibility requirements for recognition. The AKC provides a Foundation Stock Service® for rare-breed fanciers with an additional 45 breeds. The AKC classifies purebred dogs into seven categories: sporting dogs, hounds, working dogs, terriers, toy breeds, nonsporting dogs, and herding dogs. A miscellaneous group includes breeds that are not yet recognized but are considered purebred. This classification is a stepping-stone to full recognition in the AKC. Usually, six to ten breeds are in the miscellaneous class at any time. Breeds of dogs classified by category are shown in Table 16–2. The 10 most popular breeds of purebred dogs are shown in Table 16–3.

Table 16–2
AMERICAN KENNEL CLUB DOG BREEDS BY CATEGORY

Group I: Sporting Dogs

American Water Spaniel	Field Spaniel	Nova Scotia Duck Tolling Retriever
Boykin Spaniel	Flat-Coated Retriever	Pointer
Brittany	German Shorthaired Pointer	Spinone Italiano
Chesapeake Bay Retriever	German Wirehaired Pointer	Sussex Spaniel
Clumber Spaniel	Golden Retriever	Vizsla
Cocker Spaniel	Gordon Setter	Weimaraner
Curly-Coated Retriever	Irish Red and White Setter	Welsh Springer Spaniel
English Cocker Spaniel	Irish Setter	Wirehaired Pointing Griffon
English Setter	Irish Water Spaniel	
English Springer Spaniel	Labrador Retriever	

Group II: Hounds

Afghan Hound	Dachshund	Petit Basset Griffon Vendeen
American Foxhound	English Foxhound	Pharaoh Hound
Basenji	Greyhound	Plott
Basset Hound	Harrier	Redbone Coonhound
Beagle	Ibizan Hound	Rhodesian Ridgeback
Black and Tan Coonhound	Irish Wolfhound	Saluki
Bloodhound	Norwegian Elkhound	Scottish Deerhound
Bluetick Coonhound	Otterhound	Whippet
Borzoi		

Group III: Working Dogs

Akita	German Pinscher	Neapolitan Mastiff
Alaskan Malamute	Giant Schnauzer	Newfoundland
Anatolia Shepherd Dog	Great Dane	Portuguese Water Dog
Bernese Mountain Dog	Great Pyrenees	Rottweiler
Black Russian Terrier	Greater Swiss Mountain Dog	Saint Bernard
Boxer	Komondor	Samoyed
Bullmastiff	Kuvasz	Siberian Husky
Cane Corso	Leonberger	Standard Schnauzer
Doberman Pinscher	Mastiff	Tibetan Mastiff
Dogue de Bordeaux		

Group IV: Terriers

Airedale Terrier	Irish Terrier	Scottish Terrier
American Staffordshire Terrier	Kerry Blue Terrier	Sealyham Terrier
Australian Terrier	Lakeland Terrier	Skye Terrier
Bedlington Terrier	Manchester Terrier	Smooth Fox Terrier
Border Terrier	Miniature Bull Terrier	Soft-Coated Wheaton Terrier
Bull Terrier	Miniature Schnauzer	Staffordshire Bull Terrier
Cairn Terrier	Norfolk Terrier	Welsh Terrier
Dandie Dinmont Terrier	Norwich Terrier	West Highland White Terrier
Glen of Imaal Terrier	Parson Russell Terrier	Wire Fox Terrier

Table 16–2
AMERICAN KENNEL CLUB DOG BREEDS BY CATEGORY (CONTINUED)

Group V: Toys

Affenpinscher	Italian Greyhound	Pomeranian
Brussels Griffon	Japanese Chin	Poodle (Toy)
Cavalier King	Maltese	Pug
Charles Spaniel	Manchester Terrier	Shih Tzu
Chihuahua	Miniature Pinscher	Silky Terrier
Chinese Crested	Papillon	Toy Fox Terrier
English Toy Spaniel	Pekingese	Yorkshire Terrier
Havanese		

Group VI: Nonsporting Dogs

American Eskimo Dog	Dalmation	Poodle (Standard and Miniature)
Bichon Frise	Finnish Spitz	Schipperke
Boston Terrier	French Bulldog	Shiba Inu
Bulldog	Keeshond	Tibetan Spaniel
Chinese Shar-pei	Lhasa Apso	Tibetan Terrier
Chow Chow	Löwchen	Xoloitzcuintli
	Norwegian Lundehund	

Group VII: Herding Dogs

Australian Cattle Dog	Border Collie	German Shepherd Dog
Australian Shepherd	Bouvier des Flandres	Icelandic Sheepdog
Bearded Collie	Briard	Norwegian Bunhund
Beauceron	Canaan Dog	Old English Sheepdog
Belgian Malinois	Cardigan Welsh Corgi	Pembroke Welsh Corgi
Belgian Sheepdog	Collie	Polish Lowland Sheepdog
Belgian Tervuren	Entlebucher Mountain Dog	Puli
		Pyrenean Shepherd
		Shetland Sheepdog
		Swedish Vallhund

Miscellaneous Class

Breeds vary

Source: American Kennel Club, 2011.

Table 16–3
TEN MOST POPULAR BREEDS OF DOGS

Rank	2000	2005	2010
1	Labrador Retriever	Labrador Retrievers	Labrador Retrievers
2	Golden Retriever	Golden Retriever	German Shepherd
3	German Shepherd	Yorkshire Terrier	Yorkshire Terrier
4	Dachshund	German Shepherd	Beagle
5	Beagle	Beagle	Golden Retriever
6	Poodle	Dachshund	Bulldog
7	Yorkshire Terrier	Boxer	Boxer
8	Chihuahua	Poodle	Dachshund
9	Boxer	Shih Tzu	Poodle
10	Shih Tzu	Miniature Schnauzer	Shih Tzu

Source: American Kennel Club, 2011.

BREEDS OF CATS

Cats have not been developed into as many different breeds as have dogs. This is because there have been fewer uses overall for cats. Cats have been kept predominantly for their vermin-controlling habits and as pets. Thus the differentiation into breeds with highly specialized functions has not occurred. There are approximately 50 breeds of cats recognized in the United States. Table 16–4 lists cat breeds most commonly accepted by various breed associations. The 10 most popular cat breeds are listed in rank order in Table 16–5. Some breeds of cats were selected by human preference or regional diversity and have been in existence for hundreds of years. These breeds are referred to as the **natural breeds** and include Abyssinian, Birman, Burmese, Chartreux, Maine Coon, and Egyptian Mau. In some cases, modern cat fanciers have changed the natural breeds substantially through selection. The **human-developed breeds** are the livestock equivalent of composite breeds. They were created by crossbreeding and subsequent selection to fix type. Examples include crossing the Burmese and American Shorthair to develop the Bombay, and crossing the Siamese and Persian to create the Himalayan. **Spontaneous mutations** have also contributed to the development of new breeds that showcase the mutation. Examples include the American Curl (curled-back ears), American Bobtail (short-tailed), Cornish Rex (soft, short, wavy hair), Munchkin (short legs), and Scottish Fold (ears folded forward and down on the skull). There are several feline studbook organizations in the United States. The goals, rules of registration, recognized breeds, and breed standards for the different associations represent different perspectives on cat breeding and exhibition. Thus a cat that fits the standard of one association may be excluded or be inferior according to the standards of another.

Natural breeds Cat breeds selected by human preference or natural conditions specific to a region.

Human-developed cat breed Breeds that have been developed from existing breeds or crosses of existing breeds.

Spontaneous mutation A change in the DNA that creates new alleles.

BREEDS OF OTHER PET SPECIES

Rabbits are separated into distinct breeds. This is because they were first domesticated as a food species and have been used around the globe for food and fiber for hundreds of years. The remainder of the pet species are not as breed oriented. For instance, guinea pig breeds do exist, but they are largely based on coat type and color variations. Likewise, color varieties exist for several of the other rodent species. The animals are not usually individually registered, and shows of the size and type held regularly for dogs and cats are fewer in number.

Table 16–4
CAT BREEDS[1]

Abyssinian	Colorpoint Shorthair	Maine Coon	Selkirk Rex
American Bobtail	Cornish Rex	Manx	Siamese
American Curl	Devon Rex	Norwegian Forest Cat	Siberian
American Shorthair	Egyptian Mau	Ocicat	Singapura
American Wirehair	European Burmese	Oriental	Snowshoe
Balinese	Exotic	Persian	Somali
Bengal	Havana Brown	RagaMuffin	Sphynx
Birman	Japanese Bobtail	Ragdoll	Tonkinese
Bombay	Javanese	Russian Blue	Turkish Angora
British Shorthair	Korat	Scottish Fold	Turkish Van
Burmese	La Perm		
Burmilla			
Chartreux			
Chinese Li Hua			

[1]Names of breeds and standards for the breeds vary between associations.
Source: Compiled from various breed associations and cat fancy publications.

Table 16–5
TEN MOST POPULAR CAT BREEDS

Rank	1995	2000	2005	2010
1	Persian	Persian	Persian	Persian
2	Maine Coon	Maine Coon	Maine Coon	Maine Coon
3	Siamese	Siamese	Exotic	Exotic
4	Abyssinian	Exotic	Siamese	Ragdoll
5	Exotic	Abyssinian	Abyssinian	Sphynx
6	Oriental	Oriental	Ragdoll	Siamese
7	Scottish Fold	Birman	Birman	Abyssinian
8	American Shorthair	American Shorthair	American Shorthair	American Shorthair
9	Birman	Scottish Fold	Oriental	Cornish Rex
10	Ocicat	Burmese	Sphynx	Birman

Source: The Cat Fancier's Association, Inc.

The bird fancy is divided along species lines. Interesting color variations have been developed in several species. Breeders of budgerigars and lovebirds have perhaps taken this color breeding to the greatest degree. Some splendid color varieties have been developed for both species and are exhibited at shows around the country. The budgerigar breeders have also developed the exhibition of their animals to the greatest degree. As the most popular of the caged bird species, their exhibition industry is perhaps expected to be the most developed. However, an active exhibition schedule is kept for several species of caged birds in the United States. In addition, interesting color variations can be found in most of the birds that make up the bird fancy.

REPRODUCTIVE MANAGEMENT

The reproductive characteristics of the various pet species are too varied to cover adequately in one small section in one chapter. Table 16–6 explains some of the basic features of the reproductive cycles of selected mammalian species. Table 16–7 gives basic data on some avian species.

The basic structures in the reproductive tract of the **bitch** are shown in Figure 16–19. In most dogs, puberty begins at 6 to 9 months of age. The ovarian cycle of the bitch is monoestrous. The interval from cycle to cycle is influenced by breed differences and can be influenced by environmental factors as well. The time between cycles varies from 4 to 13 months, with an average of 7 months. The bitch begins to attract males before she is ready to mate. Exterior signs of heat in the bitch include behavioral changes like marking of territory, a swollen vulva, and a light bloody discharge from the vulva. Heat in the bitch is under the influence of luteinizing hormone (LH), progesterone, and estrogen (Figure 16–20). Prior to the LH hormonal surge, the bitch generally refuses the dog. After the LH surge, she generally stands for mating. The ova are released from the follicles approximately 2 to 3 days after the LH surge. The ovulated eggs are not ready for fertilization until day 4 to day 7 following estrus. The greatest number of ovulations occur 24 to 72 hours after the LH peak. Breeding should ideally occur 4 to 7 days later. Plasma progesterone concentrations rise prior to ovulation in the bitch. Thus measurement of serum progesterone concentration in the bitch can be used to determine the day of ovulation and breeding. For anyone who has ever had an unwanted litter of puppies, this may seem to be too much information. However, now that the techniques and breed association rules are in place to allow artificial insemination, the timing of appropriate semen placement can be critical in mating success or failure. In addition, valuable stud dogs can be in high demand.

Bitch A female dog.

TABLE 16-6

FEATURES OF THE REPRODUCTIVE CYCLE OF SELECTED PET SPECIES

	Dog	Cat	Guinea Pig	Hamster	Mouse	Rat	Gerbil
Age at Puberty	6–12 months	6–15 months	55–70 days	5–8 weeks	35 days	37–73 days	9–12 weeks
Cycle Type	Monoestrous, all year; mostly late winter and summer	Provoked ovulation, seasonally polyestrous, spring and early fall	Polyestrous	Polyestrous	Polyestrous	Polyestrous, all year	Polyestrous
Cycle Length	6–7 months	15–21 days	16 days	4 days	4 days	4–5 days	4–6 days
Duration of Heat	4–14 days standing heat	9–10 days in absence of male	6–11 hours	10–20 hours	9–20 hours	12–18 hours; usually begins about 7 P.M.	12–15 hours
Best Time for Breeding	4–7 days after standing	Daily from day 2 of heat	10 hours after start of heat	At start of heat, 8–10 P.M.	At start of heat	Near ovulation, which occurs close to midnight	Mid-heat
First Heat after Birth	3–5 months	4–6 weeks	6–8 hours	1–2 weeks after litter removed	2–4 days after litter removed	Within 24 hours	1–3 days
Number of Young	1–22	1–10	1–6	1–12	1–12	2–20	2–15
Gestation Period	58–70 days	58–70 days	59–72 days	14 days	17–21 days	20–22 days	24–26 days

Source: Adapted from USDA, 1984.

Table 16–7
EGG PRODUCTION AND INCUBATION FOR SOME BIRD SPECIES

Type of Bird	Egg Production per Clutch	Incubation Time
Canaries	2–7	14–15
Cockatiels	3–7	21–23
Cockatoos	2–4	28
Conures	4–6	24
Lorikeets	2–4	22–25
Lovebirds	3–8	23–24
Macaws	2–4	28
Budgerigars	4–8	18–20
Finches	2–4	14–19
Parrots	2–4	17–31

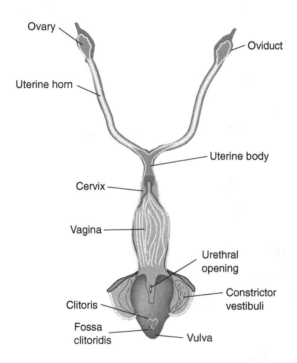

Figure 16–19
Basic structures in the reproductive tract of the bitch.

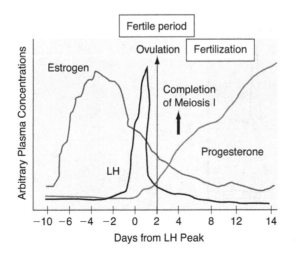

Figure 16–20
Hormonal patterns of the bitch during estrous cycle.
(Source: Adapted from Geisert, 1999. Used with permission.)

Book Refers to the number of females scheduled to be mated to a particular male.

Queen A female cat.

A mating done on the wrong day can prevent the dog from being mated with another bitch that same day. For a popular stud, it is important to mate the bitches on the appropriate days to maximize the **book** on the dog. Some owners of valuable stud dogs insist on blood hormone monitoring on all bitches to be bred to their dogs.

The basic structures of the female reproductive tract of the **queen** are shown in Figure 16–21. The average age of puberty in the queen is 10 months, with a range of 4 to 18 months. The queen is a seasonally polyestrous breeder. Photoperiod controls the period of cyclicity. Breeding season varies according to day length and is generally from March to September. Queens living indoors may cycle in the winter if lights in the house give them 12–14 hours of "daylight." Signs of heat in the queen include restlessness, vocalizations, and possibly marking of territory. The queen displays uniqueness in her reproductive function in that ovulation must be induced by copulation. Mating of the queen induces the LH surge required for ovulation (Figure 16–22). The average length of the estrous cycle is 14 to 21 days. Estrus lasts approximately 7 days, followed by a period of nonreceptivity if no mating occurs.

Figure 16–21

Anatomy of queen reproductive tract.

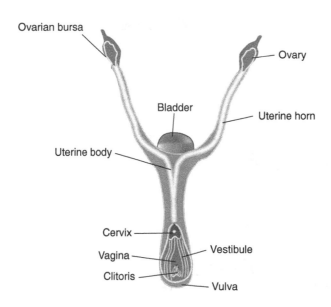

Figure 16–22

Hormonal changes during the estrous cycle in the queen. (Source: Adapted from Geisert, 1999. Used with permission.)

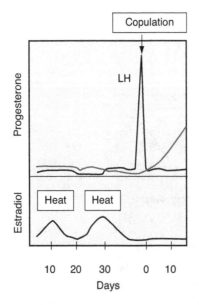

NUTRITION OF THE PET SPECIES

In addition to dogs and cats, there are several dozen other pet species. These species vary from obligate carnivores to herbivores. Monogastrics, cecal fermenters, and ruminants are included. The bird species have avian tracts, but their diets are quite varied. Thus a discussion of the nutrition of the individual species is beyond the scope of this text. Good nutrition for a pet is a responsibility of pet ownership. Learning what constitutes good nutrition for an animal can require a good deal of study and effort. The more uncommon and exotic the species being kept, the more daunting the task. See Chapters 3, 4, and 5 for basic discussions of nutrition and rations for pet species that are relevant to this discussion.

Most people who keep pets do so in limited numbers, which makes mixing rations on an individual animal basis impractical. In addition, most people do not have the knowledge to select ingredients and formulate their own rations. So most people do (and should) purchase a premixed feed for their pets. This makes the ability to choose a pet food based on the feed label information an important common denominator for all pet owners. Thus the discussion of nutrition in this chapter focuses on labels and how to interpret them. This discussion focuses on complete rations and does not include treats and specialty feeds. Figure 16–23 shows a representative pet food label.

Pet food labels are regulated, and the regulations are enforced by the FDA's Center for Veterinary Medicine (CVM). The FDA standards are the same as those that apply to livestock feeds and include proper identification of product, net quantity statement, manufacturer's address, and proper listing of ingredients. States also have the authority to establish and enforce state regulations. Many states have adopted model pet food regulations established by the **Association of American Feed Control Officials (AAFCO)** that are more specific. Aspects of feed labeling such as product name, guaranteed nutrient analysis, nutritional adequacy statement, feeding directions, and calorie statements are covered under the AAFCO standards. The requirements for labeling dog and cat foods are the most detailed and specific. This is because the needs of these species are known with enough confidence that the AAFCO can specify nutrient requirements.

Association of American Feed Control Officials (AAFCO) An organization that provides a mechanism for developing and implementing uniform and equitable laws, regulations, standards, and enforcement policies to regulate the manufacture, distribution, and sale of animal feeds.

Product Name

To keep pet food names honest to the ingredients they contain, names can only include certain words according to specific conditions named by four AAFCO rules. The "95%" rule states that for an ingredient to be used in the name of a pet food, 95% of the product must be the named ingredient, not counting the water added for processing and "condiments." If water is included, the named ingredient must still be at least 70% of the product. Ingredient lists must also be declared in the proper order of predominance by weight. Thus, "Beef Dog Food" must contain at least 95% beef, and beef must be the first ingredient listed in the ingredient list. If the food is named "Lamb and Liver Dog Food," lamb and liver combined must equal 95% of the feed. The first ingredient in the name must be the one found in greatest quantity in the feed. This rule applies only to ingredients of animal origin. So grains and vegetables cannot be part of the 95% total. "Beef and Potatoes" must still be at least 95% beef to use "beef" in the name this way.

The "25%," or "dinner," rule works the same way as the "95%" rule except the minimum requirement is that the named ingredient must be at least 25% of the product, excluding the water added during processing. The name must include a qualifying descriptive term, such as dinner, platter, entree, nuggets, formula, or other similar term. If more than one ingredient is included in a "dinner" name, they

SPARKLE 'N SHINE BRAND™ BEEF DOG FOOD

According to AAFCO model regulations this product must be 95% beef.

The "with" rule allows a statement such as this for ingredients found in a minimum of 3% in the feed.

Net Weight
5 LBS (2.26kg)

Net quantity statement tells the quantity of the product in the container.

INGREDIENTS. BEEF, POULTRY BY-PRODUCT MEAL, CORN, SOYBEAN MEAL, CORN GLUTEN MEAL, WHEAT FLOUR, CHEESE, FAT PRESERVED WITH BHA, FISH, CHICKEN, LIVER, PHOSPHORIC ACID, BREWERS DRIED YEAST, FUMARIC ACID, TRICALCIUM PHOSPHATE, SALT, SORBIC ACID (A PRESERVATIVE), CHOLINE CHLORIDE, CALCIUM PROPIONATE (A PRESERVATIVE), POTASSIUM CHLORIDE, TAURINE, DRIED WHEY, ZINC OXIDE, FERROUS SULFATE, NIACIN, VITAMIN SUPPLEMENTS (E, A, B-12, D-3), CALCIUM PANTOTHENATE, RIBOFLAVIN SUPPLEMENT, MANGANESE SULFATE, BIOTIN, THIAMINE MONONITRATE, FOLIC ACID, PYRIDOXINE HYDROCHLORIDE, COPPER SULFATE, MENADIONE SODIUM BISULFITE COMPLEX (SOURCE OF VITAMIN K ACTIVITY), CALCIUM IODATE.

Ingredients must be listed in the proper order of predominance by weight.

GUARANTEED ANALYSIS:

CRUDE PROTEIN NOT LESS THAN	24.0%
CRUDE FAT NOT LESS THAN	8.5%
CRUDE FIBER NOT MORE THAN	3.5%
MOISTURE NOT MORE THAN	10.0%
CALCIUM	0.1%
PHOSPHOROUS	0.1%

Minimums and maximums of these four must be on the guaranteed analysis label.

Other nutrients may be added to the guaranteed analysis label.

——— Daily Feeding Guidelines ———

Dog Weight	Up to 10 lbs	11 to 20 lbs	21 to 50 lbs	51 to 90 lbs	Over 90 lbs
Amount to Feed Dry*	$3/4$ to $1^1/4$ cups	$1^1/4$ to $2^1/4$ cups	$2^1/4$ to $4^1/2$ cups	$4^1/2$ to 7 cups	1 cup for each 14 lbs

AAFCO STATEMENT:

Animal feeding tests using AAFCO procedures substantiate that "Sparkle 'N Shine Brand" Beef Dog Food provides complete and balanced nutrition for all life stages.

The nutritional adequacy statement must have the appropriate life stages and how the formulation was determined (either by AAFCO Nutrient Profiles or AAFCO feed trial).

Individual dog's requirements may vary depending upon breed, size, age, exercise, and environment. Pregnant and nursing or hard working dogs may require 2-3 times these amounts.

Feeding directions. Consider these a rough guide to feeding.

FEEDING PUPPIES:

For puppies 2 to 6 months of age multiply the amount to feed, from above, by two. For puppies 6 to 12 months of age multiply the amount to feed, from above, by 1.5. Puppies that are 12 months of age to adult should be fed the amount listed in the table above.

*Based on 8oz. measuring cup.

Manufactured by Josh N' Aubry Enterprises
P.O. Box 111,
Stillwater, OK 66666
Questions? Call 1-800-111-DOGS

"Manufactured by . . . " statement identifies party responsible for quality and safety and location of the party.

Figure 16–23

Representative pet food label.

must total 25% and be listed in the same order as found on the ingredient list. The first ingredient in the name must be the one found in greatest quantity in the feed. In addition, each ingredient named must be at least 3% of the total. Grains and vegetables cannot be part of the 25% total. "Beef and Potatoes" must still be at least 25% beef to use "beef" in the name this way. The "with" or "3%" rule allows a feed name to use the designation "with" if the feed contains at least 3% of the ingredient that is named after the word "with." "Dog Food with Liver" must contain 3% liver (excluding water). "Lamb with Liver Dog Dinner" must contain 3% liver (excluding water) in addition to the minimum 25% lamb the term "dinner" indicates it contains. The feed could also be named "Lamb Dog Dinner" and have a separate entry such as "with liver" on the label that does not appear in the name. Likewise, "Doctors Brand" dog food could also carry a "with lobster" and would be required to have 3% lobster.

The "flavor" rule does not specify a minimum percentage. However, the product must have a detectable amount of the product as determined by a set of test methods using animals trained to prefer specific flavors. Pet foods often contain **digests**, which are materials treated with heat, enzymes, and/or acids to form concentrated natural flavors. Only a small amount of a "chicken digest" is needed to produce a " Chicken-Flavored Cat Food," even though no actual chicken is added. Stocks or broths are also occasionally added. Whey is often used to add a milk flavor. Often labels bear a claim of "no artificial flavors" implying something special about the feed. Actually, artificial flavors are rarely used in pet foods, so the inclusion of the wording is for perceived market advantage only. The major exception is artificial smoke or bacon flavors, which are added to some treats.

> **Digests** Produced by enzymatic degradation of animal tissues. Used to flavor pet foods.

In this discussion on the use of ingredients in product names, note that the ultimate purpose of dog and cat foods is to supply needed nutrients, not specific ingredients. Because the nutritional requirements can be met using a wide variety of ingredients, the presence or absence of a particular ingredient doesn't need to be a driving factor. However, if you choose to purchase a product on an ingredient basis, it is important to keep these rules in mind. In addition to scrutiny of the product name, also read the ingredient list to ensure that the preferred ingredient is present in a desirable amount.

Net Quantity Statement

The **net quantity statement** tells the quantity of product in the container. FDA regulations dictate the format, size, and placement of the net quantity statement on the container. The "manufactured by . . ." statement identifies the party responsible for the quality and safety of the product and its location. Regulations require that ingredients be listed in descending order of predominance by weight. Most ingredients on pet food labels have an AAFCO official definition.

> **Net quantity statement** FDA-required statement on a pet food package specifying the quantity of feed in the container.

A pet food label must state guarantees for its minimum percentages of crude protein and crude fat and the maximum percentages of crude fiber and moisture. Some labels have guarantees for other nutrients that manufacturers voluntarily include. These frequently include the maximum percentage of ash. Cat foods commonly have guarantees for taurine and magnesium. The minimum levels of calcium, phosphorus, sodium, and linoleic acid are often found on many dog food containers. The manufacturer may be willing to provide additional information on particular nutrients that are not guaranteed on the label. Nutrient guarantees are given on an " as-fed" basis.

According to AAFCO regulations, the maximum percentage of moisture content for a pet food is 78%, except for products labeled as a "stew," "in sauce," "in gravy," or similar terms. Exempted products have been found to be as high as 87.5% moisture. Moisture level can make a large difference in the amount of nutrients an animal receives from the feed. The amount of moisture in a canned food should be considered in any purchase, both in terms of the nutrients it contains and the price of the dry matter in the food.

Nutritional Adequacy Statement

The AAFCO nutritional adequacy statement is a very important part of a pet food label. A "complete and balanced," "perfect," "scientific," or "100% nutritious" pet food must have been substantiated for nutritional adequacy. This may be done by formulating the food to meet the **AAFCO Dog or Cat Food Nutrient Profiles**, or the product must be tested according to the **AAFCO Feeding Trial**. The nutritional adequacy statement must state the appropriate animal life stage(s) for which the product is suitable, such as maintenance, growth, reproduction, or all life stages. Products that are intended "for all life stages" must meet the requirements for growth and reproduction. Product labeling for a more specific use or life stage, such as "senior," or for a specific size or breed is done outside any rules governing these types of statements because the requirements have not been established in that much detail. Therefore, a geriatric diet is required only to meet the requirements for adult maintenance. Products developed outside these methods to establish nutritional adequacy must be labeled "This product is intended for intermittent or supplemental feeding only." Snack or treat foods are exempted from this rule because it is generally understood these foods aren't intended to be complete diets.

Feeding Directions

Feeding directions are designed to give the purchaser guidance as to how much of a given food should be fed to an animal. Instructions usually indicate how many cups of feed per pound of body weight to offer the animal. Feeding directions simply offer guidance in feeding an animal because many factors interact to influence the amount an individual animal may need. Companies tend to overestimate the needs of the animal in making these feeding recommendations to be sure the animals are offered enough. The best strategy for an owner is to offer the recommended amount at first, and then use judgment to adjust the amount to fit the needs of the animal.

Calorie Statement

AAFCO regulations allow calorie statements to be put on pet foods voluntarily. All products making calorie claims must include a calorie content statement on the label. Such statements must be expressed on a "kilocalories per kilogram" basis. In addition, they may appear on a per cup basis. The calorie statement is made on an "as-fed" basis, so corrections for moisture content must be made. A quick method to compare the caloric content values between a canned and a dry food is to multiply the value for the canned food by four and then compare.

For a dog food to be labeled "light," the calorie content of dry foods must be no more than 3,100 kilocalories/kilogram of metabolizable energy (ME). Canned dog foods must be no more than 900 kilocalories/kilogram ME. Light, dry cat foods must be no more than 3,250 kilocalories/kilogram ME. Canned cat foods must be no more than 950 kilocalories/kilogram ME. A dog or cat food labeled "less calories," "reduced calories," or similar words must include on the label the name of the product of comparison and the percentage of calories and feeding direction, which reflect a reduction in calories compared to feeding directions for the product of comparison. A comparison between products of different moisture content is considered misleading.

Low-fat dry dog foods must contain no more than 9% fat. Low-fat canned dog foods must contain no more than 4% fat. Low-fat dry cat foods must contain no more than 10% fat, and low-fat canned cat foods must have no more than 5% fat.

AAFCO Dog or Cat Nutrient Profiles
Nutritional standards on which nutritional adequacy statements are based.

AAFCO Feeding Trial
Standards under which a dog or cat food must be tested to qualify to use the AAFCO nutritional adequacy statement.

A dog or cat food labeled "less fat," "reduced fat," or similar terms must include on the label the name of the product of comparison and the percentage of fat reduction explicitly stated and a minimum crude fat guarantee in the Guaranteed Analysis immediately following the minimum crude fat guarantee in addition to the mandatory guaranteed analysis information. A comparison on the label between products in different categories of moisture content is considered misleading.

Other Label Claims

There is a growing trend for pet foods to be labeled as "premium," "super premium," "ultra premium," and "gourmet." None of these terms has any official regulatory standing or definition. In other words, they mean nothing in terms of a guarantee. They must be complete and balanced like any other feed, but there is no additional nutritional requirement.

AAFCO recommends the following guidelines for use of the term *natural* in the labeling of pet foods: "A feed or ingredient derived solely from plant, animal or mined sources, either in its unprocessed state or having been subject to physical processing, heat processing, or rendering, purification, extraction, hydrolysis, enzymolysis or fermentation, but not having been produced by or subject to a chemically synthetic process and not containing any additives or processing aids that are chemically synthetic except in amounts as may occur unavoidably in good manufacturing practices." The use of the term *natural* is only acceptable in reference to the product as a whole when all of the ingredients and components of ingredients meet the definition. However, exceptions for chemically synthesized vitamins, minerals, or other trace nutrients are acceptable if a disclaimer is on the bag, such as "Natural with added vitamins, minerals, and other trace nutrients." Also, a use such as "natural liver flavor" is not subject to the rule because this is not considered an implication that the whole product is natural.

Organic standards were put into effect for pet foods in March 2002 by the Department of Agriculture when it ruled that organic standards for pet foods are covered by the Organic Foods Production Act of 1990. However, comprehensive rules have not been agreed to by the USDA, the National Organic Standards Boards, and the pet food industry. The official USDA organic seal may not appear on pet foods unless the food meets the stringent standards of the National Organic Program. However, the terms "100% organic," "organic," and "made with organic ingredients" can be used.

AAFCO provides guidelines for labeling feeds that help control breath odor and reduce plaque and tartar buildup on teeth. The guidelines cover only purely mechanical (e.g., abrasive) mechanisms. Further, there can be no implication that the feed helps prevent or treat dental diseases, caries (cavities), or tooth loss. Products claiming to control breath odor may also do so if they contain chlorophyll or flavoring ingredients that are acceptable for use in animal feeds and not used in excess of amounts typical for flavoring foods.

Labels claiming that a pet feed contains ingredients that are "human grade," "human quality," "people foods," "ingredients you would eat," "food that you would feed your family," or similar claims, are considered false and misleading unless the entire product meets the USDA and FDA standards for foods edible by humans. Currently the terms "human grade" or "human quality" are not allowed by AAFCO because they are not defined. Any pet feed claiming to be human edible must be "manufactured, packaged, shipped and held under such conditions that conform to, and pass the standards set for, human edible products, and the manufacturer, shipper, distributor/wholesaler, and retailer have applicable current federal, state, and local permits, certificates, or licenses required for producing, shipping, handling, and selling products edible for people."

Additional guidelines exist for hairball claims for cat foods, for comparative claims ("Preferred by 9 out of 10 dogs over Brand X"), for fat claims, for feed ingredients, feed additives, and drugs. It is also important to note that drug claims are allowed only on prescription diets.

CHALLENGES TO COMPANION ANIMAL HEALTH

Because of the emotional bond between humans and their companion animals, the health care of pets is typically not approached from the same economical standpoint as is the veterinary care of other livestock species. Rather than dealing with disease management for an entire herd or flock, companion animal health maintenance and disease prevention is often managed in a much more individualized manner. Of course, health management of larger groups of dogs, cats or other species is essential for the successful operation of breeding or show kennels and catteries. A few common diseases that may affect pets are described below. Many other health problems, several of which are species-specific or breed-associated, are seen in pet or companion animals, but are beyond the scope of this text.

Cancer

Cancer Group of diseases caused by uncontrolled cell division that leads to abnormal growth of tissues, often resulting in the formation of masses or tumors.

Tumor Swelling or mass in a part of the body that is caused by abnormal growth of tissue.

Because of advances in veterinary care, companion animals are living longer, healthier lives. As a consequence, diseases that become more common with advancing age are increasing in frequency as life spans get longer. Cancer is one such disease, or more accurately, one such category of diseases. **Cancer** is broadly defined as the uncontrolled growth of body cells or tissues, and can in affect nearly any organ system. However, some types of **tumors** are much more common than others, and different sorts of tumors can have a wide variety of health effects. Some of the more common types of cancer to affect dogs and cats include tumors of the mouth, skin, bone, and mammary gland as well as systemic cancers such as leukemia and lymphoma. Many of these types of cancer can be treated with surgery or chemotherapy, which has the potential to add months or years of quality life for the pet. Because of the intense bond between many humans and their pets, advanced veterinary care for cancer is common and is a growing field in veterinary medicine.

Allergic skin disease

Allergies Abnormal and damaging immune responses to a particular environmental substance to which the body has become overly sensitive.

Skin problems resulting from **allergies** are common in dogs and cats and often result in itching that may be accompanied by hair loss and inflammation of the skin. Common causes of allergic skin disease include food ingredients, environmental allergens such as grass or weed pollen, and parasitic pests such as fleas. Oftentimes the precise cause of the allergic reaction is difficult to determine and treatment can be frustrating. Elimination of fleas, which are the most common cause of allergic dermatitis in dogs, is often the first step to managing skin disease and can often be a challenge. Elimination of other possible allergens in addition to medical treatments may also be helpful in controlling itching and accompanying allergic symptoms.

Pyometra

Pyometra Inflammation of the uterus leading to an accumulation of pus within the organ.

In intact females, **pyometra**, a bacterial infection of the uterus, is a potential health risk and may be life-threatening. Some factors that increase the likelihood of pyometra in bitches and queens include the administration of progestational hormonal compounds to delay or suppress estrus (in show animals, for example). However, pyometra may also occur spontaneously without previous hormonal treatments. Dogs and cats with pyometra show vague signs of disease such as lethargy, vomiting, and decreased appetite and may or may not have discharge of pus from the vulva to indicate infection of the reproductive tract. The diagnosis of pyometra is usually readily made by a veterinarian using abdominal x-ray or ultrasound. The preferred treatment is surgery to remove the infected uterus; however, nonsurgical treatment is sometimes attempted in animals that are intended for breeding in the future.

Endocrine diseases

Health problems that result from abnormal function of the **endocrine system** are relatively common in companion animals, including dogs, cats, and ferrets—and even in exotic pets such as iguanas. One such endocrine disease that frequently affects both dogs and cats is **diabetes mellitus**, which is seen most commonly in middle-aged animals. As is the case for their human companions, obese dogs and cats are at an increased risk for developing insulin resistance and diabetes. Other endocrine diseases that are common in pets include decreased thyroid function (hypothyroidism) in dogs and increased thyroid function (hyperthyroidism) in cats. Both of these disorders may have body-wide effects and can be effectively managed with appropriate veterinary care.

TRENDS IN THE PET INDUSTRY

Humanizing the Pet

The trend toward humanizing pets is growing, and no trend is quite so important as this one in defining both pet owners' views of their animal friends and their spending habits. People wish to reward their pet in human terms (Figure 16–24). This translates into demand for pet orthodontics, hotels, designer clothes, designer birdcages, rhinestone tiaras, computerized identification tags, self-cleaning litter boxes, and services from doggy spas to companies that regularly clean dog owners' yards. Add in comprehensive veterinary care, specialty food, and other pet purchases, and we have a good picture of spending on pets (Figure 16–25). An abundant supply of baby boomers who have disposable income and who are also becoming empty-nesters is driving much of this increased spending.

Endocrine system Glands that secrete hormones or other products directly into the blood. Hormones secreted by endocrine glands have a wide range of effects in maintaining normal body functions.

Diabetes mellitus Condition in which glucose absorption by cells of the body is inhibited due to decreased production of insulin by the pancreas or decreased response to insulin by body cells.

Figure 16–24
Hawkeye owns empty nesters Hank and Pam. He is shown here on "his" float. The ball in the background belongs to his dog cousin Sketch. Pam works at home, and Hawkeye spends most of his day in her company. When Hawkeye gets bored, he goes to the pool to hang out. Not much of a fan of swimming, he prefers to float his time away (Sketch is the real athlete of the family). He has a regular group of dog friends that visit frequently with their people for poolside gatherings. Hawkeye welcomes his cousin Sketch for the birthday bash he shares with Pam and her daughter-in-law, Brooke (one of Sketch's people) every September. When Hank and Pam are out of town, a sitter comes to the house to stay with Hawkeye. Hawkeye is typical of humanized pets: They enjoy and are provided many of the same things as their humans. (Photo courtesy of Pamela Damron Knight. Used with permission.)

Figure 16–25
Approximate percentage of spending on pets in the major categories. Source: National Pet Products Association. *Pet Industry Spending Figures.*

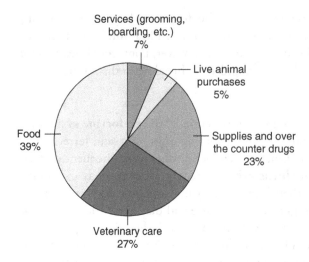

Services (grooming, boarding, etc.)
7%

Live animal purchases
5%

Food
39%

Supplies and over the counter drugs
23%

Veterinary care
27%

Pet Population

The total U.S. pet population is expected to grow and continue to be dominated by dogs and cats. The factors driving the overall increased pet population include:

- The baby boom generation's desire and ability to provide for pets
- Increased resources for pet ownership because of smaller family size
- Security and companionship of a pet against factors of modern life such as divorce, job anxiety, and geographic dispersal of families
- Surrogate bonding with the natural world through pets
- Increased ecological awareness, which is having spillover effects on a desire for pet ownership
- The dog's traditional role as protector

Registered Animals

The number of annual registrations for dogs and cats is declining. The reasons for the decrease in purebred registrations are probably multiple. However, one possible answer is that many cities are placing restrictions on breeding dogs and cats. Another is that people as a whole may be less interested in a purebred animal (Figure 16–26).

Figure 16–26
Reasons for the decline in purebred dog and cat registrations are unclear. (a) For some, owning a recognizable purebred animal like this elegant Borzoi is important. (b) For others, whether an animal is purebred is of secondary importance to simply having an animal to love. (Photos of Taylor with Alex and Thomas with Stripes courtesy Kathryn Beckett Traicoff. Used with permission.)

(a)   (b)

Hybrid dogs, in particular, are becoming more popular. Such crosses include Labrador Retriever and Poodle (Labradoodle), Pug and Beagle (Puggle), Bichon Frise and Papillon (Papichon), and dozens more.

Pet Foods

Trends in the U.S. pet food industry are truly worldwide trends because U.S. manufacturers are the leaders in the worldwide market. With a foreign market potential greater than the domestic market, manufacturers have a good deal at stake. The production of specialized products such as pet snack foods, low-calorie feeds, medicated diets for such ailments as diabetes, breed- and/or size-specific feeds, and nutrient-packed rations for athletic dogs is a major focus of the industry. Life-stage concept feed formulations and marketing are now universal throughout the pet food industry, and further offerings should be forthcoming in the near future. Diets marketed for specific types of performance are also expected to proliferate.

Owners are concerned about more than nutrition; they wish to mirror their own preferences for their pets. This has spurred the growth of organic, vegetarian, kosher, and locally sourced pet foods. The massive pet food recall of melamine-contaminated pet food in 2007 caused the same level of concern among pet owners as a baby food recall might. Consumers are demanding that ingredients put in pet foods be human-consumption grade. Manufacturing methods are being changed to reflect consumer demands such as feeds with visible vegetables. Even condiments for pet foods are becoming available on the market. The organic and "natural" pet food markets are especially strong. Specialty products generally cost more. With demand strong, companies have profit opportunities in the pet food sector and an incentive to continue developing more products.

Nutrition

The U.S. pet food market is expanding at a rapid rate. One of the major reasons for this expansion is the introduction of more specialized pet products. Up to 400 new products are introduced each year, with many directed at particular market segments. This trend is escalating. Presumably, the nutritional value of the foods will improve as companies do the research necessary to create the new feeds and comply with label regulations at the same time. An expert panel is currently at work on pet and exotic bird nutrition. The committee's purpose is the development of nutrient profiles for these species. Once accomplished (this will take years), the number of feeds available for bird species and the labeling of those feeds will improve.

An updated *Nutrient Requirements of Dogs and Cats* (The National Academies Press) was released in 2006. This publication provides nutrient recommendations based on physical activity and stage in life. It looks at how nutrients are metabolized in the bodies of dogs and cats, indications of nutrient deficiency, and diseases related to poor nutrition. This volume is a valuable resource for formulating diets, setting research agendas, developing regulations for pet food labeling, and assisting knowledgeable pet owners.

It is estimated that one in four dogs and cats in the United States is obese. With obesity comes a whole set of ailments that pets of normal weight rarely suffer. Nutrition is clearly linked to health. This pet obesity epidemic is sorely in need of attention.

Veterinary Expenditures

The total expenditures for veterinary care are increasing 8 to 10% annually. As more medical technology becomes available to pet owners, and as the baby boomer owners increasingly take advantage of those services, these costs are expected to continue to

increase. People are now demanding care for their pets that parallels what they want for themselves. In addition, there is a greater tendency for pet owners to seek regular services for pocket pets and other animals that historically received little if any veterinary care. Added to this are the increasing array of pharmaceuticals for pets for problems such as obesity and separation anxiety. Pet hospitals now routinely provide wellness plans. Pet owners are demanding and are willing to pay for human-quality care for their pets. One can even find pet liposuction, rhinoplasty, eyelifts, and other cosmetic procedures.

Mini-Trends

A variety of trends are affecting how much money is being spent on pets and on what. Several are worthy of awareness.

Upgrading necessities.   Pet owners are buying many of the same things they always have but spending more for items of higher perceived quality or status. For instance, a leather collar with charms or the must-have Signature Pet Carrier from Coach. Then there are the down-filled or memory foam dog beds, the stone-washed jean jacket for dogs, the Asian-inspired antique brown iron pet feeder, dog and cat matching towel and bathrobe sets, china food bowls, and so much more!

Pet services.   Much of the growth in pet services revolves around providing services for pets that mirror services for people. Many kennels are now near hotel quality in the accomodations they provide for pets. Doggie day care with pick-up and return services are common and expanding. Pet health insurance has entered the mainstream for pet owners. Pet funeral service providers are becoming increasingly common.

Bequeathing wealth to pets.   In most states, it is legal to establish a trust fund to be used to care for pets if the owner dies first. Legal service providers are increasing to provide for this and other needs of pet owners.

Big companies enter the market or expand.   The big pet specialty retailers (Petco and Petsmart) continue to grow and add services. By adding services, they hope to become the consumer's sole shopping place for both products and services. Other major retail outlets like Wal-Mart and Target are expanding the products they offer. A clue to which companies are investing heavily in their pet divisions can be seen in their advertising. Notice the retailers who use pets in their advertising.

Travel with pets.   A certain segment of the population takes their pets on trips, short and long. This is causing hotels to ramp up their services for pets traveling with their owners. Travel with pets is so important to some people that they consider the ease with which their pet can enter and exit a vehicle when buying transportation.

INDUSTRY ORGANIZATIONS

The following organizations are suggested for additional information.

American Cat Fancier's Association

http://www.acfacat.com

American Federation of Aviculture, Inc.

http://www.afabirds.org

American Kennel Club

http://www.akc.org

American Veterinary Medical Association

http://www.avma.org

The Cat Fancier's Association, Inc.

http://www.cfainc.org

Delta Society

http://www.deltasociety.org
An organization dedicated to promoting animals that help people improve their health, independence, and quality of life.

The International Cat Association, Inc.

http://www.tica.org
Service Dogs

Canine Companions for Independence

http://www.caninecompanions.org/
CCI trains four types of dogs: service dog, hearing dog, assisted service (social) dog, and facility dog.

Friends for Folks

http://www.doc.state.ok.us/facilities/institutions/friends.htm
The Friends for Folks Program provides senior citizens, handicapped persons, and others with a well-trained and behaved companion trained by prison inmates.

International Association of Assistance Dog Partners

http://www.iaadp.org/

National Association for Search and Rescue

http://www.nasar.org

NEADS Dogs for Deaf and Disabled Americans

www.neads.org

The Winn Feline Foundation

http://www.winnfelinehealth.org

SUMMARY AND CONCLUSION

Pet keeping probably led to the first domestication of animals. Pets and companion animals contribute depth and enrichment to the lives of people in all life stages and circumstances. We enjoy, appreciate, and benefit from pets for many reasons. It is impossible to assign a monetary value to such social, societal, and personal benefits. However, there are large economic segments to the pet industry.

The purpose of the pet and companion animal industry is to support the animals in service and companionship to people. The purpose of pets is to serve in one or more roles that include ornamental pets, status symbols, playthings, hobby animals, helpers, and companions. All regions of the United States have rates of pet ownership exceeding 50%.

There are estimated to be between 400 and 450 breeds of dogs in the world today. Only about a third of those have gained enough popularity to be included in the primary dog registry of the United States, the American Kennel Club (AKC). There are approximately 50 breeds of cats recognized by U.S. registries. Cats have not been developed into as many different breeds as dogs have because cats are put to fewer uses. However, cat breeders are actively developing new breeds. The bird fancy is divided along species lines. The remainder of the pet species are not as breed oriented as are the dog and cat.

The FDA regulates labels on pet foods. States also have the authority to establish and enforce state regulations. Many states have adopted model pet food regulations established by the Association of American Feed Control Officials (AAFCO). The regulations are more specific. Aspects of feed labeling such as product name, guaranteed nutrient analysis, nutritional adequacy statement, feeding directions, and calorie statements are covered under the AAFCO standards. The requirements for labeling dog and cat foods are the most detailed and specific. This is because the needs of these species are known with enough confidence that the AAFCO can specify nutrient requirements.

The total U.S. pet population is expected to grow modestly. However, the percentage of registered animals is declining. A major focus of the pet food industry is the production of specialized products such as pet snack foods, low-calorie feeds, medicated diets for animals with such ailments as diabetes, and nutrient-packed rations for athletic dogs. The industry is expanding to include more sales of dog and cat foods by veterinarians. Up to 400 new pet products are introduced each year, with many directed at particular market segments. The total cost of veterinary care is rising, and this trend is expected to continue.

STUDY QUESTIONS

1. Describe the rate of ownership for the various pet species in U.S. households.
2. Describe some of the generalities that can be drawn about pet owner demographics.
3. How much money is spent on pets in the United States each year?
4. Compare the percentage of U.S. households involved in the livestock industry to the percentage that have a pet or companion animal.
5. Define and differentiate among all the categories of pet animals. Include their functions.
6. In outline form, give all "value" uses for pets in modern society.
7. Give a brief history of the dog as a domestic species.
8. Give a brief history of the cat as a domestic animal.
9. Describe the distribution of pet ownership across the geographic regions of the United States.
10. Compare and contrast the types of breeding and genetics resources available for pet species to those for livestock species.
11. Describe the role of breeds in the pet species. Compare the role of breeds in the dog and cat fancies to that in the reptile fancy or the bird fancy.
12. Describe in general terms the process of mating a bitch.
13. Compare the basic structure of the reproductive tract of the dog to that of the cat. What are the similarities and differences?
14. Explain the information found on the label of a dog or cat food.
15. Describe some common health challenges for pets.
16. Describe the major trends affecting pets and the pet industry.

REFERENCES

AAFCO. 2007. *Official publication 2007.* College Station, TX: American Feed Control Officials, Inc.

American Pet Products Manufacturers Association, Inc. 2011. *2011–2012 APPMA national pet owners survey.* Greenwich, CT: American Pet Products Manufacturers Association.

AVMA. 1997. *U.S. pet ownership & demographics sourcebook.* Schaumburg, IL: Center for Information Management, American Veterinary Medical Association.

AVMA. 2002. *U.S. pet ownership & demographics sourcebook.* Schaumburg, IL: Center for Information Management, American Veterinary Medical Association.

AVMA. 2007. *U.S. pet ownership & demographics sourcebook.* Schaumburg, IL: Center for Information Management, American Veterinary Medicine Association.

Bennett, L. 2007. *Pet food trends for 2008.* Accessed online January 2008 through Small Business Trends. http://www.smallbiztrends.com/category/2008-trends.

Bennett, L. 2010. *Pet food trends for 2010.* Accessed online May 2011 through Small Business Trends. http://smallbiztrends.com/2010/01/pet-industry-trends-for-2010.html.

Campbell, J. R., M. D. Kenealy, and K. L. Campbell. 2003. *Animal sciences: The biology, care, and production of domestic animals.* 4th ed. New York: McGraw-Hill.

Case, L. P. 2003. *The cat: Its behavior, nutrition, and health.* Oxford, UK: Blackwell.

Case, L. P. 2005. *The dog, its behavior, nutrition, and health.* Ames: Iowa State University Press.

Council for Science and Society. 1988. *Companion animals in society.* Oxford, UK: Oxford University Press.

Geisert, R. 1999. *Learning reproduction in farm animals.* Stillwater: Oklahoma State University.

Irlbeck, N. A. 1996. *Nutrition and care of companion animals.* Dubuque, IA: Kendall/Hunt.

Klug, W. S., and M. R. Cummings. 2000. *Concepts of genetics.* Upper Saddle River, NJ: Prentice Hall.

Morris, D. 1999. *Cat breeds of the world.* New York: Viking.

Pet Food Institute. 2011. *Pet incidence trend report.* Pet Food Industry Reference Desk. http://www.petfoodinstitute.org.

Schwartz, M. 1997. *A history of dogs in the early Americas.* New Haven, CT: Yale University Press.

Tabor, R. 1995. *Understanding cats: Their history, nature and behavior.* Pleasantville, NY: The Reader's Digest Association.

USDA. 1984. *Yearbook of agriculture: Animal health, livestock and pets.* Washington, DC: USDA.

17

Lamoids

Key Terms

Alpaca
Bloat
Cria
Dystocia
Erythrocytes
Flehmen response
Llama
Maiden
Multiparous
Orgle
Sternal recumbancy

SCIENTIFIC CLASSIFICATION OF CAMELIDS

There are six members of the camelid family. The *camel* genus (*Camelus*) has two members: the one-humped dromedary camel (Figure 17–1) and the two-humped Bactrian camel (Figure 17–2). The llama genus (*Lama*) includes the guanaco, the llama (Figure 17–3), and the alpaca (Figure 17–4).

The *Vicugna* genus includes only the vicuna. Members of the camel family are commonly referred to as *camelids,* and members of the *Lama* and *Vicugna* genera are called *lamoids.* It is also common to refer to camels as Old World camelids and lamoids as New World camelids.

Phylum:	Chordata
Subphylum:	Vertebrata
Class:	Mammalia
Order:	Artiodactyla
Suborder:	Tylopoda ("padded foot")
Family:	Camelidae
Genus:	*Camelus* (Old World camelids); *Lama* (South American camelids); *Vicugna* (South American camelid)
Species:	*dromedarius* (dromedary camel), *bactrianus* (Bactrian camel); *glama* (llama), *pacos* (alpaca), *guanicoe* (guanaco); *vicugna* (vicuna)

Figure 17–1
Camelus dromedarius, *the dromedary camel.* (Photo courtesy of Dr. Anas Abdelqader, University of Jordan.)

Figure 17–2
Camelus bactrianus, *the Bactrian camel.* (Photo courtesy of Dr. Carlos Sañudo.)

Figure 17–3
Lama glama. *Llamas graze native pasture at 4000 meters in Bolivia.*
(FAO photo 17248/A. Odoul. Used with permission by the Food and Agriculture Organization of the United Nations.)

Figure 17–4

Lama pacos, *the alpaca.*
*Peruvian women with
their herd of alpacas.* (FAO
photo 17436/A. Odoul. Used
with permission by the Food and
Agriculture Organization of the
United Nations.)

THE PLACE OF LAMOIDS IN THE UNITED STATES

The only camelids found to any extent in the United States are the llama and alpaca; they are thus the most economically important. The New World camelids originated in the high elevations of the Andes Mountains in South America. They consist of four species in two genera: *Lama glama,* the llama; *Lama pacos,* the alpaca; *Lama guanicoe,* the guanaco; and *Vicugna vicugna,* the vicuna. All four species have 37 pairs of chromosomes and can interbreed and produce fertile hybrids. The most commonly produced hybrids are between the llama and alpaca (known as huarizo) and between the alpaca and vicuna (paco-vicuna). The guanaco and vicuna are not domesticated, although some are tame. The vicuna produces wool with the finest fiber of any animal, grading 120's on the Bradford scale. Higher numbers on the Bradford scale indicate finer wool fiber, which is more valuable for spinning and weaving into very expensive woolen material. Because of the demand for this very luxurious wool, the vicuna was hunted almost to extinction, because the animal had to be killed to obtain the fleece. To preserve the species, strict government regulations forbidding the killing of vicunas have been imposed in their native South American countries.

Llamas are very plentiful in the Andes Mountains from southern Peru to northwestern Argentina. As the largest of the lamoids, llamas have been kept primarily as a pack animal since their domestication. They are also valuable as a source of food, wool, hides, tallow for candles, dried dung for fuel, and as a provider of offerings to the gods (especially the white llamas). The alpaca, which is smaller than the llama, is often described as looking like a large goat with a camel's head and neck. The alpaca is kept and bred for its wool, which in the Suri breed can grow long enough to touch the ground.

Because of their relatively small numbers in the United States, llamas and alpacas still have a specialty status in the animal industries.

THE PURPOSE OF THE LLAMA AND ALPACA INDUSTRIES

Since the early 1970s, there has been interest in llamas and alpacas in the United States, where they are not considered a food species. However, they are used for work (packing and driving) (Figure 17–5); as guard animals (primarily for sheep and goats) (Figure 17–6); as pets and therapy animals; for fiber production; and for exhibition in shows, parades, and fairs. The llama is popular as a project animal for 4-H, Scouts,

Figure 17–5
Llamas are a useful pack animal. They carry heavy loads relative to their body weight, and cause minimal damage to fragile trails because of their padded feet. (Source: Photos.com/Thinkstock.)

Figure 17–6
Llamas serve a useful function as guard animals for sheep and goats. (Photo courtesy of Dr. Rebecca L. Damron. Used with permission.)

FFA, and other youth activities. Their most common use is as a pet, with wilderness packing as the second most common use. Llamas can carry very heavy loads, as much as a third to a half of their own weight. In the United States, llamas are often used as pack animals in wilderness areas because of their low cost and stamina on the trail. Their feet are less damaging to trails than those of horses, mules, and burros. There are several dozen commercial packers in business, and the USDA's Forest Service also uses llamas for packing. Undoubtedly, their popularity comes from a combination of need, novelty, and general appeal. The fact that they are easy to feed (grain, grass, and browse), easy to train, and generally easy to care for also contributes to their overall popularity.

HISTORY OF THE LLAMA IN THE UNITED STATES

The family Camelidae was domesticated about 4,000 to 6,000 years ago. Llamas were exported to the United States from South America in the late 19th century predominantly as zoo animals. Other importations, like that of William Randolph Hearst in the early 1900s, were for exotic species displays in game parks or on vast estates. Few alpacas were imported because Peruvian legislation enacted in 1843 prohibited

the export of live alpacas. Imports of llamas were restricted when the United States banned importation of all hoofed stock from South America in 1930 to prevent the importation of foot-and-mouth disease. At about the same time, all of the Andean countries united in an attempt to prevent the exploitation of llamas and alpacas by other countries. The only legal exportations that occurred from then until the 1980s, when the ban was lifted, were from a small herd in Canada. Thus North American llamas are descended predominantly from importations made from South America prior to 1930, some animals from Canada, a few illegal importations from Mexico, plus a few animals imported from other countries at various times. Importation from Chile began again in 1984 after Chile was recognized as being free of foot-and-mouth disease. Foot-and-mouth disease makes importations into the United States from South America difficult and expensive. The USDA's Animal and Plant Health Inspection Service (APHIS) is in charge of regulating such importation. A long, costly quarantine is necessary, and most imports have been of breeding stock. The first substantial importation of alpacas occurred in 1984.

The llama and alpaca are different from traditional meat animal species in the United States in terms of who owns them and the general attitude of the owners. The closest comparison is with the horse. Llama and alpaca owners are often not previously experienced with large animals, a situation similar to horse owners. Like horses, the llama and alpaca are often kept as a companion rather than as an investment.

GEOGRAPHIC DISTRIBUTION

According to the 2007 Census of Agriculture, there are estimated to be approximately 120,000 llamas and 120,000 alpacas in the United States. The West Coast is the most important area of the country for llama and alpaca ownership, with Oregon, Washington, and California each having greater than 10,000 combined llamas and alpacas. Texas, Colorado, Wisconsin, and Ohio also have greater than 10,000 alpacas and llamas combined.

PHYSICAL DESCRIPTION

Camelidae

Members of the Camelidae family all have long necks, small heads, and no horns or antlers. Each has a prehensile upper lip similar to that of a rabbit. They are herbivores with compartmentalized forestomachs like the ruminant, but their stomach has only three chambers, rather than the four of other ruminants. Camelidae graze many different species of plants and are more efficient than most ruminants on poor-quality feed. The red blood cells (**erythrocytes**) of camelids are elliptical, whereas in all other mammals they are circular. These elliptical erythrocytes can swell to 150% of normal size without rupturing. This allows a dehydrated animal to rehydrate very quickly. Lamoid blood contains more red blood cells per unit volume of blood than does the blood of other mammals. In addition, the **hemoglobin** of the blood reacts faster with oxygen. This gives the animals the ability to exert themselves strenuously at high altitudes and makes them well adapted to their environment. Their feet have two toes, with a very flat hoof or nail at the end of each. A thick, callused pad forms the sole of the foot.

Erythrocytes Red blood cells.

Hemoglobin Oxygen-carrying pigment found in erythrocytes.

Lamoids

The llama and alpaca are very similar. Although the llama is larger than the alpaca, there is a marked range of size. Adult llamas weigh 240–500 lbs, with little weight difference between males and females. Llamas are 40–50 in. at the shoulder, and

65–72 in. at the poll. Males should reach mature size at 3 years of age and females at 2. The alpaca ranges from 100–185 lbs and is about 36 in. at the shoulder.

Colors vary widely in the lamoids. They may be white, black, several shades of brown, red, and mixtures of these colors. They may be roan, solid, frequently spotted, or marked in a variety of other patterns.

On the llama, the fiber is found on the neck, back, and sides. Hair covers the head, belly, and legs. The fiber is 3–8 in. long and gives the llama great protection against cold, wet weather. The hair-covered areas help the llama to dissipate heat in warm climates. The fiber is oil free (no lanolin as in sheep) and lightweight. It has good spinning quality, with the fleece of the llama considered coarse and inferior to that of the alpaca. The fiber has a fine undercoat and longer, tough outer guard hair. The guard hair helps shed rain while the undercoat holds air and insulates the animal against cold. In cold weather, lamoids rest by facing the wind with their legs tucked under them. The hair-covered belly and legs are protected. In hot weather, they sit in a manner that allows air to flow under the body. The woolless areas then dissipate heat.

The alpaca is raised primarily for its wool. Alpaca wool has an extremely fine fiber that grades better than the finest wool of any sheep. The fiber of the alpaca is superior to that of the llama. It is very fine, lightweight, has good insulation value, and is dense and soft. It is a warm fiber that doesn't scratch the wearer. It is used in making items like parkas, sleeping bags, and fine coat linings, among many other things. An adult alpaca produces about 4 lbs of fiber per year. They can be sheared yearly, but, in cooler climates, it may be desirable to shear every other year so that the fiber is longer. In hot climates, yearly shearing is generally necessary to avoid heat stress. Alpacas have been selected to be gentle and submissive to facilitate shearing. These characteristics make them easy to handle as well.

Adult male alpacas and llamas are referred to as males. Breeding males are sometimes called studs. Females are not called any other name, and babies are either called babies or **crias**, which is Spanish for baby. "Gelding" refers to neutered males. Parturition is commonly called birthing.

Cria Baby llama.

GENETICS AND BREEDS

Organized breeding programs such as those that exist for livestock species have not historically been a part of llama and alpaca breeding and genetics. As with the companion animal species, breeding decisions are based primarily on subjective criteria. Knowledgeable breeders do exist and have made progress in improving these animals. Since its organization in 1988, the Alpaca Registry has required blood typing of any animal before it can be registered, and in 1998, began requiring DNA testing. In 2009, the Alpaca Registry, Inc., announced the official initiation of an industry-wide Estimated Progeny Difference program for alpacas. As increasing amounts of data are collected for the program, they should become an increasingly useful tool for alpaca breeders. The International Lama Registry requires DNA testing on sires used for outside breeding who have two or more cria and all that have more than 10 crias. In this way, both registries protect the genetics of their species.

Because the alpaca was developed for its fiber and is the primary fiber producer of the Andes regions, it is logical that breed differences should be primarily in wool type. There are two breeds of alpaca—the Suri, which produces a long, wavy fiber, and the Huacaya, which produces a more desirable, shorter, crimped fiber resembling the wool of Corriedale sheep. The predominant Peruvian breed, the Huacaya, is the breed that has been most exported to other countries. Two llama breeds are recognized in Peru. The chaku is the woolly breed. The breed with less wool is called *ccara* (*q'ara* in some literature). In the United States, two llama types are recognized, but no breeds are recognized. One type has been bred for work and is taller, heavier framed, and has shorter wool. The other is smaller, broader, and has a much heavier fleece. This type is preferred in the show ring.

HEALTH CARE

Llamas and alpacas are considered very hardy and easy to care for, are generally resistant to many diseases, and have few maintenance problems other than deworming and an occasional foot trimming. Their ruggedness is no doubt related to the harsh environment where they evolved. However, they are not immune to diseases and, in fact, are susceptible to a wide variety of diseases and parasites, with more reported each year. A good herd health program is important, and will become more so as lamoids increasingly come in contact with other domestic animals and with others of their own kind. An effective herd health program is influenced greatly by such factors as the goals of the owner (economics and purpose for the animals), the number of animals in a group, the other species with which they have contact, and geographic location. **Biosecurity** practices can reduce exposure to pathogens. Currently, no vaccines are labeled for use in llamas or alpacas. However, in populations of lamoids that are at increased risk for certain infectious diseases, veterinarians may recommend a vaccine regimen that is tailored to the specific needs of the herd. This should include a vaccination protocol for the young as well as the adults.

It is often difficult to identify an ill llama or alpaca. They are very stoic and don't show many signs of illness. Owners should develop the habit of routinely and carefully observing feed intake and grazing patterns and take the temperature of animals who are not acting "normally" to determine illness.

Llamas and alpacas are not well adapted to hot or humid climates. When the sum of temperature in degrees Fahrenheit and humidity equal or exceed 180, lamoids can suffer from heat stress. As a means of prevention, heavily wooled animals should be sheared and provided with the means to cool themselves. Shade shelters, ponds for wading, sprinkler/misting systems, fans, or an abundance of shade trees can all be effective, depending on other environmental conditions. In addition, it is best to avoid handling, exerting, or transporting lamoids unnecessarily during dangerously hot periods. Llamas with heat stress may have difficulty breathing, have rapid heart rates, and are often unable to stand, if they are severely affected. Treatment often involves cooling affected animals with cold water baths and ice packs, as well as administration of **intravenous** fluids and other medications by a veterinarian.

Enterotoxemia (overeating disease) has been frequently observed in llamas, especially the young. Apparent preventive success has been reported by immunization of the female with *Clostridium perfringens* types C and D, followed by immunization of the cria at 4 to 6 weeks of age. Tetanus can be prevented by using the *Clostridium* vaccine that contains tetanus toxoid. Llamas should also be vaccinated for rabies because they are very curious and apt to get bitten by rabid animals. Tuberculosis, anthrax, malignant edema, and Johne's disease are also possible diseases for the llama.

Llamas and alpacas in some geographical regions, especially in the eastern United States, are at risk for infection with meningeal worm, which is a nematode parasite that migrates within the spinal cord. Other internal parasites to be concerned about are coccidia, liver flukes, tapeworms, lungworms, nasal bots, and gastrointestinal nematodes. A parasite prevention regimen should be followed.

External parasites of potential concern are mange, ticks, mites, and lice. Both internal and external parasites can be treated with medicines and pesticides that are approved for cattle, sheep, and goats. Other reported diseases are leptospirosis, equine rhinopneumonitis, eperythrozoonosis, and toxoplasmosis.

Biosecurity Preventive measures that reduce risk of the spread of infectious diseases.

Intravenous Fluids and medications administered into a vein.

Problems with teeth are relatively common in camelids. In some animals, abnormal dental wear may require regular attention to prevent more serious issues from developing. The lower front teeth (incisors) grow continuously and may require periodic trimming to prevent them from becoming overgrown, which can interfere with grazing or cause an underbite. Feeding rough or stemmy forage may cause damage to the gums, which increases the risk for tooth **abscesses** seen most often in the lower cheek teeth of adults.

REPRODUCTION

There are few differences of any importance in the reproductive practices of any of the South American camelids other than some behavioral differences. Female llamas and alpacas are usually ready for their first mating at 15 to 18 months of age, but weight is an important variable in determining first mating. Reproductive ability ends at 15–18 years of age, with a normal life span of 20–25 years. In rare cases, individuals can live to be 30 years or older. Males reach full sexual maturity at approximately 3 years of age and can be mated at $2^{1}/_{2}$ years. However, younger males may be fertile and should be separated from females.

Lamoids are unusual in that they are induced ovulators and they ovulate after mating. As induced ovulators, lamoids do not have a heat cycle and will mate anytime they are not pregnant. Their wild ancestors are seasonal breeders, but this characteristic has apparently been bred out of the domestic species. Females should not be rebred until 14 to 21 days after the birth of a cria. Waiting longer than 14 to 21 days to provide additional rest between breedings may actually reduce the chances of a subsequent pregnancy. Very cold and very hot and/or humid seasons should probably be avoided as birthing seasons unless sophisticated facilities with heating and/or cooling are available.

Llamas mate with the female in **sternal recumbency** (sitting on her legs with her belly on the ground) (Figure 17–7). Because copulation lasts on the average about 18 minutes for the llama and 20 minutes for the alpaca (range of 5 to 55 minutes), the male llama will seek to assure himself he is in safe surroundings before he will copulate. If moved to a new paddock or breeding enclosure, he will inspect the surroundings, including the dung pile, and may exhibit the **flehmen response** to the scents there.

Abscess Collection of pus in a cavity as the result of infection with microorganisms or as a response to embedded foreign material, such as a splinter.

Sternal recumbency Mating position in the llama and alpaca. The female lies on the ground with her legs under her and her belly on the ground.

Flehmen response Sexual behavior of the male of several species where the male curls his upper lip and inhales.

Figure 17–7
Llamas and alpacas mate in sternal recumbancy. (Source: Nicolas Raymond/shutterstock)

Orgle The distinctive noise made by a male llama before and during mating.

Once he feels safe from rivals, he will approach an open female and begin to **orgle**. This is a term for the distinctive glutteral noise, which has been described as sounding like a cross between a gurgle and a snort. The orgling continues for the duration of the mating. An interested female clucks to the male, fans her tail back and forth, and begins to run. The male chases her. The female either stops running and sits or is forced down on the ground by the male. The male then mounts and penetrates.

During the chase, the prepuce of the male, which normally faces to the rear for urination, is pulled forward. After the male has settled on the female and positioned himself properly, he extends his penis. The penis penetrates the corkscrew-shaped opening of the cervix and the male makes rhythmic thrusts into the uterine horns, alternating between them, and deposits semen there. The male raises his tail during ejaculation. There are reports of males copulating up to 18 times per day. The female remains still, calm, and quiet during the mating. Some lie on their side. Ovulation occurs 26 to 45 hours after copulation in the female and is stimulated through hormonal action initiated by the action of the penis during copulation, the leg clasp of the male, and probably by a neural response stimulated by the male's orgling. Ninety percent of the receptive females ovulate after one copulation.

A female who has ovulated and might be pregnant (corpus luteum begins development) refuses further matings. If the male insists, the female "spits him off" or actually chases him away. Some breeders leave the mating pair together for a few days, and others hand-breed on successive days. These practices can help increase the conception rate because the female may be between ripened eggs (there is a 12-day cycle of follicular growth, degeneration, and regeneration), and also because some females need repeat matings to stimulate ovulation. Pregnancy can be confirmed by a very experienced ultrasound technician as early as 12 to 15 days postmating. A more practical time for such a procedure is 21 to 28 days post mating. Rectal palpation, in the hands of a very experienced and careful palpator, can also be used to determine pregnancy. Blood tests have also been developed to determine pregnancy. The most common blood test is the progesterone test. Blood should not be drawn from the female until 21 days after the last breeding to avoid a false positive from the corpus luteum (CL) of ovulation rather than the CL of pregnancy. Gestation length for llamas is normally 350 days, plus or minus 2 weeks. The average gestation is 335 days, plus or minus 2 weeks, for alpacas.

Most llama females give birth standing up between the hours of 9 A.M. and 3 P.M. This is no doubt a trait selected in response to the cold environment in which these animals developed. The wild vicuna of South America gives birth almost exclusively in the morning. This behavioral adaptation helps them avoid the afternoon storms in the Andes and gives the babies a better chance of survival. A baby born early in the day is able to dry, stand, and nurse before nightfall. Young born during the colder hours of the night or the wet of the afternoon are much less likely to survive. A female approaching parturition usually appears restless and loses her appetite. She separates herself from the herd, may urinate frequently, hums, and lies down and rises again repeatedly. The whole process, including placenta expulsion, takes 2 to 3 hours in a female who has had young before (**multiparous**), and somewhat longer in the **maiden** female. **Dystocia** is rare, as is retained placenta. Although females are generally good, attentive mothers, they do not lick their young or eat the placenta. A thin cutaneous membrane that covers the cria at birth, but does not restrict breathing or movement, dries up and falls from the cria's coat soon after birth. The female nudges, nuzzles, and hums to the cria to encourage it and bond with it.

Multiparous Refers to a female that has had previous pregnancies and offspring.

Maiden In this context, a female who has never given birth.

Dystocia Difficulty in birthing.

Rearing the Cria

Because of their hardy nature, little attention is usually required by the newborn cria. However, general husbandry practices such as dipping the navel cord in 7% tincture of iodine to prevent navel ill can be beneficial. Given the fact that these animals can be very valuable, other husbandry practices may be desirable.

The female llama has four teats and raises her baby on milk. Crias, like young ruminants, must have colostrum soon after birth for antibody protection. They should receive colostrum to equal 5% of their body weight within the first 6 hours after birth and 10% within the first 12 hours. If there is a problem and colostrum must be fed artificially to the cria, it should be given 4 to 8 oz at a time at 2-hour intervals. Generally, the cria is up and nursing within 90 minutes of birth. If it has not nursed naturally by 6 hours of age, the dam should be milked and the cria fed with a bottle or a stomach tube (Figure 17–8). Goat or cow colostrum can be given if the mother's colostrum is not available. Collecting excess colostrum and freezing it for future use is also a good strategy. However, excess colostrum is generally available from llamas and alpacas only in the case of a stillborn. Frozen colostrum lasts many months and can be collected from healthy, vaccinated cattle, goats, or sheep and stored for later use. The alternative is to transfuse needy babies with plasma or blood from a healthy adult llama or alpaca at a rate of 8–10% of their body weight, or to feed blood plasma in place of, or as a supplement to, colostrum.

Early growth can be monitored by weighing crias as soon as they are dry and then daily for 2 weeks. They should gain between 0.5 and 1 lb of body weight per day for the first 2 weeks and should double their birth weight in the first month of life. Crias are weaned at 5–6 months and should weigh 100–150 lbs. Baby alpacas weigh 11–20 lbs at birth and baby llamas weigh 18–40 lbs. at birth.

Crias have a functional fermentation by 2 months of age. At this age, their stomach proportions are like those of adults. They begin eating solid foods within the first 1 to 2 weeks of life and should be encouraged to do so. This early eating habit can be exploited for the cria of poor-milking mothers by providing a creep area with alfalfa and some grain. Crias who are growing well should probably be excluded from the creep area.

Figure 17–8
Generally cria are up and nursing within 90 minutes of birth. If a baby llama or alpaca fails to nurse, it must be given colostrum within 6 hours of birth by bottle or stomach tube. (Photographer Bill Tarpenning. Courtesy of USDA.)

NUTRITION AND FEED USE

Lamoids are herbivores with a complex stomach, but they have two compartments prior to the glandular stomach as compared to standard ruminants, which have three forestomachs (Figure 17–9). Regurgitation and remastication are essential features of their digestion. Anaerobic fermentation is accomplished by the presence of microorganisms in the first two compartments of the digestive system. Roughage is converted to products the animal can use to its own benefit. In general, the food mass found in the forestomachs of the lamoid is drier and not stratified into the same layers as that found in the true ruminant. **Bloat** is rare, and this is probably the reason.

By nature, llamas graze and browse. The alpaca is a grazer only. The incisor teeth are firmly fixed in the mandible like those of sheep and goats. These teeth are pressed against an upper dental pad, which assists them in shearing plant material. Their mouthparts enable them to graze close to the ground, which could allow them to harm plant communities by grazing too closely. However, their grazing habit is to move about over the grazing area and thus not damage the available forage. The habit of moving around as they graze also helps prevent them from consuming enough toxic plants to cause them harm.

The prehensile upper lip of the lamoids has a labial cleft, which allows each side of the lip to be manipulated independently of the other (Figure 17–10). This allows lamoids to check their feed carefully and prevents them from consuming rocks and other potentially harmful objects. Unlike most domestic farm species commonly found in the Western world, the lamoid tongue does not readily protrude from the mouth. This is why they do not groom their young or themselves with their tongue. This characteristic also hampers their ability to lick a salt block. They usually chew it instead.

Bloat Gas collecting in the fermentative portion of the digestive tract.

Figure 17–9

Digestive tract of the lamoid. C-1 and C-2 are used primarily as the fermentation vat. The distal portion of C-3 is glandular and can be thought of as the "true stomach," analogous to the abomasum of a ruminant.

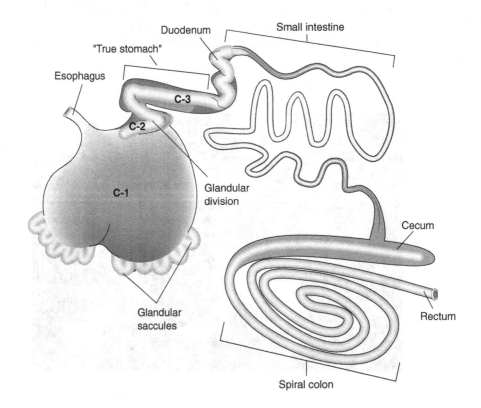

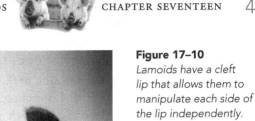

Figure 17–10
*Lamoids have a cleft
lip that allows them to
manipulate each side of
the lip independently.*

The camelids are more efficient at feed utilization than the ruminants, especially in their ability to digest and use protein and energy. This explains why llamas and alpacas are sometimes too easily fattened. Llamas are able to gain weight and prosper on native South American grasses that average 7% crude protein. The digestible energy requirement for maintenance in a llama is 75 kcal per $kg^{w.75}$. For sheep, it is 119 kcal per $kg^{w.75}$—a 37% advantage to the llama. Volatile fatty acids are the principal end products of carbohydrate fermentation in the lamoids.

There are several possible reasons for the camelid's efficiency of feed utilization, including:

- Unique anatomy
- Rapid forestomach motility, with more frequent rumination cycles
- Increased feed retention
- Increased urea hydrolysis
- Rapid liquid absorption and passage rate from the forestomachs
- More rapid and complete VFA absorption
- Low basal metabolism
- Low maintenance requirements for energy and protein

The practical implication of the efficiency of feed utilization is that camelids can be kept on low-quality pasture and range and stocked more densely than other species. In fact, they seem to have greater efficiency when consuming poor-quality forages than when consuming good-quality feeds. A llama needs 10–20% as much feed as a horse and can manage on 5% of the grazing area required by a horse. The stocking rate for alpacas is 5 to 8 animals per acre, and for llamas, 3.5 to 5.5 animals per acre. Variations depend on animal size, function, and quality of the pasture.

The large intestine and cecum are not designed for fermentation. Instead, the large intestine is spiral shaped (Figure 17–9), and decreases in size by two thirds as it spirals. Fecal pellets are formed in the large intestine.

Lamoid Feeding

The nutrition of the lamoids has been poorly researched and much is unknown. This is further complicated by the fact that much of the available literature concerns South American conditions and plant species. Because the basic nutrient requirements for these animals are not known, data from other species must be used to estimate the requirements. Recommended levels of the most important nutrients for llamas are shown in Table 17–1. The complex digestive system of the llamas, which makes them much easier to feed than monogastrics and modestly easier to feed than true ruminants, gives the llama owner a tremendous advantage. Llamas may also have some instinct about balancing their overall ration that is generally lacking in other domestic animals. Knowledgeable owners suggest that if concentrates and grains are overfed, llamas will seek very low-quality, empty browse to dilute the nutrient density of the concentrates. In practice, many llama breeders in the United States and Canada have been successfully breeding and keeping llamas since the 1930s, and a wealth of information has been gathered and disseminated to owners. Although lacking the stature of scientific information, it nevertheless gives us valuable knowledge on how to feed the llama.

If we presume that lamoids can eat 1.8% of their body weight (BW) per day in forage, and do some simple calculations on commonly available feeds, it becomes evident that many readily available feedstuffs will meet the nutrient needs of lamoids if they are provided free choice. Some feeds, if eaten at 1.8% of body weight, could easily be eaten to excess and cause obesity. Table 17–2 shows how small quantities of some common feeds meet the maintenance needs of a 330-lb (150-kg) llama. It would be necessary to limit the amounts of the higher-quality feeds listed in the table to prevent llamas from getting too fat. A good rule of thumb is to start with 1% of body weight as dry forage and increase, if necessary, to maintain body condition up to 1.5% BW. As with all species, it is necessary to increase nutrient quantities for

---

Table 17–1

RECOMMENDED NUTRIENT LEVELS FOR LLAMAS

Nutrient	Common Sources	Recommended Level in Diet
Crude protein	Forages, grains, and supplements	10–14%
TDN	Grains and forages	55–65%
Fiber	Forages/browse	25%
Calcium	Forages, especially alfalfa and supplements	0.3–0.85%
Phosphorus	Grains and supplements	0.2–0.5%
Potassium	Most feedstuffs	0.5–1.0%
Manganese	Forages and grains	40–60%
Magnesium	Forages and supplements	0.1–0.2%
Sulfur	Protein feeds	0.2–0.25%
Copper	Forages and grains	5–15 ppm
Selenium	Forages, fishmeal and supplements	0.3–0.6 ppm
Zinc	Forages/browse, some grains, and supplements	40–50 ppm
Vitamin A	Green forages	3,000–5,000 IU units/Kg
Vitamin D	Green forages, sun-cured hays	3000 IU/Kg
Vitamin E	Green forages	17–20 ppm

Sources: Carmean et al., 1992, Pond et al, 2005, Johnson, 1989a, McNamara, 2006 and Van Saun, 1999.

Table 17–2

FEED NECESSARY TO MEET DAILY MAINTENANCE ENERGY REQUIREMENTS OF A 330-LB (150-KG) LLAMA

Feedstuff	Dry Matter (kg)	% Body Weight
Alfalfa hay	1.57	1.04
Corn silage	0.77	0.52
Grass hay	1.71	1.14
Oat hay	1.77	1.18
Oat straw	1.92	1.28
Rye grass pasture, fertilized	1.21	0.81
Grass pasture, high quality	1.25	0.83
Grass pasture, average	1.49	1.00

Source: Compiled from Johnson, 1994b, p. 197, and Sell, 1993, p. 3.

production functions such as growth, lactation, gestation, and work; for environmental conditions; and so on. Grain is probably needed only in rare situations, such as when pasture conditions are poor, if animals are being worked heavily, for the crias of poor milk-producing dams, for rapidly growing animals, for heavy-milking females, and for animals in very cold environments.

Water needs can be met for lamoids by providing clean water free choice to the animals. They adjust their intake to meet their needs. Care must be taken if automatic waterers are used that require the animals to push a lever to receive their water because it may take lamoids some time to adjust. Trail llamas frequently refuse to drink during the day, especially from running water, if they are accustomed to standing water. This is not a cause for alarm—water should simply be provided at the end of the day. It is also likely that when grazing lush pastures, camelids will get most of their water from the feed, just as other herbivores do. In addition, the natural water economy of llamas allows them to take advantage of the water from dew and frost.

Vitamin and mineral needs of lamoids are very poorly known, and it is difficult to make recommendations. Lamoid rations that contain mineral levels that fill the needs of sheep are considered adequate. Because llamas and alpacas do not use their tongues to lick, many never learn to use a trace mineral block. It may be necessary to include minerals in a small amount of grain-based feed to get the animals to consume the minerals they need. Loose mineral mixes in weatherproof feeders are better than mineral blocks. Lamoids grazing or eating hay in temperate zones seem to do well enough on the forage without supplemental minerals, although problems have been observed in tropical zones. Toxicity can easily occur, and overzealous and/or novice lamoid owners need to be very careful not to overfeed. Reputable breeders in the area may be able to help new owners with mineral nutrition. Sheep breeders, extension agents, and local veterinarians should also be consulted. In lieu of other recommendations, a mixture of 50 lbs each of steamed bonemeal, dry powdered molasses, and trace mineralized salt, along with 10 lbs of ZinPro 100, offers a suitable all-around mineral mix for llamas.

General Feeding Recommendations Although it is difficult to make broad generalizations about feeding lamoids, some observations can be made to guide the novice. Good pasture, hay, or silage should meet most nutrient needs of lamoids kept in North America. Reasonable pasture, or almost any hay of 8–10% protein, is acceptable for most stages of a llama's life. Recent research has indicated that even weanlings probably need no more than 10% protein feed. Alpaca owners frequently feed protein at 14–16% of the ration, reasoning that this level is necessary to produce

Figure 17–11

It is easy to allow lamoids to overeat and become too fat because their wool makes it hard visually to evaluate their body condition. A simple condition score of 1 to 9, with 1 being emaciated, and 5 representing the ideal, is adequate.

a good fleece, although there is probably no need to do so. However, sulfur needs should be carefully met. In stress situations, such as late gestation and lactation and for the weanling, alfalfa hay can be used as a protein supplement. The addition of a mineral supplement finishes the needs.

Overfeeding is consistently more of a problem than any other nutritional ill and results in a too-fat animal. This can be difficult to detect because of the wool. Owners should weigh animals to assess feeding regimes and should learn to assess the body condition of their animals (Figure 17–11). A simple condition score index should be used. Many species of animals are condition scored on a scale of 1 to 9, with 1 being very thin and 9 representing the very obese. Just such a scale has been established for llamas.

Lamoids should be adapted slowly to new feed, especially if it includes concentrates, to avoid acidosis, which can be a problem just as it is with ruminants. If the animals learn to eat trace mineral salt mixes formulated for sheep found in the same geographic location, their mineral needs will probably be met. Body condition should be monitored, and obesity avoided because it interferes with reproduction and causes heat stress. Llamas are good at clearing brush because of their browsing habit. However, several authors warn that they can become *browse starved*. If they are allowed sudden, unlimited access, they may overeat and become ill.

BEHAVIOR

Llamas are social creatures and do best when kept with others of their species. They are often described as shy, independent, gentle, and curious (Figure 17–12). They are calm by nature and are considered easy to handle and train (Figure 17–13). However, they are naturally territorial, a trait no doubt inherited from their wild guanaco ancestors whose herd survival depended on balancing the number of animals to the carrying capacity of a territory.

Llamas use ear and tail position, various body postures, and both a humming sound and a shrill alarm call to communicate (Figure 17–14). Invasion of territory is signaled by a combination of several of these communication mechanisms. Generally, females are able to resolve disputes without physical contact. Males often fight

Figure 17–12
Llamas are generally curious creatures. This gentle young animal went from person to person, apparently smelling everyone's breath.

Figure 17–13
Llamas are generally easy to train and handle. The young llama here seems intent on determining what his young handler wants of him. This was only the second time the animal had been haltered.

Figure 17–14
Llamas use vocalizations, body postures, and both ear and tail position to communicate. In this photo, the female is signaling alarm and potential aggression with her ear and tail positions and general body posture.

Figure 17–15

Lamoids are communal dung-pile users. In the wild, this behavior probably serves to mark the territory of a family group and perhaps help control diseases.

using butts, kicks, ramming of the body, and a good deal of noise. The fight is won when one combatant is put on the ground in the breeding position, which signals submissiveness.

Males have fighting teeth—two uppers and one lower on each side, which should be removed at 3 years of age and again later if they grow out. Although llamas rarely bite humans, precaution is warranted. Llamas are prone to biting each other.

Spitting and body charging are normal herd dominance behavior patterns in males. Spitting is used by a female to signal her lack of interest to an unwanted suitor. It is also used to discourage a threat from another llama and to set the pecking order for meals. If directed at a human, spitting probably signals that the llama has been excessively or poorly handled by a human. This behavior is most evident in bottle-fed males, who tend to develop unacceptable behavior as adults, referred to as berserk male syndrome. These animals are dangerous and should be destroyed.

Lamoids are communal dung-pile users. This behavior can be considered an advantage if the dung pile is in a good place and a disadvantage if one is started in a barn or near a water supply (Figure 17–15).

TRENDS AND CHALLENGES TO THE LLAMA INDUSTRY

Research Needs

Much research needs to be done in many areas if owners are to increase their ability to care for lamoids. Finding ways and means of supporting this research is a challenge to the entire llama and alpaca industry. Identification of genetic markers to assist breeders in identifying and dealing with genetic defects would be very beneficial. Other information is needed on nutrition and health—especially approved pharmaceuticals.

Educational Needs

Owner education is important in all species, and the lamoids are no exception. Many llama and alpaca owners lack experience with large animals. The unique attributes of these animals make it especially important that owners be educated. Unfortunately, the standard livestock education routes—colleges and universities, state specialists, extension services, numerous authoritative books and publications, experienced and knowledgeable feed salespeople—are sorely lacking for the lamoid enthusiast. It is a challenge for every owner, and even for the industry itself, to develop a sound continuing education program. Also, llama owners should be educated about resources to help them with pasture management, poisonous plants, pasture rotation, economic fencing, and so on. The local extension agent has a wealth of information for the llama or alpaca owner, even though he or she may know little about camelids.

Health Care

Every llama owner should find a good veterinarian who understands lamoids or is willing to learn. One can't afford to wait until an animal is critically ill to find medical help.

ORGANIZATIONS AND SOURCES OF INFORMATION

Alpaca Llama Show Association

http://www.alsashow.net/

Alpaca Owners and Breeders Association

http://www.alpacainfo.com/

International Llama Registry

http://www.lamaregistry.com

International Camelid Institute

http://www.icinfo.org/index.html

The Alpaca Registry, Inc.

http://www.alpacaregistry.com/

SUMMARY AND CONCLUSION

Although lamoids are certainly considered a nontraditional agricultural animal in the United States, they are nevertheless becoming more common. This suggests that mainstream agriculturalists, veterinarians, and hobbyists could benefit from having more knowledge about them. Whether one is a backwoods enthusiast, a hobby farmer, a companion animal owner, or someone who makes a living with these animals, it is imperative to understand their physiology, their habits, and the industry that surrounds them.

Facts about Llamas

Birth weight:	18–40 pounds
Mature weight:	240–500 pounds
Weaning age:	5–8 months
Breeding age:	15–18 months (female); 2½–3 years (male)
Normal season of birth:	Year-round, spring and fall seasons preferred
Gestation:	350 days with +/– 14 days normal
Estrous cycle:	Induced ovulation rather than heat cycle
Birthing interval (months):	12 desirable
Names of various sex classes:	Male or stud for intact males and gelding for castrated males. Female. Baby, or cria.
Types of digestive system:	Herbivores with two fermentation compartments prior to the true stomach. Pseudo-ruminant.

STUDY QUESTIONS

1. List the genera that fall under the family Camelidae. List the species within each genus.

2. What are the two most economically important camelids in the United States?

3. Which camelid produces the highest quality wool? How does the Bradford scale work?

4. Where did llamas and alpacas originate?

5. What are the estimated populations of llamas and alpacas in the United States?

6. List the most common uses of llamas.

7. What type of digestive system do the Camelidae have? How do they compare to the more popular domestic species that have the same type of digestive system?

8. At what age do llamas reach sexual maturity? Describe the size of a mature llama.

9. How does the fiber produced from llama wool differ from that of domestic sheep?

10. Other than "baby," what are newborn llamas called?

11. List five strategies to prevent heavily wooled animals from suffering heat stress.

12. List six possible diseases of the llama. What are its most common internal and external parasites?

13. What is a more important determinant than age for when a female should be bred?

14. How long are the average gestation lengths of llamas and alpacas?

15. During what time of the day does parturition most often occur? What is the reason for this?

16. As a percentage of body weight, how much colostrum should a newborn cria consume within the first 12 hours of life?

17. What are some common methods of providing colostrum to the newborn if it has problems receiving it from the mother?

18. At what age do crias have a functional rumen?

19. Why is bloat a rare occurrence given the type of food mass found in the forestomachs?

20. What level of forage crude protein is usually sufficient to meet maintenance and growth requirements for a mature llama?

21. List the possible reasons that contribute to the increase in efficiency of lamoid feed utilization as compared to other ruminants.

22. Mature llamas on average will eat what percent of their body weight per day? To what percentage should this level be limited to prevent overconditioning?

23. What are some examples of production functions that should be considered when determining llama feeding regimes?

24. List the two most common dominance behavior patterns in males.

25. Describe the berserk male syndrome and its probable cause.

REFERENCES

For the 5th edition, Melanie A. Breshears, DVM, PhD, Diplomate ACVP, assistant professor, veterinary pathobiology, Center for Veterinary Health Sciences, Oklahoma State University, contributed material to this chapter.

Belknap, E. B. 1994. Medical problems of llamas. In *The veterinary clinics of North America, food animal practice,* L. W. Johnson, ed., Vol. 10, No. 2. Philadelphia: W. B. Saunders.

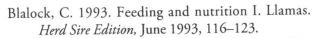

Blalock, C. 1993. Feeding and nutrition I. Llamas. *Herd Sire Edition,* June 1993, 116–123.

Bravo, P. W. 1994. Reproductive endocrinology of llamas and alpacas. In *The veterinary clinics of North America, food animal practice,* L. W. Johnson, ed., Vol. 10, No. 2. Philadelphia: W. B. Saunders.

Bravo, P. W., and L. W. Johnson. 1994. Reproductive physiology of the male camelid. In *The veterinary clinics of North America, food animal practice,* L. W. Johnson, ed., Vol. 10, No. 2. Philadelphia: W. B. Saunders.

Carmean, B. R., K. A. Johnson, D. E. Johnson and L. W. Johnson. 1992. Maintenance energy requirement of the mature llama. American Journal of Veterinary Research 53: 1696–1698.

Compton's interactive encyclopedia. 1995. Compton's New Media, Inc.

Ebel, S. 1989. The llama industry in the United States. In *The veterinary clinics of North America, food animal practice,* L. W. Johnson, ed., Vol. 5, No. 1. Philadelphia: W. B. Saunders.

Fowler, M. E. 1989a. *Medicine and surgery of South American camelids.* 3rd ed. Ames: Iowa State University Press.

Fowler, M. E. 1989b. Physical examination, restraint and handling. In *The veterinary clinics of North America,* L. W. Johnson, ed., Vol. 5, No. 1. Philadelphia: W. B. Saunders.

Fowler, M. E. 1992. Feeding llamas and alpacas. In *Current veterinary therapy XI (small animal),* R. W. Kirk and J. D. Bonagwa, eds. Philadelphia: W. B. Saunders.

Fowler, M. E. 1994. Hyperthermia in llamas and alpacas. In *The veterinary clinics of North America, food animal practice,* L. W. Johnson, ed., Vol. 10, No. 2. Philadelphia: W. B. Saunders.

Franklin, W. L. 1982a. Biology, ecology and relationship to man of South American camelids. In *Mammalian biology in South America,* M. A. Mares and H. H. Genoways, eds. Spec. Publ. 6, 457–489. Linesville, PA: Pymatuning Laboratory of Ecology, University of Pittsburgh.

Franklin, W. L. 1982b. Llama language. *Llama World* 1(2): 6–11.

Hintz, H. F., H. F. Schruyner, and M. Halbert. 1973. A note on the comparison of digestion by new world camelids, sheep and ponies. *Animal Production* 16: 303–305.

Johnson, L. W. 1989a. Llama reproduction. In *The veterinary clinics of North America, food animal practice,* L. W. Johnson, ed., Vol. 5, No. 1. Philadelphia: W. B. Saunders.

Johnson, L. W. 1989b. Nutrition. In *The veterinary clinics of North America, food animal practice,* L. W. Johnson, ed., Vol. 5, No. 1. Philadelphia: W. B. Saunders.

Johnson, L. W. 1994a. Llama herd health. In *The veterinary clinics of North America, food animal practice,* L. W. Johnson, ed., Vol. 10, No. 2. Philadelphia: W. B. Saunders.

Johnson, L. W. 1994b. Llama nutrition. In *The veterinary clinics of North America, food animal practice,* L. W. Johnson, ed., Vol. 10, No. 2. Philadelphia: W. B. Saunders.

McGee, M. 1994. Llama handling and training. In *The veterinary clinics of North America, food animal practice,* L. W. Johnson, ed., Vol. 10, No. 5. Philadelphia: W. B. Saunders.

McNamara, J. P. 2006. *Principles of companion animal nutrition.* Pearson Education, Inc.

Paul-Murphy, J. 1989. Obstetrics, neonatal care, and congenital conditions. In *The veterinary clinics of North America, food animal practice,* L. W. Johnson, ed., Vol. 5, No. 1. Philadelphia: W. B. Saunders.

Pond, W. G., D. C. Church, K. R. Pond, and P. A. Schoknect. 2005. *Basic animal nutrition and feeding.* 5th ed. New York: Wiley.

San Martin, F., and F. C. Bryant. 1989. Nutrition of domesticated South American llamas and alpacas. *Small Ruminant Research* 2: 191.

Sell, R. 1993. Llama. In *Alternative agriculture service,* D. Aakre, series ed., No. 12. NDSU Extension Services, North Dakota State University of Agriculture and Applied Science, and U.S. Department of Agriculture.

Thedford, T. R. 1992. *Some general information for the potential llama owner.* OSU Extension Facts F-9122. Stillwater: Oklahoma Cooperative Extension Service, Division of Agricultural Sciences and Natural Resources, Oklahoma State University.

Van Saun, R. J. 1999. Understanding vitamin and mineral supplements for camelids: reading between the lines. *The Alpaca Registry.* Volume IV, No 1.

18

Rabbits

Learning Objectives

After you have studied this chapter, you should be able to:

- Describe the place of rabbits in U.S. society and agriculture.
- Explain the many uses for rabbits in the United States.
- Give a brief history of the rabbit as a domestic animal.
- Describe the rabbit industry segments.
- Explain the value of breeds in the rabbit industry.
- Discuss the basics of managing rabbits for reproductive efficiency.
- Identify the major methods of feeding rabbits.
- Describe methods of maintaining healthy rabbits and some common rabbit health challenges.
- Explain the nutritional benefits of rabbits to humans.

Fancy The industry segment associated with exhibitions and shows.

Key Terms

Buck
Cecotrophs
Cecotrophy
Doe
Fancy
Fryer

Kindling
Kits
Leporarium
Nest box
Rabbitry

SCIENTIFIC CLASSIFICATION OF THE RABBIT

Phylum:	Chordata
Subphylum:	Vertebrata
Class:	Mammalia
Order:	Lagomorpha
Family:	Leporidae
Genus:	*Oryctolagus* (rabbits), *Lepos* (hares), *Ochotona* (pikas), *Sylvilagus* (cottontails)
Species:	*cuniculus forma domestica* (domestic rabbit), *cuniculus* (wild rabbit)

THE PLACE AND PURPOSE OF RABBITS IN THE UNITED STATES

The domestic rabbit is a descendant of the European wild rabbit. Compared to other animal industries in the United States, the rabbit industry is small and difficult to measure. The rabbit industry has meat-producing, pet, laboratory, and hobbyist/fancy segments, which together are estimated to have 10 million rabbits in the United States. According to the American Veterinary Medical Association, 6.17 million rabbits were kept as pets in the United States in 2006, with an estimated 1.6% of all households having a domestic rabbit as a pet (Figure 18–1). The **fancy** (owners who exhibit) is hard to measure. Of the approximately 24,000 people who belong to the American Rabbit Breeders Association, the majority raise rabbits as a hobby or to exhibit at shows. Approximately 5000 shows are sanctioned annually by the American Rabbit Breeders Association, and over 800,000 animals are exhibited. Their National Convention Show routinely attracts 20,000 entries.

Figure 18–1
In terms of the numbers of people involved, the pet rabbit segment of this industry is the largest. (Courtesy of Kellie Whipple.)

Many people keep a few rabbits in a backyard rabbitry to produce meat for the family. In addition, a viable commercial meat-producing segment of people is attempting to make a livelihood from raising meat rabbits. Large commercial operations keep hundreds or thousands of rabbits for meat production. It is estimated that 6 to 8 million rabbits are slaughtered for meat purposes annually in the United States, with only about 25% of the total processed in USDA inspected facilities. According to the 2007 Census of Agriculture, there are only approximately 6,800 rabbit farms that combined market less than 1 million meat rabbits per year (Figure 18–2). (Clearly, there is conflicting information about rabbit production available.)

Schools and universities use rabbits as teaching tools. Rabbits were used extensively in the early studies of coat color and Mendelian inheritance. They are still useful as models for teaching genetic principles. Rabbits are also raised for their skins

Figure 18–2
Rabbit meat is prized in much of the world but is a very small part of the U.S. diet. (Photo courtesy of Steven D. Lukefahr.)

Figure 18–3

The rabbit produces an excellent fur for the making of fine apparel. The skins are tanned and used for crafts, such as this one offered for sale as a curiosity.

(Figure 18–3), for their wool, and as 4-H and FFA projects (as many as 1 million animals annually). At one time, there was a viable market for the fiber produced from the Angora strains of rabbit. However, this market is currently restricted to a few hand spinners.

The rabbit is an important laboratory species. Approximately 250,000 are used as test subjects yearly. The rabbit has been a very useful animal in immunology studies, diagnostic research, eye research, pyrogen testing, fetal drug-induced teratology, parasite research, and for scores of other conditions. The rabbit has also been used extensively in the testing of human use products. The rabbit is a useful research model because it provides good repeatability of animal model studies; it is large enough for single samples; there are many stocks/strains available; it is easily managed; it provides high-quality immunologic products; and it is easy to control its reproduction.

There are several alternative uses for rabbits in the United States. These alternatives are often tapped by the meat-producing segment as markets for its surplus meat-type rabbits. These uses include:

- "Feeder rabbits" for carnivorous pet reptiles and the larger pet snakes.
- Feed for endangered carnivorous species. The Fish and Wildlife Departments of several states manage reservations for the breeding of such species as eagles, condors, alligators, and wolves. Their goal is to return the animals or their offspring to the wild. Domestic rabbits are often used as the food species of choice. In addition, most states have centers that rehabilitate injured birds of prey. Because these birds are returned to the wild if at all possible, the domestic rabbit provides a food similar to the food that the animal can find in the wild.
- Breeding stock for new producers. New producers need a source of quality breeding stock, and established breeders get higher prices for breeding stock than fryers.
- Military training. Some military bases require large numbers of rabbits for use in training soldiers in survival techniques. Part of the training is finding and killing their own food. Native, wild species are preferred, but are quickly depleted because of the large number of trainees. Thus, domestic rabbits are purchased and released.
- Sport/recreation. Greyhound racing dogs are trained to race using live rabbits. Rabbits are often an important part of petting zoos for children (Figure 18–4).
- Craft uses. For the producer with a "crafty" side, tanning pelts for craft items and making items such as rabbit foot key chains can offer an additional income.

Figure 18–4
Because they are easy to handle and not aggressive, rabbits are often included in petting zoos for children.

Rabbits are an important source of meat worldwide with annual production of approximately 1.8 million MT of meat. China is the world's largest producer with 43% of all production followed by Venezuela, Italy, Democratic People's Republic of Korea, Egypt, Spain, France, the Czech Republic and Germany. Worldwide, rabbit numbers are increasing approximately 2.5% annually.

HISTORICAL PERSPECTIVE

Fossil remains suggest that both hares and rabbits developed in the Western Hemisphere and then migrated to Asia and Europe. North and South America still have the greatest number of species compared to the rest of the continents. The exact dates of domestication are unknown. Most sources credit Spain as being the place of origin of the domestic rabbit. Some sources suggest that rabbits were domesticated as early as 600 B.C. The fact that Phoenicians traded the rabbit to all regions of the world as it was then known to be is evidence to support this early date of domestication. Romans also kept hares and then rabbits brought from Spain in the Roman **leporarium**, from which they were easily harvested for kitchen use, and thus spread the rabbit to many lands. However, neither of these facts necessarily means that rabbits were domesticated. Rather, the domestic breeds of rabbits we know today have their roots in the French monasteries where, from the early Middle Ages, rabbits were kept in hutches and raised as a food source. These species were *Oryctolagus cuniculus,* the progenitor of the modern domestic rabbit. Several breeds were known by the 16th century. In the early 17th century, "types" were described. Some present-day breeds appear little changed from those developed in the 18th and 19th centuries.

Rabbits were probably brought to the United States before the early 1900s; however, evidence to support this estimate is scant. Rabbit breeding has never had the widespread appeal in the United States that it had, and continues to have, in Europe. However, there is a thriving, if small, rabbit industry in the United States.

Leporarium Specially designed enclosure for keeping rabbits that was popular in Roman times. Both rabbits and hares were kept as a ready food supply.

GEOGRAPHIC LOCATION OF THE RABBIT INDUSTRY IN THE UNITED STATES

Some meat-rabbit production exists in every state. According to the 2007 Census of Agriculture, Pennsylvania, Florida, Arkansas, and California were the only states producing 70,000 or more per year. This is a small industry. Pet rabbits are widely

dispersed across the country with the human population, with the more heavily populated states having the most pet rabbits. The rabbit fancy has a healthy contingent in every state in the union.

THE STRUCTURE OF THE RABBIT INDUSTRY

The Rabbit Fancy

The ease of rearing, small space requirements, low initial investment required, and great variety of rabbits available in different sizes, coat types, and colors made the rabbit a natural animal around which a fancy could develop. Today an enthusiastic group of rabbit breeders and owners produce rabbits for exhibition. The animals are exhibited according to a set of rules and regulations at a large number of shows around the country. The rabbit fancy is largely centered on the activities of the American Rabbit Breeders Association (ARBA) and the activities of specific breed organizations. Youth activities are supported, and many 4-H and FFA groups encourage rabbit clubs.

Commercial Meat Production

Many producers have part-time operations consisting of 20 to 100 does. For an operation to be a full-time enterprise, it should probably have at least 300 to 500 does. Does produce from 25 to 50 live offspring a year, which yield 125–250 lbs of meat. Restaurants, wholesalers, custom meat stores, and individual buyers are the predominant markets for rabbit meat in the United States. The meat-producing sector is highly dependent on the availability of slaughtering facilities, packaging requirements, transportation costs, and potential buyers. Typical slaughter weight for rabbits is 5 lbs, which they reach at about 10 weeks of age. Rabbits at this slaughter stage are typically referred to as **fryers**.

Fryer A rabbit weighing approximately 5 lbs and no older than 12 weeks of age. Some processors stipulate no older than 10 or 11 weeks of age.

Rabbit meat sold in commercial establishments (food stores, restaurants, and so on) must be processed in accordance with local or state health codes. Requirements vary from state to state. Producers can check with the extension service and/or state meat inspection agency to determine the policies for their area. The USDA has set standards for the grading of rabbit carcasses.

Laboratory Specimen Production

Laboratory rabbit production is aimed at research laboratories, hospitals, and universities. Although the market is profitable for some, the requirements for entering the market make it difficult for individuals to become established. The specifications of the purchaser are generally stringent and often have little tolerance. In addition, the market is somewhat mercurial.

Producers for this market must be licensed under the provisions of the Animal Welfare Act (AWA). The AWA specifies that dealers selling animals to biomedical research must be licensed with APHIS, which conducts inspections to ensure compliance with the act. Violations of the provisions of the act can lead to license suspensions and/or civil penalties. The AWA requires that regulated individuals and businesses provide animals with care and treatment according to standards established by APHIS. The standards include requirements for record keeping, housing, sanitation, food, water, transportation, and veterinary care. The law regulates the care of animals that are sold as pets at the wholesale level, transported in commerce, used for biomedical research, and used for exhibition purposes.

Breeding Stock Production

Almost anyone with any size and kind of operation, a good reputation, and a knack and willingness for promotion can offer breeding stock to other breeders or new producers. The keys to success in the long term depend on how well the stock offered to the public performs in the **rabbitry** of the purchaser.

Rabbitry A place where domestic rabbits are kept.

Angora Production

Angora rabbits produce 8 to 10 in., or 12 to 16 oz, of wool per year. Most owners who raise the Angora for its wool sell their product directly to individuals or organizations who buy for mills. This market is extremely small. Some producers spin their wool and market the yarn to the general public through craft organizations and publications or on the Internet. The Jersey Wooly is also a fiber-producing breed.

BREEDS AND GENETICS

Many rabbit breeds are produced in the United States. Although the vast majority do not have registration certificates, it is possible to register rabbits with the ARBA. The procedure involves an inspection of the rabbit to be registered. Some of the major rabbit breeds are listed in Table 18–1. The ARBA maintains a website at http://www.arba.net/ where pictures of the recognized breeds can be viewed. Rabbits are generally classified by weight or hair/fur type. The weight categories are small (2–4 lbs), medium (9–12 lbs, although several breeds are smaller than this range), and large (14–16 lbs, although some breeds are larger). The hair/fur classifications are normal, rex, satin, and wool. The medium-weight New Zealand White is considered the best meat-producing breed (Figure 18–5). Californians are considered the second best meat-producing breed. Many different breeds are used in laboratories. All breeds can likely be found as pets somewhere; however, the smaller varieties and those with the most interesting coat colors are favored (Figure 18–6). The American Rabbit Breeders Association publishes a standard of perfection that gives a standard for the perfect rabbit in each breed.

The meat-type breeds of rabbits are Champagne d'Argent, Californian, Cinnamon, American Chinchilla, Creme d'Argent, French Lop, Hotot, New Zealand, Palomino,

Table 18–1
SELECTED BREEDS OF RABBITS

Breed	Size	Hair/Fur	Use	Mature Weight (lbs)
English Angora	Medium	Wool	Fur, fancy, pet, meat	9–12
American Chinchilla	Medium	Normal	Fur, pet, fancy	9–12
Californian	Medium	Normal	Meat, pet, fancy, laboratory	8–11
Champagne d'Argent	Medium	Normal	Meat, pet, fancy	9–12
Checkered Giants	Large	Normal	Pet, meat, fancy, fur	11+
Dutch	Small	Normal	Laboratory, pet	3–6
English Spot	Medium	Normal	Meat, laboratory	9–13
Flemish Giants	Large	Normal	Pet, fancy	13+
Himalayan	Small	Normal	Laboratory, pet, fancy	2–6
New Zealand	Medium	Normal	Meat, pet, fancy, laboratory	9–12
Polish	Small	Normal	Laboratory, pet, fancy	3–4
Rex	Medium	Rex	Fur, pet, fancy	8–11
Silver Martens	Medium	Normal	Fur, pet, fancy	6–10

Figure 18–5

The medium-weight New Zealand White is considered the best meat-producing rabbit breed for commercial operations. Contrary to its name, the New Zealand breed was developed in the United States. (Photo courtesy of American Rabbit Breeders Association.)

Figure 18–6

The Netherland Dwarf is a small breed used primarily for pets and for showing. (Photo courtesy of American Rabbit Breeders Association.)

Feed conversion ratio
Feed needed to produce 1 lb of gain.

Kits Baby rabbits.

Rex, American Sable, Satin, Silver Fox, and Silver Martens. The most commonly used is the New Zealand White, which is considered the best meat-type breed because of both husbandry and processor preference. The Californian is second in popularity. These two breeds have the best size, growth rates, feed conversion ratios, dress-out weights, and meat-to-bone ratios. In addition, their albino characteristics give them a cleaner, lighter dressing carcass than colored rabbits have. The pelts from these two breeds are easier to remove in processing. The production goal for meat-producing operations is to produce 4- to 5-lb fryers at 8 weeks of age. Fryers are expected to gain an average of 0.5 lb per week with a **feed conversion ratio** of 4:1.

A sound breeding program for a commercial operation should include selection for the traits that most affect profitability. These include litters per doe per year, number of **kits** per litter, number of kits weaned, longevity, weaning weights, feed conversion, and dressing percentage.

The rabbit fancy and the pet segment both rely on the purebred animal. Thus, breeding of these animals revolves around breed improvement and selection for both eye appeal and disposition. Sometimes crossbred animals are seen in the pet industry as well. Crossbreeding is a useful strategy for producing meat rabbits because of the heterosis it provides. The most popular cross is Californian bucks on

New Zealand White does. The fryers from this cross, called "smuts," are highly regarded by processors.

REPRODUCTIVE MANAGEMENT

The medium-weight breeds are mature and can be put into the breeding colony at 6 to 7 months of age. Given the same environmental conditions and breeding, **bucks** mature approximately 1 month later than does.

Outward signs of heat are not always evident in **does,** nor do does have a well-defined heat such as that found in the other livestock species. Their cycles revolve around the development and degeneration of follicles on the ovary, which occurs on a 16- to 18-day cycle. For all but 4 days of the cycle, a doe mates and is fertile. The most successful mating schemes breed on a schedule. Does that are not receptive on a given day are scheduled for rebreeding a few days later. For mating, the doe is put in the buck's cage. The buck should never be put in the doe's cage because she will fight to protect her territory. If the doe is ready, mating occurs immediately. Directly after mating, the doe should be returned to her cage to prevent fighting and possible injury. The stress of a fight can also cause the doe's temperature to rise, which is not good for the intended conception. The doe is an induced ovulator and ovulates approximately 10 hours after mating.

It is generally recommended that one buck service about 10 does. Recommendations vary on how frequently each buck should be used for mating. Certainly, using a buck two to three times a week is acceptable. Bucks may be used as frequently as once a day. Although some producers use bucks more frequently, at least for short periods, small litters may result. Artificial insemination is an option in rabbits. Rabbit semen can be extended and frozen and remain viable. Although labor intensive, artificial insemination in rabbits offers the same potential for genetic progress as it does in other livestock species. Another advantage of AI is that bucks from anywhere in the world can be mated with does found anywhere else in the world.

Gestation is 31 to 32 days. On day 28 of gestation, a **nest box** (Figure 18–7) filled half full of nesting material should be placed in the doe's hutch. A doe normally pulls some of her own fur to line a nest for the kits. An average litter is 8–10 kits. **Kindling** (birthing) normally occurs in the early morning and requires approximately 30 minutes. Within 24 and no longer than 48 hours after kindling, the nest box should be examined and any dead kits removed. Litters can be equalized between does if the kits are approximately the same age. A desirable number is seven to eight kits for each doe. Excessively large litters should either be fostered or culled to no more than eight kits. Does rarely have more than eight nipples for feeding the young. Owners in commercial operations should record the number of live and dead kits. The information is useful in making culling and selection decisions.

The nest box is removed 15 to 21 days after birth or after all of the kits have left it. Some producers prefer to leave the nest boxes; however, the young generally soil the box. Removing it allows for better sanitation and offers an opportunity to clean the box and ready it for the next litter. The kits are weaned at 28 to 30 days of age in commercial operations. At this time, they are eating well. Producers in the fancy frequently prefer to wean at 6 to 8 weeks of age. In a commercial operation, it is imperative to wean early or the operation will not be profitable. Most profitable commercial operations rebreed on a more accelerated schedule, either 14 or 21 days after kindling. A 14-day rebreeding schedule allows more litters per year. Does who lose a litter at kindling can be rebred the same day, but it is generally recommended to wait 3 days. Those who lose a litter a few days after kindling can be rebred immediately.

Buck Intact male rabbit.

Doe Female rabbit.

Nest box A box provided for the doe in which to give birth and rear the young for their first few weeks.

Kindling Parturition in rabbits.

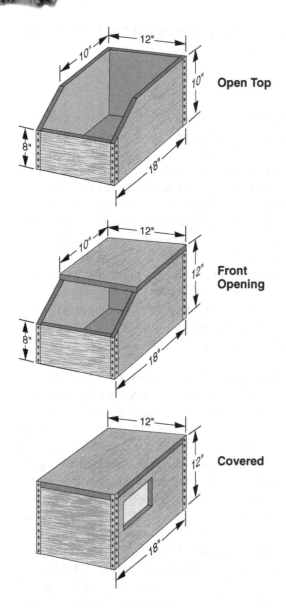

Figure 18–7
Nest boxes should provide enough room for the doe and litter but be small enough to keep the litter close together. Nest boxes can be constructed of nontreated wood, wire mesh, or sheet metal. Wood boxes should have metal reinforced edges. For winter use, the box should be enclosed with a small opening for the doe's entrance. Summer nest boxes can be open.

Fall and winter breeding slumps occur frequently in rabbitrys. Use of artificial light to extend the light hours to at least 14, and up to 16 hours, is beneficial. Recommendations suggest a 40-watt bulb at 10-foot intervals set on a timer for consistency as adequate. Bucks are frequently the problem because they are very sensitive to heat. A buck exposed to 85° temperatures for 5 or more days can become sterile for as long as 3 months. Thus, summer temperatures in much of the country can contribute to breeding problems in the fall and winter.

The reproductive tracts of the buck and doe are shown in Figures 18–8 and 18–9.

NUTRITION

The principles of nutrition are discussed in Chapters 3, 4 and 5. Refer to those chapters for more detailed information than is presented here.

Cecotrophy The act of consuming the material from the cecum in the form of cecotrophs.

The rabbit is a cecal fermenter that practices **cecotrophy**. The cecotrophic animal consumes the contents of the cecum, usually directly from the rectum. Once a day, usually at night, the contents of the large intestine are emptied of fecal material, which are hard fecal pellets. The animal allows the pellets to drop to the ground or

Figure 18–8
Reproductive tract of the buck rabbit.

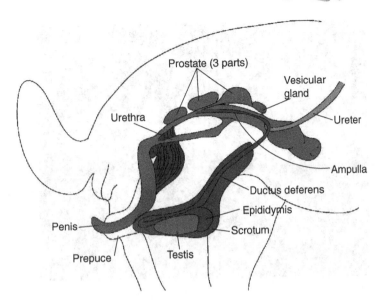

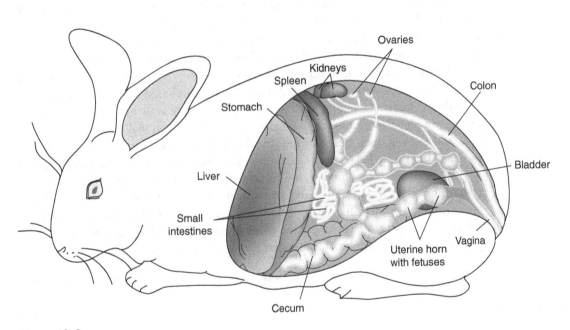

Figure 18–9
Reproductive tract of the doe.

through the cage floor. The contents of the cecum are then emptied into the lower large intestine as **cecotrophs**. These cecotrophs are higher in water, electrolytes, and protein and lower in fiber. The cecotrophs are redigested in the upper portion of the digestive tract and then become the next hard fecal pellets in the cycle. As much as 20% of the protein and 10% of the energy needs of the animal may be met by the microbial protein and the energy of the cecotrophs. Animals deprived of the practice of cecotrophy frequently develop nutritional deficiencies.

For practical purposes, there are two ways to feed rabbits. The first and most convenient method is to feed a commercially prepared and balanced complete diet. These feeds are almost exclusively pelleted rations. They are easy to feed in automatic feeders that can be fitted on the outside of the cage for ease in servicing. For large numbers of rabbits, this type of feed is the overwhelming choice. The alternative method is to

Cecotrophs Large soft pellets of cecally fermented feed, which move through the colon in a distinctly different manner than feces and are reconsumed for upper digestive tract digestion.

Figure 18–10

Rabbits thrive on commercially prepared and balanced complete diets. However, they may also be fed fresh grass and legume forage, root crops, and garden greens as a low-cost alternative. (Photo courtesy of Steven D. Lukefahr.)

feed forage, usually hay and grain. Because rabbits are herbivores, they may also be fed fresh grass and legume forage, extra garden produce such as turnips and other root crops, and limited amounts of garden greens (Figure 18–10). Owners of small numbers of rabbits may find this an attractive and low-cost alternative. Portable cages can be moved across fresh pasture, allowing rabbits to harvest their own forage.

If forage and grain rations are fed, they require individual balancing for the rabbits' needs. Commercial pelleted feeds can be purchased in one of three forms: all grain, all forage, and complete rations. Commercially available complete, pelleted rations are prebalanced to meet the rabbit's complete nutritional requirements. Pregnant and nursing does should be fed free choice. Bucks and nonpregnant, nonlactating does should be fed 6–8 oz of commercial pellets daily. It is recommended that Angora rabbits be fed complete, commercial diets exclusively because their wool gets contaminated with dust and chaff (debris) from hay, which lowers its quality. Feeding commercial pellets does not preclude the addition of small amounts of greens to the diet. Thus pet owners can use the commercial diets for their animal and still feed greens as a treat. Examples of some diets for rabbits are shown in Table 18–2.

Table 18–2
SAMPLE DIETS FOR RABBITS

	Maintenance Diet	Growth Diet	Growth Diet	Lactation Diet	Gestation Diet
INGREDIENT	PERCENTAGE OF INGREDIENT IN FORMULATION				
Alfalfa hay	52.4	45.0	60.0	36.4	50.0
Barley	18.1	34.0	15.0	—	—
Corn	—	2.7	22.0	32.5	—
Oats	9.6	—	—	—	45.5
Soybean meal	—	—	3.0	16.3	4.0
Sunflower meal	3.5	11.1	—	—	—
Wheat bran	13.0	2.1	—	10.2	—
Cane molasses	1.5	3.0	—	1.6	—
Dicalcium phosphate	1.1	1.3	—	2.2	—
NaCl	0.5	0.5	—	0.5	0.5
Vitamin, mineral, and amino acid supplement	0.3	0.3	—	0.3	—

Source: Compiled from Adams and Berry, 1987, p. 10; Kellems and Church, 1998, p. 461; and Overstreet, 1993, p. 96.

Rabbit owners commonly underestimate the amount of water rabbits require. Commercial operations generally rely on automatic watering systems that offer a continuous clean water supply. A doe and litter may need as much as 1 gal of water a day in warm weather. Standard nipple water bottles hold only a fraction of that amount. Thus, several bottles will need to be available on the cage to meet the animals' needs.

HEALTH PROGRAM

Refer to that chapter for more complete information than is presented here.

For pet rabbits, a good program of care by a veterinarian versed in rabbit diseases and health maintenance is the safest course of action. Some of the recommendations for health maintenance in commercial operations are not practical for the pet animal and animals that participate in the show circuit. Thus, diseases may be more difficult to control for the pet and fancy animal.

Providing sufficient amounts of feed and water, maintaining stringent levels of cleanliness, providing good ventilation, practicing close observation, and providing protection from sun and precipitation go a long way in protecting the health of the rabbitry. Frequent removal of loose hair as well as manure removal are necessary in an active rabbitry and help decrease disease risks.

The principles of biosecurity can be applied to a rabbitry as a means of preventing disease. At a minimum, neither human nor animal visitors should be permitted inside the rabbitry. Visitors can introduce disease and cause stress to the rabbits. Sick animals should be isolated immediately after observation. If the sick animal is in a group cage within a larger housing arrangement, the rest of the group should be isolated. The cage that housed the sick animal should be disinfected. Once the diseased animal leaves the isolation, that cage should be disinfected. In operations of all sizes, nest boxes should be cleaned and sanitized after each use, and the accumulated hair should be burned from the cages. New breeding stock should be isolated from the general herd for a period of observation. Then, a few animals from the herd should be introduced to the new animals before the new animals are introduced to the general herd. If signs of disease develop in the animals from the established herd, then a knowledgeable decision can be made about adding the new animals to the general herd. It may be prudent to dispose of both the new and exposed rabbits rather than risking exposure in the general herd.

Good records are the cornerstone of good health maintenance. Periodic review of the records with an objective eye directed at cause and effect can help spot problems and suggest long-term solutions for prevention of disease. Ear tattoos with unique numbers provide a good means of permanent identification so that individual health records can be maintained. Individual identification cards with health and reproductive information should also be kept on each cage or hutch for ease of recording. Several computer programs have been developed to assist rabbit producers with record-keeping chores. If the rabbitry contains as many as 20 does, one of these programs is probably justifiable.

Challenges to Rabbit Health

Despite good husbandry, rabbitries may still have losses due to diseases or other health issues. A few of the most common challenges to rabbit health are briefly described below.

Pasteurellosis

Pasteurellosis is a common disease in domestic rabbits and is caused by infection with *Pasteurella multocida*, a highly **contagious** bacterium. Rabbits that appear healthy may be carriers of the disease and spread it to other animals in the group. Because of

Contagious Capable of being transmitted from animal to animal.

this, it is important that new animals be quarantined or acquired from *Pasteurella*-free operations and sick animals be isolated or culled. *Pasteurella* infection can cause a respiratory disease known as snuffles or can cause problems that include eye infections, abscesses, reproductive infections, or sudden death. Veterinary treatment with **antibiotic** drugs may decrease disease symptoms but usually do not completely cure affected animals. An effective vaccine for pasteurellosis in rabbits is not available. Therefore, preventing infection within the rabbitry by purchasing disease-free rabbits and eliminating sick animals from the colony is the best method of disease control.

Antibiotic Drug used to treat bacterial infections.

Mastitis

Mastitis Inflammation of the mammary gland, often due to infection by a microorganism.

Lactating does may develop **mastitis**, especially if conditions are unsanitary. Affected rabbits often have hot and swollen mammary glands that are initially reddened and then become discolored with a bluish tint, which is referred to as blue bag. With early veterinary attention and antibiotic treatment, the doe may be saved. However, damage to mammary glands may limit future use as a breeding animal. If veterinary care is delayed or mastitis is severe, the doe may die. If a doe dies of mastitis, her orphaned kits may be hand-reared, but they should not be fostered by another doe, as that could spread the disease to the foster mother.

Diarrhea

Young rabbits may be affected by intestinal disease caused by several different microorganisms. Some intestinal infections cause diarrhea accompanied by dullness and other signs of illness that progress to death before treatment can be attempted. Vaccines for intestinal diseases are not available, but the risk of disease can be decreased by limiting stress and feeding an appropriate diet with adequate fiber.

Non-infectious diseases

Other health problems that may affect rabbits include back injuries, teeth abnormalities, hair chewing, and heat exhaustion. An improperly restrained rabbit may kick powerfully, which will potentially result in injury to the fragile spinal column. For this reason, when handling a rabbit, it is important that its hindlimbs always be supported and not allowed to kick free. Since a rabbit's teeth grow continually throughout their life, if they are not normally aligned, teeth may become overgrown and require trimming to prevent damage to the tongue and cheeks. Constant self-grooming by rabbits may result in hair accumulation in the stomach and can be prevented by daily combing to remove loose hair. Hair-chewing may be due to a low-fiber diet or boredom and damages the pelts of rabbits used for fur production. Rabbits are sensitive to hot and humid conditions, and should be kept out of extreme heat and in well-ventilated hutches with an adequate supply of cool water.

NUTRITIONAL VALUE OF RABBIT MEAT TO HUMANS

Rabbit meat is high-quality meat that is often considered a delicacy. Rabbit meat is considered white meat. It is fine grained, delicately flavored, and adaptable to many styles of cooking—from stew pot, to the barbecue, to the heights of fine Italian and

French cookery. It is high in protein and low in fat, cholesterol, sodium, and calories. A 3-oz serving of cooked rabbit meat provides the following proportion of the recommended daily dietary allowance for a young adult man:

Protein	44%
Phosphorus	32%
Iron	24%
Zinc	18%
Riboflavin	14%
Thiamin	6%
B_{12}	294%
Niacin	45%

Rabbit meat is very high in nutritive value with high nutrient density, which contains all essential amino acids needed by humans, many needed minerals, and all required vitamins except vitamin C. Although not a traditional food in many households, rabbit meat is healthful food that can be part of the diet of virtually all people.

TRENDS AND FACTORS IN RABBIT PRODUCTION

Advantages of Commercial Rabbit Production

Commercial rabbit production offers the advantage of a supplemental income that can be earned in the owner's spare time. It has a small land requirement (a huge rabbitry can be placed on less than 1 acre of land). The labor is sustained but less physically demanding than that required in many other agricultural enterprises. By comparison, the investment in facilities is less than that in most other agricultural enterprises. In addition, another source of income can be gained from producing and selling earthworms in the rabbit manure.

Disadvantages of Commercial Rabbit Production

Although the investment is less than that for most agricultural enterprises, there is nevertheless an initial investment that amounts to $70 to $150 per doe unit, depending on such factors as availability of a building and the need for cages, equipment, and breeding stock. If a building is available, initial costs can generally be halved.

As an agricultural enterprise, the rabbit industry must be considered high risk. The industry structure is simply not adequately developed to provide consistent and stable markets. The ready availability of multiple markets for livestock is one of the strongest features of the U.S. livestock industry. A similar market structure does not exist for rabbits. Individual producers must take responsibility for developing and maintaining markets, which can be challenging. In addition, ample supplies of meat can be acquired on the international market and that does not bode well for a domestic industry.

Management

Raising rabbits has a reputation of being easy. This is probably because of the fabled reproductive rates of the animal. However, rabbits are not overly easy to raise. They are like any other living creature—they require the application of good management and husbandry skills. New producers are invariably plagued with such a variety of problems that maximum production is seldom achieved for the first few years. Raising rabbits is also confining and labor intensive. During the early years of an operation, the cost of hired help can quickly deplete any profit. Attention to detail, which includes meticulous record keeping, is essential to success. Not all people are suited to these rigors.

ORGANIZATIONS AND SOURCES OF INFORMATION

American Rabbit Breeders Association, Inc.

http://www.arba.net

This organization is devoted to the rabbit fancy and to commercial production.

Maryland Small Ruminant Page

http://www.sheepandgoat.com/rabbits.html Mississippi State University Extension Service–Commercial Rabbit Production

http://www.poultry.msstate.edu/extension/

SUMMARY AND CONCLUSION

Modern domestic rabbits are descended from the European wild rabbit. The rabbit industry in the United States is a small, but quite diverse, industry. The predominant uses for rabbits in the United States are as pets, for laboratory use, and as a hobby. Many people who keep rabbits as a hobby are fanciers who participate in some part of the exhibition industry. Rabbit breeding has been evident in the United States since roughly the beginning of the 20th century but has never been practiced here to the degree that it has in Europe.

The rabbit industry is composed of the fancy, commercial meat production, laboratory specimen production, breeding stock production, fiber production, and equipment and supplies segments. Many people participate in more than one segment of the industry. More than 100 breeds of rabbits can be found worldwide, but less than half that number are found in any numbers in the United States. New breeds are being developed. Rabbit breeds are generally divided into weight categories and fur/hair categories.

Reproductive management in rabbits is not as simple as the reputation of the rabbit implies. Commercial units must work at effective reproductive management programs to remain cost effective.

The rabbit practices cecotrophy, in which cecotrophs are consumed from the anus and redigested.

Rabbits deprived of cecotrophs generally develop nutritional deficiencies. Most rabbits are fed complete commercial diets. However, information on grain and forage diets is readily available.

The principles of rabbit health maintenance are much the same as those for other species. Providing sufficient amounts of feed and water, maintaining stringent levels of cleanliness, providing good ventilation, practicing close observation, and providing protection from weather will do much to protect the health of rabbits.

Rabbit meat has high nutrient density, contains all essential amino acids, many minerals, and all required vitamins except vitamin C.

Commercial rabbit production offers the advantage of a supplemental income that can be earned in the owner's spare time, but must be considered high risk. The industry structure is not adequately developed to provide consistent and stable markets. Raising rabbits has a reputation of being easy, but rabbits are like any other animal—they require the application of good management and husbandry skills. Attention to detail, good record keeping, and hard work are required. However, a single or small number of rabbits can provide an enjoyable pet or hobby.

Facts about Rabbits

Birth weight:	Varies with breed and sex, 1.75–2.3 oz
Mature weight:	Varies with breed, sex, and condition. The weight categories are small (2–4 lbs), medium (9–12 lbs, although several are smaller than this range), and large (14–16 lbs, with some being larger).
Hair/fur classifications:	Normal, rex, satin, and wool
Slaughter weight:	4–5 lbs
Weaning age:	4–8 weeks depending on goals of the breeding program
Breeding age:	6–7 months, bucks within a breed mature approximately one month later than does
Normal season of birth:	Year round; may require artificial lighting for year-round breeding
Gestation:	31–32 days
Estrous cycle and duration of estrus:	Induced ovulation, breeds all but 3–4 days in a 16–18 day period
Kindling interval:	As little as 31–32 days; can rebreed on day of kindling; practically, 45–52 days desirable
Normal mating success:	70–90% of matings should result in a litter; seven to eight kits are the preferred litter size
Names of various sex classes:	Buck, doe, kits, fryers
Weight at weaning:	At 4 weeks—1.25 lbs, 4 lbs at 8 weeks
Type of digestive system:	Monogastric, cecal fermentation, practices cecotrophy

STUDY QUESTIONS

1. Describe the place of the rabbit in the United States.
2. How do the uses of the rabbit compare with the uses of the other species discussed in this text?
3. What are the primary and alternative uses for rabbits in the United States?
4. Give a brief accounting of the history of the domestic rabbit.
5. Describe the individual segments of the rabbit industry.
6. What are the classification categories used to distinguish among rabbit breeds?
7. In outline form, describe the basics of reproductive management in the rabbit.
8. What are the general steps necessary to get a doe's cage ready for her to kindle?
9. Describe nest box management after the kits are born.
10. Pretend you are a county agent who has been asked to give a talk to a group of grade school students who are starting a rabbit project in 4-H. What would you tell them about nutrition? What would you tell their parents?
11. What would you tell a group of potential rabbit producers about the general need for a biosecurity program if they expect to have a serious rabbit breeding program?
12. Describe at least two health challenges to rabbits.
13. In each of the chapters on food-producing species covered in this text, a section has discussed the nutritive value of the food product to humans. Create a table comparing and contrasting the information on rabbit meat to at least two other food products.

REFERENCES

For the 5th edition, Melanie A. Breshears, DVM, PhD, Diplomate ACVP, assistant professor, veterinary pathobiology, Center for Veterinary Health Sciences, Oklahoma State University, contributed material to this chapter.

Adams, A. W., and J. G. Berry. 1987. *Raising rabbits.* Circular E-8222. Stillwater: Cooperative Extension Service, Division of Agriculture, Oklahoma State University.

Clutton–Brock, J. 1999. *A natural history of domestic animals.* Cambridge, UK: Cambridge University Press.

FAO, 2011. *FAOSTAT statistics database.* Agricultural Production and Production Indices Data. http://apps.fao.org/.

Gonzalez-Mariscal, G., J. I. McNitt, and S. D. Lukefahr. 2007. Maternal care of rabbits in the lab and on the farm: Endocrine regulation of behavior and productivity. *Hormones and Behavior* 52:86–91.

Grannis, J. 2002. U.S. *Rabbit industry profile.* USDA-APHIS:VS.

Kellems, R. O., and D. C. Church. 1998. *Livestock feeds and feeding.* 4th ed. Upper Saddle River, NJ: Prentice Hall.

Lebas, F., P. Coudert, H. de Rochambeau, and R. G. Thebault. 1997. *The rabbit: Husbandry, health and production.* 2nd ed. FAO Animal Production and Health Series. No. 21. Food and Agriculture Organization of the United Nations.

Lebas, F., P. Coudert, R. Rouvier, and H. de Rochambeau. 1986. *The rabbit: Husbandry, health and production.* FAO Animal Production and Health Series, No. 21. Rome: Food and Agriculture Organization of the United Nations.

Lukefahr, S. D. 2002. Opportunities for rabbit research and human development in the Western Hemisphere: A rabbit revolution? *World Rabbit Science.* (France) 10(3):111–115.

Lukefahr, S. D., P. R. Cheeke, J. I. McNitt, and N. M. Patton. 2004. Limitations of intensive meat rabbit production in North America. *Canadian Journal of Animal Science.* 84:349–360.

McCrosky, R. 2000. *Raising rabbits in the Pacific Northwest.* BC Canada: Canadian Center for Rabbit Production Development. Accessed online July 2004. http://pan-am.uniserv.com.

McNitt, J. I., N. M. Patton, S. D. Lukefar, and P. R. Cheeke. 2000. *Rabbit production.* Upper Saddle River, NJ: Prentice Hall.

Morrow, M., G. L. Greaser, G. M. Perry, J. K. Harper, and C. C. Engle. 1998. *Agricultural alternatives: Rabbit production.* Small and part-time farming project at Penn State with support from the U.S. Department of Agriculture-Extension Service. Document Number: 28503258.

Overstreet, N. 1993. *Rabbit production handbook.* College Station, TX: Instructional Materials Service, Texas A&M University.

Sherman, D. M. 2002. *Tending animals in the global village.* Philadelphia: Lippincott Williams & Wilkins.

Smith, T. W. 1997. *Starting a rabbit enterprise.* Poultry Science Home Page, College of Agriculture & Life Sciences, Mississippi State University, Mississippi State, MS. http://www.msstate.edu/dept/poultry/rabenter.htm. E-mail: tsmith@poultry.msstate.edu.

Thompson, H. V., and C. M. King. 1994. *The European rabbit: The history and biology of a successful colonizer.* Oxford, UK: Oxford University Press.

Wright, M. A. 2005. *Raising meat rabbits.* Cornell University: Cornell Small Farms Program & Department of Animal Science Livestock Fact Sheets.

part four
Animals and Society

19

Food Safety and Consumer Concerns

Key Terms

BSE

BST

Delaney clause

Electronic pasteurization (e-beams)

Emerging pathogens

Epidemiology

Fight BAC!

Foodborne illness

GRAS list

Guillain-Barré syndrome

HACCP

Hemolytic-uremic syndrome (HUS)

Irradiated foods

Pathogen

Residue avoidance

Residue monitoring program

Septicemia

Withdrawal time

Zero tolerance

Learning Objectives

After you have studied this chapter, you should be able to:

- Describe the complexities of the food safety issues facing the food industry.
- Discuss the basics of the history of food safety during the 20th century.
- Describe the magnitude of the problem of food safety to consumers.
- Identify the most important of the foodborne pathogens.
- Differentiate between the roles of various government agencies in providing for a safe food supply.
- Describe the current and changing roles of FSIS in food safety.
- Describe HACCP and state its purpose and principles.
- Explain the level of safety associated with bovine somatotropin, growth-promoting hormones, and antibiotics in animal production.
- Describe the value of food irradiation.

INTRODUCTION

It must be said at the outset that the U.S. food supply is among the safest in the world, if not the safest. It must also be acknowledged that, despite our safe food supply, millions of Americans are made ill each year by the food they eat. According to the Food and Consumer Economics Division of the USDA, microbial **pathogens** in foods cause from 6.5 to 33 million illnesses and 9,000 deaths in the United States each year, often among the very young and the elderly. Estimates indicate that the cost of human illness for just six specific foodborne pathogens range from $2.9 billion to $6.7 billion annually. Foodborne illnesses are caused either by direct infection or the presence of a toxin. Foodborne infections result from consuming a food product contaminated by bacteria or viruses that subsequently multiply in the human body and cause illness. According to the Center for Disease Control (CDC) the bacteria that most commonly causes foodborne infections are *Campylobacter, Escherichia coli O157:H7* and Salmonella. Calicivirus, also known as the Norwalk and Norwalk-like viruses, are largely responsible for the majority of foodborne infections caused from viruses. Toxins are another source of foodborne illness. Disease caused by consuming a toxin is usually referred to as a foodborne intoxication. The toxin is usually produce by a microorganism, such as bacteria or fungi, growing in the food prior to consumption. *Staphylococcus aureus* is a bacterium that can grow in some foods and produce a toxin that causes severe vomiting. *Clostridium*

Pathogen A bacterium or virus that causes disease.

botulinum is another bacterium that can grow in canned foods if they are not processed correctly. This bacterium produces a powerful paralytic toxin. *Aspergillus* is a fungus found in many cereals, oilseeds, spices, and tree nuts. It produces the mycotoxin Aflatoxin which are not only toxic, but carcinogenic as well. Foodborne illness can result from consuming contaminated fruits, vegetables, grains, water, or animal-based foods. Threats range from disease-causing microorganisms to contamination with toxins of chemical and microbiological origin.

HISTORY OF FOOD SAFETY AS A PUBLIC ISSUE

Food safety has not always been such a high-profile public issue, although it is by no means a new issue. Concerns about the processing of food began at the turn of the 20th century. *The Jungle,* a novel by Upton Sinclair, caused great public concern by describing deplorable conditions in the meat-processing industry (Figure 19–1). Public pressure consequently resulted in the passage of the Pure Food and Drug Act of 1906 and the Meat Inspection Act of 1906, beginning the government regulation of food processing. In 1958, the Federal Food Additives Amendment made food-additive testing the responsibility of the food product's manufacturer and established that any new food additive must be demonstrated as safe before it can be added to food. A part of the 1958 Food Additive Amendment was the **Delaney clause,** which prohibited the addition of any substance shown to cause cancer in any animal at any dose. Almost from its adoption, the clause was under attack as being unrealistic. Extremely high doses of some substances may cause cancer but are perfectly safe at much lower doses. To remedy this problem, Congress passed the Food Quality Protection Act (FQPA) in August 1996. It repealed the Delaney clause, replacing **zero tolerance** with a more science-based standard of "reasonable certainty of no harm" for raw and processed food tolerances. The EPA was given 10 years to implement the law.

There was also another important outcome of the 1958 Food Additives Amendment. In effect, it created a grandfather clause for a group of compounds that were already in use when the legislation passed and were considered "generally recognized

Delaney clause Prohibited the addition of any substance to human food shown to cause cancer in any animal at any dose.

Zero tolerance Common term used to indicate restrictions imposed by the Delaney clause.

Figure 19–1
The Jungle, a novel by Upton Sinclair, described deplorable conditions in the meat-processing industry. Public outrage sparked by the novel led directly to the passage of the Pure Food and Drug Act of 1906 and the Meat Inspection Act of 1906. (Photo courtesy of Library of Congress.)

as safe (GRAS)." Compounds on this **GRAS list** were given special status and continued to be used. If they were removed from the list, it was because they had been proven to be a hazard. This list of compounds has been under constant review ever since its creation. By applying the strict provisions of the Delaney clause, several compounds have been removed from the GRAS list. The new provisions will result in some of those being returned to the GRAS list.

These measures have been highly effective and generally satisfied the concerns of the consuming public. For several decades, when food safety was discussed, the concerns focused on proper home-canning techniques to avoid botulism toxicity and the proper cooking of pork to avoid trichinosis. If there was an outbreak of food-related illness, it was usually associated with something like bad potato salad at a church social or Fourth of July picnic. Being very local, these outbreaks rarely created any media interest beyond the local paper (Figure 19–2). Perhaps the issues that most served to refocus the national attention on food safety were two incidents relating to fruits. The first was an incident with apples and the growth-regulator alar, which received sensationalized publicity because of the involvement of a well-known Hollywood actress, Meryl Streep, as spokesperson for the Natural Resources Defense Council and coverage in two *60 Minutes* programs. The second was an incident involving cyanide-tainted grapes.

The 1990s saw several episodes of food-related diseases. The most widely recognized and publicized incidents involved *Escherichia coli* (*E. coli*) O157:H7 in meat in 1993 and 1997, and in apple juice in 1996. Several incidents involved *Cryptosporidium* in drinking water. *Salmonella* caused outbreaks traced to cantaloupe in 1991, in ice cream in 1994, on alfalfa sprouts in 1995, and in homemade mayonnaise (traced to eggs) in 1996. In 1996, *Cyclospora* on raspberries from Guatemala caused an outbreak of that parasite; in 1997, oysters infected several hundred people with Norwalk virus; and in 1997, Hepatitis A–contaminated strawberries from Mexico caused an outbreak. However, the galvanizing event that brought public attention to the issue of food safety was probably in 1993 when *E. coli* O157:H7 contamination occurred in hamburgers from a well-known fast-food restaurant. The hamburger was unknowingly contaminated with the bacteria. Had it been cooked to the proper temperature, tragedy would have been averted. However, it was not properly cooked before it was served. The tragic deaths of children and the illnesses of several other individuals served to make *E. coli* a household word. From the time of that tragedy, food safety has been a national issue.

GRAS list A list of common food additives given special safe status under the 1958 food additive amendment because of their previous records as safe food additives.

Figure 19–2
Prior to the 1990s, most outbreaks of food-related illnesses were usually associated with small groups of people at a picnic or a potluck social gathering. (Source: Stockbyte/Thinkstock.)

IMPORTANCE OF FOOD SAFETY TO CONSUMERS

There is no doubt that the food safety issue is important to consumers. In a land of plenty, our consumers want the plenty to also be safe. The predominant food safety concerns of consumers are chemical residues such as pesticides and herbicides, food additives, antibiotics and hormones used on animals, **irradiated foods**, foodborne pathogens, and naturally occurring toxicants. Some are real threats, and some are exaggerated consumer perceptions of threats that are minimal. In actuality, the most significant threat to the average consumer is foodborne pathogens. Table 19–1 shows the sources, symptoms, onset, and duration of illnesses associated with common foodborne, disease-causing organisms.

Consumers generally do not understand that it is impossible to choose a diet free from all risk. This has always been true and will always be true. In addition, the potential for new risks comes with each change in food, agricultural, or processing technology, with each new trade agreement; and with each shift in eating habits. Such changes are responsible for some of the risks our food supply currently faces and have made today's food supply different than that from any time in history. We import over 46 million tons of food, much of it from developing countries (Figure 19–3).

Another issue is that the food supply is highly centralized. This is both a "curse and a blessing." It is a blessing because it makes monitoring easier and a curse because when there is a problem, it has greater potential to be a big problem. Hamburger from one plant can be processed and distributed to a dozen states in scores of food outlets per state in a manner of hours. Contaminated food can be processed and distributed in many different forms and can cause illnesses before it can be isolated (Figure 19–4). Changes in the demographics of our population also change the number of people susceptible to risk from foodborne microorganisms. The very young, the elderly, and those with compromised immune systems are at greatest risk. All of these factors make foodborne illness a different issue today than it ever was in the past.

Survey after survey has shown the level of concern consumers have for the problem. There is also a good deal of confusion on the part of the consumer as to what is a threat, how large the threats may be, and what to do to protect themselves. Much of the focus of consumer demands for solutions have centered on the government. This concern has sparked several actions at local, state, and national levels. It is outside the scope of this chapter to give a complete accounting of the actions taken and planned. Significant changes in the food system are being addressed and will continue to unfold. If properly implemented, many of the changes will lead to a safer food supply. Many already have. The much-publicized recalls of hamburger that occurred in the late 1990s are evidence of a system that is doing a better job of detecting contamination. One of the interesting ironies associated with the recalls is that segments of the consuming public and some consumer advocate groups have reacted negatively to the recalls. They have cited the recalls as evidence of an unsanitary food supply. Logically, the recalls should be comforting because the product did not get into the consumers' hands. The system worked to detect the problem before anyone became ill as a result. Unfortunately, this has not been the general response. Of course, recalls are not desirable. In 1997, Hudson Foods had to recall 25 million lbs of ground beef that was potentially contaminated with *E. coli* O157:H7. The publicity from the event was quite widespread. One of Hudson's major customers announced that it would no longer purchase from the company. A short time later, the company was sold.

One of the difficult parts of the issue from a consumer-industry perspective is that many of the problems with food and its safety are the responsibility of the

Irradiated foods Foods treated with ionizing pasteurization, which kills insects, bacteria, and parasites.

Table 19–1

FOODBORNE ILLNESS-CAUSING ORGANISMS IN THE U.S.

Organism	Common Name of Illness	Onset Time After Ingesting	Signs & Symptoms	Duration	Food Sources
Bacillus cereus	B. cereus food poisoning	10–6 hrs	Abdominal cramps, watery diarrhea, nausea	24–48 hours	Meats, stews, gravies, vanilla sauce
Campylobacter jejuni	Campylobacteriosis	2–5 days	Diarrhea, cramps, fever, and vomiting; diarrhea may be bloody	2–10 days	Raw and undercooked poultry, unpasteurized milk, contaminated water
Clostridium botulinum	Botulism	12–72 hours	Vomiting, diarrhea, blurred vision, double vision, difficulty in swallowing, muscle weakness. Can result in respiratory failure and death	Variable	Improperly canned foods, especially home-canned vegetables, fermented fish, baked potatoes in aluminum foil
Clostridium perfringens	Perfringens food poisoning	8–16 hours	Intense abdominal cramps, watery diarrhea	Usually 24 hours	Meats, poultry, gravy, dried or precooked foods, time and/or temperature-abused foods
Cryptosporidium	Intestinal cryptosporidiosis	2–10 days	Diarrhea (usually watery), stomach cramps, upset stomach, slight fever	May be remitting and relapsing over weeks to months	Uncooked food or food contaminated by an ill food handler after cooking, contaminated drinking water
Cyclospora cayetanensis	Cyclosporiasis	1–14 days, usually at least 1 week	Diarrhea (usually watery), loss of appetite, substantial loss of weight, stomach cramps, nausea, vomiting, fatigue	May be remitting and relapsing over weeks to months	Various types of fresh produce (imported berries, lettuce, basil)
E. coli (Escherichia coli) producing toxin	E. zcoli infection (common cause of "travelers' diarrhea")	1–3 days	Watery diarrhea, abdominal cramps, some vomiting	3–7 or more days	Water or food contaminated with human feces
E. coli O157:H7	Hemorrhagic colitis or E. coli O157:H7 infection	1–8 days	Severe (often bloody) diarrhea, abdominal pain and vomiting. Usually, little or no fever is present. More common in children 4 years or younger. Can lead to kidney failure	5–10 days	Undercooked beef (especially hamburger), unpasteurized milk and juice, raw fruits and vegetables (e.g., sprouts), and contaminated water
Hepatitis A	Hepatitis	28 days average (15–50 days)	Diarrhea, dark urine, jaundice, and flu-like symptoms, i.e., fever, headache, nausea, and abdominal pain	Variable, 2 weeks–3 months	Raw produce, contaminated drinking water, uncooked foods and cooked foods that are not reheated after contact with an infected food handler; shellfish from contaminated waters

(continued)

Table 19–1 (continued)

Organism	Common Name of Illness	Onset Time After Ingesting	Signs & Symptoms	Duration	Food Sources
Listeria monocytogenes	Listeriosis	9–48 hrs for gastro-intestinal symptoms, 2–6 weeks for invasive disease	Fever, muscle aches, and nausea or diarrhea. Pregnant women may have mild flu-like illness, and infection can lead to premature delivery or stillbirth. The elderly or immunocompromised patients may develop bacteremia or meningitis	Variable	Unpasteurized milk, soft cheeses made with unpasteurized milk, ready-to-eat deli meats, produce
Noroviruses	Variously called viral gastroenteritis, winter diarrhea, acute non-bacterial gastroenteritis, food poisoning, and food infection	12–48 hrs	Nausea, vomiting, abdominal cramping, diarrhea, fever, headache. Diarrhea is more prevalent in adults, vomiting more common in children	12–60 hrs	Raw produce, contaminated drinking water, uncooked foods and cooked foods that are not reheated after contact with an infected food handler; shellfish from contaminated waters
Salmonella	Salmonellosis	6–48 hours	Diarrhea, fever, abdominal cramps, vomiting	4–7 days	Eggs, poultry, meat, unpasteurized milk or juice, cheese, contaminated raw fruits and vegetables
Shigella	Shigellosis or Bacillary dysentery	4–7 days	Abdominal cramps, fever, and diarrhea. Stools may contain blood and mucus	24–48 hrs	Raw produce, contaminated drinking water, uncooked foods and cooked foods that are not reheated after contact with an infected food handler
Staphylococcus aureus	Staphylococcal food poisoning	1–6 hours	Sudden onset of severe nausea and vomiting. Abdominal cramps. Diarrhea and fever may be present	24–48 hours	Unrefrigerated or improperly refrigerated meats, potato and egg salads, cream pastries
Vibrio parahaemolyticus	*V. parahaemolyticus* infection	4–96 hours	Watery (occasionally bloody) diarrhea, abdominal cramps, nausea, vomiting, fever	2–5 days	Undercooked or raw seafood, such as shellfish
Vibrio vulnificus	*V. vulnificus* infection	1–7 days	Vomiting, diarrhea, abdominal pain, bloodborne infection. Fever, bleeding within the skin, ulcers requiring surgical removal. Can be fatal to persons with liver disease or weakened immune systems	2–8 days	Undercooked or raw seafood, such as shellfish (especially oysters)

Source: U.S. Food and Drug Administration. http://www.fda.gov/food/resourcesforyou/consumers/ucm103263.htm

Figure 19–3
There are many obstacles to providing a safer food supply including control over the millions of tons of food we import, much of it from developing nations. (Photographer Ken Hammond. Courtesy of USDA.)

Figure 19–4
The food-processing system is centralized in a way that brings lower prices and other consumer benefits but creates problems as well. Meat processed in a given batch can be packaged and distributed to many states and distributed in many consumer outlets in a matter of hours. Should contamination exist in a batch, thousands of people could potentially be affected. (Courtesy of USDA. Used with permission.)

consumer or the food handlers. Yet there seems to be an abdication of that responsibility. Whether that is from a lack of knowledge on the part of the consumer, or a general feeling that it's simply someone else's job, is unclear. The following remarks by Michael T. Osterholm, then state epidemiologist and chief of the Minnesota Department of Health's Acute Disease Epidemiology Section, were made in the wake of the massive 1997 recall of ground beef by Hudson Foods:

> Most people desperately want to believe that someone else will look out for them. We'd like to believe that just as we can drive over a bridge and not have to get out of the car and check it for safety, we can be equally confident that the government has declared our food safe. But it's not that easy. Despite our improvements . . . the problem is still present. This is not meant as a criticism either of those who raise or produce beef or of the public-health community. It is simply very difficult to eliminate the organism. . . .
>
> *Newsweek*, Sept. 1, 1997, p. 33

The livestock producer is responsible for only a very small percentage of the problem. Food safety experts estimate that 77% of all illnesses can be prevented if the food handler and preparer take proper measures. Most foodborne illnesses are caused by foods prepared in the home.

PREVENTING FOODBORNE ILLNESSES

To prevent foodborne illnesses, food preparers should be aware of a few simple, but highly effective, measures:

- Cook foods thoroughly. Cooking kills most bacteria, parasites, and viruses that are found on foods. Meat, dairy, and egg products should be cooked before being eaten. Ground beef, veal, lamb, and pork should be cooked to a temperature of 160°F. Whole cuts of beef, veal, lamb, and pork should be cooked to a minimum temperature of 145°F followed by a three-minute rest time before carving or consuming. The safe cooking temperature for all poultry products is 165°F. Reheated foods should be heated to at least 165°F (Figure 19–5).
- Prevent cross-contamination. The juices and drippings of raw meat products should not come into contact with other foods, especially those that will receive no further cooking. Be careful of refrigeration practices. Wash hands, cutting boards, spills on countertops, and other items with warm, soapy water to prevent meat juices from coming into contact with other foods.
- Refrigerate foods, including leftovers, properly. Bacteria have a hard time growing in properly refrigerated conditions. Refrigerator temperature should be set at 40°F or lower. Don't overpack the refrigerator. Keep the refrigerator clean (Figure 19–6).
- Select only the freshest meat, poultry, fish, and other food products. Do not purchase dented, bulging, or rusted cans of food. Observe the "purchase by" and "use by" dates on products.
- Freeze fresh meat, poultry, and fish that will not be used within a couple of days. Proper freezer temperature is 0°F. Thaw foods in the microwave, in the refrigerator, or under cold, drinkable running water.

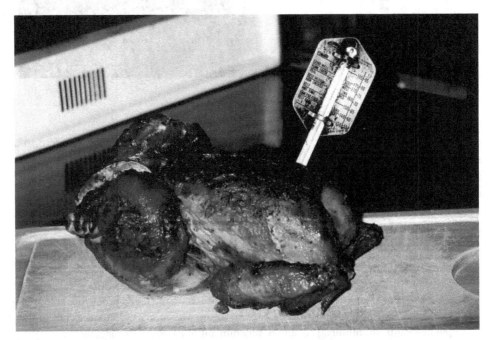

Figure 19–5
Cooking to the proper temperature is extremely important in preventing foodborne illness. Meat thermometers help ensure that safe internal temperatures are reached during cooking.

Figure 19–6
For food safety, don't overpack refrigerators. Segregate products, especially those that will not be further cooked. Keep the refrigerator clean and make sure the temperature is no warmer than 40°F. Can you spot the problems in this refrigerator?

SOME IMPORTANT MICROBIAL PATHOGENS ASSOCIATED WITH FOODBORNE ILLNESS

The surveillance and identification of new emerging foodborne diseases has always been a challenge for public health officials. Several agencies are all responsible for different aspects of food safety monitoring and testing. Historically, the communication between these agencies has been seriously lacking and as a result, made the tracking and identification of foodborne diseases very difficult. In an attempt to improve the surveillance of foodborne diseases in the United States, the CDC, in cooperation with the USDA and FDA, established in 1995 the Foodborne Disease Active Surveillance Network (FoodNet, http://www.cdc.gov/foodnet). The FoodNet surveillance started with five sites around the United States (West Coast—California; East Coast—Connecticut; South—Georgia; North—Minnesota; Pacific Northwest—Oregon). Officials felt that monitoring a site of population at different regions across the United States would prevent a data overload to the system and provide a better picture of the types of foodborne diseases occurring in the United States. Since 1995, the selected monitoring sites have expanded to 10 states with about 14% of the U.S. population being monitored. FoodNet is helping public officials better understand the **epidemiology** of foodborne disease in the United States. The following information was excerpted and edited from FDA (1997) and is found in Appendix B of that report. It is presented here to provide information about the specific pathogens and to demonstrate that the federal agencies involved do indeed have an understanding of the magnitude of the problem facing them.

Epidemiology Medical service that involves the study of the incident distribution of diseases in large populations and conditions influencing the spread and severity of diseases.

Bacteria

Salmonella *Salmonella* species cause diarrhea and **septicemia**, which can be fatal in particularly susceptible persons such as the immunocompromised, the very young, and the elderly. Animals used for food production are common carriers of *Salmonella*, which can subsequently contaminate foods such as meat, dairy products, and eggs.

Septicemia Invasion of the bloodstream by virulent microorganisms from a focus of infection.

Figure 19–7

Salmonella enteritidis is often the cause of foodborne illness. It is a difficult organism from which to protect consumers because animals used for food production are common carriers of the disease. (Courtesy of USDA).

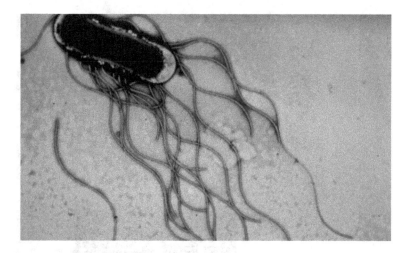

Foods often implicated in outbreaks include raw meats, poultry, eggs, milk and dairy products, fish, shrimp, frog legs, yeast, coconut, sauces and salad dressings, cake mixes, cream-filled desserts, dried gelatin, peanut butter, cocoa, and chocolate. An estimated 2 to 4 million infections occur each year in the United States, most of them as individual cases apparently unrelated to outbreaks. Between 128,000 and 640,000 of those infections are associated with *Salmonella enteritidis* (Figure 19–7) in eggs. During the 1990s, more than 500 outbreaks were attributed to *S. enteritidis*, with more than 70 deaths. In 1994, an estimated 224,000 people became ill from consuming ice cream in one outbreak alone.

Campylobacter   The bacterium *Campylobacter* (Figure 19–8) is the most frequently identified cause of acute infectious diarrhea in developed countries and the most commonly isolated bacterial intestinal pathogen in the United States. It has been estimated that between 2 and 4 million cases of campylobacteriosis occur each year with an associated 120–360 deaths. *Campylobacter jejuni* and *Campylobacter coli* (two closely related species) are commonly foodborne, and they are the infectious agents most frequently described in association with **Guillain-Barré syndrome**, as frequently as 1 in 1,000 cases. Approximately 50% of infections are associated with eating inadequately cooked or recontaminated chicken meat or from handling chickens. It is the leading cause of sporadic (nonclustered cases) diarrheal disease in the United States. Unpasteurized milk and untreated water have also caused outbreaks.

Guillain-Barré syndrome
An inflammatory disease of the peripheral nerves characterized by weakness and often paralysis of the arms, legs, breathing muscles, and face.

Listeria   Infection with Listeria monocytogene (listeriosis) was added to the list of nationally notifiable diseases in 2001. Listeriosis primarily affects older adults, pregnant women, newborns, and adults with weakened immune systems and only infrequently affects people without these risk factors. The Center for Disease Control

Figure 19–8

Campylobacter is considered the most frequently identified cause of acute infectious diarrhea in developed countries. C. jejuni and C. coli are the infectious agents most frequently associated with Guillain-Barré syndrome. (Source: USDA (U.S. Department of Agriculture).

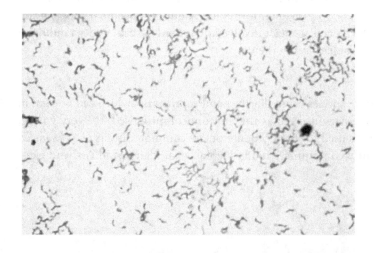

estimates there are approximately 1,600 cases of listeriosis in the U.S. annually. Listeria has been found in uncooked meats and vegetables, soft cheeses, processed meats such as hot dogs and deli meat, and smoked seafood. Unpasteurized milk and foods made from unpasteurized milk are particularly likely to contain the bacterium. Listeria is killed by pasteurization and cooking. Some contaminations have been traced to ready-to-eat foods, such as hot dogs and deli meats, contaminated after factory cooking but before packaging. Unlike most bacteria, Listeria can grow and multiply in some foods in the refrigerator. Generally, those diagnosed with listeriosis have an invasive infection: the bacteria has spread beyond the gastrointestinal tract. Symptoms include fever, muscle aches, diarrhea and other gastrointestinal symptoms, headache, stiff neck, confusion, loss of balance, and convulsions. Pregnant women generally have only a mild, flu-like illness, but infections during pregnancy can lead to miscarriage, stillbirth, premature delivery, and/or life-threatening infection of the newborn. Before 2011, the largest outbreak occurred in 2002 and was associated with turkey deli meat. Other recent outbreaks have been associated with hotdogs, sprouts and celery. In 2011, an outbreak linked to cantaloupes affected more than 120 people in at least 26 states and caused over two dozen deaths.

Shiga-Like Toxin-Producing *Escherichia coli*   Several strains of the bacterium *E. coli* cause a variety of diseases in humans and animals. *E. coli* that cause illness produce a toxin called Shiga toxin. Shiga toxin–producing *E. coli* are also referred to as STEC. *E. coli* O157:H7 (Figure 19–9) is the most commonly identified STEC in North America. However, recently there has been growing concern about the other types of STEC aside from *E. coli* O157:H7 that are being found in food, particularly meat. Some important "non-O157" STEC *E. coli* serogroups are O26, O111, and O103. STEC cause hemorrhagic colitis, which begins with watery diarrhea and severe abdominal pain and rapidly progresses to passage of bloody stools. It has been associated with **hemolytic-uremic syndrome (HUS)**, a life-threatening complication of hemorrhagic colitis characterized by acute kidney failure that is particularly serious in young children. *E. coli* O157:H7 is found in cattle, but there may be other reservoirs; the dynamics of *E. coli* O157:H7 in food-producing animals are not well understood. Approximately 73,000 cases of foodborne illness can be attributed to *E. coli* O157:H7 each year, with as many as 60 deaths resulting. However, it is estimated that non-O157 STEC may cause 36,700 illnesses each year. *E. coli* O157:H7 outbreaks have been associated with ground beef, raw milk, and minimally processed nuts, vegetables, and fresh fruit juices.

Vibrio   *Vibrio* species are gram-negative bacteria most commonly associated with seafood dishes. *Vibrio parahemolyticus* is the species most commonly reported as a cause of foodborne disease; it generally causes watery diarrhea and abdominal pain lasting 1–7 days, and commonly follows consumption of improperly handled cold

Hemolytic-uremic syndrome (HUS) A rare condition that mostly affects children under the age of 10; characterized by damage to the lining of blood vessel walls, destruction of red blood cells, and kidney failure.

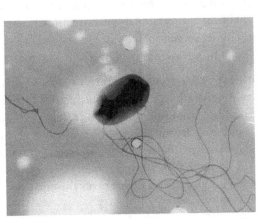

Figure 19–9
Only recognized as a pathogen in 1982, Eschericia coli O157:H7 is a gram-negative bacteria that has been associated with HUS, which is a life-threatening condition. Pictured here is a transmission electron micrograph of E. coli *O157:H7 showing flagella.* (Micrograph by Elizabeth H. White. Courtesy of Centers for Disease Control and Prevention.)

seafood salads. *V. vulnificus* is one of the more serious foodborne pathogens, with a case-fatality rate for invasive disease that exceeds 50%. Most cases of foodborne *V. vulnificus* infections occur in persons with underlying illness, particularly liver disorders, who eat raw mollusks and shellfish. Since the late 1980s, the FDA, the CDC, and the Gulf Coast states have intensified efforts to collect information on *Vibrio* infections, and on the microorganisms' ecology, to improve our ability to prevent foodborne infections.

Parasitic Protozoa

Toxoplasma Gondii   *T. gondii* is a parasitic protozoan responsible for some 1.4 million cases of toxoplasmosis and 310 deaths annually. Otherwise, healthy adults who become infected usually have no symptoms but might get diarrhea. Pregnant women who become infected can pass the disease to their fetuses. In infants infected before birth, fatality is common. Should the infant survive, the effects of infection are typically severe (i.e., mental retardation). The disease can be life threatening in persons with weakened immune systems and often is fatal to people with HIV/AIDS. *T. gondii* has been found in virtually all food animals. The two primary ways that humans become infected are consumption of raw or undercooked meat containing *T. gondii* or contact with cats that shed cysts in their feces during acute infection. A single cat can shed millions of oocysts after eating rodents, birds, or other animals infected with *T. gondii.* Under some conditions, the consumption of unwashed fruits and vegetables can contribute to infections.

Cryptosporidium Parvum   *C. parvum* is a parasitic protozoan. The most common consequence of infection in healthy people is profuse watery diarrhea lasting up to several weeks. Children are particularly susceptible. Cryptosporidiosis can be life threatening among people with weakened immune systems. The largest recorded outbreak of cryptosporidiosis was a waterborne outbreak in Milwaukee, Wisconsin, in 1993, affecting more than 400,000 people. More recently, a waterborne outbreak in Las Vegas resulted in at least 20 deaths. The first large outbreak of cryptosporidiosis from a contaminated food occurred in 1993. That outbreak was attributed to fresh-pressed apple cider. *Cryptosporidium* also is found in animal manure. Farm workers have been infected from this source.

Viruses

Norwalk Virus   Norwalk viruses are important causes of sporadic and epidemic gastrointestinal disease that involve overwhelming, dehydrating diarrhea. An estimated 181,000 cases occur annually with no known associated deaths. In January 1995, a multistate outbreak of viral gastroenteritis related to Norwalk virus was associated with the consumption of oysters. A 1993 Louisiana outbreak of Norwalk virus gastroenteritis involved 70 ill people and was associated with the consumption of raw oysters. In 1992, another outbreak resulted in 250 cases. Outbreaks of Norwalk virus intestinal disease have been linked to contaminated water and ice, salads, frosting, shellfish, and person-to-person contact, although the most common food source is shellfish. Several such outbreaks are believed to have been caused by oysters contaminated by sewage dumped overboard by oyster harvesters and recreational boaters.

Hepatitis A   Hepatitis A (HAV) is a virus that infects the liver and causes hepatitis A, an illness with an abrupt onset that can include fever, malaise, nausea, abdominal discomfort, dark urine, and jaundice after a prolonged incubation period (e.g., more than 2 months). In children less than 6 years old, most (70%) infections are asymptomatic, but in older children and adults, infection is usually symptomatic, with jaundice occurring in more than 70% of patients. Signs and symptoms of hepatitis A usually last more than 2 months, and there are no chronic consequences. About 130,000 infections with

HAV and 100 deaths occur each year in the United States. The primary mode of transmission for HAV is person-to-person by the fecal–oral route. Recognized foodborne hepatitis A outbreaks account for only 2–5% of hepatitis A cases reported in the United States each year, most of which are caused by an infected food handler. Outbreaks owing to foods contaminated before preparation, although uncommon, are associated with widely distributed products such as shellfish, lettuce, frozen raspberries, and frozen strawberries. Hepatitis A can be prevented by good personal hygiene and safe food-handling practices. It can also be prevented before exposure by hepatitis A vaccine, and after exposure by immune globulin, if given within 14 days of exposure.

GOVERNMENTAL AGENCIES AND FOOD SAFETY

Six different federal agencies bear the responsibility for the government's role in food safety. These include two agencies under the Department of Health and Human Services (HHS)—the Food and Drug Administration (FDA) and the Centers for Disease Control and Prevention (CDC); three agencies under the Department of Agriculture (USDA)—the Food Safety and Inspection Service (FSIS), the Agricultural Research Service (ARS), and the Cooperative State Research, Education, and Extension Service (CSREES); and the Environmental Protection Agency (EPA). This system has long been criticized as being unnecessarily cumbersome and wasteful as well as inefficient in the way it conducts the business of providing a safer food supply. To address these issues, Congress passed in November 2010 the Food Modernization Act. All food processors will now be required to evaluate the hazards in their facilities. In addition, the act gives FDA mandatory recall authority to swiftly remove contaminated food from the market. FDA must also conduct risk-based inspections of food processing facilities. All high-risk domestic facilities must be inspected within five years of enactment of the Food Modernization Act and no less than every three years thereafter. Finally, FDA has also been given the authority to require importers verify the safety of food from their suppliers and FDA has also been given the authority to block food from facilities/countries that refuse inspection.

The following sections explore the roles of some of these agencies in assuring a safe food supply with emphasis on animal products. Meat exported into the United States must come from countries with residue avoidance efforts equivalent to or more rigorous than the U.S. program. As a safeguard, imported meat is reinspected and tested for residues when it enters the country.

The Role of the FDA

The concerns that consumers express over food additives and the hormones and antibiotics used in animal production are largely without foundation. The government requires a rigorous approval procedure before these products can be offered for sale. This system assures the safety of the products used. The FDA is in charge of the approval process. Animal health companies are required to show that any new product they wish to offer for sale is both safe and effective. In addition, the company must provide a reliable method for detecting the drug in slaughtered animals. A new drug is approved for use only after the company has done these things. In addition to its product supervision/approval role, the FDA also limits the amounts of drug residues that can be found in animal tissue. The tolerance level for a given drug is intentionally set at 100 to 1,000 times less than a potentially harmful amount to provide a margin of safety for the consumer. Thus withdrawal times are calculated for additives and antibiotics that ensure the compound is cleared from the animal's body before it goes to slaughter. It then becomes the job of the USDA to monitor tissue samples from slaughtered animals for the compound. The agency currently monitors for over 100 compounds.

The specific FDA requirements for approval of agricultural chemicals and drugs are as follows:

1. The product must be effective at the proposed dosage level for the proposed use.
2. The drug must not create a residue in the edible tissue of the animal or bird that is at a level judged to be harmful to the consumer.
3. The drug or agricultural compound must serve a useful purpose in the production of a feed crop, animal, or bird.
4. An analytical detection method must be available that is capable of detecting the substance at or below the tolerance level.
5. The drug must be used in a manner that will not contaminate the environment or food supply.

The FDA also provides the guidelines to states for regulating the safety of milk, dairy foods, and foods served in restaurants. However, FDA delegates the responsibilities of inspecting restaurants, groceries, and other food-related operations to the states.

The Role of FSIS

The USDA, through the FSIS, has a comprehensive program in place to protect consumers from drug and other chemical residues. The FSIS inspection of carcasses at slaughter plants, as one means of protecting consumers from contaminated meat and poultry, is central to the success of the program. The sampling is done in different phases, each with slightly different goals. The comprehensive inspection is designed to ensure the safety of the consumer from drug residues and other substances.

Residue Monitoring Program   Carcasses are monitored to provide information on the occurrence of residues. Compounds tested include drugs, pesticides, and environmental and agricultural chemicals. In the monitoring program, carcasses are sampled at random in a way that produces a statistically valid sample. This requires the annual sampling of approximately 22,000 animals. Multiple samples are taken from some animals (muscle, liver, kidney, and fat). The goal of the sample procedure is to detect a 1% incidence of illegal residues and have 95% statistical confidence in the result. Results from the monitoring program suggest an industry largely in compliance with withdrawal times and appropriate use of drugs and additives. The number of illegal drug residues detected annually has been less than 1%.

If the residue data suggest an emerging problem, a special surveillance program may be implemented. One such program was initiated in 1977 because the number of sulfonamide residue violations in swine was unacceptably high. A special program of increased sampling that was specific for sulfonamides was implemented. In addition to protecting the consumer in the short run, such programs tend to focus the attention of the industry on the problem. This greatly heightened awareness helps bring the problem under control. When the sulfa drug problem occurred, those involved in industry publications, extension agents, university personnel, news reporters, and others were all working "overtime" on this issue.

The monitoring program is also used as a means of avoiding problems. Individual producers are notified when a sample produces a level of a compound that is found to be within 80–100% of the allowable residue tolerance level. Follow-up testing of animals from that producer helps the producer maintain residue levels below allowable levels.

When illegal substances are discovered, the FDA launches follow-up investigations to determine why the residues are present and who was responsible. Depending on the results of the investigation, the FDA and FSIS may initiate the surveillance program.

Surveillance Program   The surveillance program is initiated if illegal residues are found or if there are other indications of a potential for illegal residues. The surveillance program may also be used to sample sick or diseased animals. Any time an illegal drug residue is found, FDA can initiate an investigation and FSIS will prevent future shipments from the producer until tissue samples are free of illegal residues. Then, and only then, will the producer's next shipments be approved.

Residue Avoidance Program   This portion of the overall effort is educational and is designed to help producers avoid problems. It is designed to help producers understand how to prevent illegal levels of residues from occurring. The program seeks to prevent problems from birth through slaughter and processing by educating producers on the proper use of drugs and other chemicals. Producer groups and the extension service have been instrumental in working with FSIS in this portion of the overall effort.

In-Plant/On-Farm Testing   Several tests are employed to determine if illegal residues are present. The Swab Test on Premises (STOP) is used by public health veterinarians or designated consumer supply inspectors to determine if antibiotics are present. It is fast and can detect problems with a carcass before the carcass leaves the slaughter facility. A recently developed test, Fast Antimicrobial Screen Test (FAST), reduces test time from 8 hours to 6 hours. Field tests have also been developed to screen for potential antibiotic residues. These tests are not USDA/FSIS approved, but they do allow the producer to test animals on the farm. The Live Animal Swab Test (LAST) tests the urine of live animals for illegal antibiotic levels. Live animals can thus be tested before they are marketed. The Sulfa-on-Site (SOS) test screens swine serum, urine, or feed for sulfamethazine. Other tests are used in specific circumstances, and more are under development.

Responsibilities of the Federal Agencies

The FDA, the USDA, and the EPA have specified responsibilities in the residue monitoring program and responsibilities for working with states to correct detected problems. FDA has the responsibility to investigate illegal residues in animals. In some instances, the responsibility may be delegated to the state agency if there is an agreement with the state. If pesticide residues are the problem, either from direct applications or environmental contamination, EPA joins FDA and FSIS in taking corrective measures because the EPA is responsible for the proper use of pesticides. FSIS has the primary responsibility for the carcass. FDA has the authority for enforcing the proper use of animal drugs and medicated feeds. Both FDA and FSIS can seize or condemn contaminated food. In addition, the FDA has the same power with regard to animal feed. Depending on the nature of the violations, those responsible for illegal residues may face criminal prosecution, resulting in fines or imprisonment.

Changes in FSIS

FSIS also has had the responsibility for checking carcasses for diseases that may affect the wholesomeness of food. This practice originated at the turn of the 20th century when diseased animals posed a real threat to the welfare of the consuming population. This is rarely the case anymore. By and large, the animals slaughtered for human consumption are young and healthy. In recognition of this fact and in response to the need to direct more effort to foodborne pathogens, the FSIS is in the process of changing the way it works to fulfill this portion of its mission. The agency describes this change as moving from plant-based inspections to a farm-to-table consumer safety system.

The greatest risks to the food supply currently come from microbial pathogens. The type of inspection system that has been in place cannot detect those problems. Recommendations springing from studies conducted by the National Academy of Sciences (NAS), the U.S. General Accounting Office (GAO), and FSIS itself have established the need for fundamental change in the FSIS inspection program. In response to this need, the FSIS is moving to reduce its reliance on the direct inspection of carcasses and shifting to prevention-oriented inspection systems. This change will

shift resources away from inspection to a broader approach intended to minimize hazards throughout the farm-to-table food chain and thus reduce foodborne illness.

This change in focus and responsibility is tied to the Pathogen Reduction and Hazard Analysis and Critical Control Point (HACCP) Systems Final Rule, published in July 1996. The Pathogen Reduction and HACCP rule was designed to establish a system that ensures appropriate and feasible measures are taken at each step in the food-production process to prevent or reduce and, ideally, eliminate foodborne disease hazards. FSIS set as its initial goal a 25% reduction in foodborne illnesses attributed to meat and poultry and put a comprehensive program in place to achieve this goal. The program as outlined, published, and widely distributed by the FSIS includes:

- Requiring establishments to develop and implement written Sanitation Standard Operating Procedures (SSOPs) to prevent contamination.
- Requiring that all meat and poultry establishments develop and implement the HACCP system of preventive controls designed to improve the safety of their products.
- Establishing food safety performance standards and microbiological testing requirements.
- Placing clear responsibility for safe products on the establishments producing those products, backed up by rigorous FSIS monitoring and verification, with regulatory action where warranted. FSIS enforcement authorities are used to the fullest extent to address operators who violate food safety regulations and put consumers at risk.
- Enhancing FSIS's present food safety activities beyond slaughter and processing plants. This will include increased oversight of the activities and systems that affect food safety after products leave the plant, including transportation, distribution and retail, and restaurant or food service sale of meat and poultry products. FSIS will work collaboratively with other federal, state, and local agencies to help ensure this coverage.
- Encouraging research, education, and voluntary adoption of preventive strategies on the farm.
- Reshaping its workforce and the way it deploys that workforce. The agency is redeploying its resources and improving the skills and qualifications of its workforce to meet its goal of reducing foodborne illness and providing appropriate regulatory oversight within its statutory authorities along the farm-to-table continuum.
- Deploying the workforce in a manner that will enable it to protect the integrity of the mark of inspection on a product as the product moves from the controlled environment of the plant through distribution, transportation, and retail to the consumer.

These historic changes include changes to the in-plant inspection procedures. Under HACCP rules, plants assume full responsibility and are held accountable for the safety of their products. The focus of FSIS in-plant inspection changes is to verify compliance with the standards and rules. Inspection schedules are being changed. They are becoming less prescribed and instead are being designed to enhance the flexibility and effectiveness of the inspectors and their abilities to make day-to-day decisions about what food safety and consumer protection activities should be carried out in individual plants. Another part of the planned changes includes the shifting of some consumer protection activities that have nothing to do with food safety issues to other agencies or units within FSIS. This will allow inspectors to focus more on specific food safety tasks. Several other changes are being discussed and tested. All plants were required to be in compliance with HACCP as of the year 2000.

FSIS intends to improve its service in a number of ways once HACCP rules and procedures are sufficiently tested. Several of these improvements involve changes in regulatory activities beyond the processing plant. FSIS intends to monitor retail food stores, restaurants, commercial kitchens, hotels, and other institutions. FSIS will work to establish standards for postprocessing transportation, storage, and distribution systems. Educational programs are planned. The objective is to create a seamless national food safety system.

Hazard Analysis and Critical Control Points (HACCP)

The following explanation of HACCP is excerpted from documents published by FSIS to explain the HACCP final rule.

Hazard Analysis and Critical Control Points **(HACCP)** is a process control system designed to identify and prevent microbial and other hazards in food production. It includes steps designed to prevent problems before they occur and to correct deviations as soon as they are detected. Such preventive control systems with documentation and verification are widely recognized by scientific authorities and international organizations as the most effective approach available for producing safe food. HACCP is endorsed by such scientific and food safety authorities as the National Academy of Sciences and the National Advisory Committee on Microbiological Criteria for Foods (NACMCF), and by such international organizations as the Codex Alimentarius Commission and the International Commission on Microbiological Specifications for Foods.

> **HACCP** Process control system designed to identify and prevent health hazards in food.

Under the Pathogen Reduction and HACCP systems regulations, USDA is requiring that all meat and poultry plants design and implement HACCP systems. Plants will be required to develop HACCP plans to monitor and control production operations. HACCP was implemented first in the largest meat and poultry plants, with 75% of slaughter production under HACCP-based process control systems on January 26, 1998, with the remainder allowed to be phased in by January 25, 2000.

The Seven HACCP Principles

HACCP systems must be based on the seven principles articulated by the NACMCF. The seven principles are (1) hazard analysis, (2) critical control point identification, (3) establishment of critical limits, (4) monitoring procedures, (5) corrective actions, (6) recordkeeping, and (7) verification procedures.

Principle 1: Conduct a hazard analysis. Plants determine the food safety hazards that can occur as a result of the way food is processed in that establishment.

Principle 2: Identify critical control points. A critical control point (CCP) is a point, step, or procedure in a food process at which control can be applied and, as a result, a food safety hazard can be prevented, reduced to an acceptable level, or eliminated. A food safety hazard is any biological, chemical, or physical property that may cause a food to be unsafe for human consumption.

Principle 3: Establish critical limits for each critical control point. A critical limit is the maximum or minimum value to which a physical, biological, or chemical hazard must be controlled at a critical control point to prevent, eliminate, or reduce risk to an acceptable level.

Principle 4: Establish critical control point monitoring requirements. Monitoring activities are necessary to ensure that the process is under control at each critical control point. FSIS requires that each monitoring procedure and its frequency be listed in the HACCP plan.

Principle 5: Establish corrective actions. These are actions to be taken when monitoring indicates a deviation from an established critical limit. The final

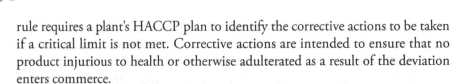

rule requires a plant's HACCP plan to identify the corrective actions to be taken if a critical limit is not met. Corrective actions are intended to ensure that no product injurious to health or otherwise adulterated as a result of the deviation enters commerce.

Principle 6: Establish recordkeeping procedures. The HACCP regulation requires that all plants maintain certain documents, including hazard analysis and a written HACCP plan, and records documenting the monitoring of critical control points, critical limits, verification activities, and the handling of processing deviations.

Principle 7: Establish verification procedures. Validation ensures that the plans do what they were designed to do; that is, they are successful in ensuring the production of safe product. Verification ensures the HACCP plan is adequate; that is, it is working as intended. Verification procedures may include such activities as review of HACCP plans, CCP records, critical limits, and microbial sampling and analysis. FSIS requires that the HACCP plan include verification tasks to be performed by plant personnel. Verification tasks are also performed by FSIS inspectors. For example, both FSIS and industry conduct microbial testing as one of several verification activities.

Additional Changes at FSIS and Other Food Safety Initiatives

Additional changes at FSIS are being heralded as a new era for food safety. One of the initiatives at FSIS is to emphasize that everyone has a responsibility for food safety. An important part of these initiatives is emphasizing that the consumer is the final critical link in preventing foodborne illness. To accomplish this, consumer education programs emphasizing "safety from farm to table" have been developed in cooperation with public and private groups to educate consumers on safe food handling. Information is provided by the USDA Meat and Poultry Hotline, through direct consumer inquiries, e-mail, and the FSIS website. The cooperation of the media, extension and public health offices, and other public and private educators has also been sought to distribute food safety information. Various programs have been developed for different audiences and are delivered in different ways. Programs are based on scientifically substantiated information. One major information campaign includes the safe handling information label: *food handling reminders.* Other food safety educational initiatives have made additional information available. Many of these initiatives are in cooperation with the FDA, the CDC, and the EPA. One example is the national education campaign called Fight BAC!, which is sponsored and coordinated by the Partnership for Food Safety Education whose membership includes federal agencies, industry organizations, and consumer groups. The Fight BAC! campaign focuses consumer attention on four critical food safety messages:

- Clean: Wash hands and surfaces often.
- Separate: Don't cross-contaminate.
- Cook: Cook to proper temperatures.
- Chill: Refrigerate promptly.

The Bioterrorism Act of 2002

The events of September 11, 2001, reinforced the need to enhance the security of the United States. Congress responded by passing the Public Health Security and Bioterrorism Preparedness and Response Act of 2002 (the Bioterrorism Act), which

President Bush signed into law on June 12, 2002. The Bioterrorism Act is divided into five titles:

* Introduction
* Title I – National Preparedness for Bioterrorism and Other Public Health Emergencies
* Title II – Enhancing Controls on Dangerous Biological Agents and Toxins
* Title III – Protecting Safety and Security of Food and Drug Supply
* Title IV – Drinking Water Security and Safety
* Title V – Additional Provisions

FDA is responsible for carrying out certain provisions of the Bioterrorism Act, particularly Title III, Subtitle A (Protection of Food Supply) and Subtitle B (Protection of Drug Supply). In September 2004, the USDA, in partnership with the FDA and the Department of Homeland Security (DHS), signed a cooperative agreement with the National Association of State Departments of Agriculture (NASDA) to further develop integrated federal-state response plans for food and agricultural emergencies. USDA's Food Safety and Inspection Service (FSIS), FDA, and DHS's Information Analysis and Infrastructure Protection are funding the development of an integrated approach to prepare for and respond to emergencies affecting national agriculture and food infrastructure. The state departments of agriculture gain technical expertise from FSIS, FDA, and DHS officials. Best practices and guidelines for federal and state food regulatory officials will be developed to address lessons learned from case studies and threat assessments. A result of this coordinated effort was the development by NASDA of a Food Emergency Response Plan (FERP) template for states to coordinate their activities with the National Response Plan (NRP).

ENSURING SAFETY OF THE MILK SUPPLY

The federal Food, Drug, and Cosmetic Act is the legislation that covers the safety procedures for milk and milk products as well as other foods shipped from state to state. FDA is responsible for enforcing the law. The Grade A Pasteurized Milk Ordinance (PMO) is the standard used in the Cooperative State Public Health Service (PHS)/FDA Program for certification of Interstate Milk Shippers (IMS). The PMO was recommended by PHS and FDA. State agencies assume the responsibility for routine inspection and sampling of milk. Each tank of milk from each producer must be tested before it is picked up for transport by the milk handler. In addition, FDA spot-checks hundreds of milk-processing plants annually. According to Anderson et al. (1991), over 99% of all samples test negative for contamination of any kind. If a milk sample is found to be contaminated, the sale of the milk is prevented. The producer is prevented from selling any subsequently produced milk until the milk tests clear of the contamination found in the earlier shipment.

As a part of the PMO, all dairy farms must be inspected at least twice a year. Some states require more frequent inspections. Part of the inspection includes examinations of animal drugs on the premises. Unapproved and/or improperly labeled drugs cannot be used or stored in the milk house, milking barn, stable, or parlor. This helps to ensure proper drug use and residue avoidance. This system has an extremely good record for ensuring the quality of dairy products. Very few incidents of foodborne diseases have ever been linked to dairy products. Most of the incidents that have been connected to dairy products were caused by mishandling during further processing or consumption of raw milk or milk products.

OTHER ISSUES OF CONCERN TO CONSUMERS

Science has brought a variety of tools to the modern livestock producer. Several of these are of concern to consumers because they are perceived to affect food quality and safety. These products are used because they produce meat and milk more efficiently or they keep animals healthier, benefitting the producer and the consumer. A brief discussion of each product follows, along with information to explain why each is considered safe. It is important to remember that each of these products has FDA approval.

Bovine Somatotropin

Bovine somatotropin (BST) is a protein hormone produced naturally by cattle from the pituitary gland. When BST is administered to dairy cows, their milk production generally increases. Some consumers have been concerned that milk from cows treated with BST will cause negative health effects when consumed by humans. Milk from BST-treated cows is safe for humans to consume and has no ill effects on human health (Figure 19–10). BST was approved by the FDA and has undergone rigorous follow-up study. There are three major reasons why BST use in cows is safe. First, BST is a species-specific protein that is active only in dairy cows. It is a protein that is structurally different from human somatotropin. The receptors for human somatotropin are sensitive to the structure (shape) of the protein. BST does not "fit" into the human structure. Second, over 90% of the BST found in milk is destroyed during the pasteurization process. Third, any BST found in milk is digested in the human digestive system as any other protein would be. (Remember, naturally occurring BST has always been found in milk. Slightly elevated levels of insulin-like growth factor (IGF-1) can be found in milk from cows treated with BST. This is not a cause for concern for three reasons. First, these levels are not above normal ranges for cows. Second, human milk has higher levels of IGF-1 and it has not caused any problems. Third, IGF-1 is not biologically active when ingested by humans and is digested by the human digestive system just as BST is. Multitudes of studies have demonstrated that BST has no effect on humans. In what should be the last word on the topic, the Institute of Food Science and Technology, through its Public Affairs and Technical and Legislative Committees, authorized a position statement on June 11, 1998.

Figure 19–10

Milk from BST-treated cows is processed along with all other milk for human consumption because BST-produced milk poses no threat to the consumer. (Photographer Charlie Rahm. Courtesy of USDA-Agricultural Research Service.)

In the summary, the institute states that objective scientific assessment of the use of bovine somatotropin (BST) to improve milk yield in cows indicates that it carries no harmful effects to humans, to the treated animals, or to the environment. The report goes on to state that the resulting milk and meat are not significantly different from milk and meat from untreated cows, in composition or quality; and in consequence there is no scientific or ethical basis for requiring distinctive labeling of milk or meat from BST-treated cows.

Hormones

Hormonal growth promotants (implants) are a tremendous tool for animal production, especially for beef production. Benefits include faster growth rate, improved feed conversion, increased amount of lean tissue gain, and decreased fat deposition. On an industry-wide basis, hormone implants improve beef production by an estimated 750,000 lbs and save 3 million tons of feed. They are a very cost-effective tool for beef production. Consumers' concerns about growth promotants are directed at whether or not the hormonal compounds can be found in the meat of implanted animals. The level of hormones that could be consumed from implanted cattle is less than 0.006% and 0.02% per 100 g consumed of estrogen and progesterone found in prepubescent boys who carry the lowest level of both hormones (CCABIC, 2006). In fact, many other foods have higher levels of hormones. According to the Council for Agricultural Science and Technology, "In a meal of mashed potatoes, whole wheat bread, green salad, green peas, and ground round steak from estrogen-treated cattle, the food that would contain by far the least estrogenic potency is the ground round steak."

Antibiotics

Antibiotics are used in animal production to treat animals suffering from infections. In addition, subtherapeutic antibiotic levels are used to maintain the health of pigs, veal calves, and poultry. This second use has been declining in recent years. Consumers are concerned with the potential for development of superbugs that are resistant to antibiotics that might threaten human health. It is important that consumers be aware that antibiotic use is tightly regulated. The length of time an antibiotic must be taken away from the animal before it goes to slaughter, or its milk can be used for feed, is called its **withdrawal time**. These withdrawal times are closely observed. Antibiotics are among the compounds that the FSIS Monitoring Program takes special interest in. Milk, meat, and poultry all have extremely good records of compliance with proper antibiotic use.

Withdrawal time The length of time an antibiotic must be taken away from an animal before the animal can be legally slaughtered.

Food Irradiation

Irradiation, or ionizing pasteurization or **electronic pasteurization (e-beams)** or cold pasteurization as it is also called, subjects the product to radiation from radioactive or machine sources. Three types of rays are used: gamma rays, electron beams, and X-rays. Gamma rays use a source of radioactive material (Cobalt 60 or Cesium 137). They emit high-energy protons that do not make the irradiated product "radioactive." This is an old technology that has been used for years to sterilize medical, dental, and household products. Electron beams, or e-beams, are produced by an electron gun. No radioactive material is used. This technology has been used in the medical field for at least 20 years. X-ray technology is the newest technology. Only commercial units have been built since 1996, and like e-beam, it does not use radioactive material (CDC, 2007). The radiation kills insects, pathogenic bacteria, and parasites. Irradiation does not make food radioactive. Its many uses include preservation of food by destroying organisms that cause spoilage and decomposition, thereby extending the shelf life of foods; sterilization

Electronic pasteurization (e-beams) Ionizing radiation from a focused beam of energy created by the acceleration of electrons using magnetic and electric fields.

so that foods may be stored without refrigeration; controlling sprouting, ripening, and insect damage in potatoes, tropical and citrus fruits, grains, spices, and seasonings; and controlling foodborne illness by destroying pathogens that cause foodborne illness. This latter use has tremendous implications for controlling *Escherichia coli* O157:H7 and *Salmonella* species. Irradiation, although a potentially useful tool for helping reduce the risks of foodborne disease, is a complement to, not a replacement for, proper food-handling practices by producers, processors, and consumers.

The history of food irradiation dates to 1895 when the first paper was published on the idea of irradiating food. Over the course of the 20th century, the process was proven effective and approved for many foods such as spices, fruits, vegetables, and grains in both the United States and several other countries. The first approval of its use on animal products in the United States came about when the FDA, in July 1985, and FSIS, in January 1986, issued rules to allow pork to be irradiated to control *Trichinella*. Subsequent rules have declared irradiation safe for poultry, raw meat, and fresh eggs. Additional products are in the process of being approved, and more will be submitted for approval.

Mad Cow Disease

Bovine spongiform encephalopathy (BSE) is a disease in cattle. It is a degenerative, central nervous system disease that causes cattle to become nervous, lose coordination, lose weight, and have difficulty walking. Cattle die 2 weeks to 6 months after these symptoms appear. The incubation period is 5–8 years. In March 1996, it was announced that a new variant of Creutzfeldt-Jakob disease in humans might be linked to BSE. Evidence accumulated since that time strongly suggests this is the case.

It is believed that the disease is spread in cattle through the feeding of mammalian-derived protein by-product feeds. On June 5, 1997, the Food and Drug Administration Center for Veterinary Medicine published a rule banning mammalian-derived protein by-product feeds for all ruminants to protect the cattle population of the United States. Since 1989, the United States has restricted importation of ruminants, ruminant products, and ruminant by-products from BSE-positive countries.

Despite all of these precautions, on December 23, 2003, the FDA was alerted to the first U.S. case of bovine spongiform in the state of Washington. A "downer" cow that suffered partial paralysis as a result of birthing difficulties had been slaughtered and, as required, a sample was sent to a USDA laboratory in Ames, Iowa, for BSE testing. Test results were positive. Unfortunately, because the results came back about 2 weeks after slaughter, the carcass had already been processed. Edible meat had been converted to hamburger and steak and edible by-products were ground and rendered to make animal feed and produce fat for soap and other products. Once notified of the positive test, the FDA took immediate action and notified the public. During the next month, over 30 officials from the FDA and various state agencies would accomplish the diligent task of tracing down all the infectious material. Within 96 hours all potentially inedible by-products had been found. By the end of the month, over 2,000 tons of meat and by-product had been destroyed.

No other BSE-infected cows were found. Quick response and the cooperation and dedication of many professionals helped to minimize damage and protect the consumer. As a result of this incident, FSIS quickly worked to implement further protections against BSE. A surveillance program to test high-risk cattle was implemented. In addition, effective December 30, 2003, carcasses from cattle intended for human food that are sampled and submitted to APHIS for BSE testing are held from further processing until results are reported. In addition, the definition of meat was clarified by FSIS not to include brain, trigeminal ganglia, spinal cord tissue, or dorsal root ganglia (all of which are central nervous system–type tissues).

Finally, slaughter and processing establishments are required to develop procedures that demonstrate specified risk materials (SRMs) are removed and not present in meat. SRMs include the brain, skull, eyes, trigeminal ganglia, spinal cord, and vertebral column and dorsal root ganglia of cattle 30 months of age and older. SRMs also include the tonsils and distal ileum of all cattle (the removal of distal ileum requires removal of the entire small intestine). SRMs have been banned because science indicates this is where infectious material accumulates.

Genetically Engineered Products

Consumers abroad, and to a lesser degree in the United States, have expressed concern about consuming genetically engineered food products. Most of this controversy has centered on plant products. However, it is inevitable that those concerns will also be directed at animals fed those plant products and then ultimately at transgenic animals themselves.

Livestock have been fed products from plants whose genetics have been altered by recombinant DNA technology (biotech crops) since those crops were first introduced in 1996. Two important types of biotech crops are crops tolerant to pesticides and crops protected from insect pests. Expected in the future are more biotech crops, many with enhanced levels of nutrients or other beneficial substances in the plant.

For those biotech crops currently available, both the levels of nutrients and antinutrients are the same as conventional crops. When fed to livestock, livestock digest and absorb the nutrients from biotech crops just as they do from conventional ones. Livestock grow and produce when fed biotech crops just as they do when fed conventional ones. The meat, milk, and eggs produced from animals fed biotech crops are the same as from conventional feeds. The proteins found in the biotech plants are broken down into smaller components during digestion and thus do not become part of the animal products. Thus, meat, milk, and eggs from animals fed biotech feeds are no different than those from animals fed conventional feeds, and they are safe for human consumption.

The use of animals with genetic alteration and of cloned animals as food is a consumer issue in the United States. In 2008, the FDA concluded that cattle, swine, and goat clones, and the offspring of any animal clones traditionally consumed as food, are safe for human and animal consumption." The issues have been debated for a number of years and will continue to be debated, at least for a time (Figure 19–11).

Figure 19–11
In 2008, the FDA concluded that "cattle, swine, and goat clones, and the offspring of any animal clones traditionally consumed as food, are safe for human and animal consumption." Meat from these clones and their offspring are considered "as safe as food we eat every day." (Photo courtesy of ViaGen, Inc.)

SOURCES OF INFORMATION

More information on the **Partnership for Food Safety Education** and the **Fight BAC!** campaign is available through the Internet at http://www.fightbac.org/.

The **National Food Safety Information Network** was part of the Food Safety Initiative of the Clinton administration. FSIS and FDA are working together to coordinate food safety information through the network. The network will coordinate and link work currently being done by both agencies' hotlines and enhance services provided by the USDA/FDA Foodborne Illness Education Information Center, which develops and maintains a database of education materials. Food safety information from FSIS is available on its website at http://www.fsis.usda.gov. Interagency food safety information is available at http://www.food-safety.gov.

EdNet is an electronic network allowing food safety educators around the country to keep abreast of new federal food safety education projects. It is a direct e-mail communication from the federal government. To subscribe, send the following message to *listserv@foodsafety.gov:* Subscribe EdNet-L firstname lastname (substitute your name for firstname and lastname).

The **Food Safety Educator** newsletter, produced by FSIS, provides a forum to communicate new initiatives and research information. The newsletter can be accessed through the FSIS website at http://www.fsis.usda.gov/News_&_Events/food_safety_educator/index.asp. To subscribe, send or fax your name and mailing address to USDA/FSIS, Food Safety Education Staff, Room 1180-South Building, Washington, DC 20250; fax (202)720-9063. Or e-mail your name and mailing address to *fsis.outreach@usda.gov.*

USDA Meat and Poultry Hotline. (202)720-3333; TTY: 1(800)256-7072; 1(888) 674-6854.

Emerging pathogens
Pathogens that have mutated to become more virulent or have only recently been recognized as a safety issue.

SUMMARY AND CONCLUSION

The food supply in the United States is arguably the safest in the world. However, in spite of the safety of the U.S. food supply, people still become ill from their food. Most illnesses are traced to one of "seven bad bugs." Actually, around 14 organisms cause problems with enough frequency to be of concern. Several of these are referred to as **"emerging" pathogens** because the problem has just begun to be realized or because some mutation in the microorganism itself has made it more of a problem than it previously was. Understandably, food safety has become an important issue with consumers. However, consumers do not always do a good job of evaluating what is and what is not a real risk. Nor are consumers especially good at taking responsibility for the safety of their own food supply.

Even though the overwhelming majority of foodborne illnesses could be prevented if better choices were made by the food preparer, the tendency of the average consumer is to look to the government to provide food safety. This task is not totally possible in a practical world. However, government agencies do have a role, and they are trying to expand that role. Various agencies in the federal government are responsible for segments of the food safety network. This is a system that has evolved since the passage of the Pure Food and Drug Act of 1906 and the Meat Inspection Act of 1906. Currently, these agencies are undergoing a transformation in the way they do business. The Food Safety and Inspection Service is dramatically changing its practices. This has been made possible by the adoption of the Pathogen Reduction Hazard Analysis and Critical Control Point Systems Final Rule, published in July 1996. Other changes are unfolding and many are still in the planning stage.

STUDY QUESTIONS

1. Describe the real versus perceived threats that the food supply poses to the average consumer. What are some events of the 1990s that focused the attention of the consumer on food safety?

2. What is the GRAS list? The Delaney clause? The Food Quality Protection Act of 1996? How do they relate to food safety?

3. What are the "bugs" that cause the majority of foodborne disease?

4. What role does the consumer have in protecting and preparing his or her own safe food supply?

5. Describe the FDA's role in ensuring a safer food supply.

6. What is the role of FSIS in ensuring a safer food supply? What are the purposes of the FSIS's monitoring program? Surveillance program? Residue avoidance program? In-plant/ on-farm testing?

7. FSIS is currently implementing and evaluating for implementation a myriad of changes in how it does business. Describe what the goals of the changes seem to be.

8. What is the Partnership for Food Safety Education and its Fight BAC! campaign? Where can you find more information about these programs?

9. Describe HACCP, its purpose, the seven HACCP principles, and when and where it was implemented.

10. Describe the safety/danger of using bovine somatotropin on cattle as it relates to the human food chain.

11. Is the use of growth-promoting hormones on food-producing animals a safe practice? Why or why not?

12. What are the benefits and risks of food irradiation? Would you eat irradiated food? Why or why not? Do you think you have already consumed any irradiated food? Why do you think consumers have been reluctant to consume foods they knew to be irradiated? If your job was to develop an advertising campaign to convince consumers to eat irradiated products, what would your slogan be?

13. What changes in animal products occur when producing animals are fed genetically engineered plant products?

14. What is FoodNet and what is its purpose?

REFERENCES

With the third and for subsequent editions, Dr. Christina DeWitt, Oregon State University, assumed co-authorship of the chapter. For the fifth edition, Dr. Siobhan Reilly, Food Protech, Stillwater, Oklahoma, reviewed the chapter and contributed new material. The author gratefully acknowledges these contributions.

Anderson, P. T., B. A. Crooker, and M. M. Pullen. 1991. *Animal products: Contributors to a safe food supply.* University of Minnesota, Educational Development System, Minnesota Extension Service.

Buzby, J. C., T. Roberts, C. T. J. Lin, and J. M. MacDonald. 1996. *Bacterial food-borne disease: Medical costs and productivity losses.* Food & Consumer Economics Division, Economics Research Service, U.S. Department of Agriculture. Agricultural Economics Report No. 741. 1301 New York Ave NW, Washington D.C. 20005-4788.

CCABIC. 2006. *Understanding hormone use in beef.* FAQ sheet prepared by the Canadian Cattlemen's Association & Beef Information Centre.

Accessed online July 2, 2007. www.cattle.ca/fact-sheets/hormal.pdf.

CDC. 2007. *Food irradiation.* Center for Disease Control & Practice. Report of Health & Human Services. Accessed online July 2, 2007 at http://www.cdc.gov/rcidod/dbmd/diseaseinfo/foodirratiation.htm.

Rothschild, M. 2011. More evidence of non-O157 STEC in ground beef. In Food Safety News by Marler Clark. Accessed May 2011 at http://www.foodsafetynews.com/2011/01/another-study-shows-stec-contamination-of-beef/

Crooker, B. A., D. E. Otterby, J. G. Linn, B. J. Conlin, H. Chester-Jones, L. B. Hansen, W. P. Hansen, D. G. Johnson, B. D. Marx, J. K. Reneau, M. D. Stern, J. F. Anderson, B. E. Seguin, J. D. Olson, R. J. Farnsworth, and W. G. Olson. 1994. *Dairy research & bovine somatotropin.* University of Minnesota Extension FO-06337. Accessed online July 2, 2007 at http://www.extension.umn.edu/distribution/livestocksystems/DI6337.

Foodborne Illness. 2011. Centers for Disease Control and Prevention. Department of Health and Human Services. Accessed Aubust 2011 at http://www.cdc.gov/ncidod/dbmd/diseaseinfo/foodborneinfections_g.htm#mostcommon

FSIS. 1998a. *Key facts: HACCP final rule.* Revised January 1998. Washington, DC: Food Safety and Inspection Service. http://www.fsis.usda.gov/index.htm.

FSIS. 1998b. Various reports. Washington, DC: Food Safety and Inspection Service, U.S. Department of Agriculture.

Mead, P. S., L. Slutsker, V. Dietz, L. F. McCaig, J. S. Bresee, C. Shapiro, P. M. Griffin, and R. V. Tauxe. 1999. Food related illness and death in the United States. *Emerging Infectious Diseases* 5(5): 1–38.

Smolin, L. A., and M. B. Grosvenor. 1997. *Nutrition science and applications.* 2nd ed. Orlando, FL: Saunders.

USDA. 2004. *Bad bug book. Foodborne pathogenic microorganisms and natural toxins handbook.* Available online at http://vm.cfsan.fda.gov/~mow/intro.html.

20

Animal Welfare and Animal Rights

Key Terms

Abolitionists

Animal rights

Animal welfare

Anthropomorphism

Downer cow

Reformists

Sentient

Speciesism

3 Rs

Vegan

Learning Objectives

After you have studied this chapter, you should be able to:

- Describe the basis for the general concern, but the lack of a consensus opinion, relating to animal welfare and animal rights.
- Compare and contrast animal welfare issues and animal rights issues. If possible, reconcile whether animal rights and animal welfare are different or the same issue to you.
- Cite the major pieces of legislation that have been passed in the United States regarding animal welfare and animal rights.
- Describe the major philosophical differences among various groups that have an interest in this subject.
- Outline a view of the issues likely to be debated for legislative action.

Sentient Creatures that experience pain and pleasure.

INTRODUCTION

Since the 1980s, no other animal-related social issue has generated as much emotion, rhetoric, and ill will as the discussion surrounding animal welfare/animal rights. Some of the uproar is simply a function of how a democratic society resolves disputes. When a major social issue emerges and beliefs and policies are challenged, anger and conflict arise. Media hype, distorted information dissemination, emotional responses, and chaotic debate usually follow. Such is true of this debate. Yet there is more to this issue. People on both sides are affected in a very visceral way. Belief systems are challenged, people feel threatened, and reason is often hard to find.

Additional factors add to the confusion on this issue. Perhaps the most important is that this is not just one issue, but many, often lumped together in people's minds. The animal rights/animal welfare issue affects **sentient** animals used for every conceivable purpose, including those used for food, research, companionship, and recreational activities. Thus, many levels of society are affected (Figure 20–1). In addition, this issue surfaced at a time when agriculture was experiencing an economic crisis of such magnitude that it changed the structure of agriculture profoundly, and with it the lives of agriculturists. The biomedical research community was also facing tough economic times, yet rapidly increasing the world's knowledge and ability to help humanity with cures and preventatives for a myriad of diseases. The research community was outraged at the notions of those who would say, "A rat is a dog is a pig is a boy" as justification for ending lifesaving research. When hunters, trappers, and product testers also came under attack, a wide spectrum of the population discovered this issue affected them.

The idea of giving an animal rights is rooted collectively in several philosophical ideas and theologies, some of which come to us from

Figure 20–1

Animal rights/animal welfare. The animal rights/animal welfare issue includes concerns over animals used for every conceivable purpose.

ancient times. Thus, the notion of having animal rights tied up in the human value system is not new. Writings from many religions have successfully incorporated animal use, rights, and admonitions about care into human mythology. Some assert animal equality on several levels, and the very existence of these writings serves to point out that humans have long considered the relationship to animals as something to ponder. Why then has this issue gained so much attention at this point in history?

The answer is complex. Several factors have contributed. In many ways, attitudes on animal use have changed because of startling advances in technology, and the efficiency those advances have brought. Technological innovation has led to profound changes in society's structure, organization, and goals. Agriculture's efficiency has freed millions of people to pursue other avenues of livelihood. This has left few people with any contact with agriculture and no reason to share the modern agrarian ethic. If they have any concept of the agrarian ethic at all, it is either that of the antique or relic family farm of 60 years ago, or it is one developed as a complete outsider of the modern reality of agriculture. Being so far removed from agriculture, the general population does not have the same contact with animals and farmers/ranchers that previous generations had (Figure 20–2). Their most common contact is with companion animals that yield no economic benefit to their owners and are often treated as a member of the family. As Rollin (1995) points out, "a primarily utilitarian view of animals has been superseded by

Figure 20–2
When more people were directly involved in agriculture, a much greater percentage of the population had some tie to a family farm. Agriculture's efficiency has freed millions from the need to grow their own food. With no ties to agriculture, most people have no reason to share the agrarian ethic. (Photographer Scott Bauer. Courtesy USDA-Agricultural Research Service.)

a more personal and comradely view." This, as well as popular culture icons such as those in Disney movies, has led many people to a highly **anthropomorphic** view of animals. With this view, it is hard for them to be objective and critical of information they receive. Technological innovations in human health are also the products of highly specialized production systems. Yet most people do not really understand that they are living longer because of research done with animals because they have no contact with the research or the researchers that make the discoveries. Nor do they tie medicinal production or product safety to animals. In sum, they do not really understand how much of their way of life depends on both agricultural and research animals. Even if they do hold such general understanding, the philosophies of the animal rights movement make the case that the animal rights philosophy does not allow humans the luxury of these pragmatic reasons for using animals. Those who argue for animal rights hold the view that humanity's quest for efficiency, productivity, knowledge, medical progress, and product safety is responsible for most of animal suffering and that these ends do not justify the means.

At the core of the focus on farm animal rights is the fact that farming is very different today in production systems compared to the more traditional role and treatment of animals in yesteryear's small family farm. Today's farm is often called a "factory farm" and the implication is intended to condemn. As Rollin (1995) points out, "The key feature . . . of traditional agriculture was good husbandry." In this traditional view, the animal's interests and the farmer's interests were so closely intertwined that few questioned that animal care was as good as it could be. Thus, very few would ever suggest that there should be laws dictating husbandry practices. However, modern, highly productive, industrial approaches to agriculture have little resemblance to the quaint family farm of the first part of the 20th century. Barnyard chicken flocks have been moved into battery cages. Baby calves that once ran by their mothers have been put into veal crates. Fenced pastures have been replaced by concrete and cable enclosures. Although many animals can be housed efficiently and food can be grown more economically in these modern systems, the general population does not have the comfort level

Anthropomorphism
Attributing human thoughts, emotions, and characteristics to animals, gods, objects, and so on.

Figure 20–3

Modern confinement systems of animal production, such as feedlots and battery cages for laying hens, bear little resemblance to production practices of the past. Many people are uncomfortable with what they view as "factory farming."
(Photographer Jeff Vanuga. Courtesy USDA-Natural Resources Conservation Service.)

with modern animal agriculture that preceding generations had with traditional agriculture (Figure 20–3).

Add to all of this the fact that activism is an established phenomenon of the post-modern age. The Vietnam War, women's issues, and the environmental movement were training grounds for a very competent breed of activist. People are also better educated on the whole than at any other point in history, and they are richer with more discretionary time. Added to this is the influence of several very effective writer/ philosophers. The writings of Jeremy Bentham in 1789, Albert Schweitzer in 1965, Peter Singer in 1975, and Tom Regan in 1983 have all influenced modern thinking. Bentham is credited by some as the originator of the animal rights movement. Singer's influence cannot be underestimated. The publication of Ruth Harrison's *Animal Machines—The New Factory Farming Industry* in 1964 brought agriculture and its animal production methods under real public scrutiny. The establishment and emergence of People for the Ethical Treatment of Animals (PETA) must be viewed as a pivotal event in the animal rights activism observed in this country today. During the decade of the 1980s, PETA and other restructured animal welfare/animal cruelty groups were able to organize, collecting millions in donations, and influence many Americans to become more animal rights minded. They successfully took their idea through the emerging stages of social consciousness and have turned it into a contemporary social issue. That is no small feat, and their skill and tenacity in this accomplishment was extraordinary.

The new animal ethic accepted and openly advocated by some, while stringently opposed by others, presents challenges to individuals who work with animals in any capacity. Who prevails, on what issues, and how society comes to view the overall issues will determine the standards society adopts for all in the future. People educated on the issues and willing to enter the public debate should determine those standards. That debate is far from over. However, both providing and receiving education on emotional and controversial issues are usually difficult. When we are angry and embroiled in conflict, opinion is easily polarized. This makes it hard to get information one can trust as being objective, and hard to truly listen to when it is presented. Even so, responsible citizenship demands of us the ability to differentiate between opinion and fact, emotional responses from objective ones, and rhetoric from information. With so much at stake, it is necessary for us all, on both sides of any issue, to come to understand the varying viewpoints. It is also morally incumbent that we find a position that is ethically defensible to support in the debate. Regardless of which position we adopt, it is further important that we be willing to inform others of our position and defend it.

ANIMAL RIGHTS VERSUS ANIMAL WELFARE

Although lines between the two tend to blur, animal rights philosophy and animal welfare philosophy are generally argued as separate issues. **Animal welfare** concerns began with the first domesticators of animals and have continued to the present with progressively responsible animal husbandry practices. The animal welfarist is concerned with an animal's treatment and well-being while the animal provides for human needs. The basis of the welfarist position is the idea that using animals obligates people to tend to basic needs considered to be good husbandry. These needs include feed, water, protection, shelter, health care, alleviation of pain and suffering, and other similar needs. Most would call these the necessary elements of humane care. In agriculture, providing for animal welfare determines whether or not animal production systems make money. Attending to welfare is an issue of biology (Figure 20–4). Providing for the welfare of an animal does not necessarily require giving it rights. Agriculturists fear that ascribing rights to animals will affect costs. As long as ascribing rights to animals does not change the way the production systems function, then there are no costs associated with the rights. However, if ascribing rights to the animals causes changes to be made purely for the sake of animal rights, then the rights have economic consequences.

Animal rights deals with philosophy, sociology, and public policy as they apply to the standing of animals in relation to human society. The most extreme animal rightists assign rights to animals that most human societies reserve for people alone, thus removing the moral barriers between people and animals. Their view is that animals have a right not to be used by humans for any purpose. To those taking the extreme animal rights position, the idea of humane care is an oxymoron. Of course, not all animal rights supporters take the extreme position. Many are more moderate and practical in their approach and work to abolish what they consider unacceptable situations of animal suffering. Many animal rightists support animal use if they can believe that both animal and human benefit. An example is keeping animals as pets. By contrast, the extreme animal rights position views pet keeping as an inappropriate exploitation that should cease. To some, biomedical research with animals is

Animal welfare The treatment and well-being of animals while they provide for human needs; humane use.

Animal rights Philosophy, sociology, and public policy as they deal with the standing of animals in relation to human society.

Figure 20–4
The animal welfarist is concerned with the animal's treatment and well-being while it is being used to provide for human needs.

Figure 20–5
To some animal rightists, biomedical research with animals is acceptable, but rodeo events, such as roping, are unacceptable exploitation.

acceptable, but calf-roping events at rodeos are not. To those who hold this position, the ultimate value of the use is what decides whether the use is justified (Figure 20–5). The anti-use animal rights philosophy leaves no room for compromise and is not open to change. It is based on a philosophy of no use. Many who subscribe to this view are **vegans**, people who use no animal products of any kind. By contrast, treatment of animals under a pro-use animal rights philosophy can change as the expectations of the greater society change and as new scientific understandings of animals develop. Some rights are already preserved in law, such as humane slaughter, and are not considered extreme by any segment of society. The new concern probably stems from the change in focus of animal rights advocates. Prior to the 1980s, almost all animal rights concerns focused on cruelty issues and generally exempted animals used for economic and recreational benefit. This distinction kept animal agriculture, research, racing, rodeo, hunting, and other similar uses from being considered in the cruelty laws. Animal rights advocates now include all of these animal uses in their agenda for change. Laws and policies are beginning to reflect the change in thought.

With this difference in philosophy, we naturally see different kinds of rights advocates—usually either reformists or abolitionists. **Reformists** may believe in the views of philosophers of the movement but generally are willing to work within the system to achieve their goals. **Abolitionists** focus on promoting total abandonment of any animal use. Some abolitionists have resorted to violence, vandalism, and theft as methods to destroy the veal and fur industries, and to stop product testing, animal research, and hunting. Regardless of the tactics, their goal is to stop animal use. Most members of these abolitionist groups use the term **speciesism**, or the placing of the interests of one's own species above the interests of another, to describe what they view as mankind's unconscionable arrogance against other species.

Bernard Rollin (1995) argues that the new animal ethic is not defined by the abolitionist view and that those opposed to animal rights make a mistake by characterizing the mainstream movement in abolitionist terms. His argument with specific regard to agriculture follows:

> Rather, it is an attempt to constrain *how* they can be used, so as to limit their pain and suffering. In this regard, as a 1993 *Beef Today* article points out, the thrust for protection of animal natures is not at all radical; it is very conservative, *asking for the same sort of husbandry that characterized the overwhelming majority of animal use during all of human history, save the last fifty or so years.* It is not opposed to animal use; it is opposed

Vegan Someone who eschews the use of any animal product, including the nonfood products.

Reformists Animal rights proponents who focus on changing methods of animal use.

Abolitionists Animal rights proponents who advocate the total abandonment of any animal use.

Speciesism Placing the interests of one species above that of another species.

to animal use that goes against the animals' natures and tries to force square pegs into round holes, leading to friction and suffering. If animals are to be used for food and labor, they should, as they traditionally did, live lives that respect their natures. If animals are to be used to probe nature and cure disease for human benefit, they should not suffer in the process. Thus this new ethic is conservative, not radical, harking back to the animal use that necessitated and thus entailed respect for the animals' natures. It is based on the insight that what we do to animals matters to them, just as what we do to humans *matters* to them, and that consequently we should respect that mattering in our treatment and use of animals as we do in our treatment and use of humans. And since respect for animal nature is no longer automatic as it was in traditional agriculture, society is demanding that it be encoded in law.

Not all people agree that animal welfare and animal rights are separate issues. Some have begun to argue that continuing to separate the ideology of animal welfare from animal rights is no longer very practical. If it is true that the vast majority of society believes in both animal use and animal rights, then the argument has merit. Rollin (1995) suggests a new way of confronting the issue: "[I]f it is the case that the notion of animals rights is a pivotal part of the emerging mainstream social ethic for the treatment of animals, there is little value in maintaining the dualism of animal welfare versus animal rights. It is rather that the traditional notion of animal welfare is being socially augmented and explicated by the notion that animals have certain rights." However, it will be difficult for some in society to accept this view. Traditional agriculturists are highly unlikely to agree anytime soon to the idea that there is no difference between animal welfare thinking and animal rights thinking. Nor are animal rights supporters likely to be in accord with this idea. In *Rain without Thunder,* Gary Francione (1996) states, "The welfarists seek the *regulation* of animal exploitation; the rightists seek the abolition. The need to distinguish animal rights from animal welfare is clear not only because of the theoretical inconsistencies between the two positions but also because the most ardent defenders of institutionalized animal exploitation themselves endorse animal welfare."

Animal agriculturists usually take the position that they are practicing animal welfarists because a well-cared-for animal performs better and thus is more profitable. However, social issues do not generally arise without provocation. Animal rightists have raised concerns about some common practices in the animal industries that reasonable people in the livestock industry have been quick to support. The entire **"downer cow"** handling that animal rightists exposed at some slaughter plants provoked a cry of outrage from many levels of agriculture.

Downer cow A nonambulatory cow.

Clearly, it is difficult to discuss this issue without becoming confused about who is a rightist and who is a welfarist, and what each wants. As a means of distinguishing between animal welfare and animal rights, the author favors using the term *animal rights* in its political sense. In this sense, animal rights describes ideas and actions that have potential political action as a possibility or goal. It pertains to such goals regardless of the species. Animal rights, then, becomes any change or attempted change in the legal status of animals that challenges the status quo. *Animal welfare,* in the author's view, refers to well-being and care in its biological sense.

PHILOSOPHY, HISTORY, AND LEGISLATION

Modern animal rights philosophy has been influenced by many thinkers and their ideas. However, the philosophies of Peter Singer (*Animal Liberation,* 1990) and Tom Regan (*The Case for Animal Rights,* 1983) have unquestionably had tremendous influence. It is outside the scope of this text to put forth the particulars of their

philosophies. Gary Francione (1996) does a good job of distilling these two theories to their basics in the first chapter of *Rain without Thunder* for those of you who wish to explore them further. Of course, a thorough understanding requires a reading of the books (and considerable reflection on the ideas). The point that is important for this discussion is that there have been philosophies put forth for people to believe in. The implications for the animal movement have been enormous.

Pro-animal use has a philosophical base also. In most of the Western world, including the United States, pro-animal use philosophy is based on the Judeo-Christian philosophy. The justification for animal use is essentially tied to the Old Testament concept of humans' dominion over animals. Interestingly, few people who oppose animal rights or abolitionist views ever evoke their philosophical reasons for doing so. Instead, they fall back on pragmatic arguments like "research saves lives" and "animal products help feed the world." Animal rights arguments, however, are usually based on adherence to a philosophical stance that is in opposition to the use of animals for any use. Peter Singer himself acknowledges the relationship between Christianity and the Western attitude toward animals. He goes on to say, "A more enlightened view of our relations with animals emerges only gradually, as thinkers begin to take positions that are relatively independent of the Church" (Singer, 1990).

In recent years, some moral philosophers have taken a stance against enhancing the moral standing of animals. In the preface to *The Animals Issue,* Peter Carruthers (1992) states that although "almost all the books and articles recently published on this issue have argued in favor of the moral standing of animals" this is simply because "most of those who take the opposite view have chosen to remain silent." His book sets forth a nonreligious, moral basis for animal use and against "forbidding hunting, factory farming, or laboratory testing of animals." He concludes his book with the flat assertion "that those who are committed to any aspect of the animal rights movement are thoroughly misguided."

In 1873, the first federal law was enacted to prevent animal cruelty in the United States. Table 20–1 lists the most important pieces of legislation enacted since that time.

ANIMAL WELFARE/ANIMAL RIGHTS GROUPS

Because opinions, beliefs, and views vary widely from individual to individual, it is logical that the same would be so of the organizations that develop around this complex issue. Groups exist on a continuum, from the most extreme militant groups on one end to pro-animal use groups on the other. Depending on how the various groups are categorized, there are probably 10,000 or so of them, all told. They are decidedly mixed in their goals and styles, and range from animal producer groups to humane societies to terrorist organizations. They may be local, national, or international. They may be pro-use or anti-use. They may be reformist, abolitionist, or protectors of the status quo. They may be political action groups or militant activists. They may count among their ranks agriculturists, militant animal rights activists, animal scientists, philosophers, and others from service industries, environmental groups, wildlife conservation groups, and nature groups. Almost all people involved have a polarized viewpoint, or they probably would not have joined any group at all. Table 20–2 offers a sampling of groups whose agendas favor either the expansion of animal rights or the opposition to the expansion of animal rights. Some focus on specific issues, while others direct their attention to a wide range of issues.

Table 20–1
SOME IMPORTANT LAWS GOVERNING HUMANE ANIMAL USE

The Federal Humane Slaughter Act of 1958, as amended in 1978, regulates slaughter practices. It requires federally inspected meat plants to meet humane slaughter conditions including rendering animals unconscious before slaughtering.

The Horse Protection Act of 1970 was enacted in order to prevent soring of Tennessee Walking Horses but covers all breeds of horses.

The Marine Mammal Protection Act of 1972 regulates the killing, capturing, and harassing of marine mammals.

The Animal Welfare Act (PL-89-544) with amendments in 1970 (PL-91-579), 1976 (PL-94-279), 1985 (PL-99-198), and 1990 (PL-101-624). This federal legislation and its amendments protects pets from theft; defines minimum holding times for pets in pounds sold to dealers; deals with basic animal management and veterinary care; and regulates research facilities, animal dealers, animal exhibitors, intermediate handlers of animals, including air and truck lines; and prohibits certain forms of animal fighting.

The Food Security Act of 1985 (PL-99-198) was the first omnibus farm legislation to include animal welfare issues. As a result of this legislation the Secretary of Agriculture is required to set standards for humane care, treatment, and transportation of animals by dealers, research facilities, and exhibitors. Included were minimum requirements for handling, housing, feeding, watering, sanitation, ventilation, shelter, veterinary care, separation of species, exercise for dogs, and the provision of an environment considered adequate for the psychological well-being of nonhuman primates. Further, research facilities were required to have a committee to monitor animal care and practices, and to provide training for anyone handling or using research animals. An information service on employee training and animal experimentation to reduce animal pain and stress was established at the National Agricultural Library.

The Health Professions Educational Assistance Amendments of 1985 provided for federal fund availability so that schools of veterinary medicine could develop curricula for humane care of laboratory species, for distress limiting methodology, and for the use of alternatives to animals in research and testing.

The Health Research Extension Act of 1985 (PL-99-158) put forth standards for research animals, which had been a matter of Public Health Service policy since 1971. Animal care committees, research plans for the reduction of or alternatives for animals in research, as well as the reduction of animal pain and discomfort were all addressed in this legislation. It was an amendment to the **Public Health Service Act** [U.S.C. 42 §§ 289d(b) & (c)], which regulates projects funded by the Public Health Service or one of its agencies.

The Public Health Service Policy on Humane Care and Use of Laboratory Animals (OPRR-NIH) was first established in 1971 and was revised several times, most recently in September of 1986 to implement the Health Research Extension Act of 1985. The policy required institutions to use the *Guide for the Care and Use of Laboratory Animals* (NIH Publication 86-23, revised 1985) as the basis for developing the institution's animal use program.

The Animal Facilities Protection Act of 1992 made destruction of animal research or production facilities a federal crime if damage exceeds $10,000. This legislation was prompted by incidents of vandalism, theft, and threats to research workers.

Good Laboratory Practice Standards were established under 3 different pieces of legislation: Toxic Substances Control Act (TSCA) (15 U.S.C. § 2603 *et seq.*) (40 C.F.R. 792.1 *et seq.*); Federal Insecticide, Fungicide, and Rodenticide Act (FIFRA) (7 U.S.C. § 136 *et seq.*) (40 C.F.R. § 160.1 *et seq.*); and Federal Food, Drug, and Cosmetic Act (FFDCA) (21 U.S.C. § 321 *et seq.*) (21 C. F. R. § 58.1). Included are regulations for the care and housing of test animals in addition to regulations for other areas of laboratory management. Data to be submitted to the Food and Drug Administration and/or the Environmental Protection Agency must be collected under these rules.

State and Local Laws address issues such as pound animals, cruelty, regulation of research facilities, and educational use of animals.

Source: Compiled from Bennett et al., 1994, pp. 3–10; Katz, 1999; and Guither and Swanson, 1999.

ANIMAL RIGHTS ISSUES PRESENT AND FUTURE

Animal rights issues involve all species of animals and could conceivably develop in an infinite number of directions. Thus, predicting the issues of the future can be difficult. Nevertheless, many indicators suggest the probable issues of the future. The most likely are discussed in this section. The directions that public policy could take include protecting the status quo, leaving the issue to individual states, controlling public lands and not private lands, and setting policy for some issues at the national level while leaving others to the states.

Table 20–2
ANIMAL RIGHTS AND ANIMAL WELFARE GROUPS

Groups targeting animal use

Farm Animal Concerns Trust

Animal Welfare Institute

Humane Society of the United States

Humane Farming Association

Animal Legal Defense Fund

Farm Animal Reform Movement

People for the Ethical Treatment of Animals

American Vegan Society

Animal Liberation Front

Groups defending animal agriculture and biomedical research

National Livestock and Meat Board

American Farm Bureau Federation

Animal Industry Foundation

Animal Agriculture Alliance

Farm Animal Welfare Coalition

Americans for Medical Progress Educational Foundation

Foundation for Biomedical Research

Groups promoting voluntary guidelines for animal use and care

Association for the Accreditation of Laboratory Care

American Medical Association

American Psychological Association

American Veal Association

American Veterinary Medical Association

Fur Farm Animal Welfare Coalition

National Cattlemen's Association

National Institute for Animal Agriculture

National Pork Producers Council

Numerous other scientific organizations

Defining and Measuring Animal Welfare

Currently, agriculturists choose management practices based on economic principles (i.e., they choose the production practices that will yield the most profit within their constraints). If government is to regulate care of agricultural animals by passing agricultural animal rights legislation, then an acceptable definition of humane care must be developed within the context of agricultural production systems. The methods for handling, transporting, and confining animals will need legal definition. Presumably, the development of such definitions would be a part of legislation aimed at restricting and directing animal management practices within production systems.

One problem with determining practices that promote the best welfare for livestock is in defining and measuring physiological welfare. Often, the production of useful product is measured. The supposition is that if the animal is gaining well or producing milk at a high level, its needs are being met. However, modern animal production systems are not always designed to measure individual production at all and, if so, only at the end of the production phase. Another problem is that good production does not prevent animals from being subjected to distress. Other indicators such as physiological measurements (blood parameters, and so on), animal behavior, preference tests, or other measures, including simple observation, may help measure an animal's state of care and distress. Measuring the psychological well-being of animals is an even more challenging task. Ultimately, a combination of measures will probably be used to measure the welfare provided in various management systems. Currently, the research necessary to make such determinations is not receiving the funding and the effort it sorely needs. Even though precise systems for measuring animal welfare need further development, those who work with animals have been developing guidelines for animal use rapidly and working to educate and implement standard practices (Table 20–3).

Regulation may involve establishment of boards and commissions that would define humane care and management, and then interpret, oversee, and arbitrate the legislative mandates. Alternatively, laws could be written through the public hearing process and enforced through regular law enforcement mechanisms. Still another alternative might include a system of labeling for food products that describes the production practices under which they were manufactured, allowing consumers to make informed spending choices.

This would no doubt increase the costs associated with food production and the cost of the products, and reduce the returns to the agricultural sector. Reduced supplies and increased consumer prices could result. The addition of new policies would also lead to regulatory bureaucracies, added taxes, and other forms of public support. However, some analysts argue, quite persuasively, that if all producers are required to make the same changes in production techniques, thereby raising costs to all and giving advantage to none, that consumers would then absorb the costs. They further argue that those costs would be so little per consumer as to be inconsequential to all but the very poorest (see Webster, 2001). If these arguments are correct, then producers would be compensated for providing improvements in the welfare of their livestock, consumers would absorb the costs, and production would continue.

It must be pointed out that certain avenues for defining animal welfare do not require broad consensus or even majority opinion and methods of enforcing

---

Table 20–3
SOME IMPORTANT GUIDELINES FOR CARE AND USE OF ANIMALS

American Association for the Accreditation of Laboratory Animal Care (AAALAC). A voluntary accreditation body that requires compliance with the *Guide for the Care and Use of Laboratory Animals* and the *Guide for the Care and Use of Agricultural Animals in Agricultural Research and Teaching*. Peer evaluation is used to ensure the proper care and use of research animals, as well as to protect people from dangers associated with conducting research with animals, and minimizing variables that can negatively affect the quality of research.

Guide for the Care and Use of Laboratory Animals. The *Guide* sets forth recommendations on policy, veterinary care, husbandry practices, and requirements for research facilities and the animals used for research in them. It further emphasizes that the responsibility for animal care is with the institution. Published by the National Research Council, the *Guide* is the resource explaining the requirements enforced under the Public Health Service Policy on Humane Care and Use of Laboratory Animals.

Guide for the Care and Use of Agricultural Animals in Research and Teaching. This guide is published by the Federation of Animal Science Societies (FASS). It is voluntary but has received wide acceptance, support, and use by those who use agricultural animals in research and teaching. It includes guidelines for institutional policies, general husbandry guidelines, health care, environmental enrichment, physical plant, handling and transport, biosecurity, genetically engineered and cloned animals, beef cattle, dairy cattle, horses, poultry, sheep, goats, and swine.

Policy on Personnel Ethics in Youth Livestock Activities. Oklahoma Cooperative Extension Service. This is an excellent example of a policy designed to retain and promote what is good about youth livestock programs. Many states have adopted policies on youth livestock programs relating to exhibitions. Such policies spell out unethical and illegal practices and the penalties for infractions.

AVMA Guidelines on Euthanasia. Presents acceptable methods of euthanasia.

Guidelines for Ethical Conduct in the Care and Use of Animals. Developed by the American Psychological Association's Committee on Animal Research and Ethics.

Source: Compiled from Bennett et al., 1994, pp. 3–10; Katz, 1999; and Guither and Swanson, 1999. Updated from various sources.

adherence to the definition, even if not all agree with the rubric assigned. Food companies have been facing mounting pressure to develop animal welfare plans, which their suppliers of animal products are then expected to follow. This gives the food companies a way to assure their consumers that the food animals are treated in a fashion they are willing to defend to their consumers. Several high-profile companies have taken this step. There seems little doubt that others will do the same. The marketplace may be the ultimate arbitrator, rendering laws unnecessary.

Webster (2001) offers the following view of welfare, "The welfare of a sentient animal is good if it can sustain fitness and avoid suffering: i.e., stay fit and happy." An avenue for supporting that definition can be found in the "Five Freedoms" (Table 20–4) put forth by the Farm Animal Welfare Council, an independent advisory body established by the British government in 1979. (Note: the FAWC closed as part of a reorganization in March 2011.) Areas considered are affective states (pain, pleasure, suffering), natural living (conditions that allow the animal's nature and adaptations), and basic health. Ultimately, a consensus will be reached through one or more avenues.

Cloning   When the world found out about Dolly, the cloned sheep, the inevitable debate ensued over the ethics of cloning animals and humans (Figure 20–6). Cloning is likely to continue as a hotly contested issue in the future. In a policy paper issued in January 2008, the FDA declared cloned animals safe to eat. Many have couched the opposition argument in animal rights terms. Legislative agendas have already developed around this issue and will continue to do so.

Table 20–4

THE FIVE FREEDOMS OF THE FARM ANIMAL WELFARE COUNCIL

The welfare of an animal includes its physical and mental state and we consider that good animal welfare implies both fitness and a sense of well-being. Any animal kept by man must at least be protected from unnecessary suffering.

We believe that an animal's welfare, whether on farm, in transit, at market or at a place of slaughter should be considered in terms of **five freedoms**. These freedoms define ideal states rather than standards for acceptable welfare. They form a logical and comprehensive framework for analysis of welfare within any system together with the steps and compromises necessary to safeguard and improve welfare within the proper constraints of an effective livestock industry.

1. Freedom from hunger and thirst—by ready access to fresh water and a diet to maintain full health and vigor.
2. Freedom from discomfort—by providing an appropriate environment including shelter and a comfortable resting area.
3. Freedom from pain, injury or disease—by prevention or rapid diagnosis and treatment.
4. Freedom to express normal behavior—by providing sufficient space, proper facilities, and company of the animal's own kind.
5. Freedom from fear and distress—by ensuring conditions and treatment that avoid mental suffering.

Stockmanship—The Key to Welfare

Stockmanship, plus the training and supervision necessary to achieve required standards, are key factors in the handling and care of livestock. A management system may be acceptable in principle but without competent, diligent stockmanship the welfare of animals cannot be adequately safeguarded. We lay great stress on the need for better awareness of welfare needs, for better training and supervision.

Source: Adapted from Farm Animal Welfare Council. http://www.fawc.org.uk/index.htm.

Figure 20–6
Dolly, the cloned sheep, was just the first of many cloned animals to follow. Many consider the ethical debate over creating clones to be issue an animal rights issue. (Photo courtesy Viagen, Inc.)

Control of Predatory Species   Predators and wild grazers affect the ability of production agriculturists to produce inexpensive food because they increase the costs of producing crops and livestock. Sheep have long been the target of coyotes. Deer and other related species can do tremendous damage to crops. In addition, several predator species have adapted to human encroachment on their space by harvesting our pets as their food supply. Herbivores freely roam some suburbs, damaging expensive landscapes. At issue is whether or not to control the problem species in order to protect the domestic plants and animals. Policy alternatives range from banning any control, to allowing almost any form of control. Alternatives in between those options include restricting some practices to minimize damage to nontargeted species, developing better control methods, and allowing the damage but instituting a method of reimbursement to those who suffer economic losses.

Hunting and Trapping   For the short term, the debate over this issue will probably center on whether or not to allow hunting on public property, whether those who interfere with hunters on public property should be restricted, and whether or not leghold traps should be allowed. Many groups have interests in this issue. Animal rights groups generally object to all hunting and trapping (Figure 20–7). Conservationists favor restrictions on hunting and trapping to ensure species health and survival,

Figure 20–7
Animal rights groups tend to object to hunting wildlife species, whereas many other groups support hunting for many reasons. (Photographer Scott Bauer. Courtesy of USDA-Agricultural Research Service.)

Figure 20–8
Advanced laboratory techniques are giving researchers tools to reduce the number of animals needed in biomedical research. Cell cultures can sometimes be used as alternatives for live animals in research. Here, animal physiologist Caird Rexroad inspects bovine embryonic cells. (Photographer Keith Weller. Courtesy of USDA.)

including both endangered and nonendangered species. The sale of hunting rights on private property gives agriculturists an economic stake. Property rights debates ensue when restrictions on private property are considered. Revenues from hunter's fees and licenses are used in conservation programs aimed at preserving wildlife species.

Research   Legislation that regulates and controls management of animals used in research already exists. The next step would be to determine if the government would exercise value judgments and determine the exact uses for animals in research, or to determine if they are to be used at all. This could mean prohibiting all animal research, or restricting some types, such as agricultural animal or cosmetics research, but allowing other types, such as biomedical research, to continue. This could negatively affect development of new drugs, cures for diseases, and the general health and well-being of the human population, and could increase the costs of health care. It is estimated that advances from animal research have added 25 to 30 years to the average American life span since 1900. Medical advances that will add even more years certainly remain to be discovered, as do discoveries that will add to quality of life. Medical research depends on the use of animals as models and will continue to do so in the near future. Animals are also used in research to benefit animal health and improve production methods, resulting in healthier, longer-lived pets and healthier, more productive livestock.

The number of animals used in research in the United States has been decreasing for several years, partly because of the costs of the regulations that have been imposed. However, a significant amount of reduction in animal use is also due to the increased use of in vitro cultures, mathematical models, and the substitution of lower organisms (Figure 20–8). Researchers have accomplished much of this through the concept of replacement, reduction, and refinement (the **3 Rs**). The success that researchers achieve in carrying out this concept may ultimately decide what laws are enacted.

3 Rs Replacement (substitute something else for higher animals), reduction (reduce the number of animals needed), and refinement (decrease in inhumane procedures).

SOURCES OF INFORMATION

The Animal Welfare Information Center (AWIC) is an information service established at the National Agricultural Library in Beltsville, Maryland. It was established as a result of the 1986 amendments to the Animal Welfare Act. Its mandate includes providing information on subjects relating to animal welfare. It is the single most important resource on this topic in the United States. Address: Animal Welfare

Information Center, National Agricultural Library, 10301 Baltimore Ave, Room 410, Beltsville, MD 20705. Phone: (301)504-6212; fax (301)504-7125; http://awic. nal.usda.gov/nal_display/index.php?info_center=3&tax_level=1&tax_subject=185.

SUGGESTED READINGS

Caruthers, P. 1992. *The animals issue: Moral theory in practice.* Cambridge, UK: Cambridge University Press.

Cohen, C. 1986. The case for the use of animals in biomedical research. *New England Journal of Medicine* 315:865.

Duncan, I., and J. Petherick. 1991. The implication of cognitive process for animal welfare. *Journal of Animal Science* 69:5017.

Finsen, L., and S. Finsen. 1994. *The animal rights movement in America.* New York: Twayne Macmillan.

Harrison, R. 1994. *Animal machines.* London: Vincent Stuart.

Jasper, J. M., and D. Nelkin. 1992. *The animal rights crusade: The growth of a moral protest.* New York: The Free Press.

Leavitt, S. E. 1978. *Animals and their legal rights.* Washington, DC: Animal Welfare Institute.

Marquardt, K., H. M. Levine, and M. LaRochelle. 1993. *Animal scam: The beastly abuse of human rights.* Washington, DC: Regnery Gateway.

Mench, J., and A. Van Tienhoven. 1986. Farm animal welfare. *American Scientist* 74:598.

Nicoll, C. 1991. A physiologist's view on the animal rights/liberation movement. *The Physiologist* 34:303.

Pardos, H., A. West, and H. Pincus. 1991. Physicians and the animal-rights movement. *New England Journal of Medicine* 324:1640.

Regan, T., and G. Francione. 1992. A movement's means create its ends. *The Animals' Agenda,* Jan/Feb:40.

Regan, T., and P. Singer, 1976. *Animal rights and human obligations.* Englewood Cliffs, NJ: Prentice-Hall.

Singer, P. 1990. *Animal liberation.* New York: Random House.

SUMMARY AND CONCLUSION

All things considered, there is little wonder that widely divergent attitudes, philosophies, and ethics that challenge more traditional values regarding animal use have developed. Thus, although animal rights is not merely some modern notion, at no time in history has the idea of rights for animals been accepted by so many and thus debated by so many. Nor have the numbers of people involved directly with noncompanion animals ever been so few. Consequently, at no other time have the conditions ever been so ripe for the issue actually to gain a following and grow.

Changing animal welfare concerns and emerging animal rights considerations have broad potential benefits and costs to humans and our society on many levels. These include philosophical, social, legal, economic, biological, emotional, and political perspectives. The interested parties encompass a range of people from agriculturists and consumers, to the most extreme animal rights abolitionist advocate. The different viewpoints pit such issues as the hard, practical consideration that animal agriculture is a major part of the economy of this country against the more esoteric considerations associated with the belief systems of those who have equated animal rights to human rights. Should the most extreme approach to animal rights be accepted by society, then all uses of animals for food,

clothing, leisure, or research purposes would cease. Few believe this could ever occur.

The level of concern for animal rights issues among the general population of the United States indicates that more concern for these issues will grow in the future. Proponents of animal rights issues will join with environmental, diet, health, and food safety groups to pursue an agenda to support their goals. It is probable that they will influence future policies. Many argue that it is only a matter of time until farm animal welfare is legislated in the United States. Agriculturists, agribusiness entities, consumers, and all the rest, along with their organizations, must join the discussion if they are to be part of the policy-making process. In fact, as Getz and Baker (1990) suggest, the process may ultimately improve animal agriculture because challenges to the status quo often lead to positive change. Many argue that it has already done so for biomedical research. Those who graduate with degrees in agriculture, biomedicine, and related fields are likely to be thought leaders of the future on this issue. It is necessary to work intelligently, follow this issue diligently, distribute good information effectively, and respond to criticisms from outside groups. The entire future of animal use in all its forms depends on informed debate.

REFERENCES

Appleby, M. C., and B. O. Hughes. 1997. *Animal welfare.* CAB International. Cambridge, UK: University Press.

Appleby, M. C., and P. Sandoe. 2002. Philosophical debate on the nature of well-being: Implications for animal welfare. *Animal Welfare* 11: 283–294.

Azjen, I., and M. Fishbein. 1980. *Understanding attitudes and predicting social behavior.* Englewood Cliffs, NJ.: Prentice Hall.

Bennett, B. T., M. J. Brown, and J. C. Scofield. 1994. *Essentials for animal research: A primer for research personnel.* Washington, DC: Animal Welfare Information Center, United States Department of Agriculture, National Agriculture Library.

Bennett, R. 1998. Measuring public support for animal welfare legislation: A case study of cage egg production. *Animal Welfare* 7:1–10.

Bowd, A. D., and A. C. Bowd. 1989. Attitudes toward the treatment of animals: A study of Christian groups in Australia. *Anthrozoös* 3:20–24.

Carruthers, P. 1992. *The animals issue: Moral theory in practice.* Cambridge, UK: Cambridge University Press.

Davis, S. L. 2000. What is the morally relevant difference between the mouse and the pig? *Proceedings of the 2nd Congress of the European Society for Agricultural and Food Ethics,* 24–26 August. Copenhagen, Denmark: Royal Veterinary and Agricultural University, pp. 107–109.

Davis, S. L. 2001. The least harm principle suggests that humans should eat beef, lamb, dairy, not a vegan diet. *Proceedings of the 3rd Congress of the European Society for Agricultural and Food Ethics,* 3–5 October. Florence, Italy. Milan, Italy: A and Q, University, pp. 449–450.

Davis, S. L., and P. R. Cheeke. 1998. Do domestic animals have minds and the ability to think? A provisional sample of opinions on the question. *Journal of Animal Science* 76:2072–2079.

Dennis, J. U. 1997. Morally relevant differences between animals and human beings justifying the use of animals in biomedical research. *Journal of the American Veterinary Medical Association* 210:612–618.

Farm Animal Welfare Council. 1993. *Second report on priorities for research and development in farm animal welfare.* Ministry of Agriculture, Fisheries and Food.

Farm Animal Welfare Council. 2004. *The five freedoms.* Accessed January 25, 2008. http://www.fawc.org.uk/freedoms.htm.

Francione, G. L. 1996. *Rain without thunder.* Philadelphia: Temple University Press.

Fraser, D. 1999. Animal ethics and animal welfare science: Bridging the two cultures. *Applied Animal Behavior Science* 65:171–189.

Fraser, D. 2001. The "new" perception of animal agriculture: Legless cows, featherless chickens, and a need for genuine analysis. *Journal of Animal Science* 79:634–641.

Fraser, D. 2008. *Understanding animal welfare: The science in its cultural context.* Oxford: Wiley-Blackwell.

Friend, T. H. 1990. Teaching animal welfare in the land grant universities. *Journal of Animal Science* 68:3462.

Getz, W. R., and F. H. Baker. 1990. Educational methodology in dealing with animal rights and welfare in public service. *Journal of Animal Science* 68:3468.

Graf, B., and M. Senn. 1999. Behavioural and physiological responses of calves to dehorning by heat cauterization with or without local anaesthesia. *Applied Animal Behaviour Science* 62(2–3):153–171.

Guither, H. D., and J. Swanson. 1999. *Animal rights and animal welfare.* University of Illinois and Kansas State University. http://unlvm.unl.edu/aniright.htm.

Heleski, C. R., A. J. Zanella, and E. A. Pajor. 2003. Animal welfare judging teams: A way to interface welfare science with traditional animal science curricula? *Applied Animal Behaviour Science* 81:279–289.

Hemsworth, P. H., and G. J. Coleman. 1998. *Human-livestock interactions: The stockperson and the productivity and welfare of intensively farmed animals.* Oxon, UK: CAB International.

Hemsworth, P. H., G. J. Coleman, J. L. Barnett, S. Borg, and S. Dowling. 2002. The effects of cognitive behavioral intervention on the attitude and behavior of stockpersons and the behavior and productivity of commercial dairy cows. *Journal of Animal Science* 80:68–78.

Hodges, J., and I. K. Han (eds.). 2000. *Livestock, ethics and quality of life.* Wallingford, UK: CABI.

Katz, L. S. 1999. *Animal rights vs. animal welfare.* Publication No. FS753. New Brunswick, NJ: Rutgers Cooperative Extension Service Agricultural Extension Service.

Kellert, S. R. 1980. American attitudes toward and knowledge of animals: An update. *International Journal for the Study of Animal Problems* 1:87–119.

Kunkel, H. O. 2000. *Human issues in animal agriculture.* College Station: Texas A&M Press.

McInerney, J. P. 1998. The economics of welfare. In *Ethics, welfare, law and market forces: The veterinary interface,* A. R. Michell and R. Ewbank, eds. Wheathampstead, Herts: UFAW.

Molony, V., J. E. Kent, and I. J. McKendrick. 2002. Validation of a method for assessment of an acute pain in lambs. *Applied Animal Behaviour Science* 76:215–238.

Paul, E. S. 2000. Empathy with animals and with humans: Are they linked? *Anthrozoös* 13:194–202.

Paul, E. S., and A. L. Podberscek. 2000. Veterinary education and students' attitudes towards animal welfare. *Veterinary Record* 146:269–272.

Pifer, L., K. Shimizu, and R. Pifer. 1994. Public attitudes toward animal research: some international comparisons. *Society and Animals* 2:95–113.

Preece, R., and D. Fraser. 2000. The status of animals in Biblical and Christian thought: A study in colliding values. *Society and Animals* 8:245–263.

Public health care policy on humane care and use of laboratory animals. 1986. Bethesda, MD: Department of Health and Human Services.

Regan, T. 1983. *The case for animal rights.* Berkeley: University of California Press.

Report of the AVMA Panel on Euthanasia. 1993. *Journal of the American Veterinary Medical Association* 202(2):229–240.

Rollin, B. E. 1992. *Animal rights and human morality.* 2nd ed. Buffalo, NY: Prometheus Books.

Rollin, B. E. 1995. *Farm animal welfare: Social, bioethical and research issues.* Ames: Iowa State University Press.

Rowan, A. 1989. The development of the animal protection movement. *The Journal of NIH Research* 1 (Nov.–Dec.):97–100.

Russell, W. M. S., and R. L. Burch. 1959. *The principles of humane experimental technique.* London: Methuen.

Singer, P. 1990. *Animal liberation.* New York: Random House.

Spinka, M. 2006. How important is natural behaviour in animal farming systems? *Applied Animal Behaviour Science* 100:117–128.

Taylor, A. A., and D. M. Weary. 2000. Vocal responses of piglets to castration: identifying procedural sources of pain. *Applied Animal Behaviour Science* 70:17–26.

Thompson, P. B. 1998. *Agricultural ethics: Research, teaching, and public policy.* Ames: Iowa State University Press.

Thompson, P. B. 1999. From a philosopher's perspective. How should animal scientists meet the challenge of contentious issues? *Journal of Animal Science* 77:372–377.

Webster, A. J. F. 2001. Farm animal welfare: The five freedoms and the free market. *The Veterinary Journal* 161:229–237.

Wells, D. L., and P. G. Hepper. 1997. Pet ownership and adults' views on the use of animals. *Society and Animals* 5:45–63.

AAFCO Association of American Feed Control Officials. An organization that provides a mechanism for developing and implementing uniform and equitable laws, regulations, standards, and enforcement policies to regulate the manufacture, distribution, and sale of animal feeds.

AAFCO Dog or Cat Nutrient Profiles Nutritional standards on which nutritional adequacy statements are based.

AAFCO Feeding Trial Standards under which a dog or cat food must be tested to qualify for use in the AAFCO nutritional adequacy statement.

Abomasum The true glandular stomach in the ruminant.

Abscess Collection of pus in a cavity as the result of infection with microrganisms or as a response to embedded foreign material such as a splinter.

Accuracy The measure of reliability associated with an EPD. If little or no information is available, accuracies may range as low as 0.01. A high accuracy would be .99.

Active immunity Immunity to a disease developed by exposure to the disease or by receiving a vaccine for the disease.

Acute diseases Diseases that are sudden or severe in onset and effect on the animal.

Ad libidum Having feed available at all times.

Adaptation The sum of the changes an animal makes in response to environmental stimuli.

Additive gene action When the total phenotypic effect is the sum of the individual effects of the alleles.

Aggressive behavior Threatening or harmful behavior toward others of the same or different species.

Agribusiness The segment of agriculture that deals in sales and service to production agriculturists and consumers.

Agriculture The combination of science and art used to cultivate and grow crops and livestock and process the products. A person who practices agriculture is an agriculturist or agriculturalist. Agricultural is the adjective that refers to things used in, relating to, or associated with agriculture.

Agroforestry Land-use systems and practices using woody perennials on the same land as livestock and/or crops.

AI stud Company that markets semen from high-quality males.

Alleles One of two or more alternative forms of a gene occupying corresponding sites (loci) on homologous chromosomes.

Allergies Abnormal and damaging immune responses to a particular environmental substance to which the body has become overly sensitive.

All-in, all-out animal management Adding animals to a facility, such as a farrowing house, at the same time and then removing them at the same time.

Alveoli Spherical-shaped structures making up the primary component of the mammary gland. Consists of a lumen, which is surrounded by secretory cells that produce the milk, and myoepithelial cells, which contract to squeeze the milk out of the lumen into the mammary gland ducts.

Airsacculitis Inflammation of the air sacs, often due to infection with a disease-causing microorganism.

American Standard of Perfection A Standard published in book form by the American Poultry Association. It lists the recognized breeds and varieties of poultry and their characteristics.

Anaerobic Conditions that lack molecular oxygen.

Anemia Disease state in which the number of red blood cells in an animal's blood are abnormally decreased.

Anestrus Period of time when a female is not having estrous cycles.

Aneuploidy A condition where an organism has a chromosome number that is not an exact multiple of the monoploid (m) number.

Animal breeding The use of biometry and genetics to improve farm animal production. The science of using the principles of genetics to make improvement in a livestock species.

Animal health The study and practice of maintaining animals as near to a constant state of health as is possible and feasible.

Animal rights movement A political and social movement that concerns itself with philosophy, sociology, and public policy as each deals with the standing of animals in relation to human society.

Animal science The combination of disciplines that together comprise the study of domestic animals. Animal science has traditionally been associated only with livestock species. However, the expanded interests of the population have caused an expansion of animal science to include additional domestic species, chiefly those in the pet and companion animal classification.

Animal welfare Concern for an animal's treatment and well-being while it is being used to provide for human needs. Humane use of animals.

Angora A specialized fiber-producing breed of goat.

Anorexia Inappetence or unwillingness to eat.

Anthropomorphism Attributing human thoughts, emotions, and characteristics to animals.

Antibodies Proteins produced by the body that attack infectious agents and neutralize them.

Antibiotic   A drug used to treat infection caused by bacteria or other microorganisms.

Antimicrobial agent   Natural or synthetic drugs which inhibit or kill bacteria. This capability makes them unique for controlling infectious diseases caused by pathogenic bacteria.

Applied ethology   The study of domestic animal behavior.

Applied or production nutritionist   A practical production-oriented nutritionist. A basic nutritionist might discover that compound X improves rate of growth. An applied nutritionist would work on practical questions such as cost effectiveness, method of delivery, carcass effects, and so on.

Aquaculture   The farming of aquatic organisms including fish, mollusks, crustaceans, and plants in fresh water, brackish water, or salt water.

Artificial insemination   The procedure for placing semen in the reproductive tract of a female animal through means other than the natural mating act in the hopes of causing a pregnancy. Commonly used in animals.

Artificial selection   The practice of choosing the animals in a population that will be allowed to reproduce.

Artificial vagina (AV)   Device used to collect semen from a male. Following erection, the penis is directed into the artificial vagina and the male ejaculates, depositing the ejaculate in a reservoir of the AV.

Ash   The incombustible residue remaining after complete combustion at 500–600°C of a sample, such as feed, animal tissue, or excreta to remove the organic matter. Considered to be the mineral matter of a feed.

Atresia   The degeneration of follicles that do not make it to the mature, or Graafian, stage. The majority of follicles in the ovary undergo atresia.

Auditory   Related to hearing.

Autosomes   All chromosomes other than the sex chromosomes.

Aversive event   A negative experience that may be painful, frightening, or nauseating. It may even involve the senses, such as a foul taste or odor or a sound like that made by a can full of rocks when tossed to the floor near a misbehaving puppy.

Avian   Pertaining to poultry and/or fowl.

Babcock Cream Test   Test for determining the fat content in milk.

Baby boomer   Demographic term for the U.S. population born between 1946 and 1964. The U.S. Census estimates there are nearly 83 million boomers.

Backfat   The subcutaneous fat on an animal's back. For hogs, backfat is highly correlated to total body fat and is often measured and used as a means of selecting lean brood stock.

Baitfish   Fish selected and produced to be used as bait for catching larger fish.

Balance trial   A type of metabolism trial designed to determine the retention of a specific nutrient in the body.

Bantam   Fowl that are miniatures of full-sized breeds. Some are distinct breeds. Usually a fourth to a fifth the weight of standard birds. Considered ornamental.

Barrow   A castrated male hog.

Barter   Trading services or commodities for one another.

Bases   One of the four chemical units on the DNA molecule that form combinations that code for protein manufacture. The four bases are adenine (A), cytosine (C), guanine (G), and thymine (T).

Basic breeder   In poultry production, a unit that produces parent stock used for multiplication of poultry, either by outcrossing, inbreeding, or other methods. Also referred to as *primary breeder*.

Basic nutritionist   A person interested in elucidating basic metabolism and nutrient action and interaction. Basic science in any discipline is necessary if practical implications are to be discovered. Think of basic science as the acquisition of knowledge for the sake of knowledge.

Beef cycle   Historic fluctuations in beef cattle numbers, which occur over roughly 10-year periods.

Behavioral ecology   The study of the relationships between a species' behavior and its environment.

Biofuel   Fuel derived from biological materials such as crops and animal waste.

Biometry   The application of statistics to topics in biology.

Biopsy   Surgical removal and examination (usually microscopic examination) of a tissue from a living body to reach a diagnosis.

Biosecurity   Procedures designed to minimize disease transmission from outside and inside a production unit.

Biotechnology   A collective set of tools and applications of living organisms (or parts of organisms) to make or modify products, improve plants or animals, or develop microorganisms for specific uses. Much of the recent innovation associated with biotechnology has been brought about by the tools of recombinant DNA technology.

Bitch   A female dog.

Blastocyst   More differentiated embryo consisting of an inner cell mass, blastocoele, and trophoblast.

Blended fisheries   A combination of aquaculture and capture fisheries. Aquaculture techniques are used to enhance or supplement capture fisheries.

Bloat   Abnormal quantities of gas collecting in the fermentative portion of the digestive tract. Can be life threatening.

Blood spots   Small spots of blood inside an egg, probably caused by blood vessels breaking in the ovary or oviduct during egg formation.

Boar An intact male hog. Boars are kept only for breeding purposes. Boar meat has a characteristic unpleasant taste.

Body condition The amount of fat on an animal's body.

Bolus A rounded mass that is ready to swallow. In the ruminant, a bolus may stay intact and be regurgitated to be remasticated during rumination.

Bomb calorimeter A device into which a substance can be placed and ignited under a pressurized atmosphere of oxygen. An insulated water jacket surrounds the "bomb" portion where the ignition takes place. By measuring the change in the temperature of the water, the amount of energy in the substance can be determined. Energy values for solids, liquids, or gases can be determined.

Book Refers to the number of females scheduled to be mated to a particular male.

Bottle Jaw Condition in which fluid accumulates and causes a swelling, under the jaw, especially in cattle, sheep or goats. It is often due to protein loss caused by severe parasitism.

Bovine somatotropin (BST) Growth hormone in cattle. Produced and secreted by the anterior pituitary gland, BST acts on various target tissues throughout the body. One of the primary mechanisms by which BST works is through a second hormone, insulin-like growth factor-1 (IGF-1). In cattle, BST increases milk production dramatically, presumably by increasing nutrient availability to the secretory cells, or by increasing the production of milk components directly.

Breed Animals with common ancestry that have distinguishable, fixed characteristics. When mated with others of the breed, they produce offspring with the same characteristics.

Breeding complementarity When the characteristics of different breeds complement each other in cross-breeding systems.

Breeding soundness exam Examination to determine the physical capacity of an individual to breed.

Breeding value The worth of an individual as a parent.

Breeds Revolution Period of great expansion in numbers of breeds of beef cattle in the United States.

British breeds Hereford, Angus, and Shorthorn; breeds of cattle that originated in England.

Broiler A chicken of either sex produced and used for meat purposes. Generally slaughtered at 6 weeks of age or younger. The term *fryer* is often used interchangeably.

Broiler duckling, also fryer duckling A young duck usually under 8 weeks of age of either sex. It must have a soft bill and weigh from 3 to $6\frac{1}{2}$ lbs.

Brood A group of baby chickens or other poultry or birds. As a verb, it can also refer to the growing of baby chicks.

Brooder A device with controlled heat and light used to warm chicks from the day of hatch to approximately 5 weeks of age. The heat is usually contained in a large reflector or hover under which the birds congregate.

Broodiness When a hen stops laying eggs and prepares to sit on the eggs to incubate them. Once the eggs hatch, the hen will care for them. Such hens are referred to as being *broody.*

Brooding The act of raising young poultry under environmentally controlled conditions during the first few weeks of life.

Broodstock Animals kept for reproductive purposes.

Browse The tender twigs and leaves from brush and trees.

Buck Term used for both an intact male rabbit and an intact male goat.

Calorie A measurement of food energy. A kilocalorie is the amount of heat required to raise the temperature of 1 gram of water 1°Celsius, from 14.5 to 15.5°C. About 4.2 joules.

Cancer Group of diseases caused by uncontrolled cell division that leads to abnormal growth of tissues often resulting in the formation of masses or tumors.

Candling Inspection of the inside of an intact egg with a light to detect defects. Incubating eggs can also be tested for dead germs and infertile eggs.

Capital requirements In this context, a combination of the capital required to integrate sufficiently to target a large enough market segment.

Capture fisheries The term used to designate the harvesting of wild aquatic animal species.

Carbohydrates Chemically defined as polyhydroxy aldehydes or ketones, or substances that can be hydrolyzed to them.

Carnivore Animals that subsist on meat.

Casein The major protein of milk.

Case-ready product A business system in which centrally prepared meats and meat items are used to increase consumer satisfaction and related profits.

Cash crop A crop grown specifically with the intent of marketing its product.

Cecotrophs Large soft pellets of cecally fermented feed, which move through the colon in a distinctly different manner than feces and are reconsumed for upper digestive tract digestion.

Cecotrophy A process in which hard fecal material is expelled from the large intestine. The cecum contracts and expels its contents, which are subsequently covered with mucus. These mucus-covered, soft fecal pellets are propelled through the large intestine by peristaltic action and consumed by the animal directly from the anus.

Cellulase An enzyme that specifically attacks and digests cellulose. Mammals do not make cellulases but some microorganisms do.

Cellulose A carbohydrate composed of thousands of glucose molecules that forms the support structure of plants.

Centrally planned economy   An economy under government control. Prices, labor, and other economic inputs are controlled and are not allowed to fluctuate in accordance with supply and demand.

Centromere   The region of a chromosome where spindle fibers attach.

Charles Darwin   An English naturalist (1809-1882). Among other contributions, he proposed the theory of evolution by natural selection.

Chick   A young chicken or gamebird of either sex from 1 day old to about 5 to 6 weeks of age.

Chromosome   The DNA-containing structures in cells. Composed of segments called genes.

Chronic   Continuing over a long period or having a gradual effect.

Chyme   The mixture of food, saliva, and gastric secretions as it is ready to leave the stomach and move into the duodenum.

Civilization   In modern context, refers to what we consider a fairly high level of cultural and technological development. An important contribution of the cultural revolution that farming brought to the process of civilization was giving people the time and lifestyle that led to the development of written language, record keeping, and artistic endeavors.

Class   In poultry, a group of breeds originating in the same geographic area. Names are taken from the region where the breeds originated.

Classical conditioning   The type of conditioning the Russian physiologist Ivan Pavlov demonstrated, hence the name Pavlovian conditioning, in which a reflex-like response can be stimulated by a neutral stimulus. In Pavlov's studies, food (an unconditioned stimulus) produced a reflex-like response in dogs, namely salivation. He coupled the ringing of a bell (neutral stimulus) with the food. He was then able to use only the bell to produce the salivation.

Clinical infection   An infectious disease in which clinical signs of the disease are expressed. Clinical signs allow detection and identification of the disease.

Clinical sign   Observable difference in an animal's normal function or state of health that indicates the presence of a bodily disorder or disease. Examples are fever, weight loss, reduced performance, decreased appetite, depression, edema, or any other signs of disease.

Cloning   Process used to produce genetically identical copies of biological entities.

Closed herd   A herd into which no new animals are introduced.

Cock   A rooster aged 1 year or older.

Cockerel   A rooster less than 1 year old.

Codominance   Both alleles are expressed in the phenotype when present in the heterozygous state.

Coffin Bone   At the bottom-most bone of a horse's leg that is encased within the hoof.

Cold blooded   Animals that cannot control their own body temperature. Poikilotherm.

Colic   A broad term that means digestive disturbance. The major symptom of colic in horses is pain. Many things can cause colic, with parasites and infections the most likely causes. However, rapid changes in diet, overeating, moldy feed, lack of water, and eating of shavings or sawdust bedding are also causes. Considered the most prevalent, costly, and dangerous internal diseases of horses.

Colostrum   Specialized milk produced in the early days following parturition to provide extra nutrients and immune function to the young. Colostrum is higher in vitamins, minerals, and protein compared with normal milk, and generally carries antibodies to aid the young in developing an immune response against potential antigens.

Colt   A young male horse.

Companion animal   An animal to whom an owner has an intense emotional tie.

Comparative method of study   A systematic method of comparing the behavior of two or more species as a way of discovering the mechanism of behavior.

Comparative psychology   The study of the mechanisms controlling behavior, learning, sensation, perception, and behavior genetics in animals and making extrapolations to humans or other animals.

Complete diet   Diet formulated to meet all the nutritional needs of an animal.

Composite breed   A breed developed from two or more previously established breeds.

Compost   Decayed organic matter used for fertilizing and conditioning land.

Conception   When the sperm fertilizes the ovum.

Condensed milk   Milk with water removed and sugar added.

Conditioning   The learned response of an animal to a stimulus.

Conformation events   Term that usually refers to a competition in which an animal's conformation is judged.

Contagious   A disease capable of being transmitted from animal to animal.

Contemporary group   A group in which animals of a given sex and age, having similar treatment, are given an equal opportunity to perform.

Continuous eater strategy   Feeding strategy employed by many prey species as a mechanism of survival. They eat many small meals throughout the day and keep on the move throughout their range. Thus they are harder to stalk by predators, generally are more alert to danger, and can take instant flight. This leads to digestive tract modifications. For example, the horse has a small stomach in relation to body size because it doesn't need storage space for huge meals. Also, it does not have a gallbladder because it has food coming to the small intestine fairly continuously and has no need for large amounts of bile at any one time.

Contract grower Producers who contract with an organization to produce a product for a price determined through a contractual arrangement.

Contract integration When one firm from one industry phase contracts with a firm at an adjacent phase for products and/or services.

Coprophagy Eating feces.

Corpus luteum (CL) Structure resulting from the conversion of the follicle (after disruption) into a structure that is responsible for the production of progesterone for the support of pregnancy. If pregnancy is not detected, the corpus luteum undergoes lysis, allowing the female to initiate another estrous cycle (plural, *corpora lutea*).

Cortisol A hormone produced by the adrenal cortex. It is elevated during stress and has been used as a gauge for the degree of stress an animal is under.

Creep An area where young nursing animals can have access to starter feeds. Creep feeds are generally high-quality feeds made available to young animals.

Cria Baby llama.

Cribbing An undesirable behavior in horses in which they bite and/or hold on to objects such as posts, fences, feed troughs, stall doors, and so on. Thought to be brought on by boredom because of stabling or confinement in a small area.

Critical period Similar to *sensitive periods,* but with a more definite beginning and end.

Crossbreeding Mating animals of diverse genetic backgrounds (breeds) within a species.

Cross-fostering Moving young from their dam and placing them with another female for rearing.

Crude fiber In proximate analysis, the insoluble carbohydrates remaining in a feed after boiling in acid and alkali.

Crude protein An estimate of protein content obtained by multiplying the nitrogen content of a substance by a factor, usually 6.25. Both true protein and nonprotein nitrogen is included in the calculation, hence the use of the designation *crude.*

Cubed hay Hay that is forced through dies to produce an approximate 3-cm product of varying lengths.

Culture In this context, the set of occupational activities, economic structures, beliefs/values, social forms, and material traits that define human actions and activities.

Cutting event A competition in which a horse cuts one cow from the herd and holds the cow away from the herd. The horse must work the cow without assistance from the rider for $2^{1}/_{2}$ minutes.

Dairy product science The science of providing milk and milk products as food.

Darwin, Charles (1809–1882) English naturalist who published *On the Origin of Species by Natural Selection* in 1859, *The Variation of Animals and Plants Under Domestication* in 1868, and *The Descent of Man* in 1871. Among other things, he proposed the theory of evolution by natural selection.

Dead germs Embryos that have died.

Defecation The act of expelling fecal matter from the large intestine via the rectum or cloaca.

Defect Unacceptable deviation from perfection. Most defects are inherited.

Deglutition The act of swallowing. Passing material from the mouth through the esophagus to the stomach or first fermentation compartment.

Delaney clause Act that prohibited the addition of any substance to human food shown to cause cancer in any animal at any dose. It was a portion of the 1958 Food Additive Amendment.

Delmarva Geographic region comprised of Delaware, Maryland, and Virginia.

Denature In protein chemistry, to disrupt the structure of a native protein, causing it to lose its ability to perform its function. Denatured proteins are generally easier to digest because the enzymes can better attack the chemical bonds.

Desertification The degradation or destruction of the biological potential of land, leading to desert-like conditions.

Diabetes Mellitus Condition in which glucose absorption by cells of the body is inhibited due to decreased production of insulin by the pancreas or decreased response to insulin by body cells.

Diagnosis The process of determining the nature and severity of a disease; art of distinguishing one disease from another.

Diagnostician An expert on diagnosing disease.

Dichromat Ability to perceive only two colors.

Diet All of the feeds consumed by an animal, including water. One can describe the diet for a full year. The diet of the animal includes mixed pasture in the summer, alfalfa hay in the winter, and trace-mineralized salt year-round.

Differentiated product A value-added product with a brand name.

Digestibility A measure of the degree to which a feedstuff can be chemically simplified and absorbed by the digestive system of the body.

Digestion The physical, chemical, and enzymatic means the body uses to render a feedstuff ready for absorption.

Digestion trial An experimental tool used to determine the digestibility of a specific feedstuff, nutrient, or ration.

Digests Produced by enzymatic degradation of animal tissues. Used to flavor pet foods.

Diluter gene   A type of modifier gene that changes a base color to a lighter color.

Diploid   Having two sets of chromosomes as opposed to the one set found in gametes.

Direct causes of disease   Exposure to, or contact with, pathogens or other substances that cause a decrease in animal health.

Dirties   Eggs with dirt, fecal material, or other material on the shell.

Disease   State of being other than that of complete health. Disturbance of normal function of the body or its parts.

Diversified Farm   Farm with multiple income-generating enterprises.

DNA (deoxyribonucleic acid)   Chemically, a complex molecule composed of nucleotides joined together with phosphate sugars. Chromosomes are large molecules of DNA. Two strands are joined together in the shape of a double helix. The sequence of the nucleotides in a segment of the chromosome called a gene determines the characteristics of the organism.

DNA polymerase   The enzyme that forms the sugar-phosphate bonds between adjacent nucleotides in a chain so that replication can occur.

DNA replication   The cellular process of making a copy of a DNA molecule.

Doe   A female goat; a female rabbit.

Dolly   A normal Finn Dorset sheep who also happened to be the first clone of an adult mammal. Cloning an adult animal was thought to be impossible before Dolly was developed. She was created by a research team led by Dr. Ian Wilmut at the Roslin Institute in Scotland. Since Dolly was born, adult mice and cattle have been cloned.

Domestic animals   Those species that have been brought under human control and have adapted to life with humans. Individuals in some species can be tamed, but have not necessarily been domesticated, such as species of exotic birds, elephants, and big cats. In general, domestic species must be able to adapt to a wide range of physical environments, must adapt to the changes that humans make in their immediate environment (artificial environment), and must respond to selection for some specialized need of humans.

Dominance   In behavior, an animal's place in the social ranking. The most dominant animal in the group exerts the major influence over other animals. A term often used to describe this is *pecking order.*

Dominant   When one member of an allele pair is expressed to the exclusion of the other.

Dorsal   The back on an animal.

Downer cow   Nonambulatory cow.

Draft   To move loads by drawing or pulling. A draft animal is one that is used to draw or pull loads.

Draft animal   An animal whose major purpose is to perform work that involves hauling or pulling. An oxen or horse pulling a plow or wagon is a draft animal.

Dressage   A competition in which horses are required to perform highly advanced maneuvers in a specified pattern. This competition may be held alone or may be part of a three-day event.

Dry matter   Everything in a feed other than water.

Drylot   A confined area generally equipped with feed troughs, automatic watering devices, shelter, and working facilities where animals are fed and managed.

Duodenum   The first segment of the small intestine. Many important digestive secretions enter the small intestine here.

Dystocia   Difficulty in birthing.

Economy of size   A relatively simple concept revolving around the maximization of the use of equipment, labor, and other costly items. Example: An owner of two poultry houses will need a tractor and spreader to clean the houses and spread the litter. However, if he or she builds two more houses, one tractor will probably suffice. The cost of owning the tractor can now be spread over the production of four houses rather than two.

Electric prods   Small handheld devices designed to give a small electrical shock. Used to keep animals moving in a chute or other handling situation. A poor substitute for good facilities and knowledge of animal handling technique.

Electronic pasteurization (e-beams)   Ionizing radiation from a focused beam of energy created by the acceleration of electrons using magnetic and electric fields.

Embryo cloning   The splitting of one embryo to produce many offspring.

Embryo transfer   Collecting the embryos from a female and transferring them to a surrogate for gestation.

Emerging pathogen   Pathogen that has mutated to become more virulent and/or has only recently been recognized as a safety issue.

Endemic   Commonly occurring or widespread within a herd or other group.

Ensiling   Glands that secrete hormones or other products directly into the blood. Hormones secreted by endocrine glands have a wide range of effects in maintaining normal body functions.

Ensiling   The process of producing silage from forage. High-moisture forage is stored under anaerobic conditions and allowed to ferment. The acids produced by the fermentation preserve the feed.

Enzymes   Proteins capable of catalyzing reactions associated with a specific substrate.

EPD (expected progeny difference)   A value equal to half the breeding value for an animal.

Epidemiology   Medical service that involves the study of the incident distribution of diseases in large population and conditions influencing the spread and severity of diseases.

Epididymis Duct connecting the testis with the ductus deferens. Responsible for sperm storage, transport, and maturation. It consists of a head, body, and tail.

Episodic The pulsatile manner in which the gonadotropic hormones are secreted by the anterior pituitary gland. Controlled by the pulse-generating center of the brain.

Epistasis Interaction among genes at different loci. The expression of genes at one locus depends on alleles present at one or more other loci.

Equine Pertaining to horses.

Eructation Belching. Removing gas from the rumen via the esophagus.

Erythrocytes Red blood cells.

Essential amino acids Those amino acids required by the body that must be consumed in the diet.

Essential fatty acids Fatty acids required in the diet.

Estrous cycle The time from one period of sexual receptivity in the female (estrus or heat) to the next.

Estrus The period when a female is receptive to mating. Synonymous with *heat.*

Ether extract In proximate analysis, the portion of a sample that is removed by extraction with a fat solvent such as ethyl ether.

Ethogram A catalog or inventory of all of the behaviors an animal exhibits in its natural environment. Originally this was the study of only wild animals, but domestic species are also studied in their surroundings. These studies are used to compare species.

Ethology The study of animals in their natural surroundings. The focus is on instinctive or innate behavior. When practiced on domestic species, especially livestock, it is often referred to as *applied ethology.*

Etiology The factor that causes a disease or the study of the factors that cause disease.

Eutrophication Promotion of excess growth of one organism to the disadvantage of other organisms in the ecosystem.

Ewe A female sheep.

Exotic fowl Nonindigenous, nonlivestock species often kept for ornamental reason. Examples include peacocks and various ornamental pheasants such as Melanistic Mutant Pheasant and Lady Amherst Pheasant.

Expected progeny difference (EPD) A prediction of the performance of an individual's progeny compared to all contemporaries for the progeny.

Expression In genetics, the manifestation of a characteristic that is specified by a gene.

Extensive agriculture Agriculture systems practiced in a manner that spreads human time and attention across vast acreages and/or large numbers of animals.

Extensive rearing systems Usually associated with range conditions in which hardy animals such as beef cattle receive little individual attention. They may be handled only once or twice per year.

F_1 Two-breed cross animals.

Fancy In the rabbit and pet industries, the segment associated with exhibitions and shows.

Farmer Anyone who practices agriculture by managing and cultivating livestock and/or crops.

Farrow In swine, the term used to indicate giving birth.

Fats One of a class of biomolecules called lipids. Lipids are substances that are insoluble in water but are soluble in organic solvents. Chemically, fats are triacylglycerides, which are composed of the alcohol glycerol, with three fatty acids attached.

Feed Foods used to feed animals.

Feed conversion ratio Amount of feed needed to produce 1 lb of gain or other product such as milk or eggs. A 3:1 ratio means that three units of feed are needed to produce one unit of gain. The smaller the ratio, the better.

Feed efficiency Product (grain, milk, eggs, and so on) per unit of feed.

Feeder pig Generally thought of as a pig weighing between 30 and 90 lbs. There is some regional difference in this range.

Feeding trial A comparatively simple experimental tool in which animals are fed to determine their performance on specific feeds or substances added to feeds.

Feedstuff Any substance that is used as animal feed. Corn, salt, prairie hay, and silage are examples.

Filly A young female horse.

Fingerlings A juvenile stage in fish. Fish usually from 1 to 6 inches long.

Finishing (phase) The final feeding stage when animals are readied for market. Finishing was once synonymous with the term *fattening.* However, the emphasis on lean meat production has made the goals of this period broader.

First-limiting amino acid The first amino acid whose lack of availability in the diet restricts the performance of an animal.

Flehmen response Sexual behavior of the male of several species in which the male curls his upper lip and inhales.

Flight zone The distance which an animal is caused to flee from an intruder.

Flighty The tendency of an animal to take sudden flight when alarmed. Also called **mobile alarm.** May be used to describe a breed or strain (i.e., Salers are more flighty than Herefords). It can also be used to describe individual animals (i.e., Bossy is more flighty than Big Bess). A type of temperament.

Flock A group of sheep.

Flocking instinct   A type of shelter-seeking behavior that has been selected for in sheep. At the least hint of danger, they move close together and move as a group. This can allow one person and a dog to shepherd a few thousand sheep.

Flushing   Feeding extra feed to stimulate estrus and ovulation rates.

Foal   A newborn horse of either sex. The term is sometimes used up to the time of weaning, after which *colt* and *filly* are more likely to be used.

Foaling   To foal. Parturition in the horse.

Follicle-stimulating hormone   Gonadotropic hormone responsible for growth, development, and maintenance of follicles in females, and the production of sperm in males. Produced and secreted by the anterior pituitary gland in a pulsatile manner in response to GnRH.

Food and Agricultural Organization of the United Nations (FAO)   The largest autonomous agency within the United Nations. FAO works to alleviate poverty and hunger by promoting agricultural development. It offers development assistance; collects, analyzes, and disseminates information; and consults with governments on policy and planning issues and provides an international forum for debate on food and agricultural issues.

Food-size fish   Fish that are grown commercially for food, usually ranging from 3/4 to 1 lb and over 12 inches in length.

Forage   Fiber-containing feeds like grass or hay. Can be grazed or harvested for feeding. Contain at least 18% fiber but are have high digestible energy (>70%).

Forestomachs   The name given to the three digestive compartments of the ruminant tract that are placed anatomically before the true stomach.

Fowl   Any bird, but generally refers to the larger birds. In this context, it refers to poultry species only.

Freemartin   Condition in cattle in which the female-born twin to a bull is infertile because of improper development of the female anatomy.

Fresh-packaged product   Traditional fresh product sold with minimal processing.

Fry   Fish in the postlarval stage.

Fryer rabbit   A rabbit of approximately 5 lbs and no older than 12 weeks of age. Some processors stipulate an age no older than 10 or 11 weeks.

Full-time equivalent   In referring to employment, a 40-hour equivalent position.

Functional foods   Enriched with nutrients that may not be inherent to the food.

Gait   Forward movement of a horse. The three natural gaits for most horses are the walk, trot, and canter or gallop. Some breeds have additional or different gaits such as the pace, foxtrot, running walk, rack, and others, and they are considered five-gaited.

Game birds   Fowl for which there is an established hunting season. Also refers to fighting chickens.

Game hen   A standard meat-type chicken packaged at a smaller size. Also called Rock Cornish game hen or Cornish game hen to reflect the influence of the Cornish breed in most of the chickens sold this way.

Gametes   Mature sperm in the male and the egg or ova in the female. The reproductive cells.

Gametogenesis   The formation of gametes.

Gander   A male goose.

Gastric ulcers   Area in which the inner lining of the stomach is lost and deeper layers are exposed to potential damage from stomach acid.

Gelding   A castrated male horse.

Gene   A short segment of a chromosome. Genes direct the synthesis of proteins or perform regulatory functions.

Gene frequency   The proportion of loci in a population that contain a particular allele.

Gene mapping   Mapping of genes to specific locations on chromosomes.

Genetically Modified Organism (GMO)   Any organism that has been modified by altering one or more genes using recombinant deoxyribonucleic acid (rDNA) technology.

Gene therapy   Transfering specific genes into mammalian cells with the goal of treating genetic disorders.

General combining ability   A term that describes a strain that contributes positively to the genetic makeup of offspring that result from mating it with several different strains.

Generation interval   In a herd, the average age of the parents when their offspring are born. Replacing breeding animals with their progeny can shorten generation intervals. Genetic progress is slowed when generation intervals are long, and hastened when the generation interval is shortened, presuming a sound selection program is being practiced.

Genetic code   The set of rules by which information encoded in genetic material (DNA or RNA sequences) is translated into proteins (amino acid sequences) by living cells.

Genetic correlation   The situation in which the same or many of the same genes control two traits.

Genetic drift   A change in gene frequency of a small breeding population owing to chance.

Genetic engineering   The term most frequently used to describe the technologies for moving genes from one animal or one species to another.

Genetic markers   Biochemical labels used to identify specific alleles on a chromosome.

Genetic testing   Process using a variety of laboratory techniques to determine if a person has, or is likely to get a genetic condition or disease.

Genetics   The science of heredity and the variation of inherited characteristics.

Genome The complete genetic material of an organism.

Genomics The study of how the genome (DNA) of any species is organized and expressed as traits.

Genotype The genetic makeup of an organism.

Genotypic frequency The frequency with which a particular genotype occurs in a population.

Gestation The period when the female is pregnant.

Ghee Clarified liquid butter.

Gilt Any female pig that has not yet given birth. Sometimes producers continue to use the term after the first litter is born and call a first-litter sow a first-litter gilt.

Gomer bull Bull rendered incapable of mating naturally that is used to detect cows in heat.

Gonads Sex organs; testis in male, ovary in female.

Grade up In animal species, the process of improving animals for some productive function by consecutive matings with animals considered to be genetically superior.

Grain-fed beef Meat from cattle that have undergone a significant grain feeding.

GRAS list A list of common food additives given special, safe status under the 1958 Food Additive Amendment because of their previous records as safe food additives.

Green Revolution Dramatic improvements in grain production in developing countries during the 1960s to the 1980s because of technological innovation and application.

Growth The process of adding tissues similar to those already present in the body to increase the size of an organism toward the goal of maturity when growth stops.

Guillain-Barré syndrome An inflammatory disease of the peripheral nerves characterized by weakness and often paralysis of the arms, legs, breathing muscles, and face.

Habituation learning A type of operant conditioning. It refers to an animal's ability to eventually ignore something that occurs often. A cat will ignore a collar after it has been on awhile. A horse will eventually ignore a train that passes by the stable or the pasture.

Hand One hand equals 4 inches. Horses are measured for height at the withers in hands.

Handling In this context, any manipulation necessary to care for or evaluate animals. It may or may not include physically touching them. Moving animals from pasture to pasture is handling of one type. Vaccinating, tagging, deworming, and so on, is more invasive handling.

Haploid A cell with half the usual number of chromosomes. Sex cells are haploid.

Hatching The process of a chick leaving the egg and emerging into the world. Birth for fowl.

Hazard Analysis and Critical Control Points (HACCP) A process control system designed to identify and prevent microbial and other hazards in food production.

Hemoglobin Oxygen-carrying pigment found in erythrocytes.

Hemolytic-Uremic Syndrome (HUS) A rare condition that mostly affects children under the age of 10; characterized by damage to the lining of blood vessel walls, destruction of red blood cells, and kidney failure.

Hen A mature female chicken or turkey.

Herbivore Animals that eat a diet of only plant material.

Herd or flock health management program A comprehensive and herd-specific program of health management practices.

Herd health program A comprehensive and herd-specific program of health management practices.

Heredity The transmission of genetic characteristics from parent to offspring.

Heritability A measure of the proportion of phenotypic variation that is caused by additive gene effects. The proportion of differences between individuals that is genetic.

Heterosis The superiority of an outbred individual relative to the average performance of the parent populations included in the cross.

Heterozygous When two genes in a pair are not the same.

Homologous chromosomes Chromosomes with the same size and shape, occurring in pairs, and affecting the same traits.

Homozygous When two genes of a pair are the same.

Horsepower Term that originated as a measure of the pulling power exerted by a horse. Technically equal to the rate of moving 33,000 lbs a distance of 1 foot in 1 minute.

Human-developed cat breed Breeds that have been developed from existing breeds or crosses of existing breeds.

Hunter under saddle At a horse show, an English division class in which movement and mannerisms are judged. Intended to depict a horse on the hunt chasing the hounds.

Hunter-gatherer Before agriculture, all people were hunter-gatherers. Hunter-gatherer peoples support their needs by hunting game, fishing, and gathering edible and medicinal plants.

Husbandry The combined animal care and management practices.

Hypothalamus Area of the brain responsible for many homeostatic functions. In reproduction, it is the region responsible for the production of GnRH, which is released into a specialized vasculature to the anterior pituitary gland. The hypothalamus is also responsible for producing oxytocin.

Ileum The last, short portion of the small intestine.

Impacted intestine Constipation in the horse and some other species.

Imprint learning Learning that has restrictive conditions and times when it can occur.

In vitro   In a test tube or other environment outside the body.

Inbred line   An established line of chickens created by intensive inbreeding. They are usually mated to other inbred lines to produce commercial varieties.

Inbreeding   Mating system in which mated individuals have one common ancestor appearing several times at least three to four generations back in the pedigree.

Inbreeding depression   A loss or reduction in vigor, viability, fertility, or production that usually accompanies inbreeding. The reverse of hybrid vigor.

Incomplete dominance   When neither allele is dominant to the other. Both influence the trait.

Incrossbred hybrid   Chickens developed by crossing inbred lines within the same breed. This technique is generally used to produce laying hens.

Incubation   The process of sitting on eggs by a hen to warm them with body heat so that the eggs develop into young. Can also be done artificially in an incubator.

Incubator   A machine that provides the environmental conditions that encourage embryonic development.

Individual cage   Small pens, perhaps 8 to 12 in. wide and 18 in. long, designed to hold one or more hens. Commercially, cages are arranged in rows with automatic watering devices and easy access to feed, and they are generally arranged so the eggs roll to an automated system of collection.

Infectious diseases   Diseases caused by living organisms, which invade and multiply in or on the body and result in damage to the body.

Infertile   An egg that is unfertilized or in which the embryo dies.

Inheritance   The transfer of gene-containing chromosomes from parent to offspring.

Intensive agriculture   Any agriculture system in which human attention and focus is directed to a small plot of land or to each animal.

Intensive systems   Animals produced in intensive systems are kept in more concentrated conditions, fed higher quality feeds, and have much more labor, technology, and overall attention directed to them.

Intravenous   Fluids and medications administered into a vein.

Involution   An organ's return to a normal state or normal size. Often used in describing the uterus after calving, or the mammary gland after completion of the lactation cycle.

Irradiated foods   Foods treated with ionizing pasteurization that kills insects, bacteria, and parasites.

Jejunum   The second and longest portion of the small intestine. The bulk of digestion and absorption of nutrients occurs in this segment.

Juvenile   Aquatic species between the postlarval stage and sexual maturity.

Kidding   Parturition in goats.

Kindling   Parturition in rabbits.

Kits   The young of some small mammals, including rabbits.

Kosher   Meat that is ritually fit for use as sanctioned by Jewish religious law.

Lactation   The process of producing milk.

Lactation curve   A plot of milk production over the life of the lactation period. Different species tend to have characteristic lactation curves.

Lactogenisis   The series of cellular changes during which mammary epithelial cells convert from the non-secretory state to the secretory state.

Lactose   Disaccharide comprised of one glucose unit attached to a lactose sugar. Made only by the mammary gland. Broken down by the enzyme lactase.

Lactose intolerance   Condition in humans where the lack of the enzyme lactase leads to stomach distress following milk consumption.

Lamb   A sheep under 1 year of age. Also, the meat from a sheep under 1 year of age.

Lambing   Parturition in sheep.

Laminitis   Commonly referred to as *founder*, an inflammation of the laminae of the hoof. It is commonly caused by overeating of grain but may also be related to eating lush pastures, to road concussion, to retained afterbirth in the mare, and to other causes.

Larva   The first stage after hatching. An independent, mobile, developmental stage between hatching and juvenile. The larva stage bears little resemblance to the juvenile or adult stage (plural, *larvae*).

Layer   A hen in the physiological state of producing eggs regularly.

Laying   Technically, the expulsion of an egg (i.e., "That hen is *laying* an egg"). However, commonly used to refer to hens in egg production (i.e., "Barn 12 is a *laying* hen barn").

Least-cost ration   A ration formulated to meet the animal's nutritional needs at the lowest cost from the feeds available.

Leporarium   Specially designed enclosure popular in Roman times for keeping rabbits and hares.

Lesion   Abnormal changes in body organs because of injury or disease.

Libido   Sexual drive.

Lignin   Polymers of phenolic acids found in plants as part of the structural components of the plant. Lignin is indigestible and can cause a decrease in the digestibility of the other fibers in the plant. Lignin generally increases as the plant ages.

Linebreeding   Mating system in which the relationship of an individual is kept close to an outstanding ancestor by having the ancestor appear multiple times on both sides of the pedigree.

Lipoproteins Compounds in the bloodstream that carry the lipids (fats) in the blood. Because lipids are not soluble in water, lipoproteins provide a special mechanism by which the lipids can carry fats from the intestines and liver to the peripheral parts of the body where they can be used as energy, or as building materials for cells. Made up of protein, fatty acids, cholesterol, and cholesterol esters, the lipoproteins exist as low-density lipoproteins (LDLs), very low-density lipoproteins (VLDLs), high-density lipoproteins (HDLs), and chylomicrons.

Literacy The ability to read and write.

Litter Material such as wood shavings, straw, or sawdust used to bed the floor of a poultry house.

Locus The specific location of a gene on a chromosome.

Long hay Hay that has not been chopped or ground; the individual forage.

Lordosis Posture assumed by females in estrus in response to pressure applied to the back.

Luteinizing hormone Gonadotropic hormone primarily responsible for providing the signal to disrupt the mature follicle in females, and the production of testosterone by the Leydig cells of the testes in the male. Produced and secreted by the anterior pituitary gland in a pulsatile manner in response to GnRH.

Luteolysis Breakdown or degeneration of the corpus luteum. Occurs at the end of the luteal phase of the estrous cycle if pregnancy is not detected.

Maiden In this context, a female who has never given birth.

Maintenance The nutritional needs of the animal exclusive of those required for a productive function such as growth, work, milk production, and so on.

Mare A mature female horse.

Marker-assisted selection Selection for specific alleles using markers such as linked DNA sequences.

Market economy Economies in which prices are freely determined by the laws of supply and demand.

Market gardening Specialized production of fruits, vegetables, or vine crops for sale.

Mash Finely ground and uniformly mixed feeds. Animals cannot separate feed ingredients; thus each bite provides all the nutrients in the diet.

Mastication The process of chewing.

Mastitis Inflammation of the mammary gland, most often caused by bacterial infection. Symptoms include redness, fever, and sloughing of white blood cells into the milk. Causes damage to the secretory cells and can be fatal if left unattended.

Maternal effect Any environmental influence that the dam contributes to the phenotype of her offspring. The contribution of the dam is environmental with respect to the calf (mothering ability, milk production environment, and maternal instinct). The genetics of the dam allow her to create this environment for her calf. Maternal effects are important during the nursing period but have diminishing effects postweaning.

Mature duck or old duck Ducks of either sex with toughened flesh and hardened bill. Their meat is used in processed products.

Mature goose or old goose A spent breeder whose meat is used in processed products.

Meat The flesh of animals used for food.

Meat science The science of handling, distributing, and marketing meat and meat products.

Meiosis The process that forms sex cells. Cells formed through meiosis have half the number of chromosomes of the parent cells.

Messenger RNA (mRNA) Nucleic acid that carries instructions to a ribosome for the synthesis of a particular protein.

Metabolism trial An advanced form of digestion trial that measures the body's use of nutrients.

Metabolic Relating to the biochemical processes that occur within a living organism, especially involving the breakdown of food and its transformation into energy.

Metric ton (MT) Approximately 1.1 U.S. tons. Equal to 1 million grams, or 1,000 kilograms.

Micturate The act of urinating.

Migration The process of bringing new breeding stock into a population.

Milk The normal secretion of the mammary glands of female mammals.

Minerals In nutrition, the specific set of inorganic elements thus far established as necessary for life in one or more animal species.

Mitosis The process of somatic cell division.

Mob A group or herd of goats.

Modifier gene Gene that influences the expression of another gene or genes.

Mohair The fiber produced by the Angora goat.

Molting The shedding of feathers by chickens. Usually egg laying is reduced or stops during molting.

Monoculture Producing only one crop or livestock species.

Monoestrus Exhibiting only one estrous cycle; for example, the bitch is seasonally monoestrus.

Monogastric Having only one stomach. A term used to differentiate between animals who have a rumen and those who do not. Some nutritionists prefer the term *nonruminant* rather than monogastric because even ruminants have only one true stomach. The additional "stomachs," or forestomachs, have very different functions than the true stomach has.

Monosomy   The absence of one chromosome from an otherwise diploid cell.

Morula   Early stage embryo, after cell division multiplies cell numbers in the zygote.

Mucous membrane   Cell layer covered in epithelial cells that both absorb and secrete.

Multiparous   A female that has had previous pregnancies and offspring.

Multiple alleles   Genes with three or more alleles.

Mustang   The term used to describe the feral horse of the American West. At one time, these were largely the descendants of the Spanish horses brought to this country beginning in 1600 to work the Spanish missions. Today, they are the descendants of many nondescript horses whose lineage and characteristics hardly compare with the original.

Mutations   Changes in the chemical composition of a gene.

Myoepithelial cells   Specialized muscle cells that surround the secretory cells of the alveoli and cause them to contract when stimulated by oxytocin.

Natural   As defined by the USDA, "a product containing no artificial ingredients or added color and is only minimally processed. Minimal processing means that the product was processed in a manner that does not fundamentally alter the product. The label must include the meaning of the term natural (such as 'no artificial ingredients; minimally processed')."

Natural breeds   Cat breeds selected by human preference or natural conditions specific to a region.

Natural selection   Selection based on factors that favor individuals better suited to living and reproducing in a given environment.

Necropsy   The examination of a body after death.

Nematode parasites   Nematodes are roundworms that are categorized in the phylum Nematoda. This is a very diverse group of organisms. Some of these worms are parasites, meaning that they survive by living inside of and gaining nutrients from another living organism, which is known as the host.

Nest box   A box provided for a rabbit doe in which to give birth and rear the young for their first few weeks. Also, a box provided for avian species to lay their eggs.

Net merit dollars   Index that includes feed costs, mastitis, milk quality costs, and productive life.

Net quantity statement   FDA required statement on a pet food package specifying the quantity of feed in the container.

Nitrogen-free extract (NFE)   In proximate analysis, a measure of readily available carbohydrates calculated by subtracting all measured proximate components from 100.

Nomadism   The practice of people without a permanent home base moving from place to place, generally in a pattern dictated by climate and/or season to find feed for their subsistence herds of livestock.

Nose tongs   Small clamp-like restraining device put in an animal's nose.

Novelty   Anything new or sudden in an animal's environment.

NPN   Non-protein nitrogen. Any nitrogen found in a feedstuff that is not part of a protein molecule.

Nucleotide   The building blocks of nucleic acids. Each nucleotide is composed of sugar, phosphate, and one of four nitrogen bases.

Nursery pig   Term often used to indicate an early-weaned pig of light weight that is housed in special, environmentally controlled nursery facilities. These pigs may be only 10–15 lbs when weaned and 14–28 days of age.

Nursing pig   A pig still nursing the sow.

Nutraceuticals   Products perceived to have both nutrient and pharmaceutical properties. Examples: Vitamins that are also antioxidants or omega-3 fatty acids that may protect against heart disease as well as supply fats in the diet.

Nutrient   A chemical substance that provides nourishment to the body. Essential nutrients are those necessary for normal maintenance, growth, and functioning.

Nutrient density   A measurement of the essential nutrients found in a food compared to the caloric content of the food.

Nutrient-dense food   A food that has a variety of nutrients in significant amounts. Meat has protein, vitamins, minerals, and other nutrients in good supply. On a per calorie basis, the consumer gets many nutrients.

Nutrition   The study of the body's need and mechanism of acquiring, digesting, transporting, and metabolizing nutrients.

Olfactory   Relating to the sense of smell.

Omnivore   Animals that eat both plant- and animal-based foods.

Oocyte   The gamete from the female.

Operant or instrumental conditioning   Learning that is primarily influenced by its effects. A positive or negative reward that either precedes or follows an act can induce an animal to repeat the act. Many types of learning fall under this category. B. F. Skinner did extensive early work in this area.

Optimal growth   When optimizing growth, such factors as cost of the ration, environment, labor, and other nonfeed inputs are considered. Sometimes optimal and maximal growth rates are the same. However, in a large number of practical production situations, they are different. For instance, a diet that maximizes growth may be too expensive to be economically feasible. A diet that produces 90% as much growth may do so in a more cost-effective way than the more expensive diet that maximizes growth. Thus, optimal growth may be 90% of maximal growth. Likewise, a growth promotant may help maximize growth. However, if the cost of the growth promotant is too high, the added gain will not pay for it.

Orgle The distinctive noise made by a male llama before and during mating.

Osteoporosis Disease in which bones are thinned with decreased mass and strength.

Outbreeding The process of mating less closely related individuals when compared to the average of the population.

Outcrossing The practice of mating unrelated breeds or strains.

Ovulation Release of the ovum or egg from the ovary.

Ownership integration An integrated operation that is under one ownership.

Oxytocin A small hormone produced in the hypothalamus and secreted by the posterior pituitary gland that stimulates contraction of muscle cells in the uterus to aid in parturition and stimulates contraction of the myoepithelial cells surrounding the alveoli to force milk out of the lumen into the mammary gland ducts.

Pacifier cow A cow that has been trained to accept moving, restraint, and other types of management. They are usually very tame and nonflighty. When mixed with less-conditioned cows, they facilitate handling of individuals or groups and have a calming influence on them. Especially useful for work in corrals and squeeze chutes.

Palatability The acceptability of a feed or ration to livestock. Influenced by taste, texture, form of the feed (whole or processed), dustiness, and several other factors, depending on the species.

Palpation Physically touching and examining with one's hands.

Papillae Small finger-like projections that greatly increase the surface area of the small intestine.

Parasite An organism that lives at the expense of a host organism. Generally must live on or in the host; a form of symbiosis.

Parent average The average predicted transmitting ability of the parents of a dairy cow.

Parturient paresis Metabolic disorder generally occurring within 72 hours of calving. Caused by low blood serum calcium level.

Parturition Process of giving birth.

Passive immunity Immunity conferred to an animal through preformed antibodies that it receives from an outside source. Antibodies are harvested from the mother's bloodstream by the mammary gland to put into colostrum as a means of conferring passive immunity to newborn mammals.

Pasteurization Controlled heating to destroy microorganisms.

Pastoralism Herding grazing animals.

Pathogen Any living disease-producing agent.

Pathogenicity The capability of an organism to produce disease.

Pathology The branch of medicine that deals with the essential nature of disease and the structural or functional changes that cause or are caused by disease. A pathologist is an expert in disease and disease processes.

Pelleting A method of processing feed in which the feed is first ground and then forced through a die to give it a shape. Pellets are generally well accepted by all classes of livestock.

Pellets Feeds that are generally ground and then compacted by forcing them through die openings.

Per capita Per unit of population.

Performance testing Evaluating an individual in terms of performance such as weight gain or milk production.

Peristalsis The progressive, squeezing movements produced by the contraction of muscle fibers in the wall of the digestive tract. The movements proceed in a wave down the length of the tract or some portion of it. The primary purpose of peristaltic action is to move material down the tract. However, it can also be used to mix the contents of the tract.

Pesticides Any agent or poison used to destroy pests, including fungicides, insecticides, herbicides, and rodenticides.

Pet An animal kept for pleasure rather than utility.

Pharming The production of pharmaceuticals from livestock or crops. Derived from the combination of "farming" and "pharmaceuticals." Gene *pharming* uses transgenic livestock to produce biologically active pharmaceuticals for human medicine.

Pharmacogenomics Branch of pharmacology that looks at how variation in human genetics leads to variation in response to drugs.

Phenotypic frequency The proportion of individuals in a population that express a particular phenotype.

Phenotypic value A measure of individual performance for a specific unit.

Phobia Excessive and unwarranted fear.

Physiology The study of the physical and chemical processes of an animal or any of the body systems or cells of the animal.

Pica A craving for and willingness to eat unnatural feedstuffs. Often caused by nutritional deficiencies.

Pig meat The meat from a hog. Synonymous with *pork*.

Pituitary gland Gland sitting directly below the hypothalamus. It is divided into the posterior pituitary gland and the anterior pituitary gland. The posterior pituitary releases oxytocin. The anterior pituitary produces and secretes several hormones, including luteinizing hormone, follicle-stimulating hormone, prolactin, and growth hormone.

Placenta   The organ that surrounds the fetus and unites it to the female while it develops in the uterus. Organ responsible for the exchange of oxygen, nutrients, and waste between the fetus and the mother. Derives from the trophoblast cells of the embryo.

Plumage   The total body feathering of poultry.

Points   The legs, mane, and tail of a horse. In other species, the head may be substituted for the mane.

Polyestrus   Exhibiting more than one estrous cycle.

Polymerase chain reaction   Molecular biology technique used to amplify specific DNA.

Polymerization   The process of building high molecular weight molecules by repeatedly chemically bonding the same compound to itself.

Polymorphism   The existence of two or more discontinuous, segregating phenotypes in a population.

Polyploidy   Condition in which the number of chromosomes an individual has is some multiple of the haploid number.

Population genetics   The study of how genes and genotypic frequencies change, and thus change genetic merit in a population.

Porcine stress syndrome   Genetic defect in which pigs are heavily muscled but have poor carcass quality and may die when subjected to stress.

Pork   The meat from a hog. In many parts of the world, the term *pig meat* is preferred.

Pork Quality Assurance Plus   A voluntary, multilevel, management education program for producers that was introduced by the National Pork Producers Council in 1989 as a tool to enhance the quality of pork sold to the world's consumers.

Posilac   Commercially available BST.

Possible change   The measure of the potential error associated with EPD values.

Postlarvae   In aquatic species, animals that are beyond the larval stage but are not yet a juvenile. They may resemble juveniles, but lack certain developmental characteristics of the juvenile.

Postpartum   After parturition.

Postpartum interval   Period of time from parturition to first estrus in the female.

Poult   Baby turkeys. Once sex can be determined, they are called young toms (males) or young hens (females).

Poultice   A soft, moist mass held between layers of cloth, usually warm, which is applied to some area of the body for therapeutic reasons.

Poultry   Domestic birds raised for eggs and meat. However, this designation has some flexibility. For example, most peafowl are kept for their ornamental plumage even though they produce eggs and can be eaten. Who would think of eating a swan? Included are the economically important species of chickens, turkeys, ducks, and geese, and those kept as hobbies, for sport, and for ornamental and aesthetic reasons. Includes ostriches, peafowl, pigeons, swans, guinea fowl, pheasants, and an assortment of other game birds.

Predicted transmitting ability   Half the breeding value.

Predicted transmitting ability net merit dollars   An economic index that measures relative lifetime profit of a dairy cow.

Predisposing causes of disease   Any condition or state of health that confers a tendency and/or susceptibility to disease.

Pregnancy disease   Also referred to as *pregnancy toxemia*. A form of ketosis in females that occurs in late pregnancy because the female cannot eat enough of the feed she is provided or is not provided enough feed. Usually occurs in cases of multiple fetuses. Common in sheep and goats.

Prehension   The act of seizing and grasping.

Prepotent   An animal that transmits its characteristics to its offspring in a consistent fashion.

Principle of independent assortment   Mendel's second law. It says that in the formation of gametes, separation of a pair of alleles is independent of the separation of other pairs.

Principle of segregation   Mendel's first law, often called the law of segregation. The law states that when gametes are formed, the genes at a given locus separate so that each is incorporated into different gametes.

Production   The general term that describes the output of usable products and services by animals.

Progesterone   Female sex steroid produced by the corpus luteum or the placenta. Has "progestational" effects, including suppression of gonadotropic secretion, decrease in uterine motility, and production of the cervical seal.

Prostaglandin   A group of fatty acid hormones, one of which is prostaglandin F2α, which breaks down the corpus luteum, allowing the female to return to estrus.

Protein   Compounds composed of combinations of alpha-amino acids.

Protein quality   A measure of the presence and digestibility of the essential amino acids in a feedstuff.

Proventriculus   The glandular stomach in fowl.

Puberty   Transitional state through which animals progress from an immature reproductive and hormonal state to a mature state. Varies with species, but timing primarily depends on age and weight.

Pullet   A young female chicken.

Purines and pyrimidines   Organic ring structures made up of more than one kind of atom (heterocyclic compounds). Purines and pyrimidines contain nitrogen in addition to carbon.

Pyometra Inflammation of the uterus leading to an accumulation of pus within the organ.

Qualitative traits Traits such as coat color for which phenotypes can be classified into groups.

Quality grade Scale that indicates quality and value of the carcass such as *prime, choice,* and so on.

Quantitative traits Those traits that are numerically measured and are usually controlled by many genes, each having a small effect. Examples are milk and egg production.

Queen A female cat.

Rabbitry A place where domestic rabbits are kept.

Rate of gain Pounds of gain per day over a specific period.

Ration The specific feed allotment given to an animal in a 24-hour period. For example, the animal's ration is 10 lbs of hay, 3 lbs of oats, 1.5 lbs of soybean meal, and trace mineral salt. The use of the term *ration* should be in conjunction with specific quantities of feed.

Recessive The member of an allele pair that is expressed only when the dominant allele is absent from the animal's genome.

Recipients Females used to carry the embryos of a donor animal throughout gestation.

Recombinant Bovine Somatotropin (rBST) Synthetic bovine growth hormone produced by recombinant DNA technology and given to dairy cows to increase milk production.

Recombinant DNA Combination of DNA molecules from different biological sources.

Recreational horses Horses of the light breeds kept for riding, driving, or nonprofessional racing and show.

Reformists Animal rights proponents who focus on changing methods of animal use.

Reining A competition in which horse and rider perform a specified pattern of advanced maneuvers. These include long sliding stops, spins (up to four 360° turnarounds at high speeds), rollbacks (180° turns after a sliding stop), and circles of different sizes.

Reliability A measure of accuracy in diary records.

Renewable resources Those resources that can be replaced or produced by natural ecological cycles or management systems.

Reproduction The combined set of actions and biological functions of a living being directed at producing offspring.

Resistance The natural ability of an animal to remain unaffected by pathogens, toxins, irritants, or poisons.

Resorption The loss of bone tissue through normal physiological means or through a pathological process.

Restriction enzyme Enzyme used to recognize a specific DNA sequence and cut it to produce DNA fragments.

Ribonucleic acid (RNA) Long chains of phosphate, ribose sugar, and several bases.

Ribosomes A component of cells that contains protein and tRNA. Ribosomes synthesize proteins.

Roaster chicken A young meat chicken, generally 12 to 16 weeks old, weighing 4–6 lbs.

Roaster duckling A young duck of either sex usually under 16 weeks of age. The bill must not have hardened completely.

Rooster A mature, male chicken. Also referred to as a *cock.*

Roughage A bulky feedstuff with low weight per unit volume. Contains at least 18% fiber but can range up to 50%. Less digestible than forages.

Rumen The largest of the ruminant forestomachs. Contains microorganisms that degrade complex carbohydrates and produce volatile fatty acids, amino acids, and vitamins to the host animal.

Ruminal bloat More correctly called *ruminal tympany.* An overdistention of the rumen and reticulum with the gasses of fermentation. Commonly referred to as *bloat.*

Ruminal tympany See *ruminal bloat.*

Ruminant Hooved animals that have a rumen and chew their cud.

Rumination The process in ruminants where a cud or bolus of rumen contents is regurgitated, remasticated, and reswallowed for further digestion.

Saddle seat pleasure An English event in which the horse's movement and mannerisms are judged.

Salivation The elaboration of the mixed secretion (saliva) produced primarily in three bilateral pairs of glands in the mouth known as salivary glands.

Saturated fats Fatty acids that are completely saturated with hydrogens, and thus do not contain any hydrogen bonds.

Savanna Tall-grass vegetation belts in the hot areas of the world. The same zone found in temperate zones is referred to as *prairie.*

Scientific literacy The minimum knowledge necessary to stay abreast of further scientific developments and innovation.

Sclera The tough white outer coat of the eyeball.

Seasonal market A time of the year when there is increased demand for a product.

Seasonally polyestrus When an animal has repeated estrous cycles but only in response to some environmental factor associated with the seasons, such as the photoperiod.

Secondary enterprise In diversified farming operations, the enterprise secondary to the one providing the bulk of the income.

Secondary sex characteristics Characteristics that differentiate the sexes from each other; occur most profoundly during and after puberty because of changes in hormonal concentrations occurring during puberty. Examples in males include such things as humps on the necks of bulls, beards on men, increased musculature in the males of most species, changes in the sound of vocalization (voice change in boys that happens at puberty). For females, includes the many characteristics lumped together that we refer to as femininity: added body fat, which creates curves where angles were once visible, mammary development, smoother hair coats, and so on. Behavioral characteristics such as "marking" territory or aggression in males are also part of the complex.

Secretory cells   The functional units of the alveoli that absorb nutrients, make the milk components, and transport the milk into the lumen of the alveoli.

Seedstock   Broodstock intended for future production.

Selection   The process of allowing some animals to be parents more than others.

Selection differential   The phenotypic advantage of those chosen to be parents. The difference in the mean of those chosen to be parents and the mean of the population.

Self-sufficient   Providing for one's own needs.

Semen   Fluid from the male that contains sperm from the testes and secretions from several other reproductive organs.

Sensitive periods   Times in an animal's life when certain types of learning are more easily accomplished. For example, imprinting behavior between the mother and offspring has a sensitive period near birth. Closely related, but more specific, is the term *critical period*. The critical period for imprinting in species X may be the first hour after birth. The critical period for puppy socialization is 3–12 weeks.

Sentient   Animals that experience pain and pleasure.

Septicemia   Invasion of the blood stream by virulent microorganisms from a focus of infection.

Setting   Placing eggs to incubate. A setting hen is a broody hen that is incubating eggs.

Sex-influenced traits   The same genotype is expressed differently depending on the sex of the animal.

Sex-limited traits   Traits expressed in one sex or the other, such as milk production in females. Both sexes carry genes for the trait.

Sex-linked cross   Sex-linked chicks can be sexed at birth by their color. Males are one color and females are another color or color pattern.

Sex-linked inheritance   Traits inherited on the X or Y chromosome and therefore inherited only when that respective chromosome is passed on.

Sheep   An animal of the genus *Ovis* that is over 1 year of age.

Shelf life   The period of freshness and wholesomeness of food items. In poultry, the length of time fresh-dressed, iced, packed poultry can be held without freezing.

Shelter-seeking behavior   Overall, behaviors that an animal exhibits to escape from weather, insects, or danger. It may include crowding together for warmth and protection, standing close to cedar trees for their insect-repelling properties, or standing head-to-tail as horses often do to swish away flies from each other's faces.

Show pigs   Pigs bred for exhibition, usually by 4-H and FFA students.

Silo   Structure in which silage is made and stored.

Singleton   An offspring born singly.

Single-trait selection   Selection for only one trait or characteristic.

Sire summary   Genetic information published on sires available within a breed.

Slash-and-burn agriculture   The practice of clearing a plot of land from the forest by cutting the trees and shrubs and then burning them. The ash from the burning fertilizes the soil. The practice has gained an undeserved bad reputation in modern times because it is poorly understood. Practiced as it has been for centuries on small rotating plots in remote, tropical areas, it has the long-term effect of preserving the forest and being a very sustainable system.

Small grains   Such grains as oats, wheat, and barley.

Social structure   The organization of a group. The patterns of the relationships of one to another.

Sociobiology   The study of the biological basis of social behavior. Especially of interest is behavior that helps pass the gene pool on to the next generation.

Somatic cells   All cells in the body other than gametes.

Sow   Female pig that has given birth.

Spat   For shellfish such as oysters, the developmental stage when they settle down and become attached to some hard object.

Spawn   To produce eggs, sperm, or young.

Specialty market   A term that suggests that a product is generally aimed at a specific segment of the overall market.

Speciesism   Placing the interests of one's own species above those of another species. This term was coined by Richard D. Ryder, a British psychologist.

Specific combining ability   When a strain only contributes positively to a cross when mated with certain, specific other lines.

Sperm   The gamete from the male.

Spontaneous mutation   A change in the DNA that creates new alleles.

Squeeze chute   A restraining device used to handle livestock. Consists of a head gate to catch the animal's head and side panels that can be adjusted to restrict the animal's movement. Used to contain the animal for management procedures like deworming and artificial insemination.

Stadium jumping   A competition in which horses jump a course of fences (jumps) in a specified order. In the first round of competition, the event is scored on a mathematical basis. Horses that receive a perfect score compete in a timed jumpoff to determine the winner.

STAGES Swine Testing and Genetic Evaluation System. A series of computer programs that analyzes performance data of purebred swine and their crossbred offspring.

Stallion A mature, male horse that is not castrated. Castrated male horses are *geldings*.

Steppes Short-grass vegetation zones. Steppe vegetation accounts for most of the land area of the world devoted to range livestock production.

Stereotyped behaviors A nonfunctional, repetitive, and intentional behavior. Stall walking, weaving, and pawing are examples in horses. Often the behaviors are rhythmic. Stalled horses often develop them in response to boredom, lack of exercise, and infrequent pasture time. Weavers appear to walk in place. Stall walkers or pacers walk or trot in a fixed pattern. This may be a line or sometimes a circle. Some incorporate a head toss at specific points. Caged primates, kenneled dogs, and caged, large carnivores also sometimes develop similar behaviors for similar reasons.

Sternal recumbancy Mating position in the llama and alpaca. The female lies on the ground with her legs under her and her belly on the ground.

Stock horse Any horse of the light breeds trained and used for working livestock, mainly cattle.

Stocker calf Weaned calf being grown prior to placement in a feedlot for finishing.

Stocker fish Fish usually 6–12 inches in length that weigh less than 3/4 lb.

Stocking The practice of placing fish from a hatchery or other source into a pond or lake to either establish a new species or augment an already existing species.

Stover The part of the plant left over after grain harvest.

Strain Families or breeding populations within a breed. They have been more rigorously selected for some trait or set of traits than the average of the breed.

Strain cross Mating different strains of the same breed and variety. Generally, the strains have been inbred to some degree and selected for different strengths to get increased production in the offspring.

Strategic alliances Partnerships between various independent segments of an industry to maximize cooperation, value, and return on investment.

Stress A physical, emotional, or chemical factor causing body or mental strain or tension. Coping with stress is a natural part of life. However, excessive amounts of stress can cause the body to suffer distress in which the body can undergo extensive, detrimental changes. Excessive stress is a contributing factor to disease.

Stud A unit of male animals kept for breeding. Also a term for a stallion.

Stud book The set of records a breed association keeps on the animals registered with it.

Subclinical No readily observable clinical signs associated with disease exist.

Submissive behavior Behaviors that a less-dominant animal exhibits toward a more-dominant animal to prevent being subjected to aggression.

Subtherapeutic Quantities too low to treat disease.

Survival of the fittest Natural selection. A process whereby those best equipped for the conditions in which they are found survive and pass their genetic material on to the next generation.

Sustainable agriculture Agriculture that meets the needs of the present generation without jeopardizing the ability of further generations to meet their own needs and without limiting their choices.

Symbiotic relationship (symbiosis) A relationship in which dissimilar organisms live together or in close association. If the relationship is beneficial to both, it is referred to as *mutualism*. Rumen microorganisms and ruminants share a mutualistic form of symbiosis.

Taboo A prohibition imposed by social custom against some action or object. Frequently found as part of religious codes and laws.

Teasing Placing a stallion and a mare in proximity to each other and observing the mare's actions. Mares that are coming into heat display specific behaviors. Signs of estrus in mares include winking of the vulva, urination, squatting, and seeking the stallion. Mares that are not in heat will either not respond or will respond in a negatively aggressive way to the stallion.

Temperament Characteristic behavior or mode of response. Long-term temperament for an individual generally stabilizes after the animal reaches sexual maturity.

Testcross Mating with a fully recessive tester animal to determine if an individual is homozygous or heterozygous.

Testosterone Male steroid sex hormone. Derived from cholesterol in the testes.

3 Rs Acronym for *replacement* (substitute something else for higher animals), *reduction* (reduce the number of animals needed), and *refinement* (decrease in inhumane procedures). Research philosophy that helps researchers gain good information from experiments using animals while reducing the pain and suffering of animals.

Three-day eventing An event of the Olympic Games since 1912. It is comprised of three parts—stadium jumping, dressage, and cross-country.

Tom A male turkey. Also called a *gobbler*.

Total Performance Index Index used by the Holstein Association to rank sires on their ability to transmit a balance of traits.

Toxin One of several poisonous compounds produced by some microorganisms, plants, and animals.

TQA   Trucker Quality Assurance Program is an education program for all involved in the transportation process of swine.

Trail event   A western event in which the horse is scored on its ability to pick cleanly through a set course that mimics outdoor trail riding.

Transcription   In protein manufacture, the process of building RNA that is complementary to DNA.

Transfer RNA (tRNA)   Molecules of RNA coded by DNA to bond with a specific amino acid. tRNA "collects" the amino acids from the cytoplasm that the ribosomes use to manufacture proteins.

Transgenic   An animal or plant that has had DNA from an external source inserted into its genetic code.

Transgenic Founder   A transgenic animal that is subsequently used to establish a transgenic line of animals.

Transhumance   The practice of moving animals seasonally from a permanent base to more abundant feed and water and then returning to the permanent base when the season changes.

Transition Economy   An economy once centrally planned that is changing to a market economy.

Translation   In protein manufacture, the process of building an amino acid sequence according to the code specified by mRNA.

Trapnest   A nest that traps a hen while she is on the nest so that her production and egg quality can be recorded.

Trimester   A third of a pregnancy. The last trimester in a ewe is approximately the last 50 days.

Trisomy   The presence of a third chromosome in an otherwise diploid cell.

Tumor   Swelling or mass in a part of the body that is caused by abnormal growth of tissue.

Ultrasonic scan measures   Measurements of body tissues taken with ultrasound waves.

Ultrasonography   Using ultrasound waves to visualize the deep tissues of the body.

Undernourished   Receiving inadequate nourishment for proper health and growth.

Unsaturated fats   Fatty acids that are not saturated with hydrogens but instead have double bonds. The number of double bonds changes the physical, biochemical, and metabolic characteristics of the fats, as compared with saturated fats.

Unsoundness   Any injury or defect that interferes with the ability of an animal to be used for its given purpose.

Value-added product   A product processed in some way that has enhanced its value.

Variety   A subdivision of a breed distinguished by color, pattern, comb, or some other physical characteristic.

Vector   1) Animal, usually an arthropod, that transfers an infectious agent from one host to another. 2) A DNA molecule that carries foreign DNA into a host cell, replicates inside a bacterial (or yeast) cell and produces many copies of itself.

Vegan   A view that eschews the use of any animal product, including nonfood products.

Vertical coordination   The process of organizing, synchronizing, or orchestrating the flow of products from producers to consumers and the reverse flow of information from consumers to producers.

Vertical Integration   The control of two adjacent stages in the vertical marketing channel from producers to consumers.

Virulence   Degree of pathogenicity.

Vitamin   Term that is used to group together a dissimilar set of organic substances required in very small quantities by the body. The term comes from a reference in 1912 by Polish scientist Casimir Funk to a "vital amine" he thought he had discovered in rice hulls. The compound he discovered was thiamin, the first vitamin to be discovered. In many ways, modern nutrition was born with that discovery.

Wean   To remove offspring from the dam and prevent them from nursing.

Weathering   Loss in nutritive value through exposure to the elements.

Western pleasure   A western event in which the manners and movement of the horse are judged. A good western pleasure horse is quiet, responsive, and gives a very smooth ride.

Western riding   A western event in which the horse is scored on lead changes through one of three potential patterns, as well as its manners.

Withdrawal time   The length of time an antibiotic must not be administered or fed to an animal before the animal can be legally slaughtered.

Wool   The fiber that grows instead of hair on the bodies of sheep.

Wool chewing   A problem of sheep. Often referred to as *wool pulling*. Animals nibble away at their fleece until they make bald spots. There may be nutritional causes. Animals on high-concentrate, low-fiber diets seem especially prone. Both confinement and crowding may be at the root of the problem.

Wool sucking   One of two major types of prolonged sucking syndrome. It is most frequently observed in cats. In both forms, cats continue to suck on objects and perhaps knead with the forepaws long after weaning. Objects may be other cats, people, dogs, themselves, and so on. Wool sucking is specifically linked to Siamese and Siamese-cross animals. The animal sucks and/or chews on wool or otherwise fluffy objects, including clothing, furniture, and bed clothes.

Work   Physical exertion as a production function.

Working cow horse A western event broken into two scored performances with those scores combined for a grand score to determine the winner. The two categories include "dry work," which is the reining portion, and "cow work," in which the horse shows its ability to control the cow.

Xenotransplantation Transplanting animal organs into humans. Scientists hope to someday have animals grow donor organs for humans that will function in the human body without being rejected. These organs could help alleviate the chronic shortage of donor organs.

Young goose or gosling A young goose weighing from 12–14 lbs. A market gosling weighs about 8 lbs. The term gosling is also used for baby geese.

Zero tolerance Common term used to indicate restrictions imposed by the Delaney clause.

Zoonotic The ability to be passed from animals to humans under natural conditions.

Zygote Cell resulting from the fusion of the sperm and oocyte.